Water and Wastewater Engineering Systems

D Barnes
BSc PhD MIWSE AMICE MIEAust

P J Bliss
BE MSc DIC ASTC MIEAust

B W Gould
BE ME MIEAust
Department of Water Engineering
University of New South Wales

H R Vallentine
BE MS ASTC FIEAust
Professor of Civil Engineering
University of New South Wales

Longman
Scientific &
Technical

Longman Scientific & Technical
Longman Group UK Limited,
Longman House, Burnt Mill, Harlow,
Essex CM20 2JE, England
and Associated Companies throughout the world.

First published by Pitman Books Limited 1981
Reprinted by Longman Scientific & Technical 1986

ISBN 0-582-99466-7

Library of Congress Cataloging in Publication Data
Water and wastewater engineering systems
Bibliography: p.
Includes index
1. Water-supply engineering 2. Sewage disposal
3. Sewage-Purification. I. Barnes, D.
TD345.W26   628.1   79-12770

National Library of Australia
Cataloguing in Publication Data
Water and wastewater engineering.
Rev. ed.
Bibliography.
ISBN 0 85896 391 4 (Pitman).
ISBN 0 582 99466 7 (Longman).
1. Water-supply engineering. 2. Sewage – Purification.
3. Sewage disposal. I. Barnes, D. (David), 1945–   .
628.1

Contents

Preface

Improvements in community health during the present century, in both industrialised and developing communities, have been due principally to advances in the field of public health engineering. The most important of these advances have been those reducing the spread of water-borne diseases by improving the quality of drinking water and effectively disposing of community wastewater and urban drainage waters.

In recent decades, the development of extensive urban areas incorporating centres of high population density and large-scale industrial plants has led to a growing awareness of the interrelationship between the essential community services of water supply and wastewater disposal and the protection of the quality of environmental waters. As a result, public health requirements and public demand for the preservation of environmental amenities impose increasingly high standards on water supply and wastewater disposal authorities in regard to the performance of their installations.

The professional responsibility for the design, construction, operation and maintenance of dams, storages, water and wastewater transmission systems and treatment facilities lies primarily with the civil engineer. This book is intended for use in a first course in water supply and wastewater engineering in an under-graduate civil engineering course. In addition, it should serve as a useful reference for students in such related fields as chemical engineering, environmental sciences, town planning, surveying and applied microbiology, and as a source of background information for students undertaking post-graduate studies in these disciplines. *It is not intended as a manual for experienced, practising engineers.* Because of its limited objective as an introductory text, the emphasis is on concepts and principles rather than on practical details. However, references to these details have been included to broaden the student's outlook and to demonstrate the application of scientific principles in the production of a system that functions satisfactorily and economically.

The book was written to meet the need for an introductory text for a course that has been given for the past nine years in the third year of the civil engineering degree course at the University of New South Wales. This course consists of 28 hours of lectures and 14 hours of laboratory and tutorial work. It is taken by students with a background of physics, chemistry, mathematics and the mechanics of solids and fluids, and a knowledge of these subjects is assumed. The authors have sought to make the book one of general rather than local application by including aspects of European, Asian and American, as well as Australian, practice and by presenting rather more detail than the minimum required for a short course.

Lecturers using the book may find it suitable for a longer course or for one in which some topics call for greater emphasis and others for somewhat less. It is suggested that an introductory course might cover Chapters 1 to 12 inclusive, with selected topics from the remaining chapters. Worked examples and qualitative review questions are presented in the text, and numerical problems, with answers, are given at the end of the book.

Students should realise that proficiency in this field requires both professional experience and further detailed study of the topics introduced. Each topic has an extensive literature of its own, whether it be flood estimation, a hydrologic process, catchment yield, urban drainage, ground-water flow, dams, tunnels, pipelines, canals, hydro-economics, water resource systems or a physical, chemical or biological treatment process. Since much of the material presented is of an introductory nature, detailed references have not been included. The student wishing to proceed further in any of the topics is advised to refer to recent comprehensive or specialised texts, such as those listed under Further Reading on page 483.

The authors acknowledge, with gratitude, the sterling efforts of Mrs M L Atkinson and Mrs J O'Keeffe who typed the numerous drafts and of Miss C Martin who prepared the diagrams. The authors also thank Professor K J Ives, of University College, London, for reviewing the text and making many helpful comments.

DB, PJB, BWG, HRV

Sydney,
November 1981

Publisher's note: Solutions Manual/Errata

A 40-page Solution Manual to many of the problems is available to lecturers who write on college letterhead direct to the publisher. This manual also lists errors in earlier printings of the book corrected in this printing.

Symbols and Abbreviations

Symbols

The symbols used throughout the text follow, as nearly as practicable, standard practice. It is inevitable, however, that the same symbol will be used for different quantities or properties when dealing with different topics. For example, the symbol L is used generally as a linear dimension, such as length of pipeline, length of tank, linear distance through a filter; it is also used as a symbol for BOD because its use elsewhere has been well established for this purpose; recently, also, it has been adopted as the symbol for the litre. Throughout the text, the symbols (with the corresponding units) are defined for the particular use, and there should be no confusion.

a   parameter as defined; area of flow in partially filled pipe
A   area (generally); paddle resistance coefficient
b   parameter as defined; linear dimension
B   basin drag coefficient
c   coefficient (various uses); filtration rate factor parameter
c' a measure of concentration
C   concentration; pipe-flow coefficient; spillway coefficient; runoff coefficient
C_D drag coefficient
d   diameter of particle; depth
D   oxygen deficit; drag force
e   linear dimension
E   energy
f   porosity; pipe friction factor
F   force; food-to-micro-organism ratio
F_s volatile solids loading rate in anaerobic digestion
g   gravitational acceleration
G   velocity shear gradient
h   head loss; height; depth of flow
H   head on a weir crest
i   mean rainfall intensity
I   light intensity

k   a coefficient (various uses); pipe roughness; Henry's law constant
K   Darcy's coefficient of permeability; a parameter; reaction rate constant
l   length of pipe element
ln logarithm to the base e
L   a linear dimension; BOD
M   moment of a force
n   number of index; Manning roughness coefficient
N   Manning roughness coefficient for full-pipe flow; bacteria concentration
p   partial pressure of gas; water pressure
P   pressure (total); power; population
P_m per cent moisture in sludge
P_v per cent volatile fraction in sludge solids
q   volume rate of flow in partially filled pipe
Q   volume rate of flow
r   specific resistance (of sludges); hydraulic radius in partially filled pipe; flow rate of return activated sludge (per cent)
R   hydraulic radius; return activated sludge flow rate; universal gas constant
R_e particle Reynolds number in settling
R   Reynolds number in flow
s   slope of partially filled pipe; drawdown
S   salinity; saturation value; slope
S_c storage coefficient
S_x solids loading rate
t   time; detention time
T   temperature; torque; thrust; transmissivity
U   uplift force; modified form of food-to-micro-organism ratio
V   velocity
$\forall$ volume
W   weight; rate of oxygen transfer; width
x   index in filter rate factor expression; an unknown parameter; linear dimension
X   mixed liquor suspended solids concentration; a parameter
X_v mixed liquor volatile suspended solids concentration
y   index in filter rate factor expression; population; depth
Y   yield coefficient
z   index in filter rate factor expression

α oxygen surface transfer coefficient ratio in impure water; a velocity ratio in flocculators
β shape factor; dissolved oxygen saturation factor

γ	unit weight
ϵ	suspension porosity
θ	temperature coefficient; an angle; proportionality constant
θ_c	mean cell residence time
λ	a parameter (rate factor in filters)
μ	absolute viscosity
ν	kinematic viscosity
ρ	density
σ	concentration of deposits in filter; surface tension
τ	shear stress
ψ	shape function
ω	angular velocity
$[\ ]_T$	total mass

Abbreviations

ADWF	average dry-weather flow in sewers
AWT	advanced wastewater treatment
BOD	biochemical oxygen demand
BOD_5^{20}	biochemical oxygen demand determined at 5 days and 20°C
CMAS	completely mixed activated sludge
COD	chemical oxygen demand
cst	capillary suction time
DO	dissolved oxygen
EP	equivalent population
FFE	falling film evaporation (for desalting)
F/M	food to micro-organism ratio (in biological wastewater treatment)
FR	fixed residue
H-W	Hazen-Williams formula
L	litre
LD_{50}	lethal dose for 50 per cent of test organisms (toxicity testing)
M	molar (concentration of chemicals); Manning formula
MCRT	mean cell residence time (in biological waste treatment)
MLSS	mixed liquor suspended solids (in activated sludge)
MLVSS	mixed liquor volatile suspended solids (in activated sludge)
MPN	most probable number (bacterial counting)
MSF	multi-stage flash distillation (for desalting)
PDWF	peak dry weather flow in sewers
pH	negative logarithm of molar hydrogen ion concentration
PWWF	peak wet-weather flow in sewers
Q/A	surface loading rate in sedimentation
RAS	return activated sludge
RBF	rotating biological filter

RMS	root mean square
RO	reverse osmosis (for desalting)
RSF	rapid sand filtration
SDI	sludge density index (in activated sludge)
SS	suspended solids
SSF	slow sand filtration
SVI	sludge volume index (in activated sludge)
TDS	total dissolved solids
TL_M	median tolerance limit (toxicity testing)
TOC	total organic carbon
TSR	total solids residue
TU	turbidity units
TWL	top water level
US	United States of America
VS	volatile solids

1 Water Demand and Sources of Supply

1.1 Introduction

A water supply project may be a complete new system providing a community with an adequate, piped supply for the first time; or it may be an augmentation, extension or partial renewal of an existing system, as is frequently the case in developed countries. Water supply for domestic and industrial purposes may be but one component of a major water resources project in which a large storage, or a series of linked storages, will serve multiple purposes such as flood control, river flow regulation, irrigation and hydro-electric power generation.

Preliminary considerations for a proposed water supply scheme include approximate estimates of the cost and assessments of the political, economic and legal feasibility of alternative proposals. Multiple-purpose schemes may require the collaboration of several governmental authorities and, if rivers forming state or national boundaries are involved, there will be a need for inter-governmental agreement. In some countries, the local community may be involved in the preliminary decision-making process, especially if all, or a major part, of the cost is to be borne locally, or if there is concern over possible effects on the local environment.

The engineering decisions of major importance in the design of water supply schemes are those relating to

a The design period, which is the number of years during which the project will be expected to meet the community's requirements
b Estimates of the population and of the types and magnitudes of commercial, industrial and agricultural undertakings to be served during the design period
c The level of service, in terms of the rate of supply, the reliability of supply and the quality of water to be provided during the design period
d The selection of the supply source
e The fixing of the capacities and operating levels of the engineering works

for the storage, treatment, transportation and distribution of the water, including provisions for supply and demand fluctuations.

The principles behind these decisions and the engineering techniques and practices involved in their implementation are the subject of this and the following chapter.

1.2 The use of water

City and municipal water supplies may be used for domestic, commercial, industrial, agricultural and public purposes. In addition, some of the supply is usually unaccounted for and is regarded as 'lost'. The supply rate of a system can be stated as a total volume provided in a given period, for example cubic metres (10^3 litres) or megalitres (10^6 litres) per day. Alternatively, the daily flow can be expressed as litres per capita (L/cap), this being the total daily volume divided by the number of residents in the community. This figure includes, in addition to personal consumption, the average resident's 'share' of water for all non-domestic use, including that of tourists and non-resident workers, as well as losses.

Domestic use

This accounts for 40 to 60 per cent of most urban supplies. It includes all water used in and around residences, including lawn sprinkling, car washing and filling swimming pools. The average daily consumption depends on climate, housing conditions and living standards; whether or not the supply to individual consumers is metered; the cost of water; and the extent to which the area is sewered.

Some 70 per cent of domestic supply is returned to the sewer system. Possibly a third of this is flushed down toilets, and the balance is bathroom, kitchen and laundry waste. The growing use of domestic appliances, such as washing machines and dishwashers, is one reason why domestic per capita consumption is increasing by 0.5 to 1.0 per cent per year. Table 1.1 shows the range of consumption rates in developed countries.

Table 1.1 Daily domestic use of water

| | Climate | |
	Temperate L/cap	Warm L/cap
Good-quality separate houses with gardens	150–250	250–650
Good-quality apartments	125–175	175–225
Old city and suburban tenements	75–100	100–150

Commercial use

This includes water used in business areas where shops, offices and light industrial units, such as garages, must provide drinking, washing and sanitary facilities for employees. Estimates of this water demand are sometimes based on the number of employees (allowing about 20 per cent of the domestic consumption per employee) and sometimes on the floor area of the commercial district.

Industrial use

This varies widely from one industry to another and among manufacturers of the same product. The type of industry, the size of the organisation, the availability and cost of water and the extent of the recycling of process water account for much of the variation. The ranges of requirements for some major industries, expressed as kilolitres of water per tonne of product (which is numerically equal to the ratio of mass of water used to mass of product) are: woollen and cotton goods 150 to 750; wood pulp, paper and steel 10 to 300; copper smelting 30 to 40; meat slaughtering and packing 15 to 25; petroleum products 3 to 10; dairy products 3 to 35.

The water demand of a single large industrial plant might be equivalent to the domestic consumption of tens of thousands of people. It is easier for the supply system of a large city to accommodate such demands than it is for a small scheme, unless adequate provision for industrial growth has been made in the design of the system. Some large industrial users arrange their own private water supply schemes.

The greater part, possibly two-thirds, of the industrial water requirement is for cooling. In many industries, less than 30 per cent of the water used is consumed, the remainder being discharged to surface or underground waters, or treated for re-use.

Agricultural use

This includes water supplied to farms, market gardens, greenhouses and dairies within the supply area. The requirements vary with climate and with local practices. Estimates of demand can be made on the basis of the average daily need per animal (ranging from perhaps 100 L for a cow to 25 L for a pig), together with an allowance for cleaning farm facilities, and provision for greenhouses (say 3 L/m²) or garden crops (possibly 15 L/m²).

Public use

This includes water used for public parks, gardens and fountains and public buildings including schools and hospitals. This demand may amount to 50 L/cap.

Loss

This is the difference between the volume supplied to a region and the total of the volumes used by individual consumers during the same period. Careful estimates for systems in which all consumer connections are metered suggest that loss, or water that is unaccounted for, may amount to 10 to 30 per cent of the total supply. Some authorities have reported much higher loss figures.

Losses may be due to a combination of factors such as leakage, evaporation or overflow from service reservoirs; leakage from mains (which may exceed 5 kL per day per kilometre length); errors in meters (which may either fail to register or under-register by several per cent); and unmetered uses such as mains flushing, road construction and fire-fighting. This unmetered consumption is usually less than 3 L/cap.d.

Total use

The total use, including losses, expressed as the average daily consumption in litres per capita (L/cap) will clearly vary considerably from one supply system to another. Table 1.2 gives some estimates for developed countries.

Table 1.2 Total daily water demand

	Climate Temperate L/cap	Warm and dry L/cap
Large cities with highly industrialised areas	400–600	500–800
Cities with light industry	250–350	350–450
Towns where most of the supply is for domestic use	150–250	250–350

Table 1.3 shows a possible distribution of water for various purposes for a city of half a million people with high living standards in a warm, dry climate, where the annual rainfall is 600 mm, falling mostly in the colder months.

In the design of a water supply system, provision should be made for a gradual increase in the per capita consumption during the economic life of the system and, in the case of unsewered towns, for a sudden increase when a sewerage system is expected to come into service. The increase in consumption results from improvements in living standards and the expansion of industry. On the other hand, greater re-use of water by industry so as to reduce pollution, increases in water charges, and the installation of meters for individual consumers in areas previously not metered, could reduce the per capita consumption.

Table 1.3 Water consumption example

Use	L/cap.d	L/cap.d	Per cent
Domestic			
Sanitation and ablution	75		
Cooking, laundry, miscellaneous	45		
Garden	80	200	40
Commercial		80	16
Industrial		100	20
Primary production		20	4
Public			
Hospitals, schools, etc	25		
Parks, street cleaning, etc	30	55	11
Losses		45	9
Total average consumption		500	100

1.3 Fluctuations in demand

The annual average rate of consumption is used in assessing the adequacy of possible sources of supply, in determining the capacity of a reservoir required to store water against dry spells and in setting water charges.

The varying rates of consumption from hour to hour during the day, and the normal year's maximum rates over periods of one hour, one day and sometimes several days, are used in fixing the capacities of various components of the water supply system. It is convenient, for purposes of comparison, to express all rates in terms of the annual average rate.

Typical values are shown in Table 1.4. In general, the maximum rates are higher in small communities than in large ones and in areas predominantly residential rather than industrial or rural.

Table 1.4 Maximum consumption ratios

Ratio	Climate Temperate		Warm, dry	
	Range	Typical	Range	Typical
Max hourly/annual average	2.0–4.0	2.5	3.0–6.0	3.5
Max daily/annual average	1.3–2.0	1.5	2.0–4.0	2.5
Max weekly/annual average	1.1–1.3	1.2	1.7–2.3	2.0

The consumption rate usually varies through the day from a minimum between 2 am and 4 am to a maximum between 8 am and noon. In residential areas, there may be a second peak during summer evenings as a result of garden sprinkling and evening meal preparation.

Isolated peak demands due to fire-fighting emergencies must be allowed for in the design of service reservoirs and distribution systems.

1.4 Population estimates

Increases in the demand on a water supply system over a period of years result from population growth, increased per capita consumption with improved living standards, and industrial development. Since it would be uneconomical and impractical to augment the system year by year to meet the growing demand, each component is designed to satisfy the estimated demand at the end of its design period. In the early part of the period, some components will therefore not be operating at their full capacity.

The selection of the design period for a component, whether a dam, a treatment plant, a pipeline, a pumping unit or a service reservoir, is based on the practical life of the component, allowing for wear and obsolescence; on the physical difficulty and the cost of enlarging or replacing it; and on financial considerations, such as expected interest rates, rates of inflation, changes in the real income of the community, methods of financing, and the availability of loans and subsidies.

The design period is usually between 10 and 50 years, long periods being appropriate for dams, tunnels and large canals, which are difficult to enlarge,

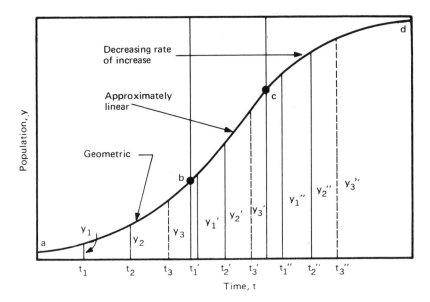

Fig 1.1 Population growth curve

and shorter periods (10 to 30 years) for pumps, pipelines, treatment plants and wells, which can be duplicated, replaced or extended more readily. The distribution network of pipes 300 mm and less in diameter is normally designed to meet the ultimate requirements of the area when fully developed and is constructed as the area is settled.

Estimates of the population to be served at the end of a particular design period are based on records of population changes to date, such as census figures and other data.

Short-term estimates, for design periods up to 15 years, can be based on a comparison of the growth curve for the previous 30 years or more with the corresponding portion of a biological growth curve. The latter curve shows the variation of the population in a culture of micro-organisms with time, from commencement of growth until attainment of ultimate size. Typically, such a curve has an 'S' shape (Fig 1.1).

If the growth curve over the previous period resembles the part ab of the biological growth curve, the growth rate is assumed to be *geometric*, that is

$$\frac{dy}{dt} = k_g y \qquad (1.1)$$

Therefore

$$\log_e y = k_g t + C \qquad (1.2)$$

and, if the populations y_1 at t_1 and y_2 at t_2 are known, the value of y_3 at t_3 can be determined.

If the growth curve for the previous period indicates a linear growth rate in recent years, corresponding to part bc of the biological growth curve, the growth is *arithmetic*, that is

$$\frac{dy}{dt} = k_a \qquad (1.3)$$

and the population y_3' at time t_3' is readily estimated from the known values at time t_1' and t_2'.

Finally, if the recent portion of the previous growth curve corresponds to the part cd of the biological growth curve, the population is growing at a decreasing rate towards a saturation value S:

$$\frac{dy}{dt} = k_d(S - y) \qquad (1.4)$$

Therefore

$$\int \frac{dy}{S - y} = k_d \int dt \qquad (1.5)$$

Insertion into Eq 1.5 of the known values y_1'' at t_1'' and y_2'' at t_2'' and an assumed value of S yields the value of k_d, and the same equation can then be used, with the values y_2'', t_2'' and t_3'', to evaluate y_3''.

The value of the population estimates arrived at in this way is limited by the fact that they do not reflect such other causes of population change as changes in birth and death rates, and gains and losses of members as a result of changes in employment opportunities and transport and accommodation facilities.

Long-term estimates, as well as short-term ones, are sometimes obtained from graphical projections based on comparisons with the growth curves of similar towns that were of the same size in the recent past, allowance being made for expected changes likely to affect the population growth of the town under consideration.

Example 1.1

A new water supply is to be provided for Civilia, an inland town with a temperate climate. Its current (1978) population is estimated to be 17 800. Census figures for it and for two larger towns A and B in the region are:

Year	A	B	Civilia	Year	A	B	Civilia
1890	7 500	4 800	1 500	1940	14 800	11 500	5 600
1900	8 300	6 400	1 930	1950	16 100	12 800	6 900
1910	9 500	8 600	2 400	1960	17 800	13 900	8 500
1920	10 800	9 700	3 900	1970	19 100	14 700	10 000
1930	12 400	10 200	4 300				

Town A has a plentiful supply from a nearby river; it is fully metered and sewered and has small but flourishing secondary industries and extensive well-kept parks and recreation areas. Town B, like Civilia, has a restricted supply which is due for renewal; it has little secondary industry, its water supply is metered, but the town is only 40 per cent sewered.

Civilia's supply will be fully metered, and it is expected that a sewerage scheme will be constructed for the first time soon after the water supply system is completed. The development of secondary industry in the town is expected to be greater than that of B, but not as extensive as that of A.

The current water consumption rates are

Town	Av daily L/cap	Max daily average	Max hourly average
A	340	1.5	2.2
B	250	1.3	1.9
Civilia	215	1.3	Not known

You are required to estimate the population, the average daily consumption, and the peak consumption rates for Civilia for design periods of 10, 25 and 50 years from 1980.

The population growth curves for the three towns from 1890 to 1970 are shown below. Predicted values for 1990, 2005 and 2030 are required for Civilia.

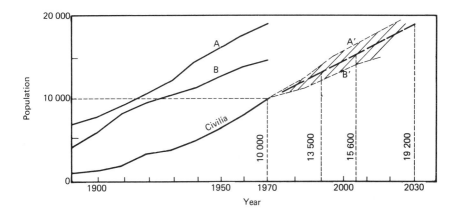

Solution

Assuming geometric growth, based on the populations in 1900 and 1978 (estimated),

$$\ln 11\ 800 - \ln 1930 = k\ (1978 - 1900),\ \text{whence}\ k = 0.0232$$

$$\ln y_{1990} - \ln 11\ 800 = 0.0232\ (1990 - 1978)$$

Therefore

$$y_{1990} = 15\ 590$$

The assumption of arithmetic growth (based on the populations in 1950 and 1978, to indicate recent trends) gives

$$y_{1990} - y_{1978} = (1990 - 1978) \times \frac{11\ 800 - 6900}{1978 - 1950}$$

Therefore

$$y_{1990} = 13\ 900$$

A graphical extension of the Civilia curve shown in the above diagram so that it falls between the transferred portions of the curves of A and B could reasonably be drawn anywhere within the shaded area. If the middle values are adopted, the recommended design population estimates are

$$y_{1990} = 13\ 500 \qquad y_{2005} = 15\ 600 \qquad y_{2030} = 19\ 200$$

To the present average consumption rate of 215 L/cap.d, it is proposed that 70 be added to allow for the new sewerage scheme, and 25 to cover any increase in general use with the lifting of restrictions and improved pressure. This would bring the 1980 consumption to 310 L/cap.d, which compares reasonably with that of A, considering the latter's more extensive industrial activity. If provision is then made for an annual increase in consumption of 1 L/cap.d to allow for industrial growth and improved living standards, and A's peak demand ratios are adopted, we arrive at the following estimates for consumption rates for Civilia:

Year	1990	2005	2030
Average daily L/cap.d	320	335	360
Max daily L/cap.d	480	503	540
Max hourly L/s	110	133	176

1.5 Sources of supply

The *hydrologic cycle* is the name given to the series of processes whereby water is evaporated from lakes and oceans, transferred as vapour over continents and precipitated as rain, hail, dew or snow. Water finds its way back to the lakes and oceans as overland flow, streamflow, underground percolating flow, or a combination of these.

The system is, in fact, considerably more complex than this. Much of the precipitation falls onto the water bodies that cover three-quarters of the earth's surface; possibly 70 per cent of the continental precipitation returns directly to the atmosphere by evaporation from the ground or river surfaces and from the foliage of vegetation after transpiration. Much water is stored, for seasons, decades or centuries, as ice, snow or groundwater. About 97 per cent of the world's water is seawater; more than 2 per cent is in polar ice and glaciers; nearly all the remainder is groundwater, only a small fraction being in lakes and rivers. Man makes relatively minor local modifications to the cycle when he diverts or regulates streamflows or draws upon groundwater for his domestic or industrial supplies and for power generation, flood mitigation, irrigation and recreation.

Rainfall, in most temperate regions, varies with respect to intensity and duration of storms and to total quantities precipitated in particular regions from month to month and from year to year. Sometimes, city water supplies can be drawn directly from rivers in which an adequate flow is assured at all times. More generally, the flow of a river fluctuates and, after long periods of little or no rain over its catchment area, it may diminish to a trickle or even cease altogether. Where a water supply scheme depends on a river as its source, it is therefore usual for a reservoir to be created by means of a dam, with a storage capacity sufficient to maintain supply to the scheme over dry spells reckoned in months or years, depending on the variability of precipitation observed in the region.

In some regions, water supplies are drawn wholly or in part from groundwater, either by means of bores or wells, or by underground galleries constructed so as to intercept percolating flows. Groundwater storages receive much of their recharge water by percolation from rivers in wet seasons, and the dry-weather flow of many rivers is the result of efflux of groundwater into the river channels. This interrelationship between surface water and groundwater is one aspect to be taken into account when assessing the long-term yield of a drainage basin or catchment. A thorough assessment involves an evaluation of the inflow volumes, outflow volumes and changes in storages in the catchment throughout the year — a procedure resembling that of cash accounting and known as a *water balance*.

The inflows include rainfall and snowfall, water transported in by pipes or channels, wastewaters discharged to surface or underground storages, and groundwater inflow from adjacent catchments. Outflows include river flows leaving the catchment area, evaporation and transpiration, and water extracted from surface and ground supplies for human use. Storages include natural and artificial surface reservoirs, groundwater up to the level of the water table, and soil moisture. These elements of the water account can be either measured directly or estimated from field studies.

For any period — a week, a month or a year — the inflow volume less the outflow volume should be equal to the increase in storage. The water balance procedure provides a check on the reliability of the water data, as well as detailed information about the hydrologic phenomena and the water resources of the catchment.

The design of water supply projects involves predictions of the likely yield of the source and estimates of the reliability of these predictions, as well as forecasts of the likely demand (previously discussed). Yield predictions are based on records of past yields from the source and sometimes, as a guide, on yields from similar sources. Flood mitigation, drainage projects and dam spillway designs require forecasts of the magnitudes, frequencies and durations of high flows. On the other hand, determining the reservoir capacity necessary to ensure a reliable supply involves predicting the frequencies and durations of flows of small magnitude, that is, forecasting droughts.

It is generally assumed that fluctuations in weather patterns are random rather than cyclic; and that, for normal design periods in water supply projects, statistical procedures of analysis, based on past records extending over 30 years or more, may be used to predict the magnitudes and the frequencies, or recurrence intervals, of high flows and low flows of streams.

The detailed analysis of past streamflow records, the arrangement of extreme flow occurrences into frequency series and the synthesising of flows to yield estimates of the probability of floods or droughts more severe than those on record are the province of the specialist in hydrology. These important and useful procedures do not lie within the scope of this introduction to water supply engineering.

1.6 Reservoirs

The function of a reservoir is to provide for fluctuations either in the supply of water from a natural source or in the demand for water by a community. A *storage* or *conservation* or *impounding reservoir* stores water in excess of demand from a natural source in periods of high flow for use in periods of low flow. A *distribution* or *service reservoir* stores water, often supplied at a steady rate from a storage reservoir, to provide for the varying demand of the community over a period of a day or several days. A storage reservoir may have a capacity equal to the total consumption of its community over a period of from one month to more than two years, depending on the variability of the river flow. The capacity of a one-day distribution reservoir is considerably less than the daily consumption. Distribution reservoirs are discussed in the following chapter.

A storage reservoir is located at a site where the average annual yield of the upstream drainage area exceeds the sum of the expected annual demand of the community at the end of the design period, the amount required to be released annually to meet the needs of users downstream and the estimated annual loss due to evaporation and infiltration from the storage. The site should provide a large storage volume, in comparison with the cost of the dam, and it should be suitable for constructing a spillway to pass flood flows downstream. The geology of the area must provide a safe foundation for the dam; seepage losses should be low and there should be suitable local construction material. The area to be inundated should have little, if any, habitation, roads or rail services, which would involve expensive relocation.

The height of the dam should ensure that the minimum water level during periods of drought is sufficient to provide a rate of flow to the service reservoir equal to the maximum daily rate of demand of the community at the end of the design period of the dam; a pumping station of adequate capacity may be necessary. The height should also be such that the volume of available storage above the minimum water level is sufficient to meet the needs of the community, the downstream users and losses during periods of drought.

A contour plan of the storage area, based on field surveys, enables a graph to be prepared showing the water surface area plotted against elevation. This can be used in estimating evaporation losses when the storage is at any particular elevation. From the area–elevation curve, a storage volume–elevation curve is prepared, each incremental volume being taken as the product of the average of adjacent surface areas and the contour interval.

Example 1.2

The areas within the natural surface contour lines immediately upstream of the site of a proposed dam are as follows:

Reduced level m	Area km²	Reduced level m	Area km²
68	0	80	0.34
70	0.01	82	0.47
72	0.03	84	0.66
74	0.06	86	0.90
76	0.12	88	1.40
78	0.22	90	2.45

Prepare surface area–elevation and storage–elevation curves for the site, assuming that the encroachment of the dam into the storage volume will be negligible.

Solution
The surface area curve is plotted directly from the above data. The storage curve is a plot of the area under the surface area curve. For example, the incremental storage between reduced levels 82 and 84 is approximately

$$\tfrac{1}{2}\,(0.47 + 0.66) \times 10^6 \times 2 = 1.13 \times 10^6 \text{m}^3 \text{ or } 1130 \text{ ML}$$

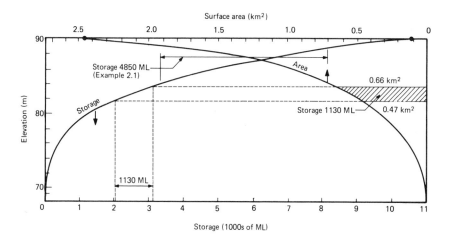

The reservoir storage required above the minimum operating level can be determined by a numerical or a graphical analysis of past records of the river during periods of critically low flow. In the numerical approach, a table is prepared which shows, month by month, for the proposed reservoir at the end of the design period, the water volume 'gains' (river inflows plus precipitation on the reservoir) and the 'losses' (town drafts plus evaporation plus infiltration plus releases for downstream use). The monthly figures for the excess of losses over gains (if positive) are totalled over each critical period, and the largest of these totals, sometimes augmented by a safety margin, is adopted as the storage capacity to be provided above the minimum operating level. The form of the table is as follows:

Month	Gains (A)		Losses (B)			Required storage for the month = (B–A), if positive	Cumu-lative storage
	River inflow	*Precipi-tation on reservoir*	*Draft*	*Evap. and infil.*	*Down-stream release*		
March April							

The graphical method of doing the above analysis, developed by Rippl, uses a mass curve showing the cumulative net inflow volume (the summation of the gains less evaporation, infiltration and essential downstream releases) plotted against time for past critical periods of low flow (Fig 1.2).

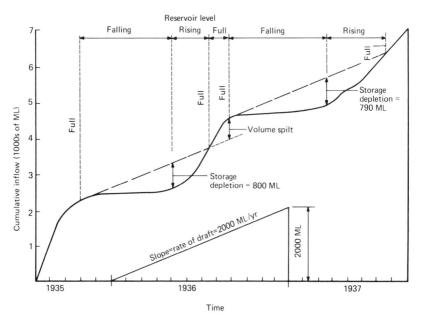

Fig 1.2 Determination of the required storage of a reservoir by the mass-diagram method

The slopes of lines on the mass curve diagram represent volume rates, so that the slope of the mass curve at any point in time represents the net inflow rate available for town use; and the slope of a line whose rise over a one-year interval equals the annual draft at the end of the design period represents the average rate of draft. Draft lines are drawn to the right from high points of the mass curve until they cut the curve again. Such draft lines will cover periods during which the total volume drawn for the town supply would have exceeded the net volume of inflow. If it is assumed that the high points represent conditions of full storage, the height of a draft line above the mass curve at any subsequent instant represents the cumulative excess of the volume withdrawn over the usable volume that has entered the reservoir.

The greatest of the heights of the draft lines above the mass curve represents the storage that would have been required in the reservoir to ensure the desired rate of draft over the period under consideration. The right-hand intersection of a draft line with the mass curve represents the full reservoir condition, and the vertical separation between adjacent draft lines represents the volume of water passing over the spillway until the water level begins to fall, following a reduction of the rate of net inflow below the rate of draft.

Mass curves can be used to determine safe rate of draft for given storage capacities. For this purpose, the maximum safe rate of draft is given by the greatest slope of a draft line drawn from a high point of a mass curve so that the maximum vertical interval does not exceed the specified storage.

1.7 Dams

Dams are structures designed to create water storage reservoirs by obstructing river flows. Their principal structural function is to withstand the thrust of the stored water, transferring it either to their foundations or to the sides of the river valley. Common types are the concrete gravity dam, the reinforced concrete buttress dam and the embankment dam of earth or rock or both, which transfer the water thrust to the foundations; and the arch dam, which transfers all or most of the thrust to the side abutments. The selection of the most appropriate type is based on consideration of the dimensions and form of the valley at the site of the dam, the capacity of the foundations and the abutments to withstand the transferred thrusts, and the availability and costs of labour, equipment and building material.

The design of dams is the function of experienced specialists, and only a few significant aspects of the subject will be mentioned here.

Gravity dams

The gravity dam is a solid structure with a cross-sectional form approximating a right-angled triangle, a horizontal base, a nearly vertical upstream face

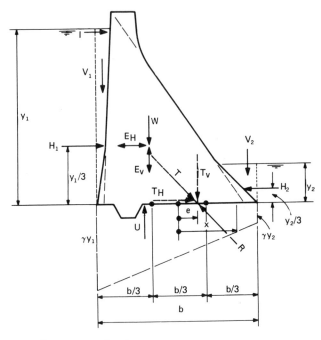

Fig 1.3 Forces acting on a gravity dam

and a top width sufficient for access along the length of the dam (Fig 1.3). In elevation, the crest is horizontal and the height varies across the valley.

The forces acting on the structure include

a The horizontal thrusts, H, of the upstream water and the downstream or tail water. If the respective water depths are y_1 and y_2 and the unit weight of the water is γ,

$$H_1 = \tfrac{1}{2}\gamma\,y_1^2 \text{ per unit length of dam}$$

$$H_2 = \tfrac{1}{2}\gamma\,y_2^2 \text{ per unit length of dam}$$

b The weights of the dam, W, and of the water, V_1 and V_2.

c The uplift force, U, exerted on the base of the dam as a result of the hydrostatic thrust of water seeping under the structure. Its maximum possible value for a base width, b, with uniform foundation material is given by

$$U_{max} = \tfrac{1}{2}\gamma(y_1 + y_2)b \text{ per unit length of dam}$$

However, special design features, such as cut-off walls extending into the foundation, and construction techniques, such as pumping cement grout into fissures in the foundation, reduce the uplift well below this value.

d Earthquake 'forces', E. In regions subject to earth tremors, the assumption is made that the dam may be subject to vertical and horizontal accelerations. For example, a horizontal acceleration of the foundation in the upstream direction of 0.1g results, in effect, in a horizontal force equal to 0.1W in the downstream direction on the dam; while such a foundation acceleration vertically downward reduces the effective weight of the dam momentarily by 10 per cent. In addition, an earthquake may result in oscillatory fluctuations in the hydrostatic thrust on the dam.

e Ice thrust, I, exerted near the level of the water surface, in regions subject to freezing.

The resulting thrust, T, due to the combination of these forces, meets the foundation at a distance e from the centre of the base. In dam-full conditions, this point is downstream from the centre (Fig 1.3).

The frictional resistance to sliding and the shear strength of the concrete key in the foundation must be sufficient to withstand the horizontal component, T_H. Similarly, the resistance of the concrete must be adequate to sustain the horizontal shear at any level within the dam.

The vertical component, T_V, acting at a distance e from the centre of the base, produces over the base a normal stress p which, at a distance x from the centre of the base, is given by

$$p = \frac{T_V}{b} \pm \frac{M\,x}{I} \tag{1.6}$$

Therefore

$$p = \frac{T_V}{b} \pm \frac{T_V\,e\,x}{b^3/12} \tag{1.7}$$

Provided that T intersects the base within its middle third, that is, provided $|e|$ is less than b/6, the normal stress p will be everywhere compressive. If e equals $+b/6$, the pressure at the upstream heel will be zero and at the downstream toe, $2T_V/b$, that is, twice the average. This middle-third rule is observed in gravity dam design not only for the base but for horizontal sections at all levels within the dam, except in the cases of dams with prestressed cables. This ensures that the dam material and the foundation are always under compression.

Excavation for a gravity dam is taken down to solid rock; frequently, cement grout is pumped into holes drilled in the foundation to seal fissures; and additional grouting, at higher pressure, is carried out during construction from galleries within the dam, to provide a grout curtain below the heel so as to reduce percolation and uplift pressure.

Buttress dams

A buttress dam has an upstream face in the form of a series of concrete slabs or barrel arches, supported by buttresses. The face usually has a slope of about 45° (Fig 1.4). This type of dam requires less than half the concrete needed for a gravity dam of similar height, but its reinforcement and formwork result in a higher unit cost of concrete. As its weight is considerably less than that of a gravity dam, it can be built on poorer foundation material.

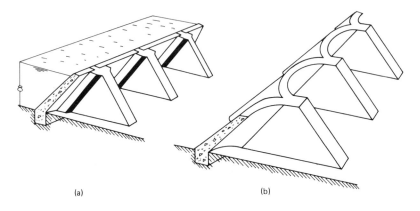

(a)   (b)

Fig 1.4 Buttress dams: (a) slab and buttress, (b) multiple arch

Earth and rockfill dams

Earth dams involve the use of cheap material and, usually, mechanised construction procedures. They can be built on earth foundations. For these reasons, they are often selected as the most economical type of dam, especially for broad valleys. Essentially, they consist of a relatively impermeable core of clay material, or sometimes a concrete diaphragm wall, extending down to an impermeable clay or rock layer and supported on the upstream and downstream sides by earth or broken rock, graded progressively from fine to coarse with distance from the core (Fig 1.5).

Earth and rockfill dams call for extensive design experience and careful construction methods and supervision, the various graded bands of material being placed in layers 0.1 to 0.3 m in thickness and compacted by rollers at the appropriate moisture content to produce maximum density.

The designer, in addition to ensuring the stability of the slopes of the embankment, must provide for the disposal of seepage without risk of erosion of the embankment material, by means of broken-rock drains.

Arch dams

An arch dam is a curved shell-like structure that relies mostly on arch action

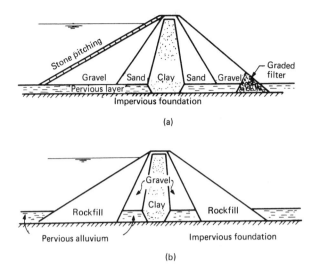

Fig 1.5 Typical cross-sections: (a) earth dam, (b) rockfill dam

to transfer the hydrostatic thrust to the sides of the valley. One method of analysis treats the structure as a series of horizontal arch slices, each transferring load to the abutments, and, at the same time, as a series of vertical cantilevers, each transferring load to its base. The water thrust on an elemental unit of the face of the dam is apportioned to the arch slice and the vertical cantilever defining the unit in such a way that the downstream deflection of the unit is the same for both the arch and the cantilever. Modern applications of three-dimensional elastic analysis involve the use of finite element techniques. Analytical approaches are sometimes supplemented by model studies.

The deflection of the arch is due primarily to the thrust of the water, but the restraining effects of the abutments, as well as temperature changes and concrete shrinkage and plastic flow must be taken into account in the design. Solid rock abutments are essential and great care is required during construction to ensure adequate resistance to seepage and weathering, since the thickness of an arch dam at its base may be less than a quarter of its height, whereas that of a gravity dam may be more than three-quarters of its height.

In a U-shaped valley, it is common to use a constant-centre or constant-radius arch dam, for which the radius of curvature of the upstream face is the same at all levels, with the centres of curvature all on a common vertical. This results in a vertical upstream face. For a V-shaped valley, the variable-centre or variable-radius dam is structurally more efficient, the angles subtended at the centres of curvature of the arch slices being constant, while the centres are not on a common vertical. This results in the upper part of the face projecting downstream of the lower part at the crown of the arch, while the reverse is the case at the abutments.

1.8 Reservoir appurtenant works

Spillways

A spillway is an essential passageway for discharging floodwaters entering a reservoir to ensure that the dam does not overflow. The spillway may be separate from the main dam structure, the floodwaters passing through a saddle or a tunnel in the surrounding hills, or it may be an integral part of the dam. As the flow usually attains a high velocity, most spillway structures are of concrete, and provision must be made for the dissipation of the kinetic energy of the flow to protect the downstream river bed from erosion.

Overflow spillways have their crest levels fixed so that, for the design flood, the top water level is below the maximum safe level for the dam. An ogee or S-shaped profile, conforming approximately to the underside of the nappe of the flow if it were to pass over a sharp-crested weir, guides the flow with a minimum of turbulence and minimum risk of separation, cavitation and vibration, which might damage the structure. The spillway discharge formula is of the form $Q = \frac{2}{3}C\sqrt{2g}\,LH^{3/2}$, where Q is the design discharge, L the length of crest, H the head on the crest and C a dimensionless coefficient, usually determined for the particular structure by hydraulic model tests. For earth dams, a length of concrete gravity dam with an ogee profile may serve as the spillway; alternatively, the flow may pass through or over a special rockfill section incorporated in the dam.

In narrow valleys where there is insufficient room for a normal spillway, the flow may be passed over a *side spillway* into a channel passing through one end of the dam, or into a *bell-mouth spillway*, which is a circular weir

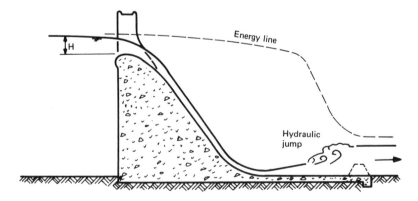

Fig 1.6 Overflow spillway

structure in the reservoir, leading via a vertical shaft into an outlet tunnel. For small flows, a *syphon spillway* through a concrete gravity dam provides a measure of automatic level control, acting as a simple weir at low flows and as a rapidly discharging outlet when the water level is sufficiently high to maintain the syphonic action.

The velocity at the base of a high spillway must be reduced to a non-scouring value before it re-enters the stream. For example, the velocity below a 50 m high spillway may approach 30 m/s, while the safe velocity for a river bed of earth or soft rock may be less than 1 m/s. One method of energy dissipation is the hydraulic jump, on a horizontal or sloping concrete apron; alternatively, a concrete 'ski-jump' bucket can be formed on the face of the spillway, to throw the water upward and outward, so that it falls onto the stream bed well downstream from the dam.

Intakes

An intake is provided to withdraw water from the reservoir for transmission to the supply system. For supplies to small communities, the flow may enter a screened pipe inlet, submerged sufficiently to prevent the entry of air and floating debris and set above the bed in order to avoid the intake of mud and sediment (Fig 1.7(a)).

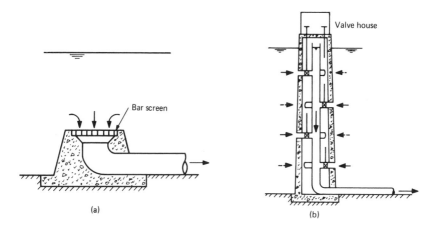

Fig 1.7 Intakes: (a) Pipe inlet, (b) Intake tower

Intakes from reservoirs serving large communities may be incorporated in the dam structure or they may be independent towers, standing in a deep part of the reservoir. Water can be admitted through any of a number of valve-controlled inlets set at different heights in the wall of the tower (Fig 1.7(b)). This provision for withdrawal of water at different levels allows for changes in the surface level of the storage and for variations with time in the quality of the water at different depths.

Water has a maximum density at 4°C. In a deep reservoir during summer, the surface layers become heated and cannot mix with the lower layers, which are at a lower temperature and greater density. As winter approaches, the surface water temperature falls until the lower layers and surface layers are at a similar temperature and hence similar density. It then becomes possible for mixing to occur throughout the reservoir — the water 'turns over'. In winter the surface water may freeze, but it will be less dense than water at 4°C which will remain at the bottom of the reservoir. This stratification will remain stable until spring, when the surface waters heat up to near 4°C and 'turnover' can occur. The temperature profiles in the reservoir depend upon the volume and depth of the reservoir and the climate. Low winter temperatures may result in two periods of turnover, while hotter climates will have only the autumn turnover. The quality of water at various depths in the reservoir reflects these changes. The concentration of oxygen in the water follows a similar pattern. When the reservoir is thermally stratified, the surface layers contain high concentrations of oxygen, while the bottom layers contain little or no oxygen. This lack of oxygen leads to the solubilisation of iron and manganese, and products of anaerobic decomposition, such as methane and hydrogen sulphide, are present. The bottom layers accumulate solid debris which settles from the surface layers. This creates silt and sludge on the bottom of the reservoir and contributes to the oxygen demand in the bottom layers. During turnover, the mixing results in a redistribution of some of the settled materials, the anaerobic products and the solubilised iron and manganese. Other factors which may affect the water quality within the reservoir include storm runoff and point discharges. Storm flows are particularly polluting if the catchment contains agricultural or urban development. The quality of water within a reservoir is not constant. It varies within the water body and is subject to diurnal and seasonal changes. A water supply reservoir should be constructed to provide sufficient flexibility so that water of reliable quality can be withdrawn at all times. Additionally, the water catchment area and the reservoir should be managed to optimise the quality of the runoff.

Sluiceways

A sluiceway is a conduit through a dam or one of its abutments set below the minimum operating level to provide for flow downstream. Sluiceways have rounded inlets to avoid cavitation near the entrance of the conduit. The entrance is protected by a screen or trash-rack and can be sealed by a vertically sliding entrance gate to shut off the flow for inspection purposes. For heads of 25 m or less, the main flow may be controlled by a gate valve within the dam or abutment, operated from a gallery above the sluiceway.

For larger heads, control is effected by a streamlined needle valve or sleeve valve located at the conduit outlet and discharging into the atmosphere.

1.9 Groundwater

In the majority of the developed countries, groundwater provides more than 20 per cent of the total water used and over 30 per cent of the domestic supplies. It is more widely distributed than surface water and generally of better quality. As it does not require the construction of costly storage reservoirs and long transmission lines, it is often an economical alternative or supplement to surface water supplies, provided that the required withdrawal rate can be maintained without unacceptable depletion of the groundwater storage.

Groundwater engineering is a specialised field dealing with the occurrence and movement in soil and rock layer, or aquifers; the extraction and treatment of groundwater and its distribution, or incorporation into a surface water supply system; and the operation of the system so that the effectiveness of the groundwater storage as a long-term source of supply is not impaired. The following brief introduction to this field presents elements of the theory of groundwater movement and the hydraulics of flow into wells.

Aquifer characteristics

Part of the precipitation that enters the ground is transpired by vegetation and part is evaporated. Some is retained in the upper soil as soil moisture, or suspended water, against the action of gravity by molecular attraction of the

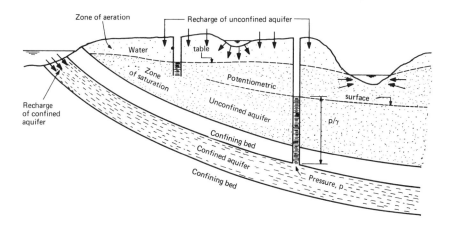

Fig 1.8 Aquifer definition diagram

soil particles and by surface tension effects. The remainder percolates through this unsaturated zone to a *zone of saturation*, where it flows as groundwater in a permeable water-bearing stratum called an *aquifer*.

The groundwater may flow with a free surface, or *water table*, or it may flow under pressure in an aquifer which is confined above, as well as below, by a relatively impermeable stratum known as a *confining bed*. For a confined aquifer, a surface analogous to the water table is that to which water would rise from the aquifer in open, cased holes extending to or above the ground level. It is called the *potentiometric surface* of the aquifer (Fig 1.8). Groundwater flow is almost always laminar. The volume rate of flow, Q, along a prismatic channel of porous aquifer material is given by *Darcy's Law*

$$Q = KAS \qquad (1.8)$$

where A is the gross cross-sectional area of the channel; S is the hydraulic gradient, being the downward slope of the water table or the potentiometric surface; and K is the *hydraulic conductivity*, also known as the *coefficient of permeability*, of the material. It has the dimensions of velocity (Fig 1.9).

The value of K depends partly on the viscosity of the water (for which reason it increases with increase in temperature) and partly on the size, shape and distribution of the pores. There is a wide range of values of K within and between the various classes of soil. For a weathered clay, K may be less than 0.01 m/yr, whereas for a clean gravel K may exceed 2000 m/d. For most natural aquifers, it lies between 0.5 and 200 m/d.

The apparent mean velocity, V, of groundwater flow is determined by dividing the volume flow rate, Q, by the gross area, A. It is less than the actual velocities in the pore spaces. From Eq 1.8,

$$V = Q/A = KS \qquad (1.9)$$

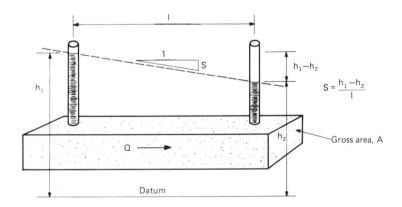

Fig 1.9 Flow through a porous medium

For example, a hydraulic gradient of 1.0 m per km (S = 0.0010), with K equal to 0.5 m/d, would result in a velocity of 0.0005 m/d; if the gradient were 20 m/km (S = 0.020) and K were 200 m/d, V would be 4 m/d.

If the thickness of the saturated aquifer is b, the flow rate through a vertical strip of unit width extending to the full depth, so that A = 1 × b, is

$$Q = KbS = TS \qquad\qquad (1.10)$$

where T = Kb is the *transmissivity* of the aquifer expressed in m^3/d per m width, that is, m^2/d.

When a saturated soil is drained under the action of gravity, the volume of water removed per unit gross volume of soil is the *specific yield* of the soil. It is dimensionless, being expressed as either a percentage or a decimal. The specific yield is less than the porosity, because some water is retained as soil moisture. The porosity of a particular sand might be 35 per cent, while its specific yield might be 25 per cent; the corresponding figures for a clay might be 45 per cent and 5 per cent.

When withdrawal of water from a bore in a confined aquifer begins, the potentiometric surface over a large area surrounding the bore is lowered. The local reduction in pressure is transmitted radially and rapidly over considerable distances by virtue of the elastic properties of the water and the aquifer material, the aquifer remaining fully saturated. The decrease in head reduces the support contributed by the water to the overlying stratum, so that the aquifer undergoes vertical compression; the reduction in pressure also permits elastic expansion of the water. These two effects result in the release of water from the aquifer, and a radial pattern of flow towards the bore develops.

In an unconfined aquifer, the radial transmission of the effects of the local lowering of the water table at the bore is much slower, for the lowering depends largely on drainage of the aquifer and the development of a hydraulic gradient towards the bore rather than on elastic effects.

The water-yielding property of an aquifer can be expressed in terms of a non-dimensional *storage coefficient*, S_c. This is the volume of water that an aquifer releases per unit surface area per unit lowering of the potentiometric surface or water table. For a confined aquifer, it is numerically equal to the volume of water released from a vertical column one square metre in cross-section when the potentiometric surface falls a distance of one metre. For an unconfined aquifer, with the water table falling a distance of one metre, one cubic metre of the aquifer is drained, and S_c is practically equal to the specific yield of the aquifer material. While the storage coefficient of a particular unconfined sand aquifer might be 0.3, that of a confined aquifer of the same material and of equal thickness might be less than 1/500 of this value. However, if the confined aquifer is of sufficiently large area, its yield may exceed that of a smaller unconfined aquifer.

Example 1.3

The sand-gravel material of a confined aquifer 21 m thick has a hydraulic conductivity of 530 m/d. The storage coefficient of the aquifer is 0.00026.

a What is the transmissivity of the aquifer?
b What would be the flow velocity and the discharge per unit width for a potentiometric gradient of 1 m/km?
c What volume of water would be released from storage over an area of 2 km² if pumping were to lower the potentiometric surface by an average of 1.5 m? Compare this volume with that which would be released from an unconfined aquifer under the same conditions, if its storage coefficient were 0.23.

Solution
a $T = Kb = 530 \times 21 = 11\ 130\ m^2/d$
b $V = KS = 530 \times 0.001 = 0.53\ m/d$
$Q = TS = 11\ 130 \times 0.001 = 11.13\ m^3/d$ per metre width
c (1) Volume $= S_c \times$ area $\times \Delta h = 0.00026 \times 2 \times 10^6 \times 1.5$
$= 780\ m^3$
(2) Volume $= 0.23 \times 2 \times 10^6 \times 1.5$
$= 690\ 000\ m^3$

The hydraulics of well flow

A well is a shaft or bore-hole sunk into an aquifer for the purpose of extracting groundwater. In the case of a confined aquifer with a potentiometric surface lying above the ground surface, water will flow from the hole, which is then called an *artesian* or *flowing bore*. For other confined aquifers and for unconfined aquifers, the static water level lies below the ground surface and withdrawal is effected by pumping from the well. The initial stage of pumping removes water in storage in the vicinity of the well, the static water level in the well being progressively lowered. In this *non-equilibrium phase*, the water table in the case of an unconfined aquifer, or the potentiometric surface in the case of a confined aquifer, is drawn down in the area surrounding the well in the form of an inverted cone, called the *cone of depression*, which increases in depth and extent with time.

(a) Unconfined aquifer equilibrium flow
In the case of an unconfined aquifer, the *drawdown*, s, at any distance, r, from the well is the depth of the modified water table below its static level. It can be measured in an *observation well* (Fig 1.10).

Continued pumping may result eventually in an *equilibrium condition*, in which no further drawdown occurs and the rate of withdrawal of water is equal to the rate at which water from distant sources is recharging the

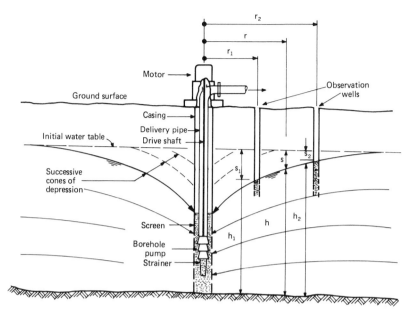

Fig 1.10 Well in an unconfined aquifer

aquifer. It may take many weeks or months of pumping for this condition to be approached. The effective limit of the cone of depression, at equilibrium, is called the *circle of influence* of the well.

In theory, the transmissivity of an aquifer can be determined from field measurements of the drawdown at two distances from the well, for a particular pumping rate, under equilibrium conditions. The drawdowns under equilibrium conditions for other rates of pumping can then be estimated. This method, due to Thiem, is based on the assumptions that the aquifer is homogeneous and isotropic, that it is horizontal and of uniform thickness, that the well penetrates the full thickness of the aquifer, and that the extent of drawdown is small in comparison with the thickness of the aquifer, so that the water movement can be assumed to be wholly in the horizontal direction without appreciable error. The volume rate of inward flow through any cylinder of radius r, with the well as axis, is

$$Q = KAS = K \times 2\pi rh \times dh/dr$$

where h is the height of the water table above the bottom of the aquifer. Integration between any two radii, r_1 and r_2, where observation wells enable the respective water depths, h_1 and h_2, to be evaluated, yields the Thiem formula

$$Q = K\pi \frac{h_2^2 - h_1^2}{\ln(r_2/r_1)} \qquad (1.11)$$

where ln signifies logarithm to the base e. With the pumping rate, Q, known, K can be evaluated, whence the transmissivity, T, follows.

(b) Confined aquifer equilibrium flow

In the case of a confined aquifer, the terms 'cone of depression' and 'drawdown' refer to the potentiometric surface (Fig 1.11). The volume of water withdrawn from the commencement of pumping to a particular instant, in the non-equilibrium phase, is the water released from storage as a result of elastic compression of the aquifer and expansion of the water following the reduction in water pressure.

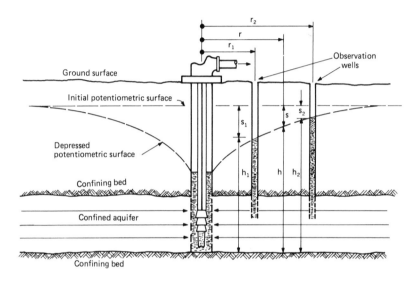

Fig. 1.11 Well in a confined aquifer

If an equilibrium condition is reached, the volume rate of inflow through any cylinder of radius r, with the well as axis, is

$$Q = KAS = K \times 2\pi rb \times dh/dr$$

from which it follows that

$$Q = \frac{2\pi Kb(h_2 - h_1)}{\ln(r_2/r_1)} \tag{1.12}$$

where $(h_2 - h_1)$ is the difference in the drawdowns at distances r_2 and r_1 respectively, and b is the aquifer thickness. The value of K for the aquifer material, and thence of T for the aquifer, follow from the insertion of field observations in Eq 1.12.

The equilibrium condition is rare, although it may be approached in an aquifer of large extent. It could occur on an island in a lake whose water provided a steady inflow to the aquifer.

Example 1.4

A confined aquifer is being pumped, under equilibrium conditions, from a fully penetrating well at a rate of 60 L/s. The drawdowns in two observation wells 20 m and 180 m from the pumped well are 3.5 m and 0.40 m respectively. If the aquifer is 25 m thick, determine its conductivity and transmissivity.

Solution

From Eq 1.12

$$K = \frac{Q\ln(r_2/r_1)}{2\pi b(h_2 - h_1)}$$

Therefore

$$K = \frac{60 \times 3600 \times 24 \ln 9}{2\pi \times 25 \times 3.1} = 23.4 \text{ m/d}$$

$$T = Kb = 23.4 \times 25 = 58.5 \text{ m}^2/\text{d}$$

(c) Non-equilibrium flow

The equilibrium method of determining aquifer characteristics is rarely used owing to the length of pumping time required before a steady state is reached. If applied to the unsteady state, an equilibrium equation yields a false, high value of K, as part of the discharge Q is coming from storage and not from recharging waters.

In the non-equilibrium phase, the rate of drawdown decreases with time. A typical form of the drawdown/time curve is shown in Fig 1.12(a). With a logarithmic time scale, the curve has the form shown in Fig 1.12(b).

Theis showed that, for an idealised aquifer such as that assumed by Thiem, the drawdown, s, at a distance, r, from a well at a time, t, after pumping has begun is

$$s = \frac{Q}{4\pi T}\left[-0.5772 - \ln\frac{r^2 S_c}{4Tt} + \frac{r^2 S_c}{4Tt} - \frac{r^2 S_c^2}{4Tt\,2(2!)} + \ldots\right] \quad (1.13)$$

The third and subsequent terms within the square brackets form an infinite series whose effect on s decreases as t increases. The effect of these terms is negligible when the value of $r^2 S_c/4Tt$ falls below 0.01. Thereafter, to a close approximation,

$$s = \frac{Q}{4\pi T}\left(-0.5772 - \ln\frac{r^2 S_c}{4Tt}\right) \quad (1.14)$$

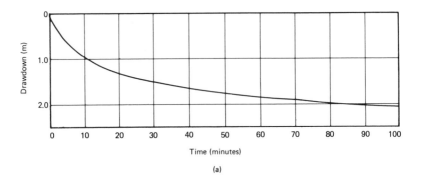

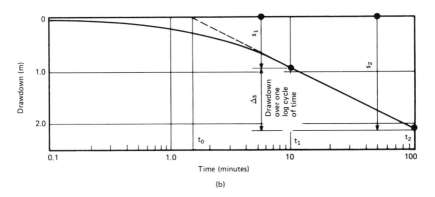

Fig 1.12 Typical drawdown/time curves for a confined aquifer: (a) natural plot, (b) semi-logarithmic plot

which is the formula for the straight portion of the curve in Fig 1.12(b). For any two points (s_1, t_1) and (s_2, t_2) on this straight portion, it follows that

$$s_2 - s_1 = \frac{Q}{4\pi T} (\ln t_2 - \ln t_1)$$

or

$$s_2 - s_1 = \frac{Q}{4\pi T} \ln \frac{t_2}{t_1}$$

$$= \frac{2.3Q}{4\pi T} \log_{10} \frac{t_2}{t_1} \tag{1.15}$$

which is Jacob's modification of the Theis non-equilibrium formula. It provides a simple method of evaluating T from a series of field observations at one observation well, extending over a few days in the case of unconfined aquifers, and a few hours in the case of confined aquifers.

If the straight portion of the drawdown curve is extended to intersect the line $s = 0$ at t_o, Eq 1.14 yields the value of the storage coefficient, since, for $s = 0$,

$$-0.5772 - \ln(r^2 S_c/4Tt_o) = 0$$

$$S_c = \frac{2.25Tt_o}{r^2} \qquad (1.16)$$

Example 1.5

If the pumping rate for the confined aquifer drawdown curve shown in Fig 1.12(b) was 23.3 L/s, estimate the transmissivity and the storage coefficient of the aquifer.

Solution
$Q = 23.3$ L/s $= 2016$ m³/d
Selecting 10 minutes and 100 minutes for t_1 and t_2, respectively, so that log $t_2/t_1 = \log 10 = 1$, and $\Delta s = s_2 - s_1 = 1.2$ m, the Jacob formula

$$\Delta s = \frac{2.3Q}{4\pi T} \log(t_2/t_1)$$

gives

$$1.2 = \frac{2.3 \times 2016 \times 1}{4\pi T}$$

Therefore, $T = 307$ m²/d

From Fig 1.12(b), $t_o = 1.55$ minutes, that is, 1.08×10^{-3} days.

Therefore

$$S_c = \frac{2.25Tt_o}{r^2} = \frac{2.25 \times 307 \times 1.08}{2500 \times 10^3} = 0.00030$$

The idealised conditions assumed in the development of the above procedures are rarely found in practice. The aquifer may not be penetrated fully by the well, it may not be homogeneous and isotropic and of uniform thickness, the drawdown of an unconfined aquifer may not be small in comparison with the aquifer thickness, or the water table or the potentiometric surface before pumping may not be close to horizontal. Furthermore, the aquifer may not extend equally in all directions from the well, being partly bounded by a water body such as a river or a shoreline or by an impermeable geological structure. Its confining strata may be partly permeable or, if it is near a sea coast, it may contain an intruding layer of saline water. Interference from adjacent pumped wells may seriously affect the drawdown. These possibilities call for a thorough study of the local conditions. In many cases, analytical techniques are available that take account of departures from the idealised conditions upon which the basic procedures are founded, but they are beyond the scope of this introductory outline.

Groundwater supply

The choice of a well type is determined by the desired yield and the depth of well necessary to achieve it, the nature of the aquifer and of the strata overlying it, the expected life of the installation and other, economic factors. Shallow wells, up to 20 m in depth, may be excavated pits, lined if necessary with brick or concrete; they may be holes with a diameter up to one metre, bored by auger; or they may be spearpoint wells, which are perforated pipes up to 75 mm in diameter, screwed to plain pipes and driven or jetted into the aquifer. Deep wells are drilled by means of cable-operated percussion rigs or hydraulic rotary drilling equipment. They are usually cased as drilling proceeds. For large supplies, a collector or radial well may be used. This consists of a concrete caisson up to 5 m in diameter, extending into the aquifer with its base sealed with a concrete plug. Perforated pipes up to 200 mm in diameter and 50 m or more in length extend radially into the aquifer to collect groundwater and convey it to the collector.

Well screens, the inlet portions of tube wells, are made of non-corrosive alloy, with holes or slotted openings of a size sufficient to pass about 50 per cent of the particles in the surrounding aquifer. An initially high rate of pumping used in the process of *well development* removes the fine material, leaving a filter of coarse material surrounding the screen. In a uniform, fine aquifer, it may be necessary to place a coarse gravel packing around the screen.

Wells should be protected against contamination from the surface and from undesirable sub-surface seepage by grouting the space between the casing and the supply pipe and by providing a concrete sealing platform over the top of the well.

The *safe yield* of a well may be loosely defined as the maximum rate of withdrawal that can be maintained over a specified period without impairing the aquifer as a suitable source, without producing such large drawdowns that pumping costs are excessive, and without resulting in contamination from the intrusion of saline or other unacceptable water. For a supply system that also uses surface supplies, intermittent withdrawal and artificial recharge of an aquifer by surface spreading or the injection into recharge wells of excess waters can increase the safe yield.

Review questions

1.1   What is meant by the term *design period*, in relation to water supply and waste-water disposal systems and equipment? Give typical values, or ranges of values, of design periods for the following, with brief justifying comments: a concrete arch dam, a pipeline from storage reservoir to distribution reservoir, pumping station equipment, laterals and branch sewers.

1.2   For a city of 100 000 people in a developed country with a temperate climate, suggest typical values for
   a   The percentage of the total water supplied for domestic purposes
   b   The percentage of the domestic supply which is discharged to the sanitary sewer system
   c   The possible percentage increase per year in the per capita domestic consumption
   d   The average daily total consumption per capita
   e   The ratios of the maximum hourly and the maximum daily consumption rates to the annual average.

1.3   List the components involved in water balance procedure. Of what value is such a procedure?

1.4   What characteristics are desirable for the site of a storage reservoir?

1.5   List the site characteristics appropriate for each of the following types of dam: concrete gravity, buttress, earth, constant radius arch, variable radius arch.

1.6   Why is it usual for intake towers to have a range of inlets at different levels?

1.7   Define the terms *hydraulic conductivity, transmissivity, specific yield* and *storage coefficient*. What are their respective dimensions?

1.8   Derive the Thiem formula for equilibrium flow to a bore in an unconfined aquifer. What are the assumptions on which it is based?

1.9   Discuss the reliability of drawdown formulae under practical conditions.

1.10 What do you understand by the term *safe yield* of a well?

2 Transmission and Distribution of Water

2.1 Transmission of water

Water may be conveyed from the source of supply to the distribution system by an open channel or a pressure conduit, or by a combination of these. Open channels include canals at ground level, elevated aqueducts or flumes, and tunnels flowing part-full, the longitudinal profile of the water surface coinciding with the hydraulic gradient. Pressure conduits include pipes and tunnels flowing full, normally lying below the hydraulic gradient so that the pressure is greater than atmospheric.

Open channels

Canals require a topography that provides a fairly direct, gradually descending route, with long straight sections connected by large radius curves and with few changes of grade and alignment. The higher the design velocity, the smaller is the size and hence the cost of the canal. Maximum permissible non-scouring velocities range from 0.5 m/s for silt and sand loams and 1 m/s for stiff clays to 4 m/s for concrete-lined channels. Economical design balances the volumes of cut and fill, keeping both to a minimum. High ground may be traversed by a tunnel flowing part-full, if an open channel around the hill would be more costly. A local depression may be crossed either by an elevated aqueduct or flume, or by a ground-level pressure conduit, sometimes erroneously called an inverted syphon.

Earth canals are trapezoidal in cross-section, with bank slopes ranging from $2\frac{1}{2}$: 1 (horizontal: vertical) in sandy soil to $1\frac{1}{2}$: 1 in firm soil. Freeboard is provided to allow for occasional flow rates in excess of the design value, and for wave action and possible increases in the water level as a result of silting or weed growth. Allowance is necessary in the design of unlined canals for seepage losses, which may range from 0.05 m^3/m^2.d for a clay soil to more than 0.5 m^3/m^2.d for sandy soil. Seepage losses and weed growth can be reduced by providing a lining of asphalt, cement-mortar or reinforced concrete. The cost of the lining is partly offset by the additional advantage of a reduction in

34

canal size, resulting from reduced flow resistance and from increased scour resistance, which permits higher design velocities.

While a canal may be less costly to construct than a pipeline, it has several disadvantages. First, a piped supply is free of seepage and evaporation losses. Second, a pipeline can be duplicated readily when additional capacity is required, whereas a canal usually has to be constructed to meet ultimate requirements, since enlargement operations would interrupt the supply. Third, canals are more susceptible than pipelines to contamination from animal, human and industrial sources and they provide obstructions to natural drainage and to land use and surface communications.

Open channel flow in water supply conduits is practically always turbulent, the criterion for laminar flow being Reynolds number, Vy/v, less than 500, where V is the mean velocity, y is the depth and v is the kinematic viscosity. If H is the head loss due to boundary resistance over a channel length L, the energy gradient, S, is H/L. The head loss for a velocity V and a hydraulic radius R can be estimated with the Manning formula which, in SI units, is

$$V = \frac{1}{n}R^{2/3}S^{1/2} \tag{2.1}$$

In terms of the discharge, with a flow cross-section A, the formula yields

$$Q = \frac{1}{n}AR^{2/3}S^{1/2} \tag{2.2}$$

In these formulae, n is a coefficient whose value depends on the roughness of the boundary surface. Typical values of n are

Smooth metal, neat cement	0.010
Asbestos pipe	0.011
Concrete	0.014
Cast iron pipe	0.015
Smooth earth, or gravel	0.018 to 0.020
Natural channels	0.025 to 0.35 +

Since the Manning formula does not allow for variation of resistance with the Reynolds number, it is strictly applicable only to the rough-wall turbulent flow regime. For this reason, and also because of the difficulty of evaluating n precisely, values of V or Q given by the formula may be in error by 5 per cent or more. Design calculations should allow for the possible increase in the value of n with deterioration of the boundary surface during the life of the channel.

Gradually varied flows under subcritical and supercritical conditions, flows in transitions and in closed conduits flowing part-full, flows at control sections, and open channel flow measurement may be involved in water supply channel design. These topics are treated in the standard hydraulics texts. Aspects of channel design that may require special attention include a Flow around channel bends, where superelevation of the water surface may call for the provision of additional freeboard; also secondary currents may result in scour of erodible material

b Flow at, or near, critical depth conditions over an extended length of channel; this may produce a wavy, unstable water surface

c Supercritical flow at bends and transitions, which results in the formation of inclined standing waves

d Flow down steep slopes, which may result in the development of roll waves and appreciable bulking as a result of the entrainment of air.

Pressure conduits

The design of a pipeline involves the selection of the route; decisions regarding the location above or below ground level; and the specification of the diameter, material and strength of the pipe, the types and capacities of pumps, if they are required, and the types and locations of essential fittings.

In plan, a pipeline follows straight lines as much as possible, but local factors, such as costly rock excavation, unstable sloping ground and access requirements, may rule out the most direct route. In elevation, the line follows the general profile of the ground. It should lie below the hydraulic gradient wherever this is practicable, so as to avoid negative pressures, and as close to it as is economically feasible, so as to minimise pressures and hence the cost of the pipe. Sometimes, excessively high pressure heads, particularly the static heads under no-flow conditions, can be avoided by providing break-pressure reservoirs at appropriate points in the line (Fig 2.1).

Excavation and maintenance costs are reduced if pipelines are laid above the ground, but the disadvantages of this practice are interference with land use, possible adverse aesthetic effects on the landscape and, in regions subject to climatic extremes, undesirable water temperatures.

The minimum pipe diameter is fixed by the design flow rate and the maximum permissible velocity. Usually, the actual velocity lies between 1.25 and 2 m/s. If minor losses are negligible, the required head is that needed to overcome pipe friction and, in the case of a rising (pumped) main, static lift. For a mean velocity V in a pipe of diameter D and length L, the friction head, according to the Darcy formula, is given by

$$H_f = \frac{fLV^2}{2gD} \tag{2.3}$$

where f, the friction factor, is a function of the Reynolds number and the relative roughness of the pipe. Charts are available for evaluating f and the rapid solution of the Darcy formula.* In terms of Q, the head loss is

$$H_f = \frac{8fLQ^2}{\pi^2 gD^5} \tag{2.4}$$

* See footnote on p 64.

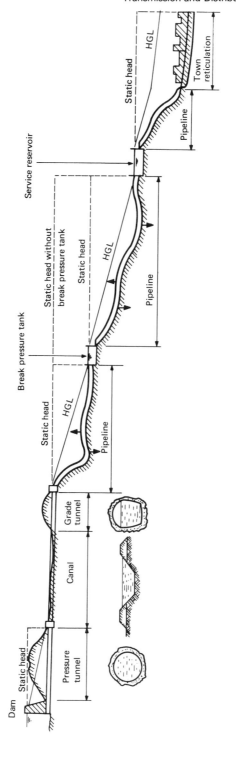

Fig 2.1 Transmission line

If the head available between the existing upstream and downstream water levels is H, Eq 2.4 gives the pipe diameter to be used provided that the velocity is not excessive. If the head is to be obtained by raising the upstream water level with a dam or by pumping, the appropriate pipe diameter will be that which results in the most economical combination of the cost of the conduit and the cost of providing the head. The lower the head, the lower is the cost of dam construction or of pumping, and the larger is the size, and hence the cost, of the conduit. For example, if the cost of the pipeline were proportional to $D^{1.5}$, the diameter and cost would be inversely proportional to $H^{0.2}$ and $H^{0.3}$ respectively. Hence an increase of 10 per cent in H would result in a decrease of 2 per cent in D and a decrease of 3 per cent in the cost of the pipe, ignoring for the moment the fact that diameters of standard pipes vary in steps of 50 mm or more.

A supply line for which the total available head is known may involve several different types of conduit, for example, a pressure tunnel, a canal and a pipeline. Usually, local conditions permit some flexibility in the distribution of head loss among the various types of conduit. The most economical distribution is that for which the change in cost per unit change in head is the same for each type of conduit. Curves of cost versus head loss for each type are plotted on the one graph and parallel tangents to the curves are located by trial such that the total of the head losses at the points of tangency equals the available head (Fig 2.2).

A similar reasoning can be used to find the optimum sizes for the sections of a transmission pipeline which has several take-offs along its length (to serve different towns, reservoirs, or districts). If it is assumed that the cost of the pipe, C, is proportional to some power of its diameter ($C = D^x$) and the head loss is jointly proportional to some function of the flow rate and some power of the diameter ($h = f(Q)D^{-z}$), then it can be shown, subject to topographical and functional constraints (such as minimum heads at high points on the pipeline), that for a minimum-cost pipeline with a given total head loss, the ratio of head loss to cost in each section should be the same ($h_i/C_i = K$).

Since the capacities of pipelines and pumps can be increased readily by duplication when required, their design periods can be shorter than those of dams, canals and tunnels, which are costly to enlarge.

A pipeline, appropriately jointed and anchored, must be capable of sustaining

a Circumferential stresses induced by the maximum static heads to which it can be subjected

b Circumferential stresses due to possible waterhammer

c Longitudinal stresses due to static pressure forces and to changes in momentum of the flow at bends, transitions and closed valves

d Longitudinal stresses due to contraction and expansion of the pipe with changes in temperature

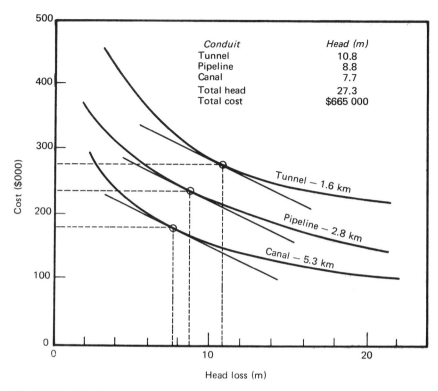

Fig 2.2 Distribution of head among conduit types for minimum cost

e Flexural stresses between supports due to back-filled soil and any likely superimposed loads.

These aspects of pipeline design are covered in hydraulics texts and in local standards relating to acceptance tests for pipes and their bedding and backfilling.

The selection of the pipe material involves consideration of the possible decrease in carrying capacity due to increasing roughness with age; strength and durability; ease of transportation and handling; the nature and effects of possible failure; leakage; cost; and maintenance required. Reinforced concrete, cement-lined spun cast iron, bitumen-lined or mortar-lined steel pipes and asbestos pipes maintain their carrying capacities; steel pipes are best for high internal pressures but are less satisfactory for large external loads and for negative pressures; while cast iron, asbestos cement and reinforced concrete pipes are satisfactory for working heads up to 125 metres. Metal pipes are subject to chemical and electrolytic corrosion both internally and externally. Protection against chemical action is afforded by protective coatings of paint, zinc galvanising, bituminous material, plastic sleeves or cement mortar. Cathodic protection against electrolytic action provides the pipe with a negative potential with respect to its surroundings so as to limit the movement of negative ions from the pipe surfaces.

Control of flow conditions in pipelines is effected by a variety of special-purpose valves. The commonest type is the *gate* or *sluice valve* in which a slightly tapered gate, operated either manually or mechanically by a threaded spindle, moves across the flow. Gate valves are placed at summits in the line, so that the lower pressures minimise the valve costs and sections of the line can be readily isolated and drained by means of *scour valves* at the sags or low points. On each side of a summit gate valve, automatic *air inlet and release valves* permit the entry of air during the draining process and the escape of air when the line is being filled and when air is released from the flowing water.

A *check, reflux* or *non-return valve* contains a metal flap, hinged at the top so that it is held open by water flowing in one direction but is closed onto a metal seat if the flow tends to reverse. Check valves are placed on the discharge side of a pump to prevent backflow; at the inlet to a pump suction line to maintain priming in the event of the pump ceasing operation; and where a rising main enters a reservoir, to prevent drainage of the reservoir if the main bursts. A *pressure-relief valve* releases flow from a pipeline by means of a spring-loaded or counterweighted plug, at a predetermined pressure, to relieve the pipeline of excessive waterhammer or other unexpected pressure. A *pressure-regulating valve* controls the flow so that the downstream pressure does not exceed a predetermined value. A feedback line from the downstream side actuates the valve to a position such that the head loss through a constricted opening maintains the required head on the downstream side. A *pressure-sustaining valve* controls the flow so that the upstream pressure is maintained, as far as possible, at a predetermined value, irrespective of the pressure downstream.

If the flow from the downstream end of a pipeline is subject to rapid variation, which could cause waterhammer in the line when the outflow is suddenly reduced, or excessive negative pressure if it is suddenly increased, the line can be protected by the installation, near the outlet, of a *surge tank*. When the outflow is reduced, part of the flow in the line is diverted into the tank, providing a head which gradually retards the upstream flow; when the outflow is increased, the tank prevents high negative pressures upstream by supplementing the flow while the velocity in the pipeline builds up gradually.

Transmission capacity

The design capacity or flow rate of a transmission line depends on the peak demand, averaged over the number of days of equalising to be provided by the service reservoir, and on the number of hours per day the line is to be in operation. For example, if the service reservoir is to equalise demand over a 24-hour period and a pumped supply line is to operate for 16 hours per day, its capacity should be such that, in 16 hours, it can deliver the maximum daily consumption for the end of the design period of the supply line.

2.2 Distribution of water

A service reservoir normally receives a steady supply from the transmission line throughout all, or a greater part, of the day. It provides equalising storage to accommodate fluctuations in demand through the day, together with a reserve storage to provide for fire-fighting and for unexpected interruptions to the main supply.

The *equalising* or *operating storage* required can be determined from an inspection of the mass curves of supply and maximum expected demand over the equalising period. Fig 2.3 shows the cumulative curves of supply and of peak demand for a 24-hour service reservoir which receives a steady supply over the period. The accompanying sketch shows the maximum and minimum water levels and the level at midnight, under normal operating conditions.

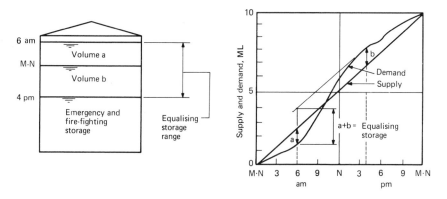

Fig 2.3 Equalising storage determination from cumulative curves of supply and demand for maximum daily consumption, with steady supply over 24 hours

For the assumed pattern of consumption, the excess of the volume supplied over the volume withdrawn since midnight reaches its maximum value, a, at 6 am, and it is stored in the reservoir. The excess of volume withdrawn over that supplied since midnight reaches a maximum, b, at 4 pm, at which time the water in the reservoir reaches its lowest level. Thereafter water rises to its initial level at midnight. The required equalising storage is therefore the sum of volumes a and b, which may amount to 20 per cent or more of the maximum daily consumption. If the supply is maintained for only part of the day, as is often the case with pumped supply, the percentage is considerably increased.

Fire-fighting storage requirements are normally set by agreement between the water supply authority and the fire authority. Some fire insurance underwriters recommend storages, flow rates and durations which vary according to the size of the community served, although it may not always be practical or economical to meet such requirements. The following figures are based on the recommendations of the US National Board of Fire Underwriters:

Population	Fireflow	Duration	Fire reserve storage
1000s	L/s	hr	ML
1	63	4	0.8
10	190	10	6.8
100	570	10	20.5

Emergency storage, to provide for failure of the transmission line, may be 25 to 200 per cent of an average day's consumption. In the case of a pressure pipeline, a burst main might interrupt supply for 12 hours or more.

The total capacity of a service reservoir is determined by the equalising, fire-fighting and emergency needs and by local economic factors and policies.

The principal types of service reservoir are the *surface reservoir*, the *standpipe* and the *elevated tank*. Surface reservoirs are usually concrete tanks, partly or wholly in excavation, located on high ground and preferably covered to prevent contamination, algal growth and the effects of extreme temperatures. Their capacities may range up to 15 ML or more and their proportions are determined by site conditions and economic factors. The depths of rectangular reservoirs are commonly between one-eighth and one-tenth of their widths. The economical depth–diameter ratio of circular prestressed concrete reservoirs is somewhat greater.

If a surface reservoir would not provide sufficient head, a standpipe or an elevated tank is required. A standpipe is a tall cylindrical tank with its base at ground level. Its upper portion contains the design storage, while the water in the lower portion serves merely as support. If the lowest level of the design storage is more than about 10 m above ground level, an elevated tank on a supporting structure may be more economical than a standpipe. The depth–capacity relationship of a reservoir should be such that the operating range of the water level does not exceed 9 m, so that excessive variations in the distribution pressures are avoided. This limitation, as well as economical structural design, may affect the proportions of the elevated reservoir.

Capacities of elevated tanks are usually less than 2 ML.

A service reservoir should be located so as to provide reasonably uniform pressures over the system. In flat localities, this means that the reservoir should be as central as is conveniently practicable. The main pipeline may lead directly to the service reservoir so that its flow is always in one direction, or it may be connected to the distribution system en route to the reservoir. In the latter case, the flow in the main between the point of connection and the reservoir may be in the reverse direction at times of high demand, with the system being supplied by both the main and the reservoir.

The distribution system should provide at all times, at every household and fire-fighting connection, the minimum pressure set by the water authority, which is usually in the range of 125 to 240 kPa, corresponding approximately to a head range of 13 to 25 m. At the householder's tap, the pressure may be less than 30 kPa owing to its elevation above the water main and the head losses in the meter, the house service line and the plumbing. The maximum static head in a distribution system is usually kept to 80 m or less, to limit leakage from the mains. For this reason, tall buildings may require booster pumps to provide adequate pressure.

Example 2.1

The water supply for Civilia (see Example 1.1) is to be provided by pipeline from a dam 12.5 km east of the town (see Example 1.2). The ground surface along the route of the line falls fairly uniformly from a reduced level of 90 m at the dam site to a reduced level of 57.6 m over a distance of 9 km. The town is expected to extend ultimately over an area of radius 1.5 km. The ground elevation in the vicinity of the town, along the route of the pipeline, is as shown.

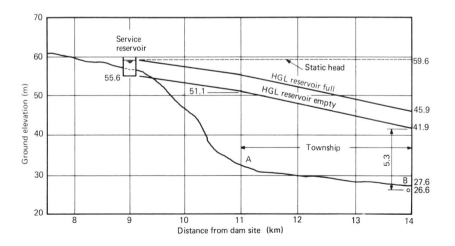

The minimum pressure in the distribution mains is to be 150 kPa, and the maximum pressure loss in the distribution system may be taken as 30 kPa per km radial distance from the service reservoir. The gravity main will provide a continuous supply and equalising will be over a 24-hour period. The required equalising storage (Fig 2.3) has been determined as 19 per cent of the maximum daily consumption for the design period of the reservoir.

Analysis of the river flows over a 35-year period shows that the average discharge is 3.65×10^6 m³/yr and that the storages required for various annual drafts are

Annual draft ML	Storage required ML
1000	1500
2000	3600
3000	6400

Site conditions limit maximum level of dam spillway crest to 90 m.

A preliminary assessment is to be made of the type, location and operating levels of the service reservoir, the diameter of the pipeline, and the minimum useful storage level and spillway level of the dam.

Solution

A   Service reservoir

The requirements for design periods of 25 years and 50 years will be considered.

			25 yr	50 yr
1	Population		15 600	19 200
2	Av daily demand (L/cap.d)	(Example 1.1)	335	360
3	Max daily demand (L/cap.d)		503	540
4	Total av daily demand (ML)		5.226	6.912
5	Total max daily demand (ML)		7.847	10.368
6	Equalising storage $0.19 \times (5)$ (ML)		1.491	1.970
7	Emergency + fire storage $0.5 \times (4)$ (ML)		2.613	3.456
8	Total storage $(6) + (7)$ (ML)		4.104	5.426

These storage magnitudes suggest a surface reservoir, if practicable. For a rectangular tank with length/breadth ratio 1.33 and depth = breadth/8

9   Approx reservoir dimensions (m) $29 \times 39 \times 3.7$ (25 years); $32 \times 42.5 \times 4.0$ (50 years). Since the 50-year reservoir dimensions are not much greater than those of the 25-year reservoir, adopt a 50-year design period

10   Equalising storage range $1970 \div (32 \times 42.5)$ (m)   1.45

11 Min distribution pressure head 150/9.8 (m)   15.3
Hence the reservoir will be on the high ground east of the town.

12 Distribution loss, A to B, 30 × 3/9.8 (m)   9.2
Head requirement at B will determine reservoir floor level. Assuming minimum depth of pipe at B is 1 m

13 Pipe level at B (m)   26.6

14 Min level of hydraulic gradient at A, (11) + (12) + (13) (m)   51.1

15 Peak hourly flow (Example 1.1) (m³/s)   0.133   0.176

16 Head loss/km in 380 mm pipe, f = 0.018 (m/km)   3.31   5.81

17 Head loss/km in 460 mm pipe, f = 0.018 (m/km)   1.28   2.24

The level of the reservoir floor, 2 m below ground level, should be such that the hydraulic gradient level is 51.1 at A. The ground levels east of the town are too low for this to be achieved with a 380 mm pipe, for the 25-year design period. Use 460 mm pipe and design for 50 years. A reservoir, 2 km from A, where the ground level is 57.6, would have a floor level of 55.6 and the head loss to A of 4.48 m would provide the required minimum head of 51.1 m. The top water level in the reservoir would be 59.6 m.

B Main supply pipeline
Determine the smallest standard pipe size and then consider the actual pipe sizes required for a range of dam heights.

		25 yr	50 yr
18	Highest possible level of spillway (m)	90	90
19	Annual draft (av daily draft × 365) (ML)	1908	2523
20	Required storage (from data and (19)) (ML)	3450	4850
21	Highest possible low water level, from storage curve (m)	88.0	86.9
22	Max available friction head [(21) − 59.6](m)	28.4	27.3
23	Max daily flow rate, from (5) (m³/s)	0.091	0.120
24	Min pipe diameter (Eq 2.4, f = 0.018, L = 9 km) (mm)	330	371

The smallest standard size is 380 mm for both periods. Hence adopt 50-year design period for the pipeline.

C Dam
(a) Pipe size 380 mm (Q = 0.120 m³/s, V = 1.058 m/s)

25 Friction head + 1 per cent allowance for minor losses   24.6

26 Lowest operating level 59.6 + 24.6 (m)   84.2

27 Spillway level, for 4850 ML storage   88.8

28 Max height of dam spillway crest 88.8 − 68.0 (m)   20.8

(b) Pipe size 460 mm (Q = 0.120 m³/s, V = 0.722 m/s)

25′ Friction + minor losses   9.5

26′ Lowest operating level 59.6 + 9.5 (m)   69.1

27′ Spillway level, for 4850 ML storage   86.4
28′ Max height of dam to spillway crest 86.4 − 68.0 (m)   18.4

A comparison of the cost of an additional height of dam of 2.4 m, with the saving resulting from the reduction in the pipe diameter from 460 mm to 380 mm, will determine the more economical combination of height of dam and pipeline diameter. An alternative to raising the height of the dam would be to instal in the line a booster pump capable of pumping 120 L/s against ahead of 15.1 m.

In calculations, the actual rather than the nominal diameter of the pipe should be used and the assumed value of the friction factor f should be checked.

The design of an urban water-distribution system involves the preparation of a contoured development map of the area to be served, showing the ultimate street layout and the planned locations of commercial, industrial, and high-density and low-density residential buildings. On a second map, or a transparent overlay, zones to be served by separate service reservoirs are delineated, consideration being given to topography, area and population density; the maximum daily demand for the design period is determined for each zone. The capacity of each reservoir is established and, allowing for hydraulic gradients across the distribution system, radially from the reservoir, of 2 to 4 per cent, the approximate operating levels, and thence the type and dimensions of the reservoir, can be fixed tentatively.

Feeders from the main supply line to the service reservoirs may connect with zone distribution systems en route (Fig 2.4).

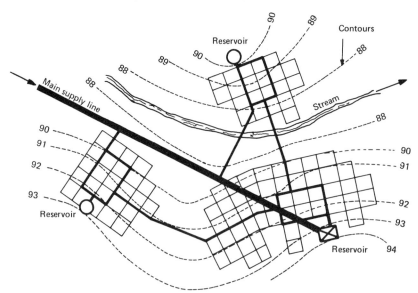

Fig 2.4 Distribution system with three service reservoirs

For each zone, a trial layout is made of a skeleton network of mains greater than 150 mm in diameter to meet the grouped maximum daily demand of each sub-area of the zone. The larger mains should be looped and inter-connected by smaller ones to ensure maintenance of supply in the event of part of the system being closed down for repair. The outflows into the minor service mains not included in the network are assumed to occur at the inter-connections, or nodes, of the skeleton system. The trial pipe sizes are determined assuming velocities of 0.7 to 1.5 m/s.

Piezometric contours for the network, compared with the ground contours, will reveal locations where the mains pressures are inadequate and changes in layout or pipe diameters are required. The trial design can be checked by a network analysis to determine the flows in each line, the piezo-metric contours and the pressures at critical points in the system. For large, complex systems, computer programs are developed for this analysis. After necessary adjustments have been made to the layout, the minor mains for the streets not served by the skeleton network are added to produce an inter-connected grid-iron pattern, with a minimum of dead ends.

Because there are many possible design variations, it is extremely time-consuming and complex to find an optimum layout. The above design procedures may have to be repeated many times, with different combinations of design parameters and strategies, before a near-optimum design is determined.

Fire hydrants are located near street intersections and others are spaced at not more than 100 m intervals. Stop valves, to enable sections of the system to be isolated for repair, are placed at intervals of 150 to 250 m, in two of the three pipes at T-junctions and in three of the pipes at cross-junctions.

If, as is usually the case, a distribution system is to be enlarged to meet growing demand rather than wholly constructed or replaced, much of the layout will be in existence and measurements of field pressures will be available. Often the essential features of the enlargement scheme will be evident to the experienced designer.

Design procedures should be precise enough for the designer to be confident that the demand and pressure requirements will be met economically. Since the range of standard pipe sizes is limited, the precise determination of a non-standard pipe size is unwarranted, although care is necessary to ensure that actual, rather than nominal, diameters of standard pipes are used in calculations. Owing to possible errors in the estimates of demand, of pipe friction characteristics and of leakage losses twenty or thirty years ahead, precision in design should be tempered with conservatism.

2.3 Pumping

An entirely gravitational system is possible for a city or town that is situated close to a high-level source of supply. Usually, it is necessary to raise the water by pumping through part or all of the main supply line. The capacity of an existing pipeline, whether a rising (pumped) main or a gravity main, can be increased by inserting a booster pump in the line.

The most common type of water supply pump is the horizontally mounted centrifugal pump in the capacity range 100 to 600 L/s (9 to 50 ML/d approximately). The size of a pump, in terms of its outlet diameter, D mm, is related to its capacity, Q L/s, by the rule-of-thumb formula

$$D = 20\sqrt{Q}$$

so that the above capacity range corresponds to a pump size range of 200 to 500 mm.

Pumps are designed to operate at peak efficiency at a particular discharge and head, the head for most pumps being between 25 m and 125 m, although special designs provide for larger heads. The head–discharge curve for a pump run at constant speed usually falls with increase in discharge. The *system head*, which is the sum of the static head and the friction and other head losses in the pipeline, increases with discharge. A system head–discharge curve can be calculated and plotted on the same graph as the pump head–discharge curve. The intersection of the two curves defines the operating head and discharge and, for economy, a pump should be chosen that operates near its point of maximum efficiency under these conditions (Fig 2.5).

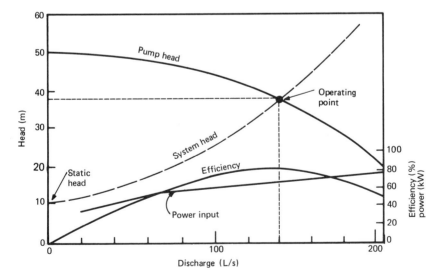

Fig 2.5 Characteristic curves of a pump operating at maximum efficiency against a system head of 38 m (static head 10 m, friction and other head 28 m) with a flow rate of 140 L/s

Operation of two similar pumps in *parallel* results in a head–discharge curve that, for a given head, yields twice the discharge of a single pump. However, the increase in discharge increases the system head, so that the resulting flow rate is less than twice that produced by a single pump. If two similar pumps are operated in *series*, the ordinates of the resulting head–discharge curve are twice those of the curve for the single pump. The intersection of the new curve with the system-head curve yields an operating head that is less than twice that of the single pump (Fig 2.6).

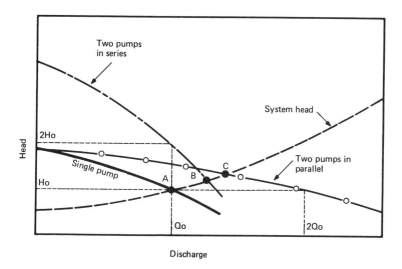

Fig 2.6 Head-discharge curves for a single pump, two similar pumps in series and two similar pumps in parallel. For the one system-head curve, the operating points are A, B and C respectively

Water supply pumping units are mostly driven at fixed speed by induction motors, either the squirrel cage or the slip-ring type. Power is usually taken from a supply authority grid but, in remote areas it may be generated by a diesel engine. Since the design of the pipeline and the service reservoirs depends on the number of hours per day the pumping station will operate, the economics of manning the station for one or more shifts and of installing automatic control devices should be considered in the overall design.

Safety precautions to be taken include the provision of a standby pump and motor, to provide at least partial supply in the event of a breakdown, and it may be necessary to provide an emergency power supply.

For heads in excess of 100 m, a multi-stage pump may be used. It contains several impellers on the one shaft, the discharge from one impeller being fed to the inlet of the succeeding one so that the effect is that of a number of pumps in series. The head imparted by each impeller is usually between 50 and 100 m. This principle is applied also in the multi-stage borehole pump, which is a compact unit lowered inside the bore casing and driven by a vertical shaft connected to a motor at the ground surface (Fig 1.10).

A critical feature in the design of a pumped supply is the necessity to limit the static suction lift. Atmospheric pressure, expressed in terms of head of water, is about 10.34 m at sea level. It decreases with elevation, and is subject to diurnal variations. These factors, together with the friction and other losses in the suction line, and the need to avoid cavitation in the regions of high velocity within the pump, effectively reduce the head available for static suction lift to 6 m or less. It may be necessary to locate the pump in a pit to meet this limitation. A reduction in the suction lift may allow a reduction in the size and cost of the pump, which, operated at a higher speed, will provide the same service as the larger pump, without cavitation. A foot (check) valve may be fitted at the suction inlet to keep the pump primed during short periods of stoppage and to prevent reversal of rotation in the event of a temporary power failure, since sudden restoration of the power supply could result in damage to the pump shaft under such conditions.

On the delivery side of the pump, a check valve is installed to prevent reversal of flow in the event of a stoppage; and a gate valve is provided to isolate the pump when it is stopped or running up to speed, to regulate the discharge, and to isolate the pump from the main for maintenance purposes.

Review questions

2.1 Discuss the possible advantages and disadvantages of canals, compared with pipelines, for a public water supply scheme.

2.2 List the sources and types of stress a pipeline must be capable of sustaining without fracture.

2.3 What are the respective functions of sluice, scour, air, check, pressure relief, pressure-regulating, and pressure-sustaining valves?

2.4 Given the estimated demand curve for maximum consumption, with steady supply over 24 hours, for a one-day service reservoir, outline the procedure for determining the equalising storage.

2.5 For a particular service reservoir site, how would you decide whether to use a surface reservoir, a standpipe or an elevated tank?

2.6 Outline briefly a procedure for the layout and design of a distribution system for a small township supplied from a single service reservoir.

3 Wastewater Collection

3.1 Introduction

The collection and disposal of water from domestic, commercial and industrial sources is necessary for public health. The water-carriage method, involving a network of underground conduits, was developed in the mid-nineteenth century, and is the most common means of disposal in developed communities. Disposal of runoff of stormwater and street washwater by surface and underground drainage systems is a much older method of protecting urban areas against health hazards, damage to property and interruption to communications by the accumulation of surface water. In some countries, one pipe network is used for both community wastes and surface runoff, in what is termed a *combined sewer system.* In others, surface waters are disposed of in a *storm sewer system*, and a *separate* or *sanitary sewer system* is used for domestic, commercial and industrial wastes. The conduits of the combined, storm and sanitary systems are called *sewers*, and the flow in sewers is *wastewater*, a term that is commonly used nowadays in preference to *sewage.*

Sewerage refers to the system of sewers and associated structures and treatment works built to collect, convey, treat and dispose of wastewater.

The combined system has the advantage that only one pipe network is required and its capacity need be little more than that of a storm sewer system, since the peak rate of flow of sanitary wastewater is usually much less than that of stormwater. On the other hand, since combined sewers are much larger than sanitary sewers, they must be designed carefully to ensure that, in dry weather, the velocity of the sanitary wastewater flow is sufficient to prevent the formation of deposits of solids in the sewer. Furthermore, if the system includes a treatment plant, either its capacity must be unnecessarily large to receive stormwater, which does not require treatment, or large quantities of polluted water must be bypassed into water-courses during periods of storm runoff. For these reasons, many countries have adopted the separate system, despite the higher installation costs.

3.2 Sanitary sewer systems

A sanitary sewer system includes:

a *Building drainage installations* — the plumbing of individual houses, apartment buildings, office blocks and industrial buildings, whose outlet sewers, or service lines, lead to

b *Collection works* — a tree-like system of pipes in which numerous small-diameter laterals converge the flows from the building service lines into larger branch sewers, which discharge into a main or trunk sewer leading either to a disposal area or to the

c *Treatment works*, whence the liquid waste is conveyed by the

d *Outfall sewer* to the final disposal area (Fig 3.1).

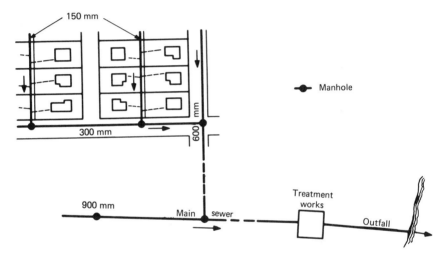

Fig 3.1 Sanitary sewer system layout

Building drainage installations are subject to local municipal regulations. Each water closet, sink, bath and wash-tub discharges through a U-shaped water-seal outlet via a waste pipe to the house service line, which leads to the public sewer. Local building codes usually require that the plumbing system of each building have at least one high, open, vent pipe. This is to ensure that the pressure in the drainage system does not fall below atmospheric pressure and so risk water being removed from the U-traps of the fixtures. Some authorities require a water-seal trap and an air-induct vent in the service line at the property boundary, to ventilate the public sewer and to prevent foul air from the sewer entering the building service line. Many authorities forbid the connection of roof and surface drains to sanitary sewers.

The conduits of the collection system are designed so that, as far as possible, the velocities are sufficiently high to prevent deposition of solid material and, except in special locations, the conduits flow either partly full or just full but not under pressure when conveying the maximum design flow. The non-pressure flow condition is intended to minimise the risk of surcharging the system and of contaminating the surrounding ground as a result of the conduits bursting or outflow leakage at joints and cracks. Short lengths of the system may be designed to carry flow under pressure, either as rising or force mains, in which the wastewater is pumped from a low-level to a high-level sewer, or as inverted syphons passing below a watercourse, a railway or highway cutting or an underground structure.

Maximum flows occur during and after heavy storms, as a result of the entry of surface water and groundwater through joints, pipe-cracks and, frequently, unauthorised connections of roof and yard water drains. In dry weather, the pipes usually flow less than half-full.

The flow in the laterals and small branch sewers is rarely steady or uniform. However, for design purposes, uncertainty about the actual flow conditions and the need to provide safety margins when fixing sewer capacities justify the simplifying assumption of steady, uniform flow.

3.3 Sewer conduits and structures

The types of conduit used in sewer construction are shown in Table 3.1. Local

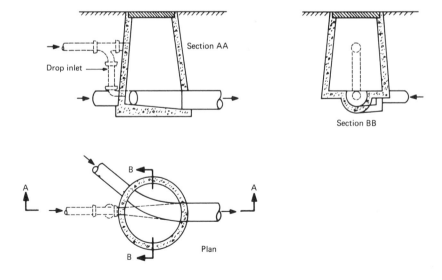

Fig 3.2 Manhole

authorities require that pipes used in sewer work conform to appropriate specifications.

Manholes

Manholes, which provide access from the ground surface to sewers for purposes of inspection, repair and clearing blockages, are installed at changes in pipe size, at abrupt changes in elevation and direction, and at junctions of sewers (Fig 3.2). They are required also on straight sections, at intervals of not more than 120 m, for pipes up to one metre in diameter, to facilitate the use of screwed rods for clearing obstructions; a larger spacing is permitted for sewers big enough for a man to enter.

A channel in the floor from inlet to outlet maintains the velocity of low flows so as to minimise deposition in the manhole. If the outlet pipe is larger than the inlet pipe, its invert, or internal bed level, is set lower than that of the inlet, so that its *soffit*, or crown, is no higher than that of the inlet, to prevent surcharge in the smaller pipe.

Table 3.1 Sewer conduits

Type	Range of diameter (mm)	Remarks
Asbestos-cement pipe	100–900	Gravity and pressure types (autoclave-cured)
Clay (vitrified) pipe	100–900	Glazed and unglazed gravity type
Concrete (plain) pipe	100–600	Gravity type
Concrete (reinforced) pipe	300–3600	Circular, elliptical and arch types
Concrete cast in place	–	For special site conditions
Iron (cast) pipe	100–1200	For pressure lines and treatment works
Plastic (solid wall) pipe	100–300	For service lines and laterals

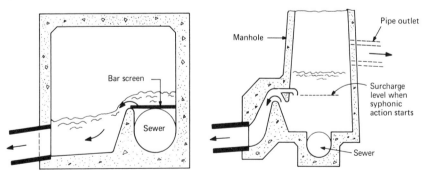

Fig 3.3 Stormwater overflow structures: (a) side spillway, (b) syphon spillway

Stormwater overflows

These are structures for discharging to local water courses the excess flows due to infiltration during storms. They may take the form of side-weirs, syphons, or pipe outlets through the walls of manholes (Fig 3.3).

Inverted syphons

Inverted syphons, to pass the flow below a natural or artificial obstruction, may consist of several parallel conduits of differing diameters. Small flows in the inlet pipe are discharged over a low weir into the smallest conduit; for larger flows, a higher weir admits water to the intermediate size conduit, and for peak flows, the highest weir feeds the excess flow into the largest conduit. The conduits are always full and under pressure, and the multiple weir arrangement ensures that, when there is flow in a conduit, the velocity is large enough to prevent deposition of solids (Fig 3.4).

Pumping stations

These may be required for the drainage of low areas and for passing the flow over high ground if a pumped main would be more economical than a tunnelled gravity main. The inflow passes through a bar screen into a totally enclosed, vented storage tank or wet-well, with steeply sloping walls near the base, to concentrate deposited solids. The pumps are located preferably below the base of the wet-well so that they remain primed when not in operation. The well storage volume and the pumping capacity should be designed to ensure that the detention time does not exceed about half an hour, to prevent excess accumulation of sludge and nuisance from odours. Automatic operation of the pumps by means of switches controlled by the liquid levels permits the use of a small-capacity pump for low flows and one of greater capacity for large flows. The station capacity must be adequate to deal with the maximum flow, but the total pumping capacity should not

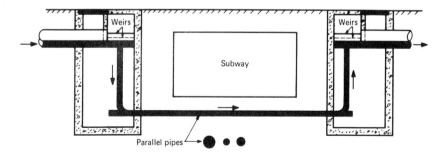

Fig 3.4 Inverted syphon

exceed that of the high-level sewer that receives the flow. A standby pump should be installed so that any one of the pumps can be taken out of service. Provision for power emergencies may include the duplication of power lines and switchgear and an alternative power source, such as an internal combustion engine.

The most commonly used type of pump is the centrifugal pump, with a shrouded impeller. It is suited to a wide range of heads and flow rates and is less subject to clogging than other types. For sewers up to 250 mm in diameter, lifts up to 15 m can be achieved economically by means of submersible pumps installed in special manholes (see Section 3.7).

3.4 Flow rates of sanitary wastewater

The capacity of a proposed sewer system is determined by the estimated requirements of the community at the end of the design period. Laterals and branch sewers are designed on the assumption that the sub-areas they are to serve are fully developed. The design periods for trunk mains, pumping stations, treatment works and outfall sewers are usually from 25 to 50 years.

The volume of wastewater discharged into the sewer system over a 24-hour period is often from 60 to 70 per cent of the volume of water supplied from municipal and private sources over the same period. In hot, dry areas the figure may be less than 50 per cent. The balance is used for lawn and garden sprinkling, street cleaning and other purposes. Hence, if the average daily water consumption is 500 L per person and two-thirds of this enters the sewers, the average daily dry-weather flow of wastewater is 333 L per person.

Some authorities make separate estimates of the domestic, public institution, commercial and industrial contributions. For example, the domestic component might be taken as 200 L per person, and the other sources may be assessed on the basis of equivalent population (EP) per institution, per factory or per hectare, or in terms of average daily rates of flow per hectare.

The rate of flow varies through the day. Flow from residential areas is lowest in the early hours of the morning, with high values in the periods 6 to 8 am and 6 to 8 pm. Flow from industrial and commercial sources occurs mostly in daylight hours, at a fairly steady rate.

The ratios of the maximum and minimum flow rates to the daily average at a point in the system vary with the size of the tributary population at that point. In the smaller, upstream sewers, the extreme flows differ considerably from the average; in the larger, downstream sewers, the extremes are less pronounced as a result of the differing travel times from the various tributary areas and the damping, or attenuation, of the peak and low flow rates as a result of channel storage effects (see Fig 3.5).

For large communities, some authorities adopt constant ratios for the

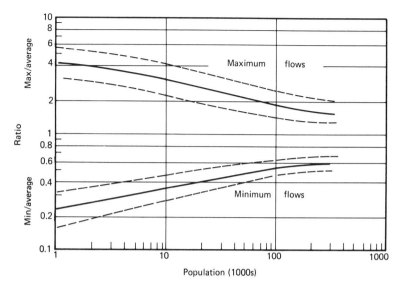

Fig 3.5 Typical ratios of maximum and minimum to average daily dry-weather flow rates

whole system. For example, the ratio of the minimum to the average rate might be taken as 0.4 and the ratio of the maximum to the average as 2.0.

The *minimum flow rate*, Q_{min}, is critical in fixing the flattest permissible slope of a sewer pipe so that the velocity is sufficient to prevent deposition of grit and accumulation of grease and slime on the sewer wall. Most authorities specify minimum 'self-cleansing' velocities in the range 0.6 to 0.75 m/s. Such velocities do not always prevent deposition, particularly in large conduits, where a criterion based on the average boundary shear stress rather than the mean velocity would seem to be more appropriate. In small sewer lines, where it may be impracticable to ensure continuous, self-cleansing flows, the slope should be large enough for the maximum dry-weather flow at the beginning of the design period to flush away deposits occurring during periods of low flow.

The *maximum dry-weather flow rate*, Q_d, at the downstream end of the system is used in determining the capacity of the treatment works, in cases where the excess flow due to infiltration of surface water and groundwater in wet weather is bypassed to storage basins or water courses.

The *maximum wet-weather flow rate*, Q_w, which comprises Q_d, plus the peak flow rate due to infiltration, is used to establish the capacities of sewers and pumping stations. Some authorities, on the basis of local experience, take Q_w at a point in the system as a factor $\times$ Q_d for that point, the factor ranging from 3 or more for population densities less than 75 per ha, to 2 or less for population densities greater than 250 per ha. Others estimate the infiltration component separately, on the basis of flow rates per ha of the tributary sewered area, or per km length of upstream sewers and house service lines, or per m diameter per km length of upstream sewers and service lines. There is a wide range in the basic rates used, typical examples of each type of rate being, in order, 0.8 L/s.ha, 0.5 L/s.km and 2.5 L/s.m.km.

Example 3.1

Estimate the values of Q_d, Q_{min} and Q_w for an urban district of area 35 ha for the following conditions:

Population density $= 50$ per ha
Av daily water supply for all purposes, per person $= 500$ L
Wastewater/water supply ratio $= 0.67$
$Q_w = 3Q_d$; $Q_{min} = 0.33 \times$ initial daily average Q

The initial daily average flow rate is estimated as one-half of the daily average rate at the end of the design period.

Solution
Design population $= 35 \times 50 = 1750$
Av daily dry-weather flow $= 1750 \times 500 \times 0.67 = 58.6 \times 10^4$ L
Peak flow/average daily flow (from Fig 3.5) $= 4.0$
$Q_d = 4 \times 58.6 \times 10^4/3600 \times 24 = 27.1$ L/s
$Q_w = 3Q_d = 81.4$ L/s; $Q_{min} = 0.3(0.5 \times 27.1) = 4.1$ L/s

Example 3.2

Estimate the peak dry-weather flow and the peak wet-weather flow from a 255 ha urban area from the following design information:

a Domestic: Area $= 205$ ha; population $= 16\,400$; av daily water supply per cap $= 200$ L; waste/supply ratio $= 0.7$;
$Q_d = 2.5 \times$ av daily rate
b Public: EP $= 1500$; $Q_d = 1.8 \times$ av daily rate
c Commercial: Area $= 11$ ha; av daily flow $= 0.5$ L/s.ha;
$Q_d = 3.6 \times$ av daily rate
d Industrial: Area $= 39$ ha; av EP $= 150$ per ha; $Q_d = 1.2 \times$ av daily rate
e Infiltration: Total length of sewers and service lines $= 154$ km.
Peak flow rate due to infiltration $= 0.85$ L/s.km

Solution

a Domestic $Q = \dfrac{16\,400\,(200 \times 0.7)\,2.5}{24 \times 60 \times 60} = 66.4$ L/s

b Public $Q = \dfrac{1500\,(200 \times 0.7)\,1.8}{24 \times 60 \times 60} = 4.4$ L/s c Commercial Q $= 11 \times 0.5 \times 3.6$ $=$ 19.8 L/s

d Industrial Q $= \dfrac{(39 \times 150)\,(200 \times 0.7)\,1.2}{24 \times 60 \times 60} =$ 11.4 L/s

$\qquad$ Q_d $= \Sigma Q$ $=$ 102.0 L/s

e Infiltration Q $= 154 \times 0.85$ $=$ 130.9 L/s

$\qquad$ Q_w $=$ 232.9 L/s

$\quad$ The ratio $\quad Q_w/Q_d = 232.9/102.0 = 2.3$

3.5 Sewer hydraulics

Partly full pipe flow

Sanitary sewers are designed to operate as open channels. For the maximum wet-weather flow, Q_w, some designers provide for the sewers to flow just full but not under pressure; others limit the flow area to pipe area ratio, a/A, to 0.75. For the smallest sewers, the ratio may be limited to 0.5 since a low estimate of the flows in these sewers could result in surcharging the house service lines.

Flow calculations can be based on the Manning formula for open channels (Eq 2.1). However, it is simpler to design a sewer for full-flow conditions with the aid of standard pipe-flow formulae or charts. For a flow rate Q, which just fills a pipe of given diameter and roughness condition, the required pipe slope is equal to the energy gradient, and this is readily computed. The pipe, laid on this slope and flowing partly full, will carry a flow, q, which depends on the ratio a/A; the relationship between q/Q and a/A is shown in Fig 3.6. Hence, for specified values of q and a/A, Q is determined and the required sewer slope is computed or read from a pipe-flow chart.

Example 3.3

a Find the slope required for a 380 mm diameter concrete pipe to convey a wet-weather flow of 125 L/s when three-quarters full, and determine the depth and velocity of the flow. Take Darcy's f as 0.033.

b What would be the depth and velocity of a dry-weather flow of 46 L/s in the pipe?

Solution

a From Fig 3.6, for $a/A = 0.75$

$\qquad d/D = 0.70;\ q/Q = 0.71;\ v/V = 0.95$

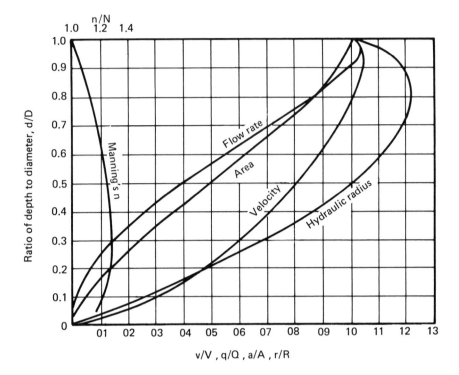

Fig 3.6 Hydraulic characteristics of circular pipes, based on the Manning formula, with n varying with the depth ratio. The lower-case terms refer to part-full conditions

Therefore

$$Q = 125/0.71 = 176 \text{ L/s}; V = Q/A = 1.55 \text{ m/s}$$

From Eq 2.3, $S = H/L = fV^2/2gD = 0.0106$

$$d = 0.70D = 266 \text{ mm}$$

$$v = 0.95V = 1.47 \text{ m/s}$$

b $q/Q = 46/176 = 0.26,$

whence, from Fig 3.6,

$$d/D = 0.39; \text{ and } v/V = 0.71$$

Therefore

$$d = 0.39D = 148 \text{ mm}; v = 0.71V = 1.10 \text{ m/s}$$

Example 3.4

The average dry-weather flow in a sewer system is based on a flow of 300 L per person per day and Q_d is taken as twice this rate. The additional peak flow in wet weather is estimated as 0.72 L/s.ha and the average population density is 50 persons per ha. If the sewers are to flow three-quarters full under peak flow conditions, determine the full-pipe flow rate in terms of the tributary population, P.

Solution

$$Q_d = 2Q_{av} = \frac{2 \times 300P}{24 \times 3600} = P/144 \text{ L/s}$$

Storm component of $Q_w = 0.72 \, P/50 = P/69$ L/s

Therefore

$$Q_w = P/144 + P/69 = P/46.7 \text{ L/s}$$

Therefore

$$Q_f = Q_w/0.71 = P/33 \text{ L/s}$$

Pipe-flow calculations

Pipe-flow charts used for sewer design include those based on the Hazen-Williams, Manning and Darcy formulae. The first two of these formulae are empirical, while the third has a sound theoretical basis. In the Hazen-Williams formula

$$V = 0.85 \, CR^{0.63} S^{0.54} \tag{3.1}$$

where C can be regarded as a non-dimensional measure of pipe roughness and 0.85 as a dimensional coefficient. In the Manning formulae (Eq 2.1)

$$V = \frac{1}{n}R^{2/3} S^{1/2}$$

where n is a roughness coefficient. The Darcy formula (Eq 2.3), with $S = H_f/L$ and $R = D/4$, can be written, for the purposes of comparison, as

$$V = (8g/f)^{1/2}R^{1/2}S^{1/2} \tag{3.2}$$

The non-dimensional friction coefficient, f, is a function of the Reynolds number VD/v, where v is the kinematic viscosity, and the relative roughness k/D, k being a linear quantity used to define the absolute roughness. In the case of slime-coated sewers, the thickness of the coating may be several times the value of k which characterises its roughness.

The ranges of the roughness measures, and typical values used in sewer design, are shown in Table 3.2.

Table 3.2 Sewer pipe roughness values

Formula	Roughness value	Best condition	Poor condition	Typical	Remarks
Hazen-Williams	C	140	< 80	110	$S \propto C^{1.85}$
Manning	n	0.010	> 0.016	0.013	$S \propto n^2$
Darcy	k(mm)	1	> 10	1.5	$S \propto f*$

* For rough-wall turbulent flow, $S \propto f \propto [\log(3.715\ D/k)]^{-2}$

The actual flow rates and the roughness conditions of pipe surfaces during the design period cannot be predicted accurately, and therefore a high degree of precision in pipe design calculations is not warranted. Nevertheless, conservative design practice requires a knowledge of the limitations of formulae used.

Flow in sewers is usually rough-wall turbulent, so that the Darcy f is independent of the Reynolds number, **R**, being simply a function of D/k, according to the Karman-Prandtl formula, which can be written

$$\frac{1}{\sqrt{f}} = 2 \log(3.715\ D/k) \tag{3.3}$$

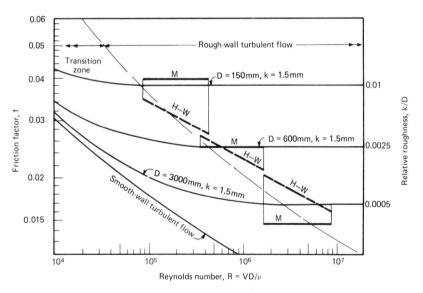

Fig 3.7 Comparison of evaluations of f in the Darcy formula by the Colebrook-White, Manning and Hazen-Williams formulae, for 150 mm, 600 mm and 3000 mm diameter pipes, with velocities between 0.6 m/s and 3 m/s; k = 1.5 mm; n = 0.013; C = 107.5; $v = 10^{-6}$ m²/s

For full-pipe flow at a specified velocity in pipes up to 1 metre in diameter, an increase in k from 1 mm to 8 mm increases the head loss by a factor of approximately 2.

In the following comparison of the three flow formulae, the Darcy formula is taken as yielding the best estimate of head loss. A k value of 1.5 mm is assumed. This roughness corresponds to a Manning n value of 0.013 for flow in a 600 mm diameter pipe, and to a Hazen-Williams C value of 107.5 for flow with a velocity of 1.0 m/s in a 600 mm diameter pipe.

The relationship between f and C, for a kinematic viscosity ν of 10^{-6} m²/s, is, from Eqs 3.1 and 3.2,

$$f = \frac{1030}{C^{1.852} \, D^{0.019} \, R^{0.148}} \tag{3.4}$$

For rough-wall turbulent flow in a 600 mm diameter pipe with k = 1.5 mm, k/D = 0.0025 and, according to Eq 3.3, f has the constant value of 0.0248 for all velocities in excess of 0.65 m/s, as is shown on the f-**R** chart in Fig 3.7. The Hazen-Williams evaluation of f, with C = 107.5, equals 0.0248 only at **R** = 6 $\times$ 10^5, corresponding to V = 1.0 m/s. Hence, the Hazen-Williams formula overestimates f, and therefore the head loss, if V < 1.0 m/s, and under-

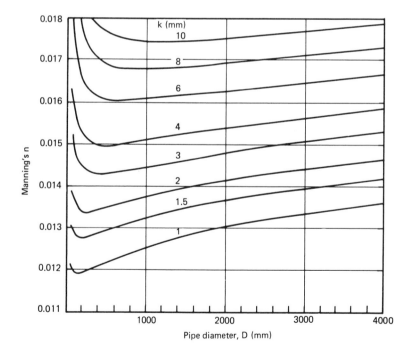

Fig 3.8 Relationship of Manning's n to k and D

estimates it if $V > 1.0$ m/s. Since, for all values of C, this formula yields sloping lines parallel to that for $C = 107.5$ on the f-**R** chart, it is not satisfactory for sewer pipe calculations.

From the Manning and Darcy formulae

$$f = 124.4\,n^2/D^{1/3} \tag{3.5}$$

Since this equation yields families of horizontal lines on the f-**R** chart, it is evident that the Manning formula applies strictly only to rough-wall turbulent flow. For the usual range of sewer velocities, flow is of this type, except when the pipes are relatively smooth ($n < 0.012$). When $n = 0.013$ and $D = 600$ mm, the Manning formula matches the Darcy formula, since Eq 3.5 yields the constant value $f = 0.0248$. For other diameters, with $n = 0.013$, the matching is less satisfactory because, for the same absolute roughness k, n varies with the diameter. Elimination of f from Eqs 3.3 and 3.5 results in the relationship

$$n = D^{1/6}[22.3 \log(3.715\,D/k)]^{-1} \tag{3.6}$$

Fig 3.8, which is based on Eq 3.6, shows that, for any particular k value, n increases from a minimum value, with increase in D, despite the practice adopted by some designers of using lower n values for the larger pipe sizes. For example, if $k = 1.5$ mm, n ranges from 0.0128 for $D = 300$ mm, to 0.0139 for $D = 3000$ mm. The adoption of $n = 0.013$ for both pipe diameters would result in the head loss in the 300 mm pipe being overestimated by 3 per cent and that in the 3000 mm pipe being underestimated by 12 per cent.

Fig 3.9 shows the percentage errors in the head loss estimates resulting from the use of the Hazen-Williams and the Manning formulae, for pipe diameters from 150 to 1000 mm and velocities from 0.65 to 3 m/s, with $C = 107.5$ and $n = 0.013$, the Darcy estimate with $k = 1.5$ mm being taken as correct. For these ranges, the Manning formula is seen to agree with the Darcy formula within $\pm$ 5 per cent, while the results from the Hazen-Williams formula are usually unreliable.

The Wallingford Charts,* based on the Darcy formula, provide a simple method of pipe-flow estimation. An alternative form of chart, suited to sewer design, is shown in outline in Fig 3.10. The abscissa is the full pipe flow, Q; actual diameters, approximating to those commonly used for sewers, are shown. For given values of Q and V, the required diameter, D, and slope, S per cent, can be read from the chart. The scale at the top of the chart has been added as an example of an abscissa that shows the tributary population. If Q_d is based on a fixed population density and if the infiltration flow is based on area, then Q_w, and hence Q, can be expressed in terms of either area or

---

* P. Ackers, *Charts for the Hydraulic Design of Pipes and Channels*, 3rd ed (metric units), HM Stationery Office, London, 1969

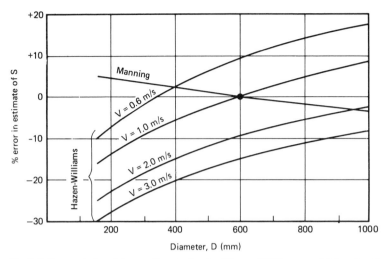

Fig 3.9 Errors in head loss estimates by the Hazen-Williams and Manning formulae, with k = 1.5 mm, n = 0.013 and C = 107.5

population, P. In Fig 3.10, the relationship Q = P/33 L/s, from Example 3.4, is the basis of the P scale. For given values of P and V, the possible D-S combinations can be read from the chart.

Self-cleansing flow

The ability of the flow to move and entrain material deposited on, or attached to, the wall of a pipe depends on the physical properties of the material, such as grain size and density, and on the boundary shear stress, or tractive stress. For a pipe of length l (Fig 3.11) flowing either just full, or partly full, with a flow cross-section, a, wetted perimeter, p, and mean tractive stress at the pipe wall, τ, the tractive force equals the component of the weight of the water in the pipe, parallel to the pipe axis of the weight of the water in the pipe. For partly filled pipe flow,

$$\tau pl = \gamma als$$

Therefore

$$\tau = \gamma rs \qquad (3.7)$$

and, for full pipe flow,

$$\tau = \gamma RS \qquad (3.8)$$

If τ is accepted as a measure of the cleansing action, a flow that partly fills a pipe will have the same cleansing effect as full-pipe flow if

$$rs = RS \qquad (3.9)$$

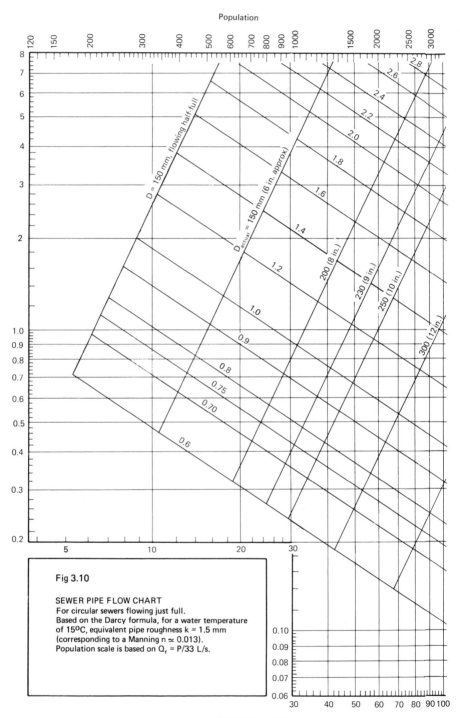

Fig 3.10

SEWER PIPE FLOW CHART
For circular sewers flowing just full.
Based on the Darcy formula, for a water temperature
of 15°C, equivalent pipe roughness k = 1.5 mm
(corresponding to a Manning n ≃ 0.013).
Population scale is based on Q_f = P/33 L/s.

Flow rate, Q (L/s)

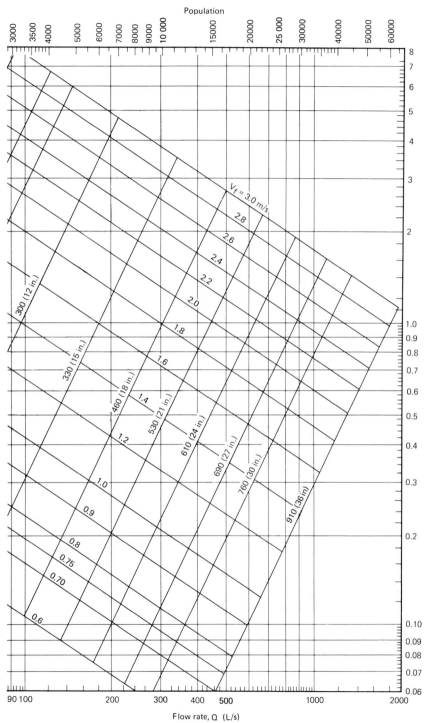

Population

Slope, S % (m per 100 m)

Flow rate, Q (L/s)

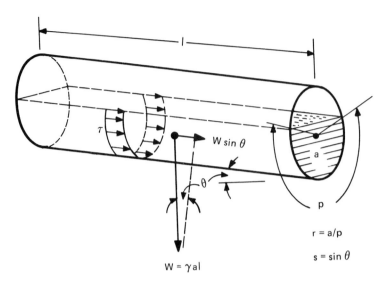

Fig 3.11 Tractive stress definition diagram

Hence, a pipe laid on a slope, S, so that, when flowing full, it is just self-cleansing, will be self-cleansing when flowing partly full with the same slope, if $r \geq R$. Fig 3.6 shows that $r \geq R$ provided that the flow at least half-fills the pipe, that is, if $q/Q \geq 0.4$, even though the velocity, v, may be less than the full-pipe cleansing velocity, V_c. If $q/Q < 0.4$, $r < R$, and from Eq 3.9, equal cleansing requires that $s = (R/r)S$. In the partly filled pipe, the cleansing velocity, v_c, corresponding to V_c for the full pipe, follows from the Manning formula and Eq 3.9

$$V_c = \frac{1}{N} R^{2/3} S^{1/2}$$

$$v_c = \frac{1}{n} r^{2/3} s^{1/2}$$

Therefore

$$\frac{v_c}{V_c} = \frac{N}{n} \left(\frac{r}{R}\right)^{2/3} \left(\frac{s}{S}\right)^{1/2} = \frac{N}{n} \left(\frac{r}{R}\right)^{2/3} \left(\frac{R}{r}\right)^{1/2}$$

Therefore

$$\frac{v_c}{V_c} = \frac{N}{n} \left(\frac{r}{R}\right)^{1/6} \tag{3.10}$$

Therefore

$$\frac{q_c}{Q_c} = \frac{a v_c}{A V_c} = \frac{N}{n} \frac{a}{A} \left(\frac{r}{R}\right)^{1/6} \tag{3.11}$$

Example 3.5

If the full-pipe cleansing velocity is 0.70 m/s, and this is provided in a 230 mm diameter pipe with a slope of 0.36 per cent, what is the cleansing velocity for a flow rate of 5.8 L/s? What slope is required to provide this velocity and what would be the velocity and capacity of the pipe, flowing full on this slope?

Solution

$$Q_c = AV_c = 0.0415 \times 0.70 = 0.0291 \text{ m}^3/\text{s or } 29.1 \text{ L/s}$$
$$q/Q_c = 5.8/29.1 = 0.20$$

whence, from Fig 3.6,

$$d/D = 0.35, \, n/N = 1.28, \, r/R = 0.77 \text{ and } v/V = 0.66$$

From Eq 3.10, $v_c/V_c = 0.748$.

Therefore

$$v_c = 0.748 \times 0.70 = 0.52 \text{ m/s}$$
$$s_c = S_c (R/r) = 0.36 \times 1.30 = 0.47 \text{ per cent}$$
$$V = v_c/0.66 = 0.79 \text{ m/s}$$
$$Q = AV = 0.0328 \text{ m}^3/\text{s or } 32.8 \text{ L/s}$$

A second iteration, with $q/Q = 5.8/32.8 = 0.18$, gives $V = 0.81$ m/s, $S = 0.48$ per cent and $Q = 33.9$ L/s.

The minimum full-pipe capacity, Q_f, based on the design flow rate, Q_w, and the specified full-pipe cleansing velocity, are critical in the determination of the pipe diameter and slope. The standard pipe size selected may have a capacity, Q, that exceeds Q_f. If the ratio of the design minimum flow rate, q,

Table 3.3 Cleansing velocities for partly-full pipes, and the corresponding velocities in full pipes on the same slope

q/Q	d/D	Full pipe cleansing velocity, V_c					
		0.60		0.70		0.75	
		v_c	V	v_c	V	v_c	V
0.40	0.50	0.49	0.60	0.57	0.70	0.61	0.75
0.35	0.47	0.47	0.60	0.55	0.71	0.59	0.76
0.30	0.43	0.46	0.62	0.54	0.73	0.58	0.78
0.25	0.39	0.46	0.65	0.53	0.75	0.57	0.81
0.20	0.35	0.45	0.68	0.52	0.79	0.56	0.85
0.15	0.31	0.44	0.72	0.51	0.84	0.55	0.89
0.10	0.26	0.43	0.77	0.50	0.90	0.54	0.97

to the capacity, Q, exceeds 0.4, q will be self-cleansing. If the ratio is between 0.1 and 0.4, q will be self-cleansing provided that the full-pipe velocity, V, exceeds 1.0 m/s. For a lesser value of V, a check on the value of q/Q and the corresponding v_c will show whether V, and hence S and Q, should be increased to ensure that the minimum flow is self-cleansing. The checking procedure is facilitated by the use of Table 3.3, which is based on Eq 3.10 and the hydraulic characteristics of circular pipes shown in Fig 3.6.

Example 3.6

Find the least slope of a 380 mm diameter sewer (k = 1.5 mm) if the design maximum and minimum flows are 80.5 L/s and 20.4 L/s, respectively, and the full-pipe cleansing velocity is 0.75 m/s. What is the least slope of a 300 mm diameter pipe for these conditions?

Solution

From the pipe-flow chart, if V_c = 0.75 m/s, the capacity, Q, of a 380 mm diameter pipe is 85 L/s and the slope is 0.22 per cent. q/Q = 20.4/85 = 0.24 and, from Table 3.3, the full-pipe velocity, V, required to provide cleansing at minimum flow is 0.83 m/s. Adopt V = 0.85 m/s, for which Q = 96 L/s and S = 0.28 per cent. (A check shows that, for q/Q = 20.4/96 = 0.21, the required V is 0.85 m/s.)

A 300 mm diameter pipe on a slope of 0.68 per cent would convey the 80.5 L/s with a velocity of 1.7 m/s. Since q/Q = 20.4/80.5 = 0.25, which requires a full-pipe velocity of only 0.81 m/s, the partly-full flow would be self-cleansing.

3.6 Sanitary sewer design

Information required for the design of the sewer system includes a contour plan of the area to be served, showing the low-density and high-density residential areas, business and industrial areas and the street layout. Detail maps should show the locations of allotments and buildings, the levels of basements to be served, street profiles including proposed changes in levels, the locations of other public utilities, depths to rock along likely sewer lines, flood levels, and details of potential sites for pumping stations (if these are required), treatment works and disposal areas.

A suitable location of the outlet from the area is selected and, from a series of trials, a plan of the most economical locations of the trunk main and its principal tributaries is prepared. Normally, they will be located along valleys. Branch lines and laterals, falling with the general slope of the ground as much as possible, are added to the system, usually being located in streets or along the rear boundaries of adjoining properties, or both, if the cross-fall of the ground prevents drainage to a lateral from the lower side. An economical layout minimises the total cost of the sewer and service lines, including excavation and installation costs, for the area, and makes full use of the capacities of small-diameter lines before they connect to the larger sewers.

The pipe sizes, invert levels and grades for a new system are determined progressively from the upstream limit of the sewered area to the outlet. (For an extension to an existing system, the level at the downstream end of the extension forms a control, and it may be necessary for the design to proceed in the upstream direction.) The diameter, grade and alignment of a sewer are kept constant between manholes. The slope of the ground may affect the diameter and grade of shallow sewers; in steep ground, a small diameter and a large gradient may be necessary to meet minimum cover requirements, while in flat areas a large diameter and a small gradient can be used to minimise excavation costs. A sewer should never be located above a water main. Local authorities have standards regarding such requirements as minimum sewer diameters and their maximum tributary populations, minimum grades in upstream sections of laterals, minimum depths of cover, and manhole details, including head loss allowances.

Example 3.7

Design the sewers shown by heavy lines between manholes 1 and 9 for this developed, residential area. The population density is 50/ha.

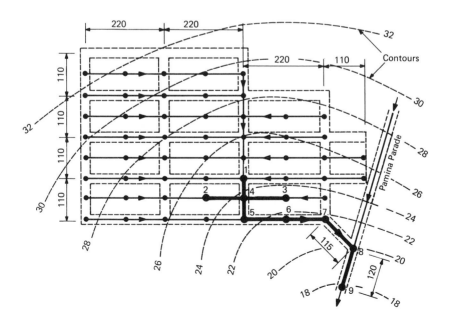

Flow details: Average dry-weather flow is 300 L per person per day; $Q_d = 2$ Q_{av} and is to be adopted as the minimum flow for design purposes; infiltration allowance = 0.72 L/s.ha; full-pipe cleansing velocity = 0.60 m/s; for the maximum wet-weather flow, a/A is not to exceed 0.75; the head loss allowance at each manhole = 0.030 m.

The peak dry-weather and wet-weather flows entering manhole 8 from Pamina Parade are 31.5 L/s and 96.5 L/s respectively, the invert level of the incoming sewer being 19.13; the lowest invert levels of the sewers entering manholes 1, 2, 3 and 5 are, in order, 22.15, 23.90, 21.24 and 23.16.

Pipe details: Available diameters are 150, 230, 300, 380 and 460 mm; k = 1.5 mm; the minimum cover, measured above the inside crown of pipes, is 0.75 m in private property and 1.4 m in roadways; the minimum grade of 150 mm sewers serving fewer than 50 people is 1.0 per cent and, from 50 to 100 people, 0.9 per cent.

Solution
The flow details are those used in Example 3.4, whence $Q_d = P/144$, $Q_{infil} = P/69$, $Q_w = P/46.7$ and $Q_f = P/33$ L/s. The area of each full street block is 2.42 ha, for which P = 2.42 × 50 = 121. The design computations are set out in Table 3.4; the ground levels shown are taken from survey data.

3.7 Sewer construction and maintenance

Leakage from sewers as a result of the failure or blockage of a pipe can lead to serious health hazards and costly repairs. Care is essential in:

a   The handling, bedding and backfilling of pipes and fittings
b   Jointing, to minimise leakage and infiltration
c   Horizontal and vertical alignment, to minimise the risk of clogging, and
d   Regular inspection and maintenance.

Pipe trenches up to 4.5 m in depth in soil are readily excavated by small mechanical excavators. For greater depths, tunnelling between shafts spaced at intervals of 1.5 to 3 times the depth may be cheaper than open trenching. Excessive depths of small sewers can be avoided if the design provides for a low-cost submersible pump to be installed in a manhole to raise the incoming flow to a shallower outflow sewer. The pump is operated intermittently by water level switches and is duplicated to guard against failure.

Public utilities usually have specified locations in streets for their electricity, telephone, gas, water and sewer lines, and accurate plans of their locations are essential so that repairs and alterations can be effected to each without disrupting the other services. Safety precautions for sewer main-

Table 3.4 Sewer design

Section (M-holes)	Length m	Tributary area ha	popu- lation	Q_d L/s	Q_{inf} L/s	Q_w L/s	Q_f L/s	Ground Upper M-hole level m	Ground Lower M-hole level m	Fall m	Dia D mm	Full-pipe V m/s	Full-pipe Q L/s	Slope S %	Fall m	Invert level Upper M-hole m	Invert level Lower M-hole m	Depth of invert Upper M-hole m	Depth of invert Lower M-hole m	Av m
1-4	55	20.57	1028	7.1	14.9	22.0	31.4	24.62	23.85	0.77	230	0.76	32	0.44	0.24	22.05	21.81	2.57	2.04	2.31
2-4	110	2.42	121	0.8	1.8	2.6	3.7	25.10	23.85	1.25	150	1.00	19	1.43	1.57	23.87	22.30	1.23	1.55	1.39
3-4	110	1.21	61	0.4	0.9	1.3	1.9	23.14	23.85	-0.21	150	0.86	15	0.90	0.99	21.21	20.22	2.43	3.63	3.03
4-5	55	24.20	1210	8.4	17.5	25.9	36.7	23.85	22.61	0.37	230	0.88	37	0.59	0.32	20.11	19.78	3.74	2.83	3.29
5-6	110	27.23	1362	9.5	19.7	29.2	41.7	22.61	21.63	0.86	230	0.85	42	0.48	0.53	19.75	19.22	2.86	2.41	2.64
6-7	110	27.83	1392	9.7	20.2	29.9	42.7	21.63	21.55	0.32	230	1.20	43	0.78	0.86	19.19	18.33	2.44	3.22	2.83
7-8	115	27.83	1392	9.7	20.2	29.9	42.7	21.55	19.80	0.95	230	1.20	43	0.78	0.90	18.30	17.40	3.25	2.40	2.83
8-9	120					126.4	181.0	19.80	17.91	1.65	380	1.59	181	0.98	1.18	17.22	16.04	2.58	1.87	2.23
				41.0	20.2	126.4	181.0													

Notes: 1 Section 2-4: The slope is determined by the minimum cover requirement at the downstream end.
2 Section 3-4: The slope is determined by the guidelines for small tributary populations.
3 In all sections, the full-pipe velocity is sufficiently high for the partly-full flows, Q_d, to be self-cleansing.

tenance staff include testing for dangerous gases before a workman enters a sewer and the presence of a second workman above ground in case of an emergency. Although gases given off by decomposed sewage may not be explosive or dangerous to health, the illegal discharge of inflammable materials into sewers and leakage from adjacent gas mains can lead to casualties and damage through asphyxiation or explosion.

3.8 Urban storm drainage

Urban storm-drainage works include street gutters, formed channels, underground pipes and storages, for the collection, transmission and disposal of stormwater from residential, business, commercial, industrial and open land within an urban area. They are distinct from flood control works, which are intended to mitigate the damaging effects of rivers overflowing their banks.

Storm runoff

Runoff does not occur immediately rain begins to fall. The early raindrops are retained on vegetation or on the ground and in natural or artificial depressions, or they infiltrate the soil, at a rate that depends on the prior wetness of the ground. When the capacity of the surface to retain water is reached, the rainwater that does not percolate into the ground flows across the surface as runoff, to be collected in gutters leading, via inlets, to underground drains.

Peak rates of runoff in gutters and pipe drains result, during a storm, from a burst of high-intensity rainfall, which may last anything from a few minutes to an hour or more. The peak flow rate at a point in the drainage system depends on the size and other characteristics of the tributary area and on the average intensity of the rainfall burst over a critical period. The length of this period, called the *time of concentration*, t_c, is generally taken as the time required for the whole of the tributary area to contribute runoff from the heavy rainfall to the flow at the point. Hence, t_c is the flow time from the most remote part of the area — in terms of travel time — to the point.

Rainfall bursts of low average intensity over a particular period occur more frequently than do those of high average intensity; for a particular frequency of occurrence, the longer the duration of the intense rainfall, the lower is the average intensity (Fig 3.12). Hence, for a given frequency, the average rainfall intensity decreases with increase in the time of concentration.

For any point in a drainage system, a value of t_c can be estimated on the basis of overland, gutter and pipe-flow hydraulics. The curves in Fig 3.12 give the mean intensity, i, of rain falling over the duration, t_c, which is likely to be equalled or exceeded once every 2, 5, 10 ... years. These average frequencies of occurrence are called *return periods* or *recurrence intervals*. The reciprocal of the return period is the probability of occurrence in any one year. For

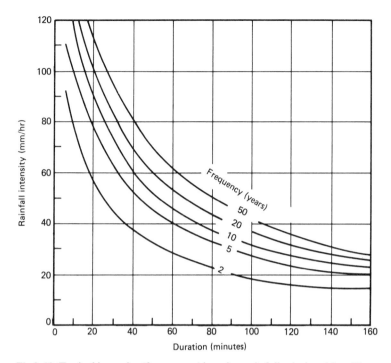

Fig 3.12 Typical intensity/frequency/duration rainfall relationships. The curves vary with locality and are developed from local observations

example, the probability that a rainfall event with a 5-year return period will occur in a particular year is 0.2.

Rainfall events of equal duration and mean intensity do not result in equal peak runoff rates at a point in a drainage system. The differing temporal and area patterns of the rainfall and the differences in the wetness of the area prior to the heavy rain largely account for the variation. However, the *average* of the peak runoff rates can be considered to be related to the mean rainfall intensity. On this basis, the peak runoff rate for a particular frequency is related, statistically, to the rainfall event of the same frequency.

Considerations of cost limit the capacity of drainage systems to cope with high flow rates, so that most systems can be expected to surcharge from time to time. For a residential area, surcharging once every 3 years may be tolerable, whereas for a commercial or shopping area, possible damage and inconvenience may warrant drains with such capacities that surcharging would be less frequent, perhaps once every 10 years, on average. In the first case, the design return period would be 3 years, and in the second, 10 years.

The peak runoff rate at a point in a drainage system, for a given return period, can be estimated by several methods, details of which can be found in recent hydrologic publications. The one most commonly used for suburban areas up to 15 km² is based on the rational formula

$$q = 0.278\,CAi \qquad\qquad (3.12)$$

where q is the peak flow rate (m³/s) at the point; A is the drainage area (km²) upstream of the point; i is the mean rainfall intensity (mm/hr) for a duration equal to t_c, for the specified return period; C is a dimensionless *coefficient of runoff*. It can be considered as relating the mean rainfall rate to the probable instantaneous peak runoff rate with the same return period, for a particular type of surface. An average prior wetness of the surface is assumed.

A major difficulty in the use of the Rational formula is selecting an appropriate value of C. Typical values adopted for return periods up to 10 years, for different classes of land, are

City and commercial	0.7 to 0.95
Industrial	0.6 to 0.9
Residential, high-density	0.6 to 0.75
low-density	0.25 to 0.5
Parks and undeveloped land	0.1 to 0.3

As the intensities of storms increase, the proportional effect of retention decreases. Hence, for recurrence intervals greater than 10 years, these values of C should be increased. For a drainage area that includes a range of types of surfaces, a composite value of C is sometimes applied to the whole area.

A second difficulty lies in estimating the time of concentration, the greater part of which often consists of the *inlet time*, comprising overland and gutter flow times. There is little reliable information about overland velocities, particularly on pervious ground. Assumed inlet times for residential areas range from less than 10 to more than 25 minutes. The *flow time* in a pipe drain can be estimated more readily. With the velocities usually in the range 0.75 to 1.5 m/s, the flow time for the upper reaches of a system is usually less than 5 minutes, and hence an error in estimating inlet time in the upper reaches may have a major effect on the value of t_c, and hence on i and q.

Example 3.8

Find the probable peak flow rate at a point in a drainage system in a residential suburb, for a 2-year return period, if the tributary area is 4.84 ha and the time of concentration is 28 minutes. Use Fig 3.12 to obtain the rainfall intensity.

Solution

For a duration equal to t_c, i = 50 mm/hr (Fig 3.12). Adopting a value of 0.35 for C,

$$q = 0.278 \ CAi$$
$$= 0.278 \times 0.35 \times 0.0484 \times 50 = 0.235 \ m^3/s \ or \ 235 \ L/s$$

Storm sewer design

The pipe drainage system follows the general fall of the ground to the disposal area. Inlets from gutters, through openings in the kerb or grates in the gutter, or both, are provided at low points in a street, at important street intersections and at points where the gutter capacity is reached.

Example 3.9

Find the capacity of a gutter with a 0.15 m kerb height, if the longitudinal slope of the gutter is 2 per cent and the transverse slopes of the gutter and the street shoulder are 1 in 12 and 1 in 24 respectively. The width of the gutter is 0.5 m. Take Manning's n as 0.018. If the runoff to the gutter from an area is 50 L/s.ha, what tributary area would fill the gutter to capacity?

Solution

$$A = 0.21 \ m^2; \ P = 3.25 \ m; \ R = 0.063 \ m$$

$$V_f = \frac{1}{n} R^{2/3} S^{1/2} = 8.8 S^{1/2} = 1.25 \ m/s$$

$$Q_f = AV = 1.81.S^{1/2} = 0.256 \ m^3/s = 256 \ L/s$$

Tributary area $= 256/50 = 5.12 \ ha$

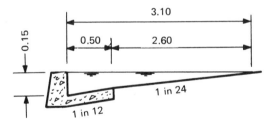

The drainage pipes are designed to flow just full for the peak runoff rate, although some authorities permit a small surcharge. Since heavy storm runoff carries grit and debris into the system, the minimum pipe diameter is normally 300 mm, to reduce the risk of blockages; and the minimum design velocity is 0.75 m/s to transport the gritty materials. The drains are dry most of the time and, as low flows carry little sediment load, there is no need to consider partly full flow conditions. The requirements regarding depth of cover, manhole details and the stepping down of inverts where the pipe diameter increases, are as for sanitary sewers.

Example 3.10

The portion of a suburban residential area shown in the diagram has paved streets and gutters with 0.15 m kerb heights. It is proposed to provide a pipe drain running south along Corcoran Street. The design frequency is once in 2 years and Fig 3.12 can be assumed to apply to the locality. The directions of overland and gutter flow are as indicated by arrows and the time for overland flow to gutter d-e is 25 minutes; n for the gutter flow is 0.018 and k for the pipes is 1.5 mm. Determine the location, diameter and size of the pipe.

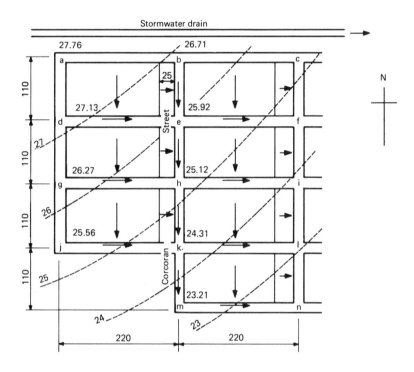

Solution

The gutter capacities are as for Example 3.9, therefore $Q_f = 1.81 \, S^{1/2} \, m^3/s$

Gutter d-e: $S = 0.0055$; $Q_f = 0.134 \, m^3/s$; $V_f = 0.65 \, m/s$

Gutter e-h: $S = 0.0073$; $Q_f = 0.155 \, m^3/s$; $V_f = 0.75 \, m/s$

Using V_f to obtain a conservative estimate of flow time:

Gutter d-e: $t_c = 25 + 220/0.65 \times 60 = 30.6$ min, therefore,

    $i = 46 \, mm/hr$
    Tributary area $= 2.15$ ha and, taking $C = 0.35$,
    $q_e = 0.278 \, CAi = 0.278 \times 0.35 \times (2.15 \times 10^{-2}) \times 46 = 0.096 \, m^3/s$,
    which is within the capacity of the gutter.

Gutter e-h: $t_c = 30.6 + 110/0.75 \times 60 = 33.0$ min; $i = 43$ mm/hr,

$A = 2.15 + 0.27 = 2.69$ ha
$q_h = 0.278 \times 0.35 \times (2.69 \times 10^{-2}) \times 43 = 0.112$ m³/s

Gutter g-h: q_h will be approximately the same as $q_e = 0.096$ m³/s.

The total peak gutter flow reaching h will be about 0.20 m³/s, which is in excess of the capacity of gutter h-k. Hence, an inlet must be provided to a pipe at h.

Pipe h-k: For h, $t_c = 33.0$ min; $i = 43$ mm/hr, as above;

$A = 4.24$ ha; therefore $q = 0.278 \times 0.35 (4.84 \times 10^{-2}) \times 43 = 0.202$ m³/s
From the pipe-flow chart, 202 L/s would require a 300 mm diameter pipe with $S = 4.2$ per cent and $V = 2.8$ m/s, or a 380 mm diameter pipe with $S = 1.2$ per cent and $V = 1.75$ m/s. In view of the ground slope h-k (0.73 per cent), use the 380 mm pipe.

Pipe k-m: $t_c = 34.0$ min; $i = 41$ mm/hr; $A = 7.26$ ha; $q = 0.290$ m³/s; therefore $D = 460$ mm; $S = 0.96$ per cent; $V = 1.77$ m/s.

A suitable tabular form for drainage computations provides for a single-line entry for each section of pipe between manholes. Separate columns show the location of the section, the values of A, t_c, i, C and q for the downstream end of the section, and the pipe details, Q, V, fall, and upstream and downstream levels and depths of inverts. The overland and gutter flow times and the locations of inlets to the sewers can be incorporated in the table or they can be determined separately.

Runoff estimates can be made more accurately if there are records of measured rates of runoff, or of surcharges of existing drains, for past heavy falls of observed intensity and duration in the region. For areas greater than 15 km², modified forms of the Rational method have been found to yield satisfactory estimates of runoff rates, particularly in regions for which they were developed. Alternatively, various methods involving the runoff hydrograph can be used. In these methods, rainfall intensity, which is treated as constant in the Rational formula, is generally assumed to vary in accordance with a selected design storm pattern, or *hyetograph*. This is transformed, with allowance for storage and varying rates of loss within the system, into a design *runoff hydrograph*, which is then routed through the sewer system.

Reduction of storm sewer flow

The peak rates of inflow to storm sewers, and hence the required capacities and the costs of the sewers, can sometimes be reduced by means of open catch drains which intercept runoff from open upstream land and divert it around the area to be sewered.

Another method involves the storage of runoff in a *detention basin*, formed by constructing a low earth embankment across the outlet from the open area. A conduit through the embankment passes low flows to the pipe drain system. When the rate of inflow to the basin exceeds the rate of outflow, the volume of water stored in the basin increases until the inflow rate falls below the outflow rate. The effect of the basin in prolonging the period of runoff and so reducing the peak rate of runoff into the sewer system depends on its storage volume, the capacity of the outlet pipe and on the characteristics of the runoff hydrograph for the design storm on the upstream area.

3.9 Combined sewers

In regions subject to high-intensity rainfall, wastewater flows may be negligibly small in comparison with those due to storm runoff, and the pipes can be designed as storm sewers, cleansing during dry weather being achieved by the provision of adequate pipe grades or by periodic flushing.

If the wastewater flows, including infiltration flows, are significant in comparison with those due to storm runoff, as is the case in regions less prone to high-intensity storms, they are taken into account. For example, the peak flow rate for design purposes may be taken as the sum of the estimates of the peaks of the wastewater and the runoff flows, or simply as a multiple of the peak wastewater flow.

A compromise sewerage system has been recommended for climates which do not usually experience extreme storm flow. It is a partly-separate system in which a small amount of storm flow is deliberately admitted to the sanitary sewer to prevent excessive accumulation of sediments, particularly when the sewer flow would otherwise be below design capacity. Most of the storm-water passes to a stormwater sewer.

3.10 Other methods of wastewater collection

Pretreated wastewater collection

If the solids of sanitary wastes are removed or liquefied in domestic septic tanks, and grit is removed from sullage and ablution water in settling pits, economies can be effected in the design of a sewer system, especially in the upper reaches. The pretreatment reduces the likelihood of pipe blockages and grit accumulation so that, compared with conventional sewer design practice, smaller pipe sizes and flatter grades can be used. Also, the storage effects of the septic and grit tanks reduce the peak flows in the system. Pretreatment involves the installation of septic and settling tanks for each household. It may be economical for scattered communities, in regions where the soil is unsuitable for the local disposal of septic tank and sullage wastes.

Vacuum system of wastewater collection

This is also known as the Liljendahl system. It uses air rather than water as the transporting medium. The pipe system, which serves only the sanitary closets of the community, is maintained at approximately one half of the atmospheric pressure by means of a central vacuum pump installation. Each closet operation admits some 18 L of air together with the closet content and 1 L of flushing water, and the discharge is conveyed as a plug by the excess upstream pressure resulting from successive flushings. The system involves power costs for the pump operation and an efficient maintenance service is required. However, the conduits, which are commonly of rigid PVC, are smaller than those of conventional systems and the quantities of wastewater are much less. Since flow does not rely on gravity, the conduits can be laid on negative gradients where necessary, so that costly excavation can be avoided. This system is suitable for locations where a conventional system would involve high construction costs and where sullage water can be disposed of locally without nuisance.

'Magic Flush' toilet system

This involves the installation of a waste storage tank for each residence. A clear, odourless, non-reacting mineral fluid, less dense than water, operates in a closed cycle for flushing the toilet wastes to the tank, where the solids settle and the clear fluid is returned to the toilet cistern. The stored wastes can be removed and conveyed by tanker to a central treatment plant. This system is suited to locations where water is scarce and expensive and where the local disposal of sullage water presents no problem.

Chemical sanitation

This is widely used as a means of holding toilet wastes in a hygienic form prior to treatment or disposal. Such units are employed in caravans, trains, buses, aircraft, sickrooms, small boats, large ships and at sites distant from main drainage. The chemical closets are charged with a fluid which prevents microbial growth but does not treat the wastes. The most commonly used fluids are based upon formaldehyde, sodium hydroxide or coal tar products. The first two types of chemical can be discharged into conventional treatment works, provided adequate dilution is available; coal tar products require separate disposal. The liquids from these units have a high BOD_5^{20} ($\sim 10\,000$ mg/L) because little additional water is added to dilute the wastes.

Review questions

3.1 Discuss the relative merits of combined and separate sewer systems.

3.2 Why are there restrictions on the velocity of flow and on the hydraulic pressure in sewer conduits?

3.3 What is the justification for the usual assumption of steady, uniform flow in a length of sewer pipe between manholes?

3.4 Give typical values for the ratios of maximum and minimum sewer flow rates to the average dry-weather flow rate for a sewer with a tributary population of 10 000.

3.5 In the design of a sewer system, what are the reasons for estimating Q_{min}, Q_d and Q_w?

3.6 Comment briefly on the reliability of the Manning formula and the Hazen-Williams formula for estimating head loss in sewer flows.

3.7 Why is the minimum cleansing velocity in a pipe flowing part-full less than that for full-pipe flow?

3.8 Define the terms *inlet time, flow time* and *time of concentration.*

3.9 Show in a sketch the typical qualitative interrelationship of rainfall intensity, rainfall duration and return period. In the design of a storm sewer, on what basis is the return period selected?

3.10 What is the purpose of a detention basin?

4 Chemical Structure and Microbial Degradation

4.1 Sources of waters and wastewaters

The chemical and microbiological content of a water sample depends upon the physical, chemical and biological characteristics of the 'catchment' which supplied that sample. A raw water collected from a highland catchment area, with low agricultural use and minimal human occupation, will be a high-quality water with few impurities, but it may be discoloured. The greater the impact of man on the catchment area, the poorer the quality of the surface water. Waters which drain from rich agricultural land may contain agri-culturally-based constituents such as fertilisers, insecticides and animal waste products; surface water which drains from residential or industrial areas can include considerable contamination from paved surfaces and even effluent discharges.

Wastewaters are subject to some variation. The basic domestic uses of water — washing, food preparation and water closet flushing — provide a relatively uniform wastewater. Variations are caused by modifications to this 'normal' use. For example, the widespread use of water-consuming household devices — dishwashers and automatic washing machines — tends to increase the volume of water used and produce a weaker wastewater. The inclusion of industrial effluents can further modify the characteristics of the wastewater. Most regulatory authorities impose standards on the volume and composition of the wastewaters discharged to municipal sewerage systems. These standards should ensure that industrial effluents are not toxic and do not appreciably change the average strength of municipal sewage.

4.2 General classification of constituents

A complete, time-consuming analysis of any type of sample would be very expensive and it is unlikely that the results would be of real value in the design or operation of a treatment plant. The diversity and complexity of samples are best illustrated by wastewaters which usually contain materials as varied as solid faeces, detergents, hydrocarbon oils, common salt, clay and food particles. The analyses which are usually carried out are intended to group materials in a manner relevant to treatment processes.

Solubility and settlement

Materials can be classified according to their ability to form a solution in water, or their insolubility and hence their tendency to settle out of water. Large, dense, insoluble particles settle from a sample in a very short time and can be removed easily by the settlement process. The smaller and less dense a particle, the less readily it will settle. Small particles take an uneconomic and impractical length of time to settle; they can be modified for the settlement process by the addition of chemicals to form a large, scavenging, settleable floc (common in water treatment) or by the addition of suitable micro-organisms and the creation of proper conditions in which they will metabolise the small particles and produce a large, settleable, biological mass (common in wastewater treatment). Completely soluble materials cannot be removed by simple settlement; they must be converted by chemical or biological means into a settleable form or into a gaseous product, or they must be subjected to other separation processes.

Organic and inorganic materials

Chemical compounds can be divided into those which are based upon carbon skeletons (organic compounds) and those which do not contain carbon skeletons (inorganic compounds). Inorganic compounds such as sodium chloride, NaCl, and calcium bicarbonate, $Ca(HCO_3)_2$, are largely unaffected by the simple unit processes of settlement and biological growth. Certain inorganic forms can be removed by chemical processes — for example, calcium and magnesium salts are removed by an ion exchange process, or by chemical precipitation to soften hard water. The majority of inorganic species can be removed only by processes that are prohibitively expensive for large-scale use, except in arid areas (distillation, reverse osmosis or electro-dialysis). Organic compounds can often be degraded, and this process is particularly important in wastewater treatment. The ease of degradation depends on the structure of the molecule; this is discussed in subsequent sections.

Viable and non-viable cells

It is important to distinguish between living (viable) cells and non-living (non-viable) cells. The term *viable* implies that the object is capable of living. Some micro-organisms go into dormant states if the environment is unfavourable, but can become active again if their environment becomes more congenial. It is particularly important that effective counts of viable bacteria are carried out on drinking water supplies.

4.3 Chemical structure

The basic concepts of atomic and molecular structures, together with chemical bonding, are treated in elementary chemistry texts. In this text, attention will be given to certain more complex structures which are important in wastewater treatment.

Water treatment is primarily concerned with the removal of small, suspended particles and the processes are physical and mechanical rather than chemical or biochemical. Chemical and biochemical actions are responsible for taste and odour formation and for certain changes which occur both in reservoirs and in treatment processes.

Organic molecules are formed with carbon skeletons. Carbon is capable of forming four symmetrical single bonds. A basic linear skeleton can be formed by the joining of the carbon atoms in straight chains:

$$- C - C - C - C - C - C - C - C -$$

or in branched chains:

$$- C - C - C - C - C - C - C -$$

or in cyclic structures:

The properties of the compounds are determined by the chain length and structure, by the degree of unsaturation or multiple bonding ($C = C$, $C \equiv C$) in the carbon chain, and by the groups attached to the carbon chain. Simple substitutions with hydrogen are referred to as hydrocarbons; other functional groups are aldehydes ($-C {\underset{O}{\overset{H}{\lessgtr}}}$), acids ($C {\underset{OH}{\overset{O}{\lessgtr}}}$) and amines ($-NH_2$). Molecules based upon simple hydrocarbon structures are referred to as *aliphatic;* other groupings include aromatic compounds, based upon benzene skeletons ($C_6 H_6$) in a cyclic stabilised form (⌬), and heterocyclic compounds, based upon ring structures, substituted with atoms other than carbon (commonly N, O and S).

Food and foodstuffs are mainly organic, and the chief constituents of living organisms are also the major constituent organic types in waterborne samples. The main constituents of naturally-synthesised organic materials are carbon (C), hydrogen (H) and oxygen (O); also present in significant amounts (0.1–5 per cent) are nitrogen (N), phosphorus (P) and sulphur (S). These six elements usually account for at least 99 per cent of the chemical composition of biological material. Certain inorganic ions — calcium (Ca^{2+}), magnesium (Mg^{2+}), sodium (Na^+), potassium (K^+) and chloride (Cl^-) — are required for biological growth. The proportion depends upon the type of organism. Vertebrates require more calcium and magnesium (for their bone structure) than do invertebrates. The trace elements such as iron (Fe), zinc (Zn), copper (Cu), bromine (Br) and iodine (I) are needed in small amounts for biological activity. For wastewater treatment, the most important classes of organic molecules are certain large molecules — the carbohydrates, proteins and lipids. It is therefore useful to consider the decomposition or degradation of these molecules by micro-organisms.

Carbohydrates

Carbohydrates are composed of carbon, hydrogen and oxygen in the molecular form $C_n H_{2n} O_n$. A simple carbohydrate, such as glucose ($C_6 H_{12} O_6$), is referred to as a *monosaccharide*; two simple units when joined together form a *disaccharide* (as in common sugar, sucrose). Organic material acts as a food and energy source for the micro-organisms and, in this way, the organic molecules are degraded. The simple carbohydrates are readily degraded in the presence of oxygen to yield water and carbon dioxide, and to liberate energy which can be used by the micro-organisms. For example, for glucose, the process is

$$C_6 H_{12} O_6 + 6O_2 \longrightarrow 6CO_2 + 6H_2O + energy \qquad (4.1)$$

The process of building monosaccharides into disaccharides can be continued to produce polymeric chains or *polysaccharides*, which may be resistant to degradation by micro-organisms.

Proteins

Proteins are composed of amino acids, which have the general formula

$$
\begin{array}{c}
H \\
| \\
R - C - COOH \\
| \\
NH_2
\end{array}
$$

In a protein structure, there are 22 units possible for the group R, ranging from simple structures such as $R = CH_3$ in alanine, $CH_3CH(NH_2)CO_2H$, to more complex structures such as that in arginine, where $R = NH_2C(=NH)NH(CH_2)_3$. An amino acid can join other amino acids by forming a bond between the amino group (NH_2) of one amino acid and the acidic (COOH) group of another amino acid. This bond, referred to as a *peptide bond*, permits the formation of long chains of linked amino acids known as proteins

$$
\begin{array}{c}
H \quad O \quad R_1 \quad H \quad O \quad R_2 \quad H \quad O \quad R_3 \quad H \\
| \quad \| \quad | \quad | \quad \| \quad | \quad | \quad \| \quad | \quad | \\
-N-C-CH-N-C-CH-N-C-CH-N-
\end{array}
$$

The nature of the groups R in the structure of an individual protein tends to confer particular properties on that protein — for example, a strong linear protein, as in muscle or hair fibre, or a rounded globular structure, as in blood proteins.

In the presence of oxygen, proteins are degraded to their constituent amino acids, which are subsequently degraded to ammonia, carbon dioxide and water.

Lipids

The term *lipid* is used to describe several types of compound (oils, waxes and fats) which are insoluble in water. These compounds include a long hydro-carbon structure, which usually has a more ionic group (such as COOH) at one end. Animal fats and oils have mainly saturated carbon bonds ($-C-C-$), while plant products contain some unsaturation ($>C=C<$). These structures form water-soluble layers, or group together to form emulsions. Degradation of these molecules is slow, owing to the insoluble nature of the compounds and the basic stability of hydrocarbon structures. In the presence of oxygen, the lipids decompose into carbon dioxide and water.

4.4 Aerobic and anerobic processes

The degradation of large molecules has been described in terms of the final products, assuming that the micro-organisms are operating in the presence of oxygen. These conditions, in which free dissolved oxygen is present in the water phase and is utilised by the micro-organisms, are referred to as *aerobic* processes. If free oxygen is not available for use by micro-organisms in the water phase, the micro-organisms take oxygen from inorganic salts which contain bound oxygen (nitrate, NO_3^-, sulphate, SO_4^{2-}, phosphate, PO_4^{3-}). This mode of operation is termed *anaerobic.* The presence or absence of oxygen in a water or wastewater sample is therefore of considerable importance. It limits the type of micro-organism which can be active and this, in turn, influences the products likely to be formed in the water or wastewater.

Oxygen gas (O_2) is only sparingly soluble in water. Approximately 9 mg/L is the maximum (saturation) concentration of oxygen in clean distilled water at 25°C. This dissolved oxygen is used by aerobic micro-organisms as they degrade organic material. It is important to recognise that this low concentration of oxygen in water has a critical function in both water and wastewater treatment. The terms aerobic and anaerobic refer to oxygen in the water phase; the overall effect of aerobic processes is to consume this dissolved oxygen to produce carbon dioxide, water and other oxidised forms such as nitrate, phosphate and sulphate. During this process, the micro-organisms gain some energy. A generalised equation would be

$$C, H, O, N, P, S \dots + O_2 \xrightarrow[\text{micro-organism}]{\text{aerobic}}$$

$$CO_2 + H_2O + NO_3^- + PO_4^{3-} + SO_4^{2-} + \text{new cells} + \text{energy} \qquad (4.2)$$

The products of aerobic processes are not usually objectionable.

Anaerobic processes must take oxygen from dissolved inorganic salts and so produce the reduced forms of the constituent elements: nitrogen (N_2) from nitrate ions, phosphine (PH_3) from phosphate ions, and hydrogen sulphide (H_2S) from sulphate ions. Additionally, the micro-organisms produce methane (CH_4) and carbon dioxide. A generalised anaerobic process can be written as

$$C, H, O, N, P, S + NO_3^- + PO_4^{3-} + SO_4^{2-} \xrightarrow[\text{micro-organism}]{\text{anaerobic}}$$

$$CO_2 + CH_4 + N_2 + PH_3 + H_2S + \text{new cells} + \text{energy} \qquad (4.3)$$

The products of anaerobic processes are usually more objectionable than those of aerobic processes. Methane and phosphine are combustible gases, while hydrogen sulphide and other products, like mercaptans and amines, are malodorous.

The micro-organisms carry out the degradation of organic material to gain energy and build structures for their own metabolism. Micro-organisms will therefore be more successful if they can gain more energy, and in a mixed system, the most successful micro-organisms will predominate. The energy

yields for the degradation of pyruvate ions, which are common inter-
mediaries in aerobic and anaerobic processes, are as follows:

Aerobic process	Energy yield (kJ/mole)

$$\tfrac{1}{10} CH_3COCOO^- + \tfrac{1}{4} O_2 \longrightarrow$$

$$\tfrac{1}{5} CO_2 + \tfrac{1}{10} HCO_3^- + \tfrac{1}{10} H_2O \qquad 114 \qquad (4.4)$$

Anaerobic processes

$$\tfrac{1}{10} CH_3COCOO^- + \tfrac{1}{2} NO_3^- \longrightarrow$$

$$\tfrac{1}{5} CO_2 + \tfrac{1}{10} HCO_3 + \tfrac{1}{2} NO_2^- + \tfrac{1}{10} H_2O \qquad 72 \qquad (4.5)$$

$$\tfrac{1}{10} CH_3COCOO^- + \tfrac{1}{8} SO_4^{2-} + \tfrac{1}{10} H^+ \longrightarrow$$

$$\tfrac{1}{4} CO_2 + \tfrac{1}{10} HCO_3^- + \tfrac{1}{16} H_2S + \tfrac{1}{16} HS^- + \tfrac{1}{10} H_2O \qquad 15 \qquad (4.6)$$

A micro-organism will gain most energy by carrying out an aerobic
process. Therefore, if dissolved oxygen is present in a sample, aerobic
degradation will occur and aerobic micro-organisms will predominate. The
next most favourable process uses nitrate as an oxygen source, and this is
fortunate because the product gas, nitrogen, is less objectionable than the
other anaerobic products.

Certain micro-organisms use dissolved oxygen if it is available, but convert
to anaerobic processes when oxygen is absent; these organisms are termed
facultative. Organisms which can use only dissolved oxygen are strict *aerobes*
and those with only an anaerobic metabolic process are strict *anaerobes*.

Implications for water treatment

The presence of organic material in water encourages the growth of micro-
organisms and the consumption of oxygen. In a water supply, it is therefore
advisable to minimise the organic content of the water, so minimising
biological growth. This will reduce the loads on the treatment plant and
prevent microbial growth in the distribution system. The oxygen demand
resulting from the degradation of organic material in a reservoir causes a
reduction in the oxygen concentration in the lower layers of the reservoir. The
bottom waters of a deep reservoir, being low in dissolved oxygen, usually
contain products of anaerobic degradation, and such waters may be
unacceptable as a raw water supply. Microbial growth is not widely used in
water treatment, but in slow sand filters there is a layer of active biological
growth which has an important function in the performance of the filter (see
Section 13.4).

Inorganic ions are usually restricted to ensure a palatable water with no toxic effects (see next chapter), but the presence of nutrients can encourage the growth of algae which may be unacceptable (see below).

Implications for wastewater treatment

Wastewaters contain a high concentration of degradable material and so consume a great deal of oxygen. Treatment plants rely upon separation processes and biological growth to remove this material. In a settlement process, oxygen is not usually supplied externally, and therefore any system with a long retention time could consume sufficient oxygen to become anaerobic. The gases so released cause the settled solids to rise, and an unsatisfactory effluent results. An aerobic biological process must be supplied with sufficient oxygen to maintain aerobic conditions throughout the treatment plant.

Anaerobic processes are more suited to the treatment of very strong wastes or to systems involving a long retention time, where it is not feasible or economical to supply oxygen externally. In both aerobic and anaerobic systems, the effluent is likely to contain a concentration of inorganic materials similar to that of the raw wastewater, but the organic material will be significantly reduced. The degradable organic material that does remain will continue to require oxygen for aerobic processes in the receiving water. If large amounts of degradable organic materials are present, so much oxygen may be required that it cannot be replaced by natural aeration. The receiving water may then become depleted of oxygen and, in extreme cases, become anaerobic. One of the criteria used in setting effluent standards is that the quality of the receiving water be acceptable for subsequent water use. The dissolved oxygen concentration is usually one of the main criteria used in assessing water quality.

4.5 Microbial species in water and wastewater treatment

Several types of micro-organism are important in water and wastewater treatment systems. An introductory survey of the characteristics and functions of bacteria, protozoa, fungi, algae, worms and larvae, and viruses is given in the subsequent sections.

Bacteria

Bacteria are small single-celled micro-organisms which exist in a variety of shapes and carry out a variety of metabolic processes. The basic bacterial cells have a diameter between 10^{-7} to 10^{-6} m, although several types of bacteria aggregate to form larger clusters. Bacteria can use soluble substances as a food source, and they have a high metabolic rate. They can therefore consume organic material rapidly, converting it partly into bacterial cells. Bacteria can be aerobes, anaerobes or facultative. They are the only common microbial group containing both anaerobic and facultative species and are usually the most important group in aerobic and anaerobic processes; pathogenic bacteria are dangerous to man. Drinking waters are usually supplied with a minimum of viable bacteria. The principles of and techniques for counting bacteria are outlined in later sections.

Protozoa

Protozoa are single-celled animals which can use solid substances, including bacteria, as a food source and which reproduce by simple division. They can function only aerobically and they can become a predominant microbial type in waters which contain little organic degradable material. In a sequential, aerobic, biological treatment process (for example, plug flow activated sludge), the first stages are effected almost entirely by bacteria. In the later stages, protozoa consume bacteria and exist in a more stable aerobic environment. In these stages, protozoa are more numerous and are important in maintaining a balanced population and creating a clear effluent.

Protozoa exist in a range of shapes and sizes (Figs 4.1 and 4.2). The motile ones, such as free-swimming ciliates, are capable of self-propelled motion. Some, such as stalked ciliates, are non-motile. Some, such as the ciliates, have a fixed shape, while others, such as the amoeba, can change shape.

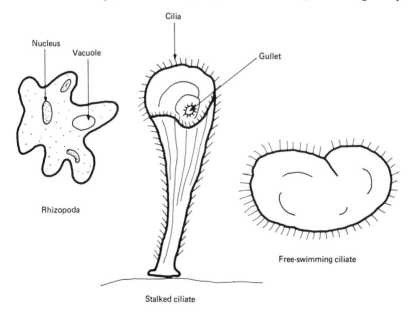

Fig 4.1 Representative protozoa

Fungi

Fungi are multicellular, non-photosynthetic plants which use organic matter as a food source. They have metabolic requirements similar to those of bacteria, but require less nitrogen and can grow at lower pH values. Fungi are larger than bacteria (Fig 4.2) but have poorer settling properties. They are important in such processes as composting, and are significant in some fixed film processes such as the rotating biological disc, when relatively large segments of biomass shear off the discs and can be settled (see Chapter 14). In free-floating aerobic processes, such as the activated sludge process, it is usual to discourage the formation of fungi.

Algae

Algae are singled-celled plants. They convert carbon dioxide into cell biomass and generate oxygen in the presence of sunlight. They do not consume organic material as do the previously-described micro-organisms; rather they are producers of organic material. Algae require adequate supplies of nutrients to grow effectively, and the most critical nutrients are usually nitrogen as nitrate and phosphorus as phosphate. If these nutrients are available in sufficient amounts, large growths of algae, known as algal blooms, can develop. This process, by which nutrients are accumulated in a water body with a consequent growth of algae, is termed *eutrophication*. The eutrophication of some waters has become a major problem in recent years because large amounts of nutrients enter the water cycle as a result of the use of chemical fertilisers and the discharge of sewage effluent into natural waters.

Algae create a water treatment problem. Their presence in a water supply can produce tastes and odours, and the presence of numerous small algae can

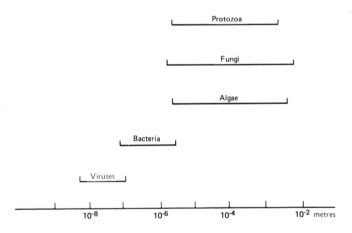

Fig 4.2 Size of micro-organisms commonly encountered

interfere with the filtration of a water. It is therefore preferable that a raw water supply does not contain significant numbers of algae.

In wastewater treatment, algae are of importance only in oxidation ponds, where the oxygen they generate provides part of that required in treatment processes (see Chapters 11 and 14).

Worms and larvae

A range of higher animals has been detected in the upper layers of trickling filters and of slow sand filters. These animals either live entirely on the filter or spend part of their life cycle on it, as in the case of the larvae of some insects. These higher animals can metabolise fairly large particles and they 'graze' on the lower life forms. This maintains an open structure in the filters and reduces the total organic mass. Soluble material is metabolised by bacteria, bacteria by protozoa, and protozoa by higher animals. Each stage reduces the total organic mass as some material is 'burnt' to create energy for the consuming organism.

Viruses

Viruses are small organisms less than 10^{-7} m in size (Fig 4.2). They reproduce only if they can colonise a living cell and, having done so, they can multiply very rapidly. As viruses are responsible for several human diseases such as hepatitis, there is concern to minimise their transmission via water or wastewater. The determination of numbers of viruses is a difficult procedure which is not normally carried out on a routine basis.

4.6 Microbiological analysis

As we have seen, some micro-organisms are pathogenic, that is, capable of producing disease in humans, while many others are non-pathogenic. It is important to ensure that drinking water supplies (and to a lesser extent, wastewater effluents) are free of pathogenic micro-organisms. Unfortunately, the wide range of pathogens and the inherent difficulties of analysis make direct determination of their numbers impractical on a routine basis. Routine microbiological analysis of waters and wastewater leans heavily on detecting indicator organisms. These are species which exist in large numbers in the intestines of man and are therefore present in large numbers in domestic wastewaters, but they are not necessarily pathogenic. The detection of indicator organisms suggests that human contamination of the water has occurred, and that other, more dangerous organisms could be present.

The most common micro-organisms are bacteria of the coliform group. Members of the coliform group *Escherichi coli (E coli)* exist in large numbers in the human intestine. *E coli* is not pathogenic when ingested, and it is present in such high concentration that, even after dilution, routine analysis is feasible. It is important to recognise that this is an indicator only; the absence of *E coli* does not guarantee the absence of pathogens.

The small size of all microbiological species restricts direct enumeration. The bacteria may be detected either by the growth of visible colonies on plates of gel (plate counts), by reactions in special solutions in small fermentation vessels (most probable number), or by observation through a good quality microscope (microscopy).

Plate counts

As bacteria multiply, their accumulated mass increases to form a colony visible to the human eye. This observation can be quantified by the following method: 0.1 to 1.0 mL of the sample is added to a sterile, agar-based growth medium in a shallow Petri dish; the sample is covered; the agar sets and is incubated for 24 or 48 hours, during which time each bacterial cell can form a colony large enough to be seen and counted. If a suitable growth medium is selected, this method can be used to count *E coli*.

A plate count technique is also used in membrane filtration. A volume of water is passed through a sterile membrane filter which traps the bacteria. The membrane is then transferred to an agar plate, where it is incubated. The visible bacterial colonies can then be counted.

Determination of most probable number (MPN)

An alternative method for determining the number of bacteria in a sample is the technique of most probable number determination. A number of small fermentation vessels which contain a growth medium are inoculated with the sample. Statistical analysis of the vessels which show bacterial growth after incubation is used to determine the most probable number, MPN, of bacteria in the original sample.

Lactose can be fermented by the coliform group of bacteria, resulting in the formation of carbon dioxide. A series of diluted samples can be incubated in lactose broth; the small fermentation vessel contained in a small inverted tube which is also filled with lactose broth. A sample which contains coliform bacteria will generate carbon dioxide; this will be seen in the inverted tube when the broth becomes cloudy. From serial dilution and statistical tables, the MPN of coliform bacteria in the original sample can be determined. This analysis is not specific, because other groups of bacteria can ferment lactose; hence the test yields a presumptive MPN. The fermented tubes can be inoculated into lactose broth, which contains chemicals that inhibit the growth of non-coliform bacteria. Positive results in this reincubated test are taken as indicating coliforms of human origin.

Microscopic examination

Micro-organisms can be observed with the aid of a simple optical microscope with a magnification of 200 to 1000 diameters. With experience, this method can be used to make a preliminary identification of micro-organisms — a useful first step in estimating species in a water supply or a biological treatment process.

4.7 Microbial processes in treatment

The interrelationship between the chemical and microbiological processes that take place in water and wastewater and their implications for the design and operation of treatment plants are important aspects of water and wastewater engineering. Treatment plants often rely on optimising biological processes which would otherwise occur slowly and produce an adverse environmental effect. A wastewater treatment plant therefore attempts to optimise the settlement and microbial processes so that the discharge effluent will cause only minor changes which have little deleterious effect on the receiving water. Similarly, an understanding of algal growth is essential to efficient management of catchments and reservoirs.

Review questions

4.1 Describe the characteristics of bacteria, protozoa and algae. Relate these characteristics to the role of bacteria, protozoa and algae in water and wastewater treatment.

4.2 Why are non-pathogenic micro-organisms counted when they pose little hazard to human health?

4.3 Why is nitrate desirable in waters which may become anaerobic?

4.4 Why are lipid molecules more difficult for micro-organisms to degrade than simple carbohydrate molecules?

4.5 A solution of common salt in water would 'pollute' a clean freshwater stream. What are the difficulties involved in removing salt from water?

4.6 Why do facultative bacteria carry out aerobic rather than anaerobic processes in the presence of oxygen?

5 Characterisation of Waters and Wastewaters

5.1 Necessity for testing

Waters and wastewaters are analysed for a number of purposes:

Design

To design an efficient system, the characteristics of the water and wastewater to be processed must be known. For example, it is necessary to know the amount of oxygen consumed by a particular wastewater in order to determine, among other things, the oxygen requirement in the treatment stage.

Operation

In the day-to-day management of a plant, regular testing is essential so that the plant can be altered to accommodate changing loads. Routine tests may reveal the need to modify the chemical dosage of chlorine or coagulant, or a process variable; for example, if a sample shows changes in settlement characteristics, the settlement stage of the process can be modified accordingly.

Record keeping

By indicating such things as change in load and process efficiency, routine testing allows the long-term performance of plant to be assessed. This information can be used in upgrading the plant, in designing new plant, in optimising performance and in timing augmentation of the plant.

Statutory requirements

The discharge of effluents is controlled by statutory bodies, which may insist on regular sampling and analysis.

5.2 Types of test

The type of test to be performed depends upon the degree of accuracy required, the use of the data and the use of the water. Tests for plant operation control must be performed rapidly, often by persons with little formal training in analysis. The analyses required by statutory authorities are usually carried out by trained personnel in a well-equipped laboratory. The type of analytical tests for a drinking water supply will differ from that for a raw wastewater.

The types of test used on water and wastewater can be broadly classified as:

a Tests for gross pollution, such as biochemical oxygen demand, chemical oxygen demand, suspended solids, ammonia and grease. These tests are used extensively for wastewaters.

b Tests for appearance and aesthetic acceptability of waters, such as taste, odour, turbidity and colour. These tests are widely used for water supplies.

c Microbiological tests, which are used mainly for detecting indicator organisms in water supplies and effluents, but can also be used to detect other species (see Chapter 4).

d Tests for toxins. Only specified amounts of toxic materials are permitted, particularly in water supplies but also in wastewaters, effluents and sludges. Heavy metals (lead, cadmium, mercury), radioactive materials and some organic compounds (herbicides, pesticides) are toxic in small quantities, and very sensitive analytical procedures are required to detect them.

e Tests for materials that are a health risk. Certain materials have specific effects on human health and need to be controlled. Fluoride is often added to water to improve dental health. A fluoride concentration of 1 mg/L is considered to be optimum; additional fluoride may adversely affect tooth structure. Nitrate (NO_3^-) is toxic to infants less than 6 months old, for they do not have a fully-developed stomach and cannot detoxify the nitrite ions (NO_2^-) formed in the stomach. The haemoglobin becomes blocked and cannot transfer oxygen; a condition known as methaemoglobinaemia develops, which can be fatal. The chloride ion imparts a salty taste to water at approximately 200 ppm. A concentration of 600 ppm of chloride causes kidney damage. Magnesium sulphate is a laxative; the concentration of magnesium and sulphate is usually restricted in drinking waters. Irrespective of the reason for performing an analysis, the method of analysis depends upon the chemical characteristics of the sample.

f Tests which determine suitability for incidental uses. It is important that waters and wastewater can be reticulated and have no adverse effect on fittings. Tests which assess corrosivity (see Section 5.10) on the basis of dissolved gases, pH and dissolved salts may be required. Iron and manganese are soluble in their reduced forms but, on oxidation, they form insoluble salts which can block distribution systems and block or stain fittings. Calcium and magnesium salts in a water prevent soap from lathering, and can be precipitated when the water is heated. Domestic equipment may be stained by coloured ions, such as copper, in a water.

g Operational tests, used to optimise or check plant performance. These tests are relatively simple and are not dealt with in this chapter. They include the jar test for assessing coagulation and flocculation (Chapter 9), tests for assessing sludges and simple analytical tests.

Points (a) to (g) are illustrated further in Section 5.9 and in the associated Tables 5.1 and 5.2. Section 5.3 describes the theory of chemical equilibrium in water. Applications of this theory are given in later sections.

Colorimetric methods may be used for ammonia, lead, fluoride and chloride residual. It is therefore more convenient to discuss the principles of the analytical methods rather than the type of test. The purpose of the following outline is not to give practical details, nor to provide a rigorous discussion of the methods. Instead, some of the relevant principles are stated, together with their advantages and disadvantages. More information is given about more recent instrumental methods of analysis than about conventional methods. The length of discussion does not necessarily reflect the relative importance of a method.

5.3 Chemical equilibria, pH and buffers

Many chemical reactions can be described as equilibria, in which reactants A and B form products C and D.

$$A + B \rightleftharpoons C + D \qquad (5.1)$$

In such a case the reaction does not go completely to the right-hand side. Some A and B will remain even after an infinite time, and similarly a mixture of C and D will form some A and B. The equilibrium constant K of the reaction is used to define the equilibrium.

$$K = \frac{[C][D]}{[A][B]} \qquad (5.2)$$

[A], [B], [C] and [D] are the concentrations (strictly activities) of A, B, C and D when the reaction system has reached equilibrium.

The concept of equilibrium constant and several related concepts (such as solubility product and dissociation constant) are valuable in predicting the behaviour of several important species in water and wastewater engineering. The concept can be applied to water which is in equilibrium with a small concentration of protons (H^+) and hydroxide ions (OH^-).

$$H_2O = H^+ + OH^- \qquad (5.3)$$

$$K = \frac{[H^+][OH^-]}{[H_2O]} \qquad (5.4)$$

The concentration of protons and hydroxide ions is so small that $[H_2O]$ can be taken as constant. Eq 5.4 can be written as

$$K_w = [H^+][OH^-] \qquad (5.5)$$

where K_w is the ionic product of water which, at $25°$ C, is 1×10^{-14}; therefore,

$$[H^+] = [OH^-] = \sqrt{10^{-14}} = 10^{-7} \qquad (5.6)$$

This simple derivation is the basis of the definition of acids and alkalis. A solution with 10^{-7} moles/L (that is, 10^{-7}g/L) of protons is a neutral solution; with more than 10^{-7}, it is alkaline. This definition is cumbersome, so it is transformed to a logarithmic scale of pH, where

$$pH = -\log_{10} [H^+] \qquad (5.7)$$

For example, if

$[H^+] = 10^{-7}$, pH $= 7$, signifying a neutral solution

$[H^+] = 10^{-2}$, pH $= 2$, signifying an acidic solution

$[H^+] = 3 \times 10^{-10}$, pH $= -\log_{10} (3 \times 10^{-10})$
$= -\log 3 + 10 \simeq 9.5$, signifying an alkaline solution.

Buffers

An understanding of how solutions resist changes in pH is particularly important when treatment processes add acidity or alkalinity to a sample, as in anaerobic digestion, nitrification, chlorination, coagulant addition and pH correction. Biological processes are usually optimum at neutral pH values and can be sensitive to changes in pH.

The ability of a sample to resist changes in pH is referred to as its *buffering capacity*. Buffers are usually composed of mixtures of weak acids (or bases) and the salts of a weak acid. A weak acid is one which does not dissociate to any great extent, and so does not yield a high concentration of protons. For a weak acid, HA,

$$HA \rightleftharpoons H^+ + A^- \qquad (5.8)$$

$$K = \frac{[H^+][A^-]}{[HA]} \qquad (5.9)$$

The equilibrium constant, K, is small.

For the dissociation of acids, K is usually referred to as the ionisation, or dissociation, constant K_a, and

$$[H^+] = \frac{[HA]}{[A^-]} K_a \qquad (5.10)$$

If the acid is mixed with a salt of the same anion, for example, the sodium salt, NaA, the salt will dissociate almost completely:

$$NaA \rightleftharpoons Na^+ + A^- \tag{5.11}$$

Thus, in a mixture of the salt and acid, the anion concentration $[A^-]$ in Eq 5.10 is numerically similar to the concentration of salt added, while $[HA]$ is numerically similar to the concentration of acid added initially. Thus,

$$[H^+] = \frac{[HA]}{[NaA]} K_a \tag{5.12}$$

$$= \frac{[\text{acid added}]}{[\text{salt added}]} K_a \tag{5.13}$$

Eq 5.13 can be transformed to a logarithmic pH scale:

$$pH = pK_a + \log_{10} \frac{[\text{salt added}]}{[\text{acid added}]} \tag{5.14}$$

Example 5.1

A solution of 0.1 M acetic acid and 0.1 M sodium acetate has the following pH:

$$pH = pK_a + \log_{10} \frac{[\text{salt added}]}{[\text{acid added}]}$$

$$= 4.76 + \log_{10} \frac{[0.1]}{[0.1]} = 4.76$$

If 20 mL of 1 M hydrochloric acid (HCl) is added to 1 L of this buffer, the protons of the hydrochloric acid will combine with any acetate ions (A^- in Eq 5.8). Thus, the molar concentration of undissociated acid $[HA]$ will increase from 0.1 to 0.12 (ignoring dilution factor) and the acetate ion concentration will decrease to 0.08. From Eq 5.10,

$$pH = pK_a + \log_{10} \frac{0.08}{0.12}$$

$$= 4.76 - 0.18 = 4.58$$

In the presence of the buffer, the pH has been reduced by only a small amount from 4.76 to 4.58, while 20 mL of 1 M HCl in 1 L of pure water would give a pH of 1.7.

Several salts are commonly found in waters and wastewater—for example, carbonates, bicarbonates, phosphates and acetates. They usually maintain a pH near to neutral. The degree of buffering capacity can be measured by titrating with N/50 acid and is recorded on a calcium carbonate scale as alkalinity. Australian waters have very low concentrations of carbonate and bicarbonate; they are low in alkalinity ($<$ 200 ppm) and it is difficult to maintain reliable pH values. High alkalinity waters, which are more common in Europe and North America, are less subject to this problem.

5.4 Physical tests

Tests for colour, turbidity, taste and odour are widely used to establish the aesthetic quality, or potability, of waters. The tests are rarely used to examine wastewaters or effluents. Physical tests do not attempt to specify the chemical or group of chemicals responsible for a particular effect. The methods of analysis for colour and turbidity are relatively simple and are widely used in routine analysis and plant control. The assessment of taste and odour in waters is subjective and a panel of 'testers' is needed to carry out the analysis. Other physical tests, such as the determination of temperature, do not warrant separate discussion, while the determination of conductivity can provide a simple analytical method for some waters and wastewaters.

Turbidity

Turbidity is a measure of the ability of a water to scatter light. Small particles in water scatter and absorb light, so that the light does not pass directly through the water. Therefore, the water appears cloudy or turbid. Turbidity can be caused by any small particles which are suspended in the water, for example clay, algae and organic material. The turbidity of a sample will depend upon the number, size, shape and refractive index of the particles in suspension. Therefore, there is not a universal relationship between measured turbidity and the amount of material suspended in the water, although for specific samples there may be proportionality between turbidity and suspended solids concentration. Turbidity is measured on a turbidity scale of units established for a standard suspension. A commonly employed method of turbidity measurement uses a formazin polymer as the standard suspension and balances the scattered and transmitted light intensities for defined conditions of illumination. The turbidity of waters is determined by the same experimental technique using the calibration curve of the standard suspension.

Colour

Colour in water means that the water will absorb light energy in the visual spectral range (400–700 nm). Water (H_2O) is colourless, so the presence of impurities in a sample records the presence of impurities in that sample. Particles in suspension confuse the determination of colour, because light is absorbed and scattered by the particles. True colour is determined on samples which have low turbidity or have been filtered (apparent colour can be removed by filtration). Again, colour can be caused by many different chemicals; for example, industrial dyestuffs, dissolved minerals, plant and animal byproducts and decomposition products. Many waters examined for colour are in a water supply system. A major colouration is the 'humic acid' materials produced by plants; this type of material is common in waters collected from uplands and low-grade agricultural land. A yellow-brown colouration is imparted to the water. Colour is determined by visual comparison with standard solutions of the chloroplatinate ion, which are similar in colour to the natural colours present in waters. The test can be carried out as a simple comparison between the sample and the standards. The standards can be freshly prepared solutions of chloroplatinate ion or glass discs tinted to match the chloroplatinate-ion colouration. Potable waters are usually analysed by visual comparison. The presence of unusual colours (due, for example, to the presence of industrial wastewaters) requires the use of a spectrophotometer to measure the colour at different wavelengths.

Taste and odour

The presence of taste and/or odour in a water is recognised by the response of human cells to particular chemicals. Many chemicals can give rise to tastes or odours; for example, the byproducts of micro-organisms, hydrogen sulphide, dissolved salts and decaying vegetable matter. Some chemicals will give rise to taste or odour only; for example, the presence of sodium chloride (salt) in water produces a salty taste but no odour. For other chemicals it is difficult to define the effects because the odours are apparent only when the water is in the mouth. An aim of a water-supply undertaking is to provide water which is not objectionable to the consumer, therefore taste and odour are assessed by panels of individuals. Detailed procedures have been devised for the production of odour and taste-free water and for the testing of samples. The samples can be rated on a scale which describes their acceptance to consumers, or the dilution required to eliminate a taste or odour can be recorded as the threshold of the taste or odour.

Conductivity and total dissolved solids

The conductivity of a water measures the ability of the sample to carry an electric current. Compounds which dissociate in solution to give separate ions will have a high conductivity, while compounds which do not dissociate have a low conductivity. Therefore, the major influence upon conductivity is the concentration of dissolved inorganic salts in the water. The relationship between conductivity and dissolved substances depends upon the materials present, the temperature, concentrations and pH-value of the sample.

Therefore, a universal relationship between conductivity and total dissolved solids cannot be expected, but for particular samples, where there is one major contribution to the conductivity (for example, sodium chloride or calcium bicarbonate) correlation is possible. As with other physical tests, conductivity is used to gather routine data and to highlight changes in the water which may warrant further investigation. Conductivity is determined by measuring the electrical resistance of a sample between two electrodes. Resistivity is the product of the resistance and the distance between the electrodes. Conductivity is the reciprocal of resistivity (units seimen) for a sample 1 cm square, and is conveniently measured at 25°C.

5.5 Principles of analytical chemical methods

Concentrations are normally determined on a mass per volume basis. They are conveniently expressed in mg/L, which is equivalent to g/m^3; and, since 1 L of water has a mass of approximately 1 kg, these values can be taken also as parts per million (ppm). The types of analytical method used in water and wastewater analysis can be described as titrimetric, colorimetric, spectral and potentiometric. The first two are more traditional analytical techniques, while the last two are based more on instrumental techniques.

Titrimetric analysis

The general experimental techniques of titrimetric analysis involving the use of pipettes, burettes and coloured indicators are well established. The method gives reliable results down to concentrations of 1 mg/L but not lower; the equipment required is relatively inexpensive and is widely used for several important determinations such as dissolved oxygen, alkalinity and hardness.

Colorimetric analysis

The colour intensity of a particular compound is related to the concentration of that compound in a solution. The absorbance, A, of light by the solution is taken as the logarithm of the ratio of the intensity of the incident light, I_o to that of the transmitted light, I. It is directly proportional to the concentration, C, of coloured species in the sample and to the path length, P_L, of the sample through which the light passes:

$$A = \log_{10} \frac{I_o}{I} = k' P_L C \qquad (5.15)$$

where k' is a constant.

For samples of the same path length, the absorbance, A, is directly proportional to the concentration of absorbing substance in the solution:

$$A = kC \qquad (5.16)$$

where k is a constant.

Several experimental techniques can be used with the colorimetric method:

a Direct comparison by sight with the colour of standard solutions of the species
b Comparison of the colour of the sample with calibrated coloured discs
c Measurement of the light absorbance at the wavelength of maximum absorbance; the reading is converted to concentration from a calibration curve
d Machines are available which will perform these processes automatically, the reagents being mixed and pumped to a spectrophotometer for light measurement.

Colorimetric methods are sensitive and flexible, and they can be relatively inexpensive. They are used to identify significant species such as ammonia, nitrite and chlorine. The major disadvantage is interference: other species may give a similar colour to that used for the analytical determination.

Spectral methods

When common salt (NaCl) is added to a flame, an intense yellow colour is observed; this effect has an analytical application. Heating the sample causes electrons in the stable lower energy ground state of sodium to be promoted to a higher energy-excited state. The electrons are unstable in this higher energy state and fall back to the ground state, losing the additional energy as emitted light. The yellow light intensity can be measured and compared with a calibration curve for standard solutions of sodium ions. If simple gas/air flames are used, only easily excited atoms can be determined, for example, sodium, potassium, lithium, calcium and magnesium.

The other important spectral method is atomic absorption spectrophotometry, which measures the light absorbed by species injected into a flame. For example, for the determination of copper concentration, light of the exact wavelength necessary to excite copper atoms is produced from a hollow cathode copper lamp (Fig 5.1). This light is shone into a flame in which the sample for analysis is also burnt. The light intensity passing through the flame is reduced as light is taken up by each copper atom to promote electrons from its ground state to the excited state. The intensity of the 'copper' light detected beyond the flame is therefore less than it would be in the absence of copper in the flame. This difference is related to the amount of copper in the flame, and hence in the original sample.

Simple flame methods of atomic absorption spectrophotometry are widely used for metal analyses and they give reliable results at or below concentra-

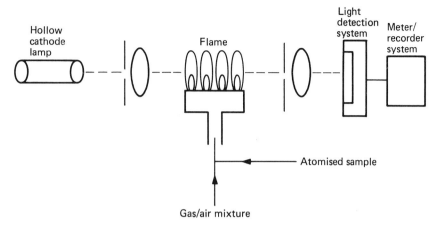

Fig 5.1 Schematic representation of atomic absorption spectrophotometry

tions of 1 mg/L. The use of a specific wavelength of light for a specific metal reduces interference, although, flame effects do influence the results. The instrument required for such tests costs several thousand dollars, and separate hollow cathode lamps are required for each metal.

Potentiometric methods

A potential difference (voltage) is generated if a piece of metal, M is placed in a solution which contains a solution of the divalent metallic ions M^{2+}. This potential difference can be taken as a measurement of the ease of dissolving the metal. For a system

$$M \rightleftharpoons M^{2+} + 2e^- \qquad (5.17)$$

the potential difference, E, is given by the 'Nernst' equation

$$E = E_o + \frac{RT}{nF} \log \frac{[M^{2+}]}{[M]} \qquad (5.18)$$

where E_o is the standard electrode potential of the M/M^{2+} system under standard experimental conditions; R is the universal gas constant; T is temperature in $^\circ K$; n is the number of electrons transferred (two in this case); F is the Faraday, which is a constant; and $[M^{2+}]$ and $[M]$ represent the activity of the ions and the metal.

At $25^\circ C$, the value of RT/F is 0.059, and the activity of the metal can be taken as unity. Therefore,

$$E = E_o + \frac{0.059}{n} \log [M^{2+}] \qquad (5.19)$$

Thus for this process in which n = 2, the potential generated is proportional to log $[M^{2+}]$, the intercept at zero activity (concentration) gives E_o, and the gradient is 29.5 mV/unit activity. It is therefore possible to measure concentration by determining the potential difference generated between the metal and an unknown concentration of metallic ions in a solution. Experimentally, it is necessary to have a reference electrode for measuring this potential difference in the external circuit. Potentiometric methods are used in specific ion electrodes and in pH (glass) electrodes.

Specific ion electrodes have been developed for a range of ions including fluoride, chloride and nitrate. The fluoride electrode contains a crystal of lanthanum fluoride, which acts as a membrane separating the sample from an internal measuring solution and electrode. The membrane is sensitive to the fluoride concentration in the sample, and can register the differences of potential between the outside sample and the internal reference solution. This potential difference is measured and used to determine the concentration of fluoride ions. The specific ion electrodes require careful use and checking; but, for certain determinations, they give accurate, reliable results.

The pH or glass electrode operates on similar general principles, except that the membrane is a glass bulb formulated so that it responds to the presence of protons in solution (Fig 5.2). The outside surface of the glass is sensitised by the protons in the sample and the inside surface by a standard solution of hydrochloric acid, in which there is a silver/silver chloride electrode. The differences in potential across the glass are measured and displayed on a pH scale.

As with all specific ion electrodes, the response depends on the condition of the membrane, and the electrode requires regular calibration with standard buffer solutions of known pH. This electrode system is widely used and is a rapid, reliable means of determining pH.

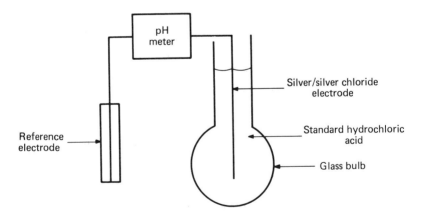

Fig 5.2 Glass (pH) electrode

5.6 Solids determination

There are several methods for determining the amount and type of solid material dissolved or suspended in a water sample. The various tests used to measure different types of solid material are discussed below.

Total solids

To determine the total amount of solid material present in a water sample, a fixed volume of the sample is evaporated and the residue dried at 105°C and weighed. As no separation is involved, soluble materials such as sugar and salt are included in the result, together with clay particles and non-volatile oils.

Suspended and/or soluble solids

To determine the amount of material not in solution (the amount of suspended solids), the sample is centrifuged or filtered and the dried residue weighed. Soluble solids can be separated from the filtrate and then weighed, or they may be determined by subtracting the suspended solids from the total solids. The determination of suspended solids indicates the material which might be removed by a settlement process.

Volatile solids and/or fixed residue

If a sample is heated to 600°C in air, the organic material will burn and the weight loss can be attributed to the organic content of the sample. This is usually interpreted as the degradable fraction of the sample, although not all organic materials are degradable and some inorganic compounds including calcium carbonate decompose and lose weight at this temperature. The material remaining after heating is recorded as the fixed residue.

Settleable solids

The volume of settleable solids can be ascertained by permitting a sample to settle for a period of 30 minutes or one hour. The test is usually performed in a one-litre cone graduated at the base, known as an Imhoff cone. The values obtained are on a volume/volume basis, for example 15 mL/L, and not on the more usual mg/L basis. This test is incorporated into the sludge volume or sludge density index.

All these solids determinations give only a generalised indication of the amount of material measured. They do not specify the particular compounds or groups of compounds in a sample.

5.7 Determination of dissolved oxygen

All aerobic organisms require oxygen for respiration. Therefore, the presence of oxygen in water and wastewater is important to the maintenance of the quality of surface water, and an adequate supply of oxygen is required for wastewater treatment. The determination of biochemical oxygen demand, BOD, which is the major parameter in water pollution control, requires the determination of dissolved oxygen. The two methods in general use are a titrimetric method (Winkler) based on chemical procedures, and an instrumental method based on a detecting electrode.

Winkler method

The concentration of oxygen in a water sample cannot be determined by a simple titration. Instead, the oxygen is replaced by its equivalent in iodine, which is easily titrated. Solutions of manganous sulphate and alkaline potassium iodide are added to the sample for analysis. In alkaline conditions, the manganese ions form a white precipitate of manganous hydroxide:

$$Mn^{2+} + 2OH^- \rightleftharpoons Mn(OH)_2 \tag{5.20}$$

The manganous hydroxide reacts with any oxygen in the solution to form a brown precipitate of manganic oxide (MnO_2). The oxygen oxidises the manganese and in so doing becomes fixed in the precipitated oxide:

$$Mn(OH)_2 + \tfrac{1}{2}O_2 \rightleftharpoons MnO_2 \downarrow + H_2O \text{ (brown precipitate)} \tag{5.21}$$

On the addition of sulphuric acid, the manganic oxide reacts with the iodide ions added initially as potassium iodide, re-forming manganous ions which do not precipitate in the acidic solution; iodine is then formed:

$$MnO_2 + 2I^- + 4H^+ \rightleftharpoons Mn^{2+} + I_2 + 2H_2O \tag{5.22}$$

The oxygen originally in solution is replaced by iodine, which can be titrated with sodium thiosulphate, the blue/black starch indicator being used to detect the endpoint of the titration:

$$2S_2O_3^{2-} + I_2 \rightleftharpoons S_4O_6^{2-} + 2I^- \tag{5.23}$$

These reactions constitute a series of oxidation and reduction processes, and therefore other oxidising and reducing agents can interfere with the determination. The most common interfering ion is nitrite (NO_2^-). This problem can be overcome by the routine inclusion of sodium azide in the original potassium iodide solution. The azide reacts with nitrite and eliminates any interference:

$$NaN_3 + H^+ \rightarrow HN_3 + Na^+$$

$$HN_3 + NO_2^- + H^+ \rightleftharpoons N_2 + N_2O + H_2O \tag{5.24}$$

Dissolved oxygen electrode

Oxygen can be reduced at a metal cathode, provided that an appropriate potential is applied to the electrodes. The current due to the reduction of oxygen is proportional to the concentration of oxygen in the solution. In practice, it is necessary to prevent access by other reducible species to the electrodes. A gas-permeable membrane separates the solution from the electrodes (Fig 5.3). The oxygen in the bulk of the solution is proportional to the oxygen which permeates the membrane and is recorded as a current on reduction. The electrode requires regular calibration, but provides a simple experimental method of measuring dissolved oxygen.

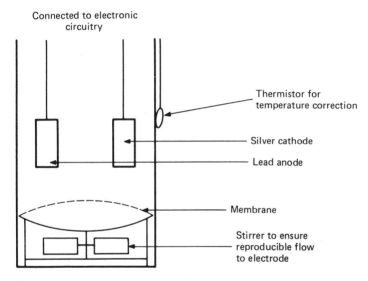

Fig 5.3 Schematic representation of a dissolved oxygen electrode

5.8 Measuring organic pollution

The oxygen demand exerted by degradable organic materials present in waters and wastewaters can be determined experimentally. The most widely used method is the biochemical oxygen demand test, although the chemical oxygen demand and the total organic carbon determinations are also used.

Biochemical oxygen demand (BOD) test

This test measures the oxygen required by micro-organisms during the degradation of a water sample. In a simple test, the dissolved oxygen concentration, DO, is determined at time zero, DO_0; another sample of the same wastewater is placed in a sealed bottle and incubated at 20°C for five days. During the incubation, the DO decreases and DO_5 is determined. The 5-day BOD at 20°C is equal to the difference in the DO values:

$$BOD_5^{20} = DO_0 - DO_5 \qquad (5.25)$$

Such a simple test is possible only for samples with a small BOD. The maximum dissolved oxygen concentration in clean water at 25°C is 9 mg/L. Thus, if the demand for oxygen over 5 days exceeds 9 mg/L, a DO_5 of zero will be recorded and so it is not possible to determine the BOD. Samples are therefore diluted until the diluted sample has a BOD_5^{20} of between 2.0 and 7.5 mg/L. This usually necessitates several dilutions of the sample to ensure that at least one dilution is of an appropriate concentration. The samples are diluted with oxygenated water which contains trace amounts of nutrient materials required by micro-organisms (N, P, S, Fe, Ca ...) but which does not consume oxygen. Samples which are sterile, inhibitory to bacterial growth or toxic, will require pretreatment and seeding with bacteria. In all cases, a blank is incubated consisting only of the dilution water which has been subjected to the same pretreatment as the samples.

The BOD test is subject to the normal statistical errors of chemical analysis plus the errors inherent in projecting bacterial growth. For a standard solution (glucose and glutamic acid), an error of ± 5 per cent is normal; for actual samples, the error is usually much higher (± 10 to 20 per cent).

Kinetics of carbonaceous BOD

The simplest mathematical analysis of BOD is based on the assumption that the reaction is first order; that is, that the rate of loss of a component, dC/dt, depends only on the concentration of that component, C, and is proportional to C, i.e.

$$\frac{dC}{dt} \propto -C \qquad (5.26)$$

In the BOD test, the concentration in Eq 5.26 is that of the undegraded organic material. This is conveniently represented as L, the ultimate oxygen demand by that material (see Fig 5.4):

$$\frac{dL_t}{dt} \propto -L_t$$

or

$$\frac{dL_t}{dt} = -k' L_t$$

where k' is a constant.

Integration between the limits $L = L$ at time $t = 0$ and $L = L_t$ at time $t = t$, gives

$$\log_e \frac{L_t}{L} = -k't$$

Expressed to the base 10 with $k = k' \log_{10} e$

$$\log_{10} \frac{L_t}{L} = -kt$$

or

$$\frac{L_t}{L} = 10^{-kt} \tag{5.27}$$

The remaining oxygen demand, L_t, at any time, t, is therefore given by

$$L_t = L10^{-kt} \tag{5.28}$$

where k is the BOD rate constant, and the measured BOD is the difference between the ultimate and remaining oxygen demands:

$$\begin{aligned} BOD_t &= L - L_t \\ &= L(1 - 10^{-kt}) \end{aligned} \tag{5.29}$$

Thus, for a five-day BOD,

$$BOD_5 = L\,(1 - 10^{-5k}) \tag{5.30}$$

The form of such a relationship is plotted in Fig 5.4.

The rate of the reactions, and hence the degree of completion, is implicit in the rate constant, k. Fig 5.5 shows BOD versus time for three rate constants, $k = 0.5d^{-1}$, $0.1d^{-1}$, and $0.01d^{-1}$, all with an ultimate BOD of 400 mg/L. The BOD_5^{20} represents 99.7 per cent, 68.4 per cent and 10.4 per cent respectively of the ultimate oxygen demand, L.

The observed BOD-versus-time curve for municipal wastewaters is commonly quoted as having a rate constant, k, of $0.17d^{-1}$.

Example 5.2

A sample of wastewater gave a BOD_5^{20} of 200 mg/L ($k = 0.2d^{-1}$). Calculate the ultimate BOD (L).

Solution
From Eq 5.30

$$BOD_5 = L(1 - 10^{-5k})$$

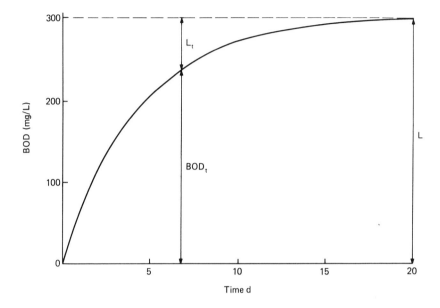

Fig 5.4 Form of a BOD-time curve

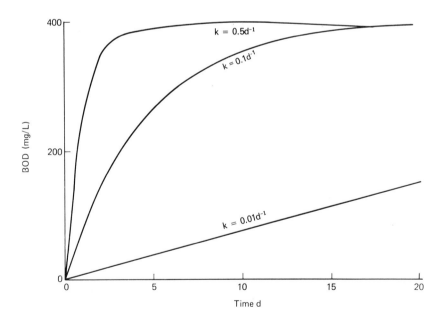

Fig 5.5 Form of a BOD-time curve for various rate constants

$$200 = L(1 - 10^{-5 \times 0.2})$$

$$L = \frac{200}{0.9} = 222.2 \text{ mg/L}$$

The experimentally-observed BOD-versus-time curve can be considered as a summation of the oxygen demand curves of all the materials in the sample, including materials which are degraded rapidly ($k = 0.4d^{-1}$ or greater) and those degraded slowly ($k = 0.05d^{-1}$ or less). This is represented schematically in Fig 5.6. At any time, t, the total observed oxygen demand expressed as the BOD curve represents the summation of all the individual oxygen demand curves 1, 2, 3, 4 ....

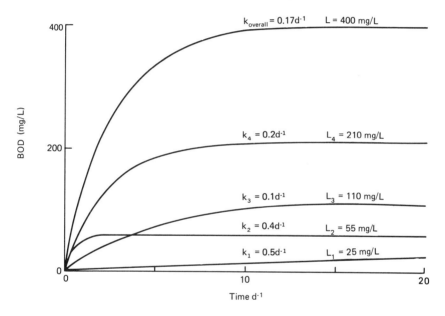

Fig 5.6 Diagrammatic representation of the summation of individual oxygen demand curves

The commonly-quoted BOD reaction rate constant $k = 0.17d^{-1}$ expresses only the average degradation rate. After five days, for a rate constant of $0.17d^{-1}$, 86 per cent of the ultimate carbonaceous BOD will have been exerted. However, molecules which are difficult to degrade, such as fats and oils, will be oxidised to a much lesser degree and will have exerted a much smaller percentage of their ultimate carbonaceous BOD in this time. Readily degraded molecules, such as simple sugars, could be almost completely oxidised after five days and so will have exerted almost 100 per cent of their individual ultimate carbonaceous BOD.

This discussion of the BOD process should be considered as a simplified overview. The individual reactions which occur during the biological degradation of molecules include several series of interlocking reactions. The treatment of BOD as a first-order process is a convenient formulation which often approximates to observed experimental results.

Nitrification in the BOD reaction

The processes described in the previous sections as the BOD reaction refer only to the oxidation of carbon-based molecules. In practice, a second-stage oxygen demand is observed. In the case of raw or settled sewage, this second stage usually becomes apparent after approximately eight days of incubation at 20°C (Fig 5.7). In this second stage, oxygen is consumed in the oxidation of ammonia, producing nitrate ions in the process termed *nitrification*.

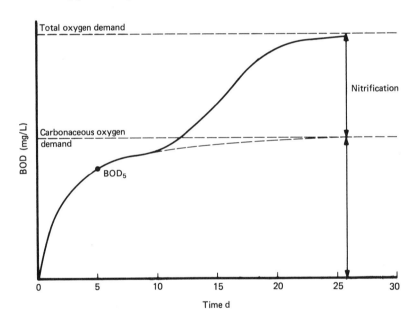

Fig 5.7 Oxygen demand for carbonaceous oxidation and nitrification

A large percentage of the nitrogen in water and wastewater originates from proteins (Section 4.3): the protein molecules are degraded to release ammonia. The oxidation of ammonia is carried out by two specialised bacteria — *Nitrosomonas*, which oxidise ammonia to nitrite ions, and *Nitrobacters*, which oxidise nitrite ions to nitrate ions:

$$2NH_3 + 3O_2 \xrightarrow{Nitrosomonas} 2NO_2^- + 2H^+ + 2H_2O \qquad (5.31)$$

$$2NO_2^- + O_2 \xrightarrow{\textit{Nitrobacters}} 2NO_3^- \tag{5.32}$$

The process of nitrification consumes significant amounts of oxygen so that the total oxygen demand for nitrification is often comparable with the carbonaceous demand. Nitrification also generates protons, thus increasing the acidity of a water sample.

Use of the BOD test

The BOD test is widely employed, particularly in wastewater treatment and water quality control. The BOD forms the basis of discharge standards for effluents and is fundamental in the design of treatment plants. It relies on biological action and is an approximation to the actual processes which occur in a receiving water or in an aerobic treatment plant. The test is slow, taking at least five days to yield a result. It can give only historical data, and it is not suited to rapid process control. It is well suited to the analysis of domestic wastewaters, but it is less reliable for industrial wastewaters. The presence of chemicals which are toxic or inhibitory to micro-organisms will produce an erroneously low value for BOD_5^{20}. Similarly samples which are deficient in nutrient elements can be degraded only slowly and so they too give BOD_5^{20} values which err on the low side.

Chemical oxygen demand (COD) test

The BOD test is lengthy (5 days), and prone to difficulties with the micro-organisms. A much faster chemical test, the chemical oxygen demand test, has been developed.

Strong oxidising chemical reagents can be used to oxidise a sample, and the consumption of chemical oxidant can be related to an oxygen demand. Potassium dichromate is used in boiling concentrated sulphuric acid with a silver catalyst. Under these extremely strong oxidising conditions, organic material (plus some inorganic material) is degraded and the dichromate is reduced to trivalent chromium:

$$Cr_2O_7{}^{2-} + 14H^+ + 6e^- \rightleftharpoons 2Cr^{3+} + 7H_2O \tag{5.33}$$

The oxidation is carried out for two hours, and the remaining dichromate is determined by titration with a solution of ferrous ion (Fe^{2+}). The difference in dichromate concentration between a blank and a sample solution is expressed as chemical oxygen demand (COD), conveniently determined as mg/L. The most common interference in this test is caused by chloride ions which are oxidised to chlorine by dichromate and registered as COD. The effect of chloride ions is overcome by adding mercury ions which react with chloride ions and form a stable compound, mercuric chloride, which is resistant to oxidation by potassium dichromate.

Because of the extremely strong oxidising conditions, the results of the

COD test are usually higher than for a BOD_5^{20} test. The COD represents the complete oxidation of many organic compounds and some inorganic compounds. Ammonia is not oxidised. As a first approximation, the COD can be taken as double the BOD_5^{20}. The actual ratio of BOD_5^{20} to COD varies from sample to sample. A reliable correlation can be made only if sufficient data have been collected to validate such a correlation.

Another method of performing a COD test involves using potassium permanganate as the oxidising chemical. This determination is referred to as the *permanganate value* (PV). The test is carried out in dilute sulphuric acid at 27°C for four hours. Under these milder conditions, the PV values are less than the COD values and are usually comparable with, or smaller than, the BOD_5^{20} values. The permanganate value can be determined after three minutes of reaction. During this short reaction time, a large percentage of the inorganic species and a small percentage of the organic material will be oxidised. The ratio of three-minute to four-hour permanganate values can be taken as the ratio of inorganic to organic reducing material in a sample.

The tests for COD and PV are particularly useful for industrial wastewater samples. They are not affected by toxic and inhibitory chemicals as there is no biological activity and they have the further advantage that the results are available after a short period, measured in hours rather than days.

Total organic carbon (TOC) test

The determination of total organic carbon can be completed in a few minutes and does not require the use of wet chemicals. The results give the total concentration of carbon present as organic compounds in a sample. The technique involves combusting a small amount of the sample in air and measuring the carbon dioxide evolved. The results are displayed on a recorder. The instruments are provided with two separate reaction paths. One includes a low-temperature furnace (150°C) with an acidic packing; a sample passed through this stream will yield carbon dioxide from the decomposition of inorganic carbonates. The carbon dioxide evolved from this low-temperature stream represents the inorganic carbon content of the sample. A second sample, passed through the high-temperature stream (1000°C), will yield carbon dioxide from the carbonates and from the combustion of organic compounds. The organic carbon content of the sample can be obtained by subtracting one result from the other. A schematic representation of a TOC instrument is shown in Fig 5.8.

This instrumental method is capable of producing results in a relatively short time (15 minutes). The instrument must be carefully maintained, and as it analyses only a small sample, the method is very prone to sampling errors. The analytical method again involves extreme reaction conditions. It would be expected that all organic material would be combusted at 1000°C in the presence of a catalyst. The method is not necessarily related to the biode-

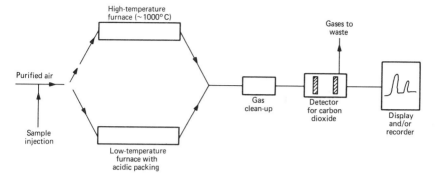

Fig 5.8 Schematic representation of an instrument for the determination of total organic carbon

gradability of the sample — a piece of plastic would register a TOC but would not be biodegradable in a reasonable time and so would not register a BOD_5^{20}. The TOC is therefore a parameter different from both the BOD and COD. The numerical value of TOC is likely to be lower than BOD_5^{20}, because it is the carbon which is being determined and not the oxygen consumption.

The TOC test is particularly useful for industrial samples, which are likely to be nutrient deficient or contain toxins. It is also valuable when a rapid analysis is required.

5.9 Standards and analytical results

The analysis required for each type of sample depends on the intended use of that sample. The general principles set out in Sections 5.1 and 5.2 are used to select the appropriate analysis.

For drinking water supplies, the major criteria are appearance (turbidity, colour), toxicity (metals, bacteria, organics), potability (taste, odour), health (bacteria, chloride, nitrate, magnesium sulphate) and, inevitably, cost. These general conditions are listed in Table 5.1, which summarises the criteria for drinking water standards set by various authorities. In most cases, drinking waters will meet these standards, but if the only available water supply cannot be treated at reasonable cost, it will be necessary to use substandard water with, in some cases, a consequent risk to health.

The standards for water quality will reflect the current state of knowledge or level of available technology. Therefore, as water treatment and analytical methods have improved, so the water quality standards have become more stringent. For example, drinking water standards in 1914 required the bacterial plate count not to exceed 100/mL with an MPN of $\leqslant$ 2.2/100 mL; by 1942 the coliform MPN had to be $\leqslant$ 1/100 mL and there were more

Table 5.1 Comparison of physical and chemical standards for water supplies

Approximate limits proposed for certain substances which may give rise to trouble in piped supplies (mg/L except where shown otherwise)

Substances	(a) ES 1970	(b) IS 1963 Permissible	(b) IS 1963 Excessive	(c) IS 1971 Permissible	(c) IS 1971 Excessive	(d) USPHS DWS	(e) USSR	(f) AS 1971 Treated	(f) AS 1971 Other
Fluoride (as F^-)	*	≤1.0	1.5	*		*	1.5	1.5	1.5
Nitrate (as NO_3^-)	<50	<45	–	45		45	44	45	45
Copper (as Cu)	0.05	1.0	1.5	0.05	1.5	1.0	1.0	0.30	1.00
Iron (as Fe)	0.1	0.3	1.0	0.1	1.0	0.3	<0.3	0.30	1.00
Manganese (as Mn)	0.05	0.1	0.5	0.05	0.5	0.05	–	–	–
Zinc (as Zn)	5.0	5.0	15.0	5.0	15.0	5.0	5.0	5.0	5.0
Magnesium (as Mg)	30	50	150	30	150	–	–	–	–
Sulphate (as SO_4^{2-})	250	200	400	200	400	250	500	–	–
Chloride (as Cl^-)	200	200	600	200	600	250	350	–	–
Phenolic compounds (as phenols)	<0.001	0.001	0.002	0.001	0.002	0.001	–	–	–
Aggressive carbon dioxide (as CO_2)	0	–	–	–	–	–	–	–	–
Ammonia (as NH_4^+)	0.05	0.5 (as NH_3)–	–	–	–	–	–	–	–
Dissolved oxygen	>5.0	–	–	–	–	–	–	–	–
Total hardness (as $CaCO_3$)	100–500	–	–	100	500	–	≤350	–	–
Total solids	–	500	1500	500	1500	500	1000	500	1500
Colour (1)	–	5 units	50 units	5 units	50 units	15 units	22°	5 units	50 units
Turbidity (2)	–	5 units	25 units	5 units	25 units	5 units	2 mg/L	5 units	25 units
Taste	–	unobjectionable	unobjectionable	unobjectionable	unobjectionalbe	–	≤2 points	unobjectionable	unobjectionable
Odour (3)	–	unobjectionable	unobjectionable	unobjectionable	–	Threshold odour no 3	≤2 points	unobjectionable	unobjectionable
Magnesium and sodium sulphate	–	500	1000	–	–	–	–	–	–
pH range (pH units)	–	7.0–8.5	6.5–9.2	7.0–8.5	6.5–9.2	–	–	7.0–8.5	6.5–9.2
Carbon chloroform extract	–	0.2	0.5	0.2	–	0.2	–	–	–
Alkyl benzene sulphonates	–	0.5	1.0	0.2	1.0	0.5	–	0.5	0.5
Hydrogen sulphide (as H_2S)	0.05	–	–	–	–	–	–	–	–

(1) Units on platinum-cobalt scale.
(2) Units on turbidity scale.
(3) Threshold odour number is the number of times by which the odour-bearing sample has to be diluted with odour-free water for the odour to be just detectable.
* Lower, upper and optimum concentrations of fluoride are related to average maximum daily air temperatures.

Maximum allowable concentrations of toxic substances

Substances (units in mg/L)	(a) ES 1970	(b) IS 1963	(c) IS 1971	(d) USPHS DWS	(e) USSR	(f) AS 1971
Lead (as Pb)	0.1	0.05	0.1	0.05	0.1	0.05
Arsenic (as As)	0.05	0.05	0.05	0.05	0.05	0.05
Selenium (as Se)	0.01	0.01	0.01	0.01	0.01	0.01
Chromium (as Cr hexavalent)	0.05	0.05	not included	0.05	0.1	0.05
Cadmium (as Cd)	0.01	0.01	0.01	0.01	0.01	0.01
Cyanide (as CN)	0.05	0.2	0.05	0.2	0.1	0.01
Barium (as Ba)	1.0	1.0	not included	1.0	5.0	1.00

(a) European Standard for Drinking Water 1970.
(b) International Standard for Drinking Water 1963.
(c) International Standard for Drinking Water 1971.
(d) United States Public Health Service Drinking Water Standards 1962.
(e) Draft of proposed revision of the 1954 USSR Drinking Water Quality Standard.
(f) Australian Capital Cities—Criteria & Objectives for Public Water Supplies.

stringent requirements on the number and frequency of sample collections and analyses. Similarly, radioactivity in drinking water was not considered a significant parameter until the second half of the twentieth century; subsequent standards included recommendations for the permitted levels of radioactivity.

Many organic chemicals are released into waters and may be present in drinking waters. Specific maximum concentrations have therefore been proposed, particularly for pesticides; for example, the total concentration of organophosphorus and carbamate compounds should be less than 0.1 mg/L, while DDT should not exceed 0.042 mg/L. Trihalomethane compounds, such as chloroform ($CHCl_3$), can be formed during water treatment and distribution. They are considered undesirable and the suggested concentration limit is approximately 0.1 mg/L. Low turbidity (0.5) has been suggested; although little aesthetic improvement is achieved below 5 turbidity units, there are less viruses in the lower turbidity waters.

Several of the authorities quoted in Table 5.1 are preparing, or have prepared, revised standards for water supplies. However, the limits set for the major parameters are not radically different from those set out in Table 5.1. The major new proposals relate to specific compounds or groups of compounds which are included separately, for example pesticides and trihalomethanes.

Standards have been prepared for raw waters to be used as a water source. The standards set upper concentration limits at which waters can be used. For example, colour in excess of 300 units will require special treatment to provide water of drinking water standard, as would waters which contain very high number of coliform bacteria ($> 50\,000/100$ mL). In general, raw waters are selected such that the highest quality of reliable supply is used with the least treatment to meet drinking water standards. Waters used in industry will have specific requirements depending upon the applications; waters used in the food and beverage industries will need to meet standards at least as stringent as those for drinking water; while cooling waters can contain much higher concentrations of impurities.

The standards set for the discharge of effluents usually reflect the downstream uses of the receiving water. A simple approach is to ensure that the BOD_5^{20} of a receiving water does not exceed 4 mg/L, so that a high dissolved oxygen concentration is maintained. The total mass of BOD_5^{20} in the water after an effluent is discharged equals the sum of the separate BOD_5^{20} masses of the receiving water and effluent. If the receiving water dilutes an effluent eight times, and the water prior to receiving the discharge has a BOD_5^{20} of 2 mg/L, the mass of BOD_5^{20} in 8 litres of stream water before it receives the discharge is 2×8 mg ($= 16$ mg). The mass of BOD_5^{20} in 1 litre of effluent, with a BOD concentration of x mg/L, is x mg.

If n litres of effluent are mixed with 8n litres of stream water at the junction of the effluent outfall and the stream, the BOD mass balance would be

BOD into junction = BOD out of junction

effluent BOD + upstream BOD = downstream BOD

$$nx + 8n \times 2 = 9n \times y \tag{5.34}$$

where y is the concentration of the BOD downstream of the junction. Division by n, simplification, and substitution of 4 as the maximum value of y gives

$$x + 16 \leqslant 36$$

or

$$x \leqslant 20 \tag{5.35}$$

This was the basis of a standard initiated by the UK Royal Commission on Sewage Treatment (1912) whereby, for effluents discharged to clean streams giving a dilution factor of at least eight, the BOD_5^{20} must be 20 mg/L or less. The standard is usually expressed as 20 mg/L of BOD_5^{20} and 30 mg/L of sus-

Table 5.2 Discharge standards and treatment processes

Possible situation	Effluent standards		Treatment process
Large dilution, small flow	No floating material No gross solids		Screening
Large dilution	BOD_5^{20} SS	< 150 mg/L < 150 mg/L	Grit removal and primary settlement in addition
Reasonable dilution in receiving waters, e.g. 8 times	BOD_5^{20} SS	< 20 mg/L < 30 mg/L	Aerobic biological treatment and secondary settlement in addition
Little dilution in receiving waters	BOD_5^{20} SS	< 10 mg/L < 10 mg/L	Efficient biological and settlement processes and perhaps filtration
Little dilution with particular concern to maintain high oxygen concentration	BOD_5^{20} SS NH_4-N	< 10 mg/L < 10 mg/L < 5 mg/L	Aerobic processes capable of nitrifying effluent
Extreme sensitivity of receiving water to nutrient loading	BOD_5^{20} SS Removal of nitrogen and phosphorus	< 5 mg/L < 5 mg/L	Additional tertiary treatment processes for nutrient removal

pended solids, and is termed a 20/30 effluent standard. Such an effluent can usually be achieved by settlement and aerobic biological processes.

The important condition of eight times dilution in the receiving water does not apply to all situations. The requirements for effluents discharged into the sea can be less stringent. Effluents discharging into receiving waters where they will be diluted less than eight times and, in some cases, to a dry watercourse, may be subject to more stringent standards. The requirements imposed are usually what could be achieved by available technology. Table 5.2 summarises some discharge standards and the treatment processes likely to be employed for municipal wastewaters.

The main considerations in dealing with effluents are therefore the parameters which estimate major pollution, BOD and suspended solids. As well, levels of nutrient materials such as nitrogen and phosphorus, and the presence of floating materials and gross solids must be considered.

Table 5.3 Typical analytical results for wastewater samples concentrations (mg/L)

Sample	Total solids	Suspended solids	BOD_5^{20}	Org-N	$NH_4 - N$	NO_3
Raw municipal wastewater	600	250	250	40	30	< 5
Settled wastewater	500	100	180	30	20	< 5
Secondary treated wastewater	500	30	20	15	25	5
Nitrified effluent	500	10	10	5	5	30

The pollutional load of wastewater varies from region to region, depending on such factors as water usage, industrial input, standard of living, groundwater infiltration and local practices. The results of analysis of a typical sample of municipal wastewater and the effects of various treatment processes are listed in Table 5.3. The BOD_5^{20} is usually between 100 and 400 mg/L, with a similar concentration of suspended solids. These amounts can be reduced to less than 30 mg/L by conventional processes. Nitrogen is present in raw wastewaters as organic nitrogen — mainly from protein — and as ammonia nitrogen; these can be successively transformed into nitrate as described for nitrification. The total solids concentration shows little variation during treatment processes because inorganic ions tend to pass through most processes. The losses during the treatment processes represent transfers to the sludge solids (see Chapters 11 and 12) and to the atmosphere. Both effects can be significant.

The types of analysis and the analytical results for other classes of sample, for example, analyses of raw reservoir waters and river waters, will depend upon the proposed use of the water. The more urbanised the catchment area, the more polluted the water will be, and the analysis required will include the wastewater types of analyses such as those for solids and BOD, but fewer of the type such as those for turbidity and colour.

5.10 Corrosion and corrosion control

It is important that waters and wastewaters should not corrode the structures, fittings or mechanical equipment with which they come in contact. This condition is included in the standards set for waters and wastewaters. Some discussion of corrosion and corrosion control, as it affects structural materials such as iron and concrete, is given in this section.

Theory of metallic corrosion

Corrosion may occur as a result of either electrochemical or microbiological activity, or through a combination of both. Electrochemical corrosion takes place when electrochemical cells are formed as a result of varying electrochemical potentials at different points on a metal surface in contact with a solution (such as water containing impurities). These differences in potential can originate from the contact of dissimilar metals, or from differences in properties of a metal from point to point (for example, either different crystals of metal may have different amounts of alloyed material or there could be small amounts of carbon or other substances) or from differences in the concentration of impurities, such as oxygen and salts, in the water. These differences of potential cause a flow of current between the water and the metal, creating anodic areas where the current leaves the metal, and cathodic areas where it enters it. For corrosion to occur, there must be anodic and cathodic areas and a flow of electrons to complete a circuit.

A type of corrosion cell for iron is shown in Fig 5.9. For the passage of four electrons, the *anode reaction* is

$$2Fe - 4e^- \longrightarrow 2Fe^{2+} \tag{5.36}$$

and the ferrous ion goes into solution. Gradual removal of iron molecules from the metal will cause a hole or pit to form. The ferrous ion will either stay in solution to cause an increase in the iron content of the water delivered to consumers, or it will become oxidised to ferric iron, which will precipitate as red ferric hydroxide or carbonate, either in suspension or attached to some portion of the metal, depending on the nature of the water.

At the *cathode*, the electrons leave the metal and can react with the hydrogen ions, giving hydrogen gas. A layer of hydrogen would act as an insulator, causing polarisation, thus reducing or stopping the current and hence the corrosion. In the presence of dissolved oxygen, however, the

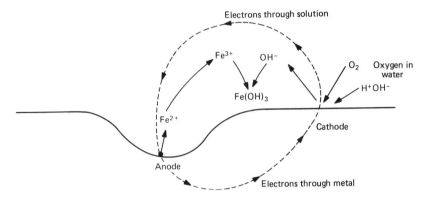

Fig 5.9 A simple electrochemical corrosion cell for iron

reaction is likely to be

$$2H^+ + 4e^- + O_2 \longrightarrow 2OH^- \qquad (5.37)$$

or, more fully,

$$2H_2O + 4e^- + O_2 \longrightarrow 4OH^- \qquad (5.38)$$

but, in the presence of calcium bicarbonate, it is likely to be

$$2Ca(HCO_3)_2 + O_2 + 4e^- \longrightarrow 2CaCO_3 \downarrow + 2CO_3{}^{2-} + 2H_2O$$
$$(5.39)$$

Under suitable conditions, the calcium carbonate may precipitate as an insulating film over the cathodic area, thus greatly reducing the flow of current and, consequently, the rate of corrosion.

Rate of corrosion

Electrochemical corrosion occurs when a metal is in contact with water containing dissolved substances. There is no *one* index or equation for the prediction of corrosion rates, because there are so many interrelated factors to be considered. These include properties of both the water and the metal.
    The *water-related* properties affecting corrosion rates are

a *Dissolved oxygen concentration* At pH values above 5, the only way the polarising hydrogen gas film can be removed from the cathodic areas is by oxidation, mainly by dissolved oxygen. Therefore, at the usual pH values of 6 to 8.5, oxygen is needed for corrosion to continue

b *pH of the water* This is important because it controls the electrode potentials of metals, thus affecting the strength of the cells, and it controls the solubility of materials like calcium carbonate and ferric hydroxide, which can form protective scales. At low pH values, the discharge of protons is the major cathodic reaction and corrosion is rapid; this is supported by the observation that many metals are dissolved by acids

c *Carbon dioxide concentration* This is related to the pH of the water and to the carbonate equilibrium system. Excessive carbon dioxide lowers the pH, thus dissolving protective films more readily and increasing corrosive activity

d *Concentrations of other ions* Of particular concern are chloride, sulphate, bicarbonate and calcium ions. Some ions promote and others hinder the formation of protective films. Calcium, bicarbonate, phosphate and silicate ions assist in film formation. Chlorides and sulphates may cause reduction or breakdown of films. If the water has a high conductivity, the rate of corrosion is increased; an increase in any dissolved salts will increase the conductivity of the water

e *Temperature* This is important because chemical reactions are more rapid at higher temperatures. An increase of about 10°C will approximately double the rate of corrosion. In *hot climates*, corrosion control is particularly important

f *Water velocity* This causes turbulence to carry the reaction products away from the anode and cathode areas. Reaction products in contact with the anode and cathode tend to reduce the electrochemical potential difference and hence the rate of corrosion. If they are removed rapidly, the corrosion will continue at its highest rate

The main characteristics of a metal which affect the rate of corrosion are

a Its relative position in the galvanic series. Magnesium, for example, tends to corrode easily, whereas copper and silver do not

b Its ability to form insoluble protective coatings. Aluminium and zinc can form such coatings

c Any non-uniformities, such as non-uniform scales, inclusions, microstructure differences and stress differentials

d Connection to a dissimilar metal

Corrosion control

There are five methods of corrosion control in waterworks practice:

a Use of non-corrosive materials, such as concrete, asbestos cement, or plastic, or the more expensive non-corrosive metals such as stainless steel, copper, brass and bronze

b Use of sacrificial metallic coatings such as zinc (galvanising) or aluminium to protect metals

c Use of inert coatings to separate the corrosion-prone metals and the water. These include various resins, enamels, paints and membranes

d Treatment of water to remove excess carbon dioxide and sometimes oxygen, to adjust the pH, and to add such chemicals as will deposit protective films on the metal without other significant adverse effects

e Artificial maintenance of an electric potential between the water and the metal, so that all points on the metal structure become cathodic. This is known as *cathodic protection.*

Bacterial oxidation of iron

If water in a pipeline, or other dark place, contains ferrous iron in solution, it can support the growth of iron bacteria, the commonest of which are *Leptothrix, Crenothrix* and *Gallionella.* These bacteria form colonies on the walls of pipelines and similar places, and obtain some of their life energy from the oxidation of ferrous iron to ferric iron, which then precipitates in large gelatinous slimy lumps or 'tubercles' of ferric hydroxide. These tubercles roughen the surfaces of the pipe and reduce its water-carrying capacity. When the bacteria die, their decomposition can cause objectionable tastes and odours in the water.

Corrosion of concrete

A discussion of the physical and chemical properties of cement and concrete is beyond the scope of this book. Cement is manufactured by the controlled incineration of an intimate mixture of limestone and clay. When cement powder is mixed with water, a series of chemical reactions occur to form a mixture of calcium, aluminium, iron and silica compounds, which will set to a rock-like material. Acidic conditions will leach lime ($Ca(OH)_2$) from the concrete and weaken it. Sulphate ions react with tricalcium aluminate, a component of the concrete, to produce calcium sulphoaluminate. This increases the volume and changes the internal structure, thus weakening the concrete. Hydrogen sulphide given off from anaerobic wastewater will pass into the atmosphere above the liquid (Fig 5.10). Bacteria can exist in the water droplets on the inside of the sewer. These bacteria convert the hydrogen sulphide into sulphuric acid which attacks the concrete structure of the sewer. This phenomenon is very marked in hot climates, where wastewater is likely to be anaerobic and where rates of microbial action are high.

It is necessary to control the pH and sulphate content of materials in contact with concrete. Under adverse conditions (in hot climates, for example) it is necessary to use corrosion-resistant cements or to provide protective coatings.

5.11 Sampling

The results of any analysis are of value only if the sample is known to represent accurately the water or wastewater being sampled. Problems are associated with taking a representative sample from a large flow, particularly

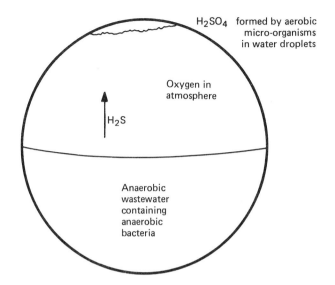

Fig 5.10 Corrosion of concrete sewers by combined aerobic and anaerobic microbial processes

if the flow rate varies with time and the water contains a range of materials of differing physical and chemical properties. The simplest type is a grab sample, which only corresponds to the flow at the time when the sample is taken. Even assuming that it is representative of the flow at that time, it is usually necessary to take multiple grab samples to form a reliable assessment of the water. For a wastewater flow, diurnal variation with significant loads in the morning and evening and with little load during the night would require grab samples taken several times in a day and during any periods of change such as at weekends, on holidays or during storm flows. For a raw water supply there is usually some diurnal variation, but the effects of seasonal changes often require some study.

Individual samples can be combined into composite samples in proportion to the flows. Analysis of such composite samples is particularly useful in establishing average conditions, but it can mask transient effects. The most useful form of analysis provides a continuous record of a particular parameter; unfortunately, few analytical methods provide reliable data in a continuous form.

Serious problems are associated with the storage and transport of samples. The fact that waters and wastewaters contain micro-organisms means that their properties will change continually. The shortest possible time interval between sampling and analysis is desirable. If the sample has to be stored, low temperature (4°C) limits rates of change. For certain analyses, it is possible to add chemicals to prevent biological changes, but this is clearly of no use for a BOD test. For the determination of dissolved oxygen, the addition of manganous sulphate and alkaline potassium iodide/azide solution effectively fixes the oxygen for titration later.

Direct analysis in the field, at the time of sampling, alleviates many of these difficulties; unfortunately not all analytical methods are suited to use in the field. Volumetric and colorimetric analysis can be used in the field but instrumental methods are less suitable, as is analysis which requires accurate weighing or controlled incubation. For the BOD test, an error of $\pm 1°C$ during incubation can result in up to 5 per cent error in the analytical results.

Any analytical determination is only as good as the validity of the sample. There is little point in carrying out a $100 analysis on one cent samples. Due attention has to be paid to the methods of sampling, and effective liaison between the analyst and the persons taking the sample is clearly advantageous.

Review questions

5.1 Why is it necessary to analyse the effluent from a wastewater treatment plant?

5.2 What problems could arise if distilled water were supplied as a municipal drinking water supply?

5.3 What is the relevance of determining the alkalinity of drinking water to the treatment of municipal wastewater?

5.4 Why does the pH of many Australian wastewaters drop below 6.5 if nitrification is attempted without pH correction?

5.5 Why is the pH of hydrochloric acid less than that of acetic acid for the same strength of solution?

5.6 Why is titrimetric analysis unsuitable for routine determinations of concentrations less than 1 mg/L?

5.7 Why are colorimetric procedures lengthy or difficult for analysis of raw sewage samples?

5.8 Which type of analytical method would be used for
   a Studying ground water infiltration by adding lithium chloride to the sewers
   b The chlorine concentration in a swimming pool
   c The concentration of calcium in a drinking water?

5.9 Would a water sample with 10 mL/L of settleable solids be suitable for direct discharge to a small stream?

5.10   What are the advantages and disadvantages of the Winkler titration and electrode method for measuring dissolved oxygen?

5.11   What are the advantages and disadvantages of the BOD, COD and TOC tests?

5.12   How can a sample of municipal wastewater have a $BOD_3^{20} = 200$ mg/L and $BOD_{30}^{20} = 400$ mg/L?

5.13   What possible explanations can account for a wastewater sample with $BOD_5^{20} = 150$ mg/L and COD $= 180$ mg/L?

5.14   Why is 200 mg/L of chloride in drinking water the permissible limit, while 600 mg/L is the excessive limit?

5.15   Why is the total amount of nitrogen in a final effluent less than the total amount of nitrogen in a raw municipal wastewater?

5.16   What problems are encountered as a result of sulphate in waters and wastewaters?

6 Environmental Pollution

6.1 General

Pollution is an inevitable product of most of man's activities, whether urban or rural. The type of pollution produced varies with the type of activity, while its significance depends on both the type and amount of pollutants, and also on the intended uses of the portion of the environment which they enter. Thus, pollution may be at the same time both a product of land use and an important factor in determining the use for which the receiving environment is suitable.

Pollution control is therefore aimed at reducing the impact of various activities on the environment by limiting the amounts of pollutants which may be discharged, to a level compatible with all intended uses. The principal forms of control are concerned with air, land and water pollution. While the main concern of this book is with water pollution, it should be noted that both air and land pollution can contribute significantly to the problem. Air pollutants may enter surface waters directly by fallout of particulates or by solution of gases, or indirectly by being incorporated in precipitation. Similarly, materials deposited on land may be washed into waters by storm waters and other surface runoff. This is why legislation to control water pollution often includes regulations concerning waste disposal on land.

To 'pollute', according to the *Concise Oxford Dictionary*, is 'to destroy the purity or sanctity of'; 'to make foul or filthy'. Water pollution, within the meaning of these definitions, may therefore be considered as the alteration of the quality of a receiving water body, for example by a wastewater discharge, in such a manner as to make it unfit for some intended use. It may also refer more generally to any change in the inherent physical, chemical or biological characteristics of the receiving stream caused by material entering the water. The latter is a very comprehensive definition, often adopted in water pollution control legislation so as to bring all forms of discharge under control.

For practical purposes, however, it is necessary to take account of the intended uses of receiving waters when setting quality standards for discharge to them. Quality requirements for drinking water (the highest of the common beneficial uses of water) will be found in Chapter 5. The general objectives of pollution control are to protect the *health* of the community, to maintain waters in a state inoffensive to the senses of sight, taste or smell (*aesthetics*) and to prevent excessive disruption to the balance of plant and animal life in the waters (*ecology*). All of these objectives, however, must be achieved within the limits of the community's capacity to pay for the necessary controls (*economics*). Thus, although the requirements for drinking water represent the most stringent standards that a surface water body could be required to meet, and thus would impose the strictest demands on pollution controls, only in the most exceptional circumstances has it been considered economically justifiable to apply such standards to effluent discharges.

6.2 Sources of pollution

Fig. 6.1 summarises the main sources of pollution associated with land use in both rural and urban environments. Some of the major water uses, and quality considerations associated with the more important of them, are shown, along with an outline of the main engineering development works involved in urban water supply and wastewater disposal systems. It is evident from Fig. 6.1 that water use and pollution are so closely related to all aspects of land use and development that effective water quality control requires very close co-ordination of all levels of planning and development within a river basin. This approach is exemplified in England and Wales, where all water development and control activities have been consolidated into a relatively small number of Regional Water Authorities.

Until recently, pollution control in most countries was directed mainly at the most readily definable sources, such as sewer outfalls and industrial discharges — often referred to as *point sources* of pollution. There are two important reasons for this. Firstly, the large concentrations of pollution from domestic and industrial wastewaters and the potential health, aesthetic and economic effect of uncontrolled discharges demand that effective disposal systems be provided. Secondly, the fact that these sources of pollution are so concentrated, mainly within urban areas, simplifies the problem of providing sewerage systems for collecting and conveying wastewaters to a small number of plants so that they can be treated to the required standard prior to discharge. This results in economies of scale in plant construction and operation.

Since the early 1970s, increasing attention has been paid to *non-point* (or diffuse) *sources* of pollution such as stormwater runoff in both urban and rural areas, and other forms of rural pollution. Although their diffuse nature tends to make them relatively insignificant for much of the time, these sources can give rise to particularly heavy pollution during storms, when the storm intensity is high enough to produce surface runoff. The effects of

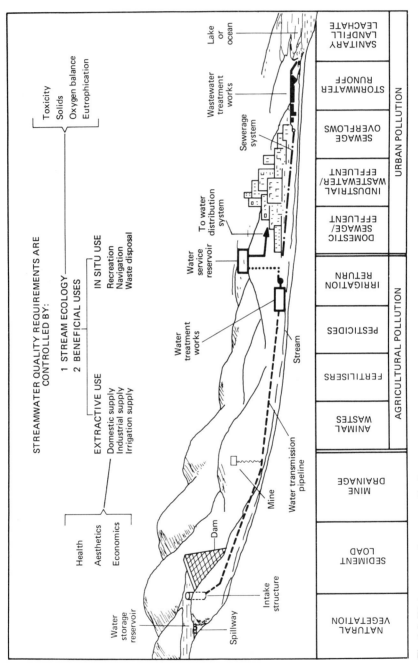

Fig 6.1 Water use and water pollution

pollutants from these sources can be especially important where streams discharge either to large inland water bodies, such as natural lakes and man-made impoundments, or to poorly-flushed estuaries.

Rural pollution

Most of the important forms of pollution in rural areas arise from non-point sources, although the increasing trend towards intensive confinement feeding of livestock makes point-source pollution an increasing problem in many areas. Some characteristics of the main types of rural pollution shown in Fig 6.1 are briefly discussed here.

Decaying vegetation Washed into surface waters, this can use up oxygen from the water, and also contribute to organic colour caused by various forms of relatively non-degradable humus-like organic residues.

Mine drainage This can occur either from a mining operation itself or from tailings dumps. It can carry sediment and dissolved materials. These materials, the nature of which depends on the type of mining, may range from dissolved metals from metalliferous mining to large amounts of black sediment from coal mining. Mine drainage is frequently acidic.

Sediment This is a major constituent of surface runoff into streams as a consequence of natural erosion, which is greatly accelerated by activities such as construction (for example of roads and highways), mining operations (as noted above) and the clearing of land for agricultural development. Where adequate controls are not provided, soil erosion and the resulting heavy sediment loads can be serious, not only because soil surfaces are denuded but because sediment tends to accumulate in streams and impoundments. This may reduce the capacity of stream channels, so increasing flood hazards. In the long term, it can also tend to reduce the storage capacity of impounding reservoirs.

Agricultural pollution This is related to the type of activity, land management practices and climate. *Sediment* can be a serious problem, especially in dry areas where, although the rainfall is usually poor and unreliable, high-intensity storms can occur quite frequently. In such cases, soil loss from croplands may be especially severe. Fertilisers and pesticides also may be washed into surface waters from agricultural lands. Many of these materials are strongly adsorbed to soil particles and are thus mainly associated with the sediment load. Nitrogen forms, however, are readily soluble, and in areas where nitrogenous fertilisers are extensively used high concentrations of nitrate have been found in underlying groundwaters. *Animal wastes* may be deposited either directly into surface waters or on stream banks and other surfaces, from which they may be washed into streams. The main forms of pollutants associated with animal wastes are organic matter, nitrogen, bacteria and sometimes pathogens.

Problems with animal waste disposal have been aggravated by the relatively recent development of intensive animal production methods, involving confinement feeding. This results in a large volume of highly concentrated wastes in a small area, requiring extensive treatment before disposal. Even with such treatment, effluent quality is rarely suitable for discharge directly to surface waters. Therefore disposal is usually to land surfaces. Adequate controls on frequency and rate of application are then necessary to prevent pollution from surface runoff.

Irrigation return water This usually contains a considerably higher dissolved salt concentration than the raw water source. For example one of the major problems associated with the Murray River, Australia's largest inland stream, is salinity build-up resulting from return waters from irrigation areas. This causes such a high salt concentration that the water is becoming unsuitable for further irrigation.

Urban pollution

Some general characteristics of the main sources of urban pollution listed in Fig 6.1 are the following.

Domestic wastewaters These are generally about 99.9 per cent water, the remaining 0.1 per cent (or 1000 mg/L) comprising various types of solid in dissolved or suspended form. The suspended matter includes organic faecal matter and food scraps as well as rags and a high concentration of human enteric micro-organisms which may be accompanied by a variety of pathogens. The dissolved material includes enough plant nutrients (such as nitrogen and phosphorus) to cause frequent troubles with excessive weed growths and algal blooms. Conventional wastewater treatment is effective in removing the majority of the suspended matter, most of the dissolved organic matter and, especially if disinfection is practised, a large proportion of the indicator and pathogenic organism content. The dissolved solids content is little affected, however, and only about 20 per cent of the plant nutrients is removed by conventional treatment. *Sewage overflows* are provided in most separate sewer systems in order to relieve the sewers of excessive flows resulting from wet-weather infiltration. They may discharge sewage from mains to surface streams during storms.

Sanitary landfill leachate This is produced as rainwater percolates through decaying garbage, collecting as it goes a fairly high concentration of putrescible organic material, nutrients and dissolved material such as iron.

This material can cause considerable pollution, but where sites are well planned and operated, the quantity of leachate is kept to a minimum, and that which is generated is collected and treated before it is allowed to enter a stream. Leachate may also contain waste chemicals where they have been ill-advisedly deposited in the landfill.

Urban stormwater This is a non-point source of pollution. It may contain a wide variety of materials washed from gardens, streets and other surfaces. These materials may include inorganic sediment, chemical cleansers and detergents, pesticides, fertilisers, animal faecal matter, garden clippings, oils, and even lead residues derived from motor fuels.

6.3 Effects of pollution

The effects of the various forms of pollutant mentioned above may be measured in terms of changes to the physical, chemical and biological characteristics of the receiving water. Some general effects of pollution, and ways in which some of the standard measures of water quality mentioned in Chapter 5 apply to the measurement of pollution, are described below. It should be noted, however, that a complete system for describing the pollutional status of a water body should include as a major component a statement about stream biology and microbiology. Description in terms of physical and chemical quality parameters alone is essentially a compromise commonly adopted because these are relatively easy to measure. Some understanding of the general characteristics of micro-organisms, and of aspects of biological growth discussed in Chapter 4, will be found useful as a background to the consideration of stream pollution.

Effects on oxygen resources

Dissolved oxygen (DO) is essential to all normal forms of aquatic life; 5 mg/L is widely considered to be the minimum DO required to support a balanced population of desirable aquatic flora and fauna. When it is recalled that saturation DO at 15°C and 25°C are only 10.2 and 8.4 mg/L respectively, it is evident that any pollutant that greatly decreases the dissolved oxygen resources of a surface water will therefore have a potential effect on the aquatic life.

The main effects of pollutants on DO in surface waters arise from discharges of

a *Organic materials*, which cause oxygen to be used up, and thus create an 'oxygen demand' as they undergo biodegradation

b *Reducing agents*, which deplete oxygen resources as they are chemically oxidised in the receiving stream c *Fats, oils and greases*, which form surface films, inhibiting transfer of oxygen from the atmosphere into the water

d *Surfactants* and other materials, which may either affect oxygen transfer into the water or alter the saturation DO concentration

e Large volumes of *hot water*, which raise the temperature of the receiving water, thus reducing the possible oxygen resources available and at the same time increasing the rate of oxygen demand by increasing the rate of biological activity.

Of these, the most generally significant effects are those caused by biodegradation of organic matter, a fact that led to the development of the BOD test, which is specifically aimed at simulating the effects of organic wastes on a river. Temperature effects also may be important in waters receiving cooling water discharges from power stations or industrial establishments.

Effects of solids – suspended and dissolved

The most immediate problem caused by solids is their unpleasant appearance. Coarse suspended and floating matter is unsightly, especially when recognisably of sewage origin, and fine suspended matter gives the water a turbid appearance and restricts light penetration. This not only restricts visibility for the observer, but may reduce the variety of aquatic plants which rely on light for their photosynthesis, as well as reduce the populations of all but the coarser types of fish. Sedimentation of the settleable fraction of suspended solids may form banks of sludge on the stream bed, either smothering the bottom organisms (especially if the solids are inert) or changing the DO level in bottom water layers, if they are organic and undergo biodegradation.

Dissolved solids, in very high concentrations, reduce the solubility of oxygen in water. At much lower concentrations, they may affect the suitability of water for uses such as drinking and irrigation water supply. Domestic wastewaters typically contain 300 to 400 mg/L of dissolved solids more than the water supply to the area.

Effects of toxic materials

Many waste products from industrial activities are poisonous to aquatic life. Heavy metals, various synthetic organics and materials such as pesticides have been implicated in killing fish in water receiving wastewater effluents. Such materials often have a similarly deleterious effect on biological wastewater treatment processes, requiring that their admission to sewers be strictly controlled.

Toxicity may become apparent either as dramatic, short-term effects (acute) or as long-term cumulative effects (chronic). Some organisms are able to adapt to using some organic toxins (such as cyanide) as food sources, provided they are given the opportunity to acclimatise to these toxins over a range of slowly increasing dosage rates.

Ammonia is toxic to fish in concentrations above about 0.5 mg/L, especially when present as NH_3, which is the predominant form at high pH. The effects of toxic agents are also enhanced if the organisms concerned are subjected to the stress of other adverse environmental conditions. Where more than one toxic substance is present, the combined effect may in some cases be greater than the sum of the effects of the individual toxins. This is known as *synergism*.

Effects of plant nutrients

Enrichment of surface waters by plant nutrients from wastewater, stormwater runoff and other discharges — eutrophication — is becoming a matter of increasing concern to pollution control authorities in many countries. Materials such as nitrogen, normally present in municipal wastewaters and treated effluents in concentrations between 20 and 50 mg/L, and phosphorus, present in increasing quantities as a result of its use in washing powders, may contribute to heavy growths of aquatic plants and algae. Microscopic algae may impart colour and turbidity to the water, while larger forms of algae, plants and weeds may grow so thickly as to completely choke the waterway. Such growths tend to be seasonal and cyclic, a period of very rapid growth being followed by death and decay of the plant material. Oxygen demand exerted as the plant material decays in the waters and around the shoreline may exceed the resources of the water body, leading to anaerobic conditions and serious odour problems.

These more extreme effects of eutrophication are most likely to occur in lakes, reservoirs, sluggish streams and poorly-flushed estuaries where nutrients tend to accumulate. In fast-flowing streams and estuaries with good flushing characteristics, the problem is less marked.

Even where eutrophication in inland streams and impoundments occurs to a less spectacular extent, growth of microscopic algae can seriously affect the quality of water for domestic purposes, often giving rise to unpleasant tastes and odours and, in some cases, imposing a heavy load on water filtration plants.

It is also worth noting that streams receiving wastewater effluents often exhibit growths of filamentous bacteria attached to the stream bed for some distance downstream of the outlet. These growths are often mistakenly called 'sewage fungus'.

Effects of enteric micro-organisms

The main problem with enteric micro-organisms discharged into receiving waters that are to be used for consumption (as a source of domestic water supply) or contact recreational purposes (such as swimming) is that they are a danger to health. Of primary concern are pathogenic organisms, principally bacteria and viruses, although by far the greatest numbers of organisms routinely present in human body wastes belong to the coliform bacteria group. Because of their larger numbers, and also because analytical techniques for estimating their numbers are much simpler than those for pathogens, coliforms (specifically faecal coliforms) are widely used as indicators of faecal pollution.

Since environmental conditions differ greatly from those within the human body with respect to temperature, pH and nutrient supply, enteric organisms tend to decrease in numbers fairly rapidly when discharged into natural surface waters. Other factors that contribute to the reduction in organism numbers include competition from organisms better adapted to the aquatic environment, sedimentation, predation by other organisms and the bactericidal effects of sunlight. As a result of all these self-purification effects, the bacterial quality of streams improves as the water flows downstream away from the effluent outfalls.

Over 100 distinct serotypes of virus have been found in sewage and polluted waters. Various studies have shown that (a) virus concentration in raw sewage is of the order of 1 to 1000 units per litre, (b) removal in conventional secondary treatment is of the order of 50 to 99 per cent, and (c) ordinary effluent chlorination does not guarantee complete inactivation of viruses. Virus survival in water decreases with increasing temperature, and the time required for a 99.9 per cent reduction in concentration has been reported to range from 2 to 100 days for various members of the enteric virus group.

Because of their very small (colloidal) size, viruses have a surface charge and tend to be strongly adsorbed to the surfaces of soil particles and organic solids. Therefore, turbidity and other solids in waters are potential adsorption sites for any viruses present in the water. Particulate matter may also tend to shield adsorbed viruses from the effects of chemical disinfectants. For this reason, turbidity standards for domestic water supply generally have been raised in recent years.

Other health effects of pollution

Apart from the microbiological and toxic aspects of pollution which affect the suitability of water for human consumption, there are several other effects that relate to health. *Nitrates*, from wastewater effluents or agricultural runoff or resulting from biological nitrification in streams receiving discharges of ammonia nitrogen, are important because they are toxic to babies if the water is used in making up powdered milk formulae (causing methaemoglobinaemia).

There is concern that many *synthetic organic* compounds may be responsible for causing cancers (carcinogenic), birth defects (teratogenic) or mutations (mutagenic). Although many of these effects have been observed in laboratory animals, they have usually resulted only at concentrations many times higher than those likely to occur in surface waters as a result of waste discharges. Analytical techniques for detecting trace amounts of many of these compounds among the background of normal organic products of microbial degradation have only recently been developed, so that there is, as yet, little direct evidence linking the presence of these substances in the water with public health problems. Among substances that have given rise to suspicion are chlorinated hydrocarbons, possibly formed by the reaction of chlorine, used for disinfection, with simple organic compounds. Precautionary monitoring of substances such as trihalomethane is a recent addition to the list of routine water quality tests required for major city water supplies in the United States.

6.4 Oxygen demand and replenishment

It was noted above that the main effect when organic wastes are discharged into streams is the oxygen demand exerted as the organic matter is degraded by aerobic micro-organisms — an effect used in the laboratory BOD test as a measure of the strength of an organic waste.

The effect of this oxygen demand is to reduce the DO concentration in the stream. This is often expressed in terms of increasing the oxygen deficit, D (the amount by which the DO level is below its saturation value). The rate of change of oxygen deficit, dD/dt, can then be written in terms of ultimate carbonaceous oxygen demand, in the absence of re-aeration, as

$$\frac{dD}{dt} = K_1 L_t \tag{6.1}$$

where K_1 is the BOD reaction rate constant (d^{-1}); L_t is the ultimate BOD at time t (mg/L); $D = C_s - C$ (mg/L); C_s is the saturation DO concentration in water (mg/L); and C is the actual DO concentration in water (mg/L).

Oxygen replenishment — re-aeration

To satisfy the demand exerted during processes such as degradation of organic matter, oxygen must be present in sufficient quantities to prevent stream DO levels from falling to the point where the water cannot support the normal range of aquatic life. At saturation (or equilibrium), this oxygen is present in proportion to the partial pressure of oxygen in the atmosphere above the water surface (Henry's Law) — under normal temperatures to the extent of only 8 to 10 mg/L. In normal surface waters the actual DO level is usually less than saturation, since there is usually some organic matter undergoing degradation even in relatively unpolluted streams. In such cases, there is always an oxygen saturation deficit (that is, a difference between the saturation concentration and the actual concentration), and this produces a tendency for more oxygen to pass into solution to restore the equilibrium between the DO in the water and the oxygen level in the atmosphere. The rate of oxygen transfer into the water is then given in terms of the oxygen saturation deficit as

$$\frac{dD}{dt} = -K_2 D \tag{6.2}$$

The minus sign indicates that the oxygen transfer tends to reduce the oxygen deficit. K_2 is the system re-aeration coefficient (d^{-1}).

If there is no oxygen demand, this expression may be integrated for the initial condition of DO deficit D_a, and DO deficit D_t at time t, to give

$$D_t = D_a e^{-K_2 t} \tag{6.3}$$

The DO sag curve

It will be seen that the actual DO level in a stream at any time will be governed by the summation of the rates of oxygen use and oxygen replenishment. For a simple case, where it is assumed that oxygen use in carbonaceous oxidation of organic matter and atmospheric re-aeration are the only processes operating, this can be represented by the dissolved oxygen sag curve (Fig 6.2). The DO sag curve may also be formulated by combining Eqs 6.1 and 6.2 to give

$$\frac{dD}{dt} = K_1 L_t - K_2 D \tag{6.4}$$

Analytical solutions of this equation may be obtained by integration if it is further assumed that there are no other sources of pollution and no change in stream flow to alter the concentrations of organic matter and DO.

The expression that results from integrating, changing to the base 10 and making the substitution $k = 0.4343K$ is

$$D_t = \frac{k_1 L}{k_2 - k_1}(10^{-k_1 t} - 10^{-k_2 t}) + D_a 10^{-k_2 t} \tag{6.5}$$

where L is the value of the ultimate biochemical oxygen demand.

The point at which DO reaches a minimum — the critical point defined by t_c, D_c — may be found by setting $dD/dt = 0$, whence the following expressions are obtained:

$$D_c = \frac{k_1}{k_2} L 10^{-k_1 t_c} \tag{6.6}$$

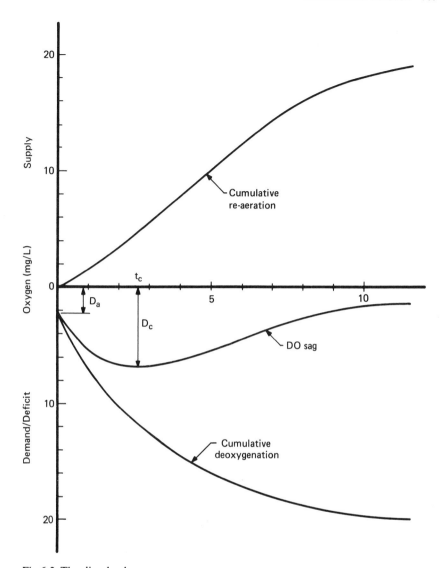

Fig 6.2 The dissolved oxygen sag curve

$$t_c = \frac{1}{k_2 - k_1} \log \left\{ \frac{k_2}{k_1} \left[1 - \frac{D_a(k_2 - k_1)}{Lk_1} \right] \right\} \tag{6.7}$$

Where there are changes in streamflow or further inflows of pollutants, or both, it is possible to adapt Eq 6.4 for numerical solution by computer for the particular flows and waste inputs concerned.

The value of k_1 varies with the type of waste. For sewage at 20°C, it is usually about $0.17d^{-1}$. The value of k_2 varies considerably according to the characteristics of the stream. Since oxygen transfer takes place only at the surface of the water, the mass transfer rate depends on the rate at which oxygen dissolves at the surface layer, the rate at which it diffuses throughout the water volume, and the rate at which the more highly saturated surface layers are mixed with the water volume. Therefore the stream re-aeration rate depends on the degree of turbulence and is greatest in shallow, swift-flowing streams with rough stream beds. Deep, sluggish streams may have very poor re-aeration characteristics. Surfactants and mono-molecular layers of materials, such as oils, also affect the value of k_2.

Example 6.1

A wastewater treatment plant serving a population of 50 000 receives a per capita flow of 250 L/d and a per capita BOD_5 loading of 70 g/d. Effluent from the plant is discharged into a stream which has a flow of 1.0 m³/s, a BOD of 2 mg/L and a DO concentration of 9.0 mg/L. If the BOD_5 of the stream immediately below the outfall is not to exceed 4.0 mg/L, what is the maximum BOD_5 which may be permitted in the plant effluent and what would be the required percentage BOD_5 removal efficiency of the treatment plant?

Solution

Required effluent BOD_5 is calculated from a mass balance. Since mass of BOD_5 = flow × BOD_5 concentration, therefore

$$
\begin{bmatrix} \text{Upstream flow} \\ \times \\ \text{BOD concentration} \end{bmatrix} + \begin{bmatrix} \text{Effluent flow} \\ \times \\ \text{BOD concentration} \end{bmatrix}
$$

$$
= \begin{bmatrix} \text{Downstream flow} \\ \times \\ \text{BOD concentration} \end{bmatrix}
$$

$$
\text{Effluent flow rate} = \frac{50\ 000 \times 250}{60 \times 60 \times 24 \times 1000} = 0.145 \text{ m}^3/\text{s}
$$

Substituting this value, along with data, then gives

$$
(1.0 \text{ m}^3/\text{s} \times 2 \text{ mg/L}) + (0.145 \text{ m}^3/\text{s} \times BOD_5)
$$

$$
= (1.145 \text{ m}^3/\text{s} \times 4 \text{ mg/L})
$$

$$
\text{Therefore, effluent } BOD_5 = \frac{(1.145 \times 4) - (1.0 \times 2)}{0.145}
$$

$$
= 17.8 \text{ mg/L}
$$

BOD concentration of sewage entering plant

$$= \frac{\text{per capita BOD}_5}{\text{per capita flow}} = \frac{70\ 000\ \text{mg}}{250\ \text{L}} = 280\ \text{mg/L}$$

Therefore, BOD removal efficiency $= \dfrac{280 - 17.8}{280} \times 100$

$$= 93.6\ \text{per cent}$$

Example 6.2

For the conditions described in Example 6.1, what is the critical DO concentration in the stream and at what distance below the outfall does it occur? Temperature is $20°C$ throughout, $k_1 = 0.1\ \text{d}^{-1}$ for the effluent/stream water mixture, $k_2 = 0.3\ \text{d}^{-1}$, stream velocity $= 0.1\ \text{m/s}$, saturation DO concentration is $9.17\ \text{mg/L}$ and effluent DO concentration is $5.0\ \text{mg/L}$.

Solution
Critical DO deficit and critical time are calculated from Eqs 6.6 and 6.7. To use these equations, it is necessary to calculate the initial DO deficit, D_a, and the initial ultimate BOD of the effluent/water mixture, L_a. The DO immediately downstream of the outfall is calculated from a mass balance:

Downstream DO

$$= \frac{(1.0\ \text{m}^3/\text{s} \times 9.0\ \text{mg/L}) + (0.145\ \text{m}^3/\text{s} \times 5\ \text{mg/L})}{1.145\ \text{m}^3/\text{s}}$$

$$= 8.49\ \text{mg/L}$$

Whence, $D_a = 9.17 - 8.49 = 0.68\ \text{mg/L}$

Ultimate BOD is calculated from Eq 5.29

$$L = \frac{L_t}{(1 - 10^{k_1 t})} = \frac{4.0}{(1 - 10^{-0.1 \times 5})} = 5.85\ \text{mg/L}$$

From Eq 6.7

$$t_c = \frac{1}{0.3 - 0.1}\ \log\left\{\frac{0.3}{0.1}\left[1 - \frac{0.68(0.3 - 0.1)}{5.85 \times 0.1}\right]\right\} = 1.81\ \text{days}$$

And from Eq 6.6

$$D_c = \left(\frac{0.1}{0.3}\right) \times 5.85 \times (10^{-0.1 \times 1.81}) = 1.29\ \text{mg/L}$$

Therefore, critical DO concentration $= 9.17 - 1.29 = 7.88\ \text{mg/L}$ and distance below outfall $= t_c \times$ velocity

$$= (1.81) \times \left(\frac{86400}{1000}\right) \times 0.1 = 15.64\ \text{km}$$

Effect of temperature on rate constants k_1 and k_2

Both the BOD reaction rate (constant k_1) and the re-aeration rate (constant k_2) are temperature dependent. In order to calculate the critical effect of an organic waste discharge, it is therefore necessary to take into account the temperature likely to be encountered in the stream. The effect of temperature on the rate of chemical reactions can be described by an equation in the following form:

$$k_T = k_{20}\theta^{(T-20)} \tag{6.8}$$

where k_T is the reaction rate at temperature $T°C$; k_{20} is the reaction rate at a base temperature of $20°C$; and θ is the temperature coefficient.

The BOD reaction rate has been found to correlate with Eq 6.8, with a temperature coefficient, θ, of 1.047. The re-aeration rate also follows Eq 6.8, but does not depend as much on temperature, having a temperature coefficient, θ, of 1.02.

Example 6.3

If the temperature of both the stream and the effluent described in Example 6.1 is $35°C$, what is the critical DO concentration and how far below the outfall would it occur? The saturation DO at $35°C$ is 7.1 mg/L, and for this case the upstream DO is 6.9 mg/L.

Solution

$$\text{Downstream DO} = \frac{(1.0 \times 6.9) + (0.145 \times 5)}{1.145} = 6.66 \text{ mg/L}$$

whence, $D_a = 7.1 - 6.66 = 0.44$ mg/L

If the effluent BOD and stream BOD are the same as in Examples 6.1 and 6.2 above, initial ultimate BOD is unchanged, i.e., $L = 5.85$ mg/L.

Values of k_1 and k_2 at $35°C$ are calculated from Eq 6.8, using appropriate values of the temperature coefficient, θ:

$$k_{1_{35}} = k_{1_{20}} (1.047)^{(T-20)} = 0.1 \times 1.047^{(15)} = 0.20 \text{ d}^{-1}$$

$$k_{2_{35}} = k_{2_{20}} (1.02)^{(T-20)} = 0.3 \times 1.02^{(15)} = 0.40 \text{ d}^{-1}$$

Then

$$t_c = \frac{1}{0.4 - 0.2} \log \left\{ \frac{0.4}{0.2} \left[1 - \frac{0.44(0.4 - 0.2)}{5.85 \times 0.2} \right] \right\} = 1.34 \text{ days}$$

and

$$D_c = \left(\frac{0.2}{0.4}\right) \times 5.85 \times (10^{-0.2 \times 1.34}) = 1.58 \text{ mg/L}$$

Therefore, critical DO concentration $= 7.1 - 1.58 = 5.52$ mg/L

and distance below outfall $= 1.34 \times \left(\dfrac{86\,400}{1\,000}\right) \times 0.1 = 11.58$ km

Other factors affecting DO

There are many factors that affect DO in surface waters in addition to those that are considered in formulating the DO sag curve. Oxidation of ammonia — *nitrification* — may result in very large oxygen demands in streams receiving secondary effluents, especially when they are partly nitrified in the treatment plant and are thus well seeded with nitrifying organisms.

Other factors are summarised in Fig 6.3. They include the *bioflocculation* and *sedimentation* of solids at normal flows and the reverse process of *resuspension* during high stream stages; the release of soluble *products of anaerobic decay* within the bottom sediment and the escape of insoluble gases formed during this process, with the possibility of some purging action by these gas bubbles on DO (probably a minor factor); the addition of DO in *photosynthesis* by aquatic plants and algae during daylight hours and subsequent oxygen demand in *respiration* during the night; and oxygen demand in the respiration of all forms of aquatic animals.

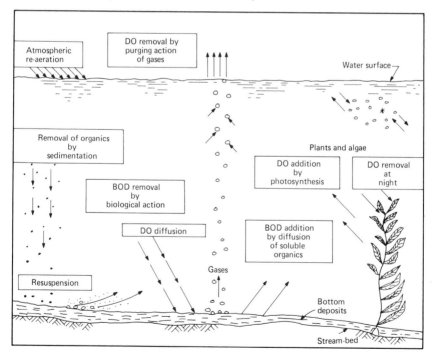

Fig 6.3 Factors affecting dissolved oxygen in streams

Attempts have been made to allow for many of these effects by including additional terms in Eq 6.4 and then using numerical techniques for computer solution of the resulting differential equations, and also by using empirically determined values of the many constants involved. These approaches are beyond the scope of this text.

The effect of aquatic plants on DO levels does merit some further comment, however, since these plants introduce a significant diurnal component into the pattern of DO variations. Since plants contribute oxygen to the water during daylight, it is not uncommon for DO levels to reach super-saturation during this period. During the night, plants use up oxygen by respiration and thus add to the other sources of oxygen demand, with the result that DO levels may fall to low values in the hours before daylight. Hence, the critical DO level may differ significantly from the value indicated by the simple DO sag curve.

Salinity is also important in estuaries and ocean waters because the saturation DO is reduced by the high concentration of dissolved salts.

Limitations of dissolved oxygen as a measure of pollution

Because of its importance to all forms of aerobic life and the ease with which it can be measured, dissolved oxygen is the single most useful chemical indicator of the degree of organic pollution in a surface water body. Other forms of chemical pollution may be present without affecting DO, however, and they are often responsible for killing fish — for example, spills of pesticides and other highly toxic chemicals occasionally result in the death of large numbers of fish and other organisms, without any accompanying effects on DO. Similarly, the sudden inflow of large volumes of fresh water into salt water estuaries can interfere with the normal balance of aquatic organisms.

6.5 Measurement of toxicity

Toxicity measurement, because it involves the effects of chemicals on living organisms, can be made only by subjecting some forms of test organism to measured concentrations of the suspect chemical under carefully-controlled conditions. Fish are often used as sensitive indicator organisms for this purpose, under specified environmental conditions of temperature, pH and salt concentrations.

The technique involves subjecting equal numbers of healthy specimens of the test organisms to various concentrations of the toxic material and noting the percentages surviving at the end of some standard period — usually 48 or 96 hours. The concentration at which 50 per cent of the test organisms survive at the end of the test period is then quoted as a measure of acute toxicity. This concentration is known either as the 'median tolerance limit', TL_M, or the lethal dose to 50 per cent of test organisms, LD_{50}.

Chronic toxicity effects are likewise determined by bio-assay procedures, but over a much longer period and preferably over several generations of test organisms.

Review questions

6.1 What is the importance of dissolved oxygen in streams? Explain why some pollutants affect the amount of dissolved oxygen.

6.2 Discuss the aspects of water pollution which are related to the suitability of water as a source for domestic water supply. Include comments on the requirements for health, aesthetic acceptability and the cost of required treatment.

6.3 Discuss the practicability of controlling all the sources of pollution which may contribute impurities to a typical river.

6.4 Describe some of the important considerations which are neglected in the formulation of the DO sag curve equation (Eq 6.5). How would these other factors affect the validity of the conclusions reached when they have been neglected?

7 Introduction to Treatment Processes

7.1 Need for treating water and wastewater

Water from many surface and groundwater sources is not suitable for potable supply purposes in its untreated state. Treatment may be required to protect the health of the consumer, to make the water acceptable to the senses of sight, smell and taste, or sometimes for economic reasons, such as to prevent scaling or corrosion in pipework, hot water services and boiler installations, or even to avoid staining clothes during laundering.

Wastewater, the water discarded after it has been used for domestic, commercial or industrial purposes, usually requires treatment before discharge, in order to protect the receiving environment.

In many parts of the world, water demands have increased to the extent that available resources have already been developed close to their economic limits. Many of these areas are facing the necessity of directly reclaiming wastewaters for re-use before the end of the century. Indeed, many cities at present practise a form of indirect re-use, since their water supply intakes are downstream of the sewage outfalls of other towns and cities on the stream. In periods of low streamflow, sewage effluent may comprise a significant percentage of the raw water supply to such cities. This often places a heavy demand on both the upstream wastewater treatment plants and the downstream water treatment plants. On the one hand, wastewater effluent quality for discharge to the stream must be sufficiently high to ensure that the streamwater quality is adequate for the required beneficial uses; on the other hand, the water treatment plants of downstream communities must be of sufficiently high standard to ensure that health and aesthetic requirements are met in the water supplies.

Design of water and wastewater treatment plants to meet the required quality objectives under such conditions may often demand the development of new processes, modifications of existing processes, or new combinations of conventional processes. Optimal design of treatment plants requires a clear understanding of the principles and capabilities of each of the available unit processes, of which the most commonly used are discussed in Chapters 8 to 12 inclusive. Other processes, which may require consideration on occasions, are discussed in Chapters 13 and 14, while a few of the more specialised processes which may be required in industrial water and wastewater treatment are dealt with in Chapter 15, and aspects of advanced wastewater treatment and water reclamation are discussed in Chapter 16.

In most municipal treatment plants, it is possible to meet the quality objectives for water and wastewater by means of standard sequences of treatment processes. Flow sheets for some of these conventional process sequences are presented in Chapters 13 and 14 respectively, and will be found useful as illustrations of the ways in which the most important unit processes are commonly applied.

Treatment of water supplies for, and of wastewaters from, industries in many cases involves unit operations and process sequences similar to those used in municipal systems. In other cases, however, the required water quality may be much higher than that of the municipal water supply, necessitating special treatment methods. Similarly, the wastewater produced may differ in composition and concentration to the extent that special treatment is required to render it acceptable for discharge either to surface waters or to the municipal sewerage system. Some aspects of industrial water supply and wastewater treatment requirements are discussed in Chapter 15.

7.2 Objectives of treatment

The main objective of water and wastewater treatment is to separate undesirable impurities from the product water. These impurities, which are drawn off in concentrated form as sidestreams to the main process, often require further treatment (especially in wastewater treatment plants) before they can be returned to the environment.

In some cases treatment may be required to make up a deficiency in some quality in the water. For example, fluoride is added to many municipal water supplies for the protection of children's teeth, while oxygen is sometimes added by aeration processes in water and wastewater treatment.

7.3 Water and wastewater quality and treatment

The choice of treatment processes for any particular application depends on the quality of the raw water, the required quality of the treated water, and the economic resources available to pay for both the capital and operating costs of the treatment plant. A detailed discussion of common parameters for measuring water and wastewater quality, together with quality requirements for drinking waters and wastewater effluent discharges, is given in Chapter 5. Consideration of costs is outside the scope of this text.

Of great importance in selecting treatment processes for particular applications is the general physical form, as well as the chemical and biological nature, of the impurities to be removed. A classification of impurities on this basis is shown in Fig 7.1.

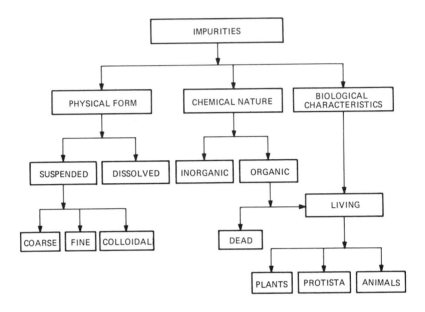

Fig 7.1 Nature of impurities in waters and wastewaters

In *physical form*, impurities may be either dissolved or suspended, and the suspended matter may be coarse, fine or colloidal in size. Another important way in which the various types of impurity may be distinguished on the basis of physical behaviour is their settling characteristics. Coarse material and some of the fine matter are generally readily settleable and may be conveniently removed by simple gravity sedimentation. Dissolved and colloidal matter and the remainder of the fine suspended matter, however, is not removed by conventional sedimentation and the choice of treatment processes for removing these forms of impurity depends largely on their *chemical* and *biological* characteristics.

Treatments appropriate to the removal of the various forms of impurity are similarly classified under the broad headings of physical, chemical and biological processes. Relationships between the various forms of impurity and some treatment processes commonly used to remove them are shown in Fig 7.2.

Physical processes are generally the simplest forms of treatment and comprise, principally, screening, sedimentation and filtration. Other

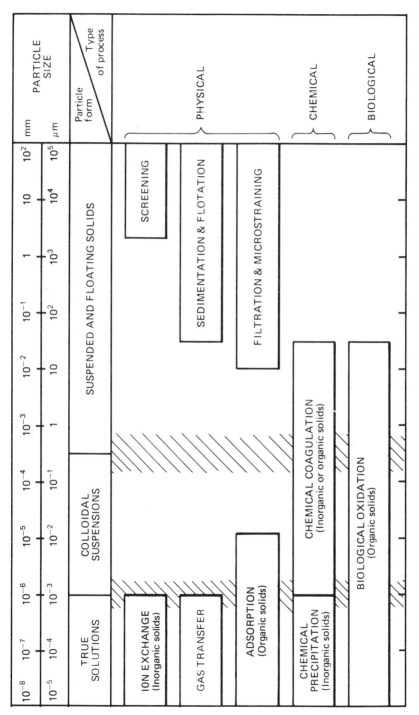

Fig 7.2 Applications of unit processes

physical processes such as flotation, gas transfer and adsorption are also important in particular cases.

Screening by racks, coarse or fine screens, or comminutors is carried out at the head of most treatment plants, where it constitutes a form of preliminary treatment for removing coarse material which might otherwise interfere with subsequent treatment processes or pumping equipment.

Sedimentation, alone or in conjunction with other processes, in both water and wastewater treatment plants, is involved in removing the major part of the removable impurities. Where impurities are present in solution or in suspensions too fine for removal by sedimentation, other processes are used to convert them into a settleable form. In the case of some inorganic dissolved salts, chemical precipitation is used, while organic and inorganic colloids and fine suspended matter may be rendered settleable by *chemical coagulation* followed by *flocculation*. Organic matter in solution or suspension may be *oxidised biologically* by micro-organisms, which, under correctly-controlled conditions, are themselves settleable.

Filtration, by passing the flow through a bed of fine porous material, is normally carried out after sedimentation in water treatment (and sometimes after final sedimentation in wastewater treatment) to remove fine particles that escape in the sedimentation tank effluent.

If there are objectionable dissolved impurities which cannot be removed by these processes, there are further processes which can be used.

Sometimes, *chemical treatment* can successfully alter the nature of a substance so that the products formed are no longer objectionable, although they remain in solution. Colour in water can be bleached, offensive odours oxidised to inoffensive compounds and nitrates reduced to nitrogen gas; disinfection can kill bacteria without removing the material of which they are composed.

Some impurities can be removed by *adsorption* onto the active surfaces of some solids, such as activated carbon, or by exchange onto ion exchange materials.

Phase change is a method, albeit an expensive one, of separating dissolved impurities from water. Methods using distillation and freezing are described in Chapter 13.

Semi-permeable membranes are used for removing unwanted material in the reverse osmosis and electrodialysis methods of desalination (Chapter 13).

Review question

7.1 What general processes are available for removing or changing unwanted suspended and dissolved impurities in water and wastewater?

8 Physical Treatment Processes

The general importance of physical processes in water and wastewater treatment has been shown in Chapter 7. The principles of these processes are presented in this chapter, while further details of their application are discussed in Chapters 13, 14 and 15.

8.1 Screening

River waters and raw wastewaters may contain coarse suspended and floating matter which may damage or interfere with the operation of pumps and treatment plant equipment. This material is usually removed by simple screening devices, which in treatment plants are classified as *preliminary treatment*.

In *water supply systems*, screens are usually located at intakes from rivers, lakes or open storage reservoirs, where they serve to prevent the entry of logs and sticks or even fish and animals. In *sewerage systems*, screens are sometimes provided at the inlet to sewage pumping stations, where rags, paper and other coarse materials could cause damage by fouling pump impellers, and on sewer overflow structures where it is desirable to prevent coarse materials from fouling the receiving environment. Screens are usually installed at the inlets to wastewater treatment plants to remove materials which otherwise may become entangled in pumps, scrapers and aeration devices, or may foul weirs and channels.

Classification of screens

Screens may be classified variously according to their clear opening size (as coarse, medium or fine), their configuration (racks, bar screens and mesh screens), the method used to clean the entrapped material from the screen surface (manually, mechanically raked, or water-jet cleaned), and also according to whether the screen surface is fixed or moving. Combined screening and maceration devices are sometimes used at wastewater treatment works.

Fixed screens

Racks and bar screens These are the simplest forms, and are widely used at inlets to wastewater treatment plants, and on river intakes for water supplies.

Bar screens (Fig 8.1(a)) consist of parallel metal bars with 20 to 60 mm clear openings in coarse screens, and 10 to 20 mm clear openings in fine to medium screens. Fine screens are usually preceded by coarse screens in order to prevent the risk of damage by large objects, or excessive head loss as screenings accumulate.

Bar screens may be cleaned reasonably satisfactorily by manual raking in small installations. Large installations, however, are generally provided with mechanical devices for removing screenings at regular intervals. Such devices may be operated either by time clocks or by pressure-sensing probes which are activated when the head loss across the screen becomes excessive. A large number of proprietary screens with mechanical rakes are currently available. In most cases, manufacturers provide design charts to facilitate selection of appropriate screen sizes.

Mesh screens These are used mainly in water supply and water treatment installations. They have square openings ranging in size from 1 mm to 25 mm or even more, according to design requirements. Most fine mesh screens are used in locations where relatively small amounts of material are to be removed, and they are usually manually cleaned. Such screens, for example, may follow bar screens on water intakes to prevent small fish from being drawn into the intake.

Moving screens

Drum screen This is a continuous screening device consisting of a hollow drum, usually 2 to 5 m in diameter, which rotates about its horizontal axis (Fig 8.1(b)). One end of the drum is closed. Water enters the drum through the other end and passes out either through perforations or mesh openings in its periphery. As the drum rotates, screenings caught on it are carried clear of the water surface and are deposited in a collecting trough. Water jets help to clean the entrapped material from the screen surface.

Disc screen This consists of a large rotating metal disc, often set at an angle of about 30° to the vertical, partly immersed. Solids caught on the face of the disc are carried to the top, where they are removed by revolving brushes.

Fine belt screens These are made of flexible woven wire mesh. They are only rarely used in the treatment of water or municipal sewage, but are commonly used for industrial wastes. The rotation of the screen is an aid to cleaning. Some belt screens are vibrated to increase efficiency and prevent clogging when screening out fine material like spent grain from a distillery or fine organic wastes from a canning factory.

Medium belt screens These are used for continuous operation in removing floating and suspended debris from water supply intakes. They consist of sections of mesh attached to frames which are hinged together and mounted on a chain belt (Fig 13.2(b)).

Microstrainers These are a development of the drum screen in which the screening fabric is woven stainless steel micromesh (Fig 8.1(c)). Meshes are available with apertures ranging from 15 to 64 μm for removing very fine suspended matter from feed water. Microstrainers are usually 0.8 m to 3 m in diameter and rotate at a maximum peripheral speed of 0.5 m/s. Effective cleaning of microstrainers requires high-pressure water jets using good-quality water. To control the growth of slime bacteria, which would rapidly clog the micromesh, the drum surface can be bathed in ultraviolet light.

Microstraining has found its principal application in pretreating some types of water supply, before other treatment processes; in the case of some good-quality upland waters, it may be all the treatment that is necessary for removing some types of algae and other planktonic organisms. In wastewater treatment, microstrainers are also used at a tertiary stage to further improve a good-quality secondary effluent by removing suspended solids escaping from the final sedimentation tanks. In these applications, microstrainers fulfil a function more usually associated with filters than with conventional screens.

Loading rates of 350 to 2300 m^3/m^2.d have been claimed for micro-strainers, but in any particular application the design should be based on tests carried out on the water to be treated. For design purposes, conventional water analyses, such as that for suspended solids, do not provide adequate information, since the number, size and shape of particles all affect the rate of removal by microstrainers.

Disposal of screenings

Screenings removed at water supply intakes usually comprise leaves, sticks and other vegetable matter which is relatively inoffensive and may be returned to the river downstream of the intake.

Sewage screenings are often heavily contaminated with faecal matter and need to be carefully disposed of as quickly as possible, usually by burial, incineration, or maceration and return to the flow.

Design of screens

The main factors to be considered in screen design are the strength and durability of the screening medium, the clear screen area, maximum flow velocity through the screen apertures so that screenings will not be dislodged, minimum velocity in the approach channel to prevent settlement of suspended matter on the channel floor, and the head loss through the screen. In most cases mild steel is satisfactory for making screens, but other materials may need to be considered in abnormally corrosive environments. The strength of the screen media should be sufficient to withstand impact of large floating objects and also the forces which may be generated by mechanical cleaning devices.

Velocity through screen apertures should generally not exceed 0.6 to 1.0 m/s, depending upon the nature of the materials to be removed and their susceptibility to being forced through the screen at higher flow velocity. The minimum velocity required in approach channels to prevent deposition of sand and other suspended matter is related to the size and density of the

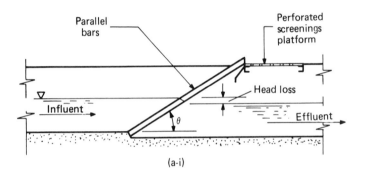

(a-i)

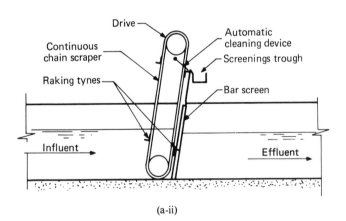

(a-ii)

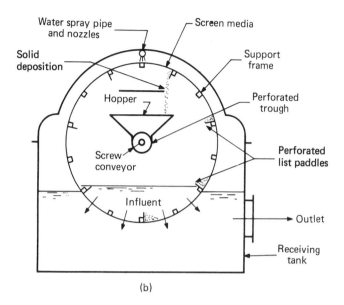

(b)

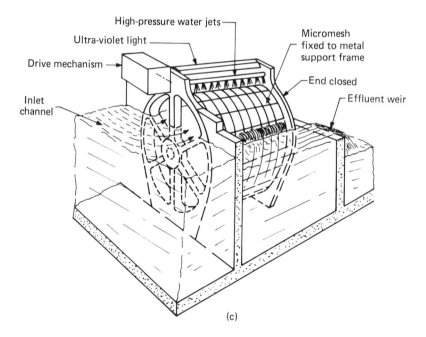

(c)

Fig 8.1 Examples of screens: (a-i) manually-raked bar screen, (a-ii) mechanically-raked bar screen, (b) drum screen, (c) microstrainer

suspended impurities, and to the flow velocity in the channel from which the water or wastewater was drawn. A minimum velocity of 0.3 to 0.4 m/s is usually sufficient to prevent excessive accumulation of settled materials in approach channels.

Head loss through screens

The minimum loss through clean screens can be estimated by considering the screen to approximate an orifice or a short conduit, or even by applying a minor loss expression.

A widely-quoted equation of this last type, useful for estimating minimum head loss through clean bar screens is

$$h = \beta \left(\frac{w}{b} \right)^{4/3} \frac{V_a^2}{2g} \sin \theta \qquad (8.1)$$

where h is the head loss across the screen (m); w is the maximum bar width (mm); b is the minimum aperture width (mm); V_a is the velocity in the approach channel (m/s); β is the shape factor ($\simeq$ 2.4 for square-edged rectangular bars); and θ is the angle of inclination of the bars to the horizontal (commonly 30°).

This expression is of use in determining the minimum hydraulic losses through screens at the various rates of flow that occur, but is of no value in determining head loss once material begins to accumulate on the screen surface. Design should take into account the maximum increase in head loss likely to occur under the critical conditions of maximum flow and minimum cleaning frequency. With mechanically-raked screens, this can be readily accommodated by providing an automatic cleaning system. Manually-raked screens, however, should have liberal freeboard in the upstream channel to avoid the danger of overtopping the channel at high flows.

8.2 Sedimentation

Definitions

Sedimentation may be defined as the removal of solid particles from a suspension by settling under gravity.

Clarification is a similar term which refers specifically to the function of a sedimentation tank in removing suspended matter from the water to give a clarified effluent.

Thickening in sedimentation tanks is the process whereby the settled impurities are concentrated and compacted on the floor of the tank and in the sludge-collecting hoppers.

Concentrated impurities withdrawn from the bottom of sedimentation tanks are called *sludge*, while material that floats to the top of the tanks is called *scum*.

Application of sedimentation processes

In *water treatment*, sedimentation is commonly used to remove impurities that have been rendered settleable by coagulation and flocculation, as when removing turbidity and colour. Precipitates formed in processes such as water softening by chemical precipitation are also removed by sedimentation. Less frequently, preliminary sedimentation may be used to remove settleable materials from waters drawn from fast-flowing streams which may on occasions carry a heavy sediment load.

In *municipal wastewater treatment*, sedimentation is the main process in primary treatment, where it is responsible for removing 50 to 70 per cent of the suspended solids (containing 25–40 per cent of the BOD) from the wastewater. After biological treatment, sedimentation is used to remove the biological floc produced by micro-organisms in these processes, so that effluent quality will approach a standard suitable for discharge into inland waterways. The removal of grit in the preliminary stage of treatment is commonly carried out by means of a differential sedimentation process in which heavy grit is permitted to settle while lighter organic matter is retained in suspension.

Sedimentation is also required where phosphorus removal is effected by chemical precipitation separately from primary or secondary treatment. Other less obvious applications of sedimentation are in the separation of digested sludge from supernatant liquor in secondary (unstirred) sludge digesters, and also in sludge lagoons.

An understanding of the principles governing the various forms of sedimentation behaviour is essential to the effective design and operation of sedimentation tanks.

Classification of settling behaviour

Several classes of settling behaviour may be distinguished on the basis of the *nature* of the particles to be removed and their *concentration*. Thus individual particles may be discrete (sand grains) or flocculent (most organic materials and biological solids), while particle concentrations may vary from very low, through moderate, to high concentrations in which adjacent particles are actually in contact. Common classifications of settling behaviour are

Class I   — Unhindered settling of discrete particles
Class II   — Settling of dilute suspensions of flocculent particles
Class III — Hindered settling and zone settling
Class IV   — Compression settling (compaction).

Ideal settling behaviour — Sedimentation Class I

The simplest form of sedimentation is that involving discrete particles in such low concentration that each particle settles freely without interference from adjacent particles (that is, unhindered settling).

When a particle settles in a fluid it accelerates until the drag force due to its motion is equal to the submerged weight of the particle. At this point, the particle will have reached its terminal velocity, V_p.

A definition sketch for settling of an idealised spherical particle is shown in Fig 8.2, where V_p is the particle settling velocity (m/s); D is the drag force; W is the submerged weight of the particle; d is the diameter of the particle (m); A_p is the projected area of particle normal to direction of motion (m²); V_p is the volume of the particle (m³); ρ is the density of the particle (kg/m³); ρ_ℓ is the fluid density (kg/m³); μ is the dynamic viscosity of the fluid (N.s/m²); and C_D is the drag coefficient.

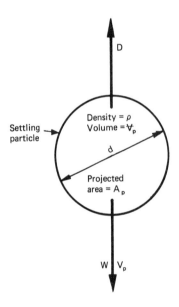

Fig 8.2 Definition sketch for particle terminal settling velocity

An expression for V_p may be derived by equating expressions for submerged weight, W, of the settling particle and the fluid drag force, D.

The drag force on a particle is given by

$$D = C_D \rho A_p \frac{V_p^2}{2} \tag{8.2}$$

The submerged weight of the particle can be expressed as

$$W = (\rho - \rho_\ell)g\,V_p \tag{8.3}$$

Equating the above expressions after substituting for A_p and V_p and rearranging, results in the following expression for V_p

$$V_p = \sqrt{\frac{4}{3}\frac{(\rho - \rho_\ell)}{\rho}\frac{gd}{C_D}} \tag{8.4}$$

In practice, it is found that C_D is a function of the Reynolds Number, R_e, and, for spherical particles, it can. be represented by the following expressions

$$\text{For } R_e < 1, C_D = \frac{24}{R_e}$$

$$\text{for } 1 < R_e < 10^4, C_D = \frac{24}{R_e} + \frac{3}{(R_e)^{1/2}} + 0.34$$

$$\text{and for } 10^3 < R_e < 10^5, C_D \simeq 0.4$$

Substituting the above expression for $R_e < 1$ (laminar flow) in Eq 8.4 and noting that $R_e = \rho_\ell V_p d/\mu$, results in the following equation, known as Stokes's Law:

$$V_p = \frac{g}{18}\frac{(\rho - \rho_\ell)}{\mu}d^2 \tag{8.5}$$

At high values of R_e, where $C_D \approx 0.4$, the equivalent expression is

$$V_p = \sqrt{3.33\frac{(\rho - \rho_\ell)}{\rho}gd} \tag{8.6}$$

It is seldom possible to apply Eqs 8.4, 8.5 and 8.6 directly to practical sedimentation processes, because particle diameter and density are usually not known, and in practice particles are irregular in shape. Nevertheless, the general conclusion that V_p depends on particle diameter, particle density and, under some conditions, also on fluid viscosity and hence on temperature, is of value in understanding sedimentation behaviour. Furthermore, in practical sedimentation tanks, the terminal settling velocity is quickly reached, so that, for non-flocculent particles and uniform fluid flow the settling velocity is constant throughout the settling time. This fact can be usefully applied to a study of settling in an *ideal sedimentation tank* to give an important design parameter for sedimentation processes.

Idealised representations of three common types of sedimentation tanks are shown in Fig 8.3: (a) rectangular horizontal flow, (b) circular radial flow and (c) upflow tanks.

The *ideal rectangular horizontal flow sedimentation tank* is considered to be divided into four zones (Fig 8.3(a))

a Inlet zone — in which momentum is dissipated and flow is established in a uniform forward direction
b Settling zone — where quiescent settling is assumed to occur as the water flows towards the outlet
c Outlet zone — in which the flow converges upwards to the decanting weirs or launders
d Sludge zone — where settled material collects and is moved towards sludge hoppers for withdrawal. It is assumed that once a particle reaches the sludge zone it is effectively removed from the flow.

In the settling zone of an ideal rectangular sedimentation tank, the critical particle for design purposes will be one that enters at the top of the settling zone, at point A, and settles with a velocity just sufficient to reach the sludge zone at the outlet end of the tank, at point B. The velocity components of such a particle are V_h in the horizontal direction and V_p, terminal settling velocity, in the vertical direction.

From the geometry of the tank it is apparent that the time required for the particle to settle, t_o, is given by

$$t_o = \frac{H}{V_p} = \frac{L}{V_h}$$

but, since $V_h = Q/WH$, then $V_p = Q/WL$, where Q is the rate of flow, and L, W and H are the length, width and depth of the tank, respectively. Since the surface area of the tank, A, is WL, then

$$V_p = Q/A \tag{8.7}$$

According to this relationship, the slowest-settling particles which could be expected to be completely removed in an ideal sedimentation tank would have a settling velocity of Q/A. Hence this parameter, which is called the *surface loading rate* or *overflow rate*, is a fundamental parameter governing sedimentation tank performance.

This relationship also implies that sedimentation efficiency is independent of tank depth — a condition that holds true only if the forward velocity is low enough to ensure that settled material is not scoured and resuspended from the tank floor.

A similar analysis of an *ideal circular radial flow sedimentation tank* is summarised in Fig 8.3(b), from which it is seen that the same relationship, $V_p = Q/A$, is obtained.

In an *ideal upflow sedimentation tank* (Fig 8.3(c)), it is apparent that a particle will be removed only if its settling velocity exceeds the water upflow velocity. In this case the minimum upflow velocity is given by the flow rate divided by the surface area of the tank (Q/A), so once again the minimum settling velocity for a particle to be removed is $V_p = Q/A$.

In an ideal sedimentation tank with a horizontal or radial flow pattern,

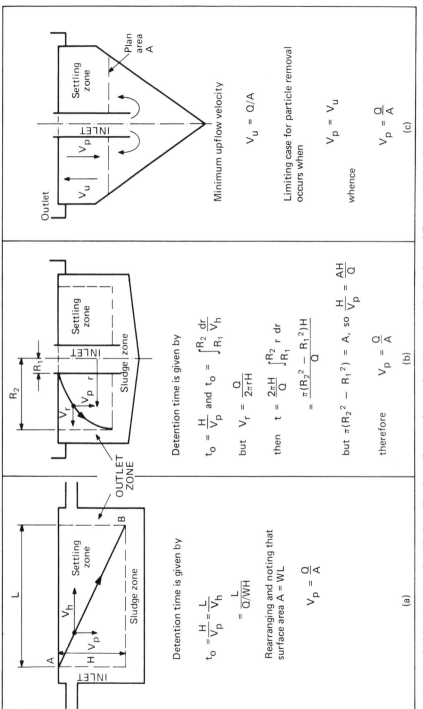

Fig 8.3 Definition sketches for ideal settling in sedimentation tanks: (a) rectangular horizontal flow tank, (b) circular radial flow tank, (c) upflow tank

particles with settling velocities less than the critical value of $V_p = Q/A$ — say, V_p/n — will also be removed in the proportion $1/n$. By contrast, in an ideal upflow tank, no particles with settling velocities $V_p < Q/A$ will be removed.

Sedimentation Class II — settlement of dilute suspensions of flocculent particles

The most common type of sedimentation in water and wastewater treatment involves flocculent particles, such as flocculated impurities, organic waste matter and biological solids, present in relatively low concentrations.

Settling of flocculent (Class II) suspensions differs from that of ideal (Class I) suspensions in that Class II sedimentation involves a variety of particle sizes settling at different rates so that larger, faster-settling particles may overtake slower-settling particles. Colliding particles may then coalesce to form larger aggregates with an increased settling velocity, so that the typical path followed by flocculent particles is curved, as shown in Fig 8.4.

One important requirement of sedimentation tanks for treating flocculent suspensions is, therefore, that the depth should be great enough to provide the opportunity for particle agglomeration to occur. This may be confirmed by reference to Fig 8.4, which compares the behaviour of Class I and Class II settling if the depth of the sedimentation tank is reduced. For a tank with depth H, consider typical critical particle settling paths, ACB for a discrete particle and ADB for a flocculent particle. If the tank depth is reduced to H/2, the forward velocity will be doubled, while the total time of travel through the tank will be halved. Hence the depth to which the particles have settled at the mid-point of the full-depth tank (AX and AY) will represent the depth reached at the outlet end of the settling zone in the half-depth tank. The

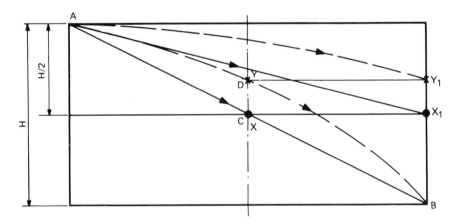

Fig 8.4 Theoretical effect of tank depth on removal of discrete and flocculent particles

corresponding paths of the two particles will then be AX_1 and AY_1. It is apparent that the discrete particle will again just reach the bottom of the reduced-depth settling zone. The flocculent one, however, will not have reached the tank floor and hence will be drawn off in the tank effluent. This is an oversimplification, since it is possible that an increased forward velocity may result in greater turbulence. This may promote a faster rate of particle collision and agglomeration, and hence help to promote an increased settling velocity, thus compensating in part for the reduced depth in which flocculation can occur. Nevertheless, it is generally considered that the overall effect of reducing tank depth is to reduce removal efficiency when treating flocculent particles.

Hence, although the surface loading rate again represents the minimum average settling velocity that a particle must have in order for it to be removed in a Class II sedimentation tank, attention must also be given to the depth or detention time provided. These three parameters are interrelated, so that once values for any two are chosen, the third is fixed, as may be seen from the following:

Detention time is given by $t = \dfrac{\forall}{Q} = \dfrac{WLH}{Q}$

since $WL = A$, $t = \dfrac{H}{Q/A}$ \hfill (8.8)

where L, W and H are, respectively, the length, width and depth in metres of the settling zone; $\forall$ is the volume of the settling zone (m³); and Q is the flow rate (m³/s).

Some effects of depth and detention time on solids concentration for flocculating particles can be determined, if representative samples of the water or wastewater to be treated are available, by quiescent settling tests in columns having a height equal to the maximum depth to be considered for the sedimentation tank in question. The column should be provided with sampling points, so that samples can be drawn from various depths at suitable time intervals throughout the settling period. From the results of suspended-solids tests carried out on the samples, the percentage removal of suspended solids at each time and depth can be calculated, and plotted as in Fig 8.5.

Lines of equal solids-removal efficiency can then be drawn. Hence, a combination of depth and detention time could be chosen for any required suspended-solids removal efficiency. While it may be feasible to obtain suitable samples of water for testing in this way, there are many problems with this approach. In the case of wastewaters, it is difficult to obtain representative samples at any single time, while for a proposed new scheme it is usually impossible to obtain samples at all.

Other investigations on primary sedimentation tanks in wastewater treatment have shown that efficiency depends greatly on the suspended-

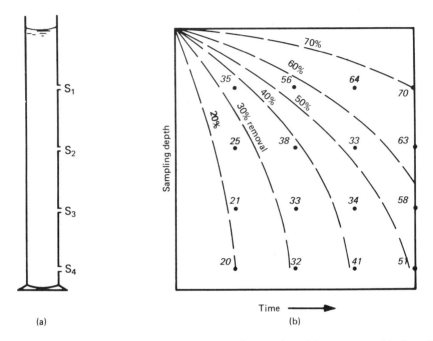

Fig 8.5 Settling column test for Class II sedimentation: (a) apparatus, (b) plot of results

solids concentration in the influent. Sedimentation efficiency was shown to increase as suspended-solids concentration increased (a finding which is consistent with the greater opportunities for particle collisions, and hence flocculation, provided by higher particle concentration).

Sedimentation Class III — hindered settling, zone settling and sludge blanket clarifiers

As the concentration of particles in a suspension is increased, a point is reached where particles are so close together that they no longer settle independently of one another but the velocity fields of the fluid displaced by adjacent particles overlap. There is also a net upward flow of liquid displaced by the settling particles. This results in a reduced particle-settling velocity and the effect is known as *hindered settling*.

The most commonly encountered form of hindered settling occurs in the extreme case where particle concentration is so high that the whole suspension tends to settle as a 'blanket'. This is termed *zone settling*, because it is possible to distinguish several distinct zones, separated by concentration discontinuities. Fig 8.6 represents a typical batch-settling column test on a suspension exhibiting zone-settling characteristics. Soon after leaving such a

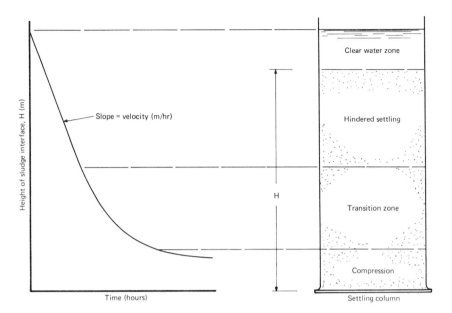

Fig 8.6 Settling column test for a suspension exhibiting zone-settling behaviour

suspension to stand in a settling column, there forms near the top of the column a clear interface separating the settling sludge mass from the clarified supernatant. This interface moves downwards as the suspension settles. Similarly, near the bottom there is an interface between that portion of the suspension which has settled and the suspended blanket. This interface moves upwards until it meets the upper interface, at which point settling of the suspension is complete.

It is apparent that the slope of the settling curve at any point represents the settling velocity of the interface between the suspension and the clarified supernatant. This once again leads to the conclusion that in designing clarifiers for treating concentrated suspensions (Class III), the surface loading rate is a major parameter to be considered; unless the surface loading rate adopted is less than the zone-settling velocity (V_{sz}) of the influent suspension, solids will be carried over in the effluent.

An important application of zone settling is in the final sedimentation tanks of activated sludge processes.

Hindered settling is also important in upflow clarifiers in water treatment. These units often operate with a high concentration of solids (consisting of chemically-formed floc and impurities) in suspension. By simple comparison with the ideal upflow sedimentation tank in Fig 8.3(c), it may be seen that a suspension will be retained in an upflow clarifier only if the settling velocity of the suspension interface, V_s, is equal to the upflow velocity of the water,

V_u. This is important because many practical clarifiers are designed to maintain a high concentration of solids in suspension in order to take advantage of the increased opportunity for particles to collide and agglomerate. This assists in removing many of the very fine particles which might otherwise be carried over in the effluent.

In both these cases involving hindered settling of concentrated suspensions, the settling velocity of the suspension, V_s (or V_{sz}) is dependent on its concentration: as concentration increases, V_s (or V_{sz}) decreases.

The relationship between the velocity of settling (hereafter called simply V_s) and the volumetric concentration of the particles in the suspension has not yet been determined analytically for hindered settling situations. It is therefore necessary to use empirical equations to define an approximate relationship.

Many equations for this relationship have been proposed. The combined advantages of mathematical simplicity and reasonable accuracy over a wide range of concentrations are features of the empirical equation proposed by Richardson:

$$V_s = V_p \epsilon^n \tag{8.9}$$

where $\epsilon = (1 - c)$, the porosity of the suspension; c is the proportion of the total suspension volume occupied by particles; and n is an index depending on the Reynolds number and the size and shape of the particles.

For smooth spheres, the value of n varies from 4.65 for fully laminar flow conditions to about 2.5 for turbulent flow conditions around the particles. For irregular particles, many of which are both fragile and porous and for which the value of c cannot be directly determined, the formula may be modified to

$$V_s = V_p (1 - kc')^n \tag{8.10}$$

where c' is the concentration in some convenient reproducible unit; k and n are parameters so chosen that the resulting formula closely approximates the performance of the particular suspension.

Suitable values of k and n may be selected by plotting experimental values of $\log V_s$ against values of $\log (1 - kc')$ for different selected values of k until a value is found to give a good approximation to a straight line over an appropriate range. The corresponding value of n may be calculated from the slope of the line. The value of V_p is given by the extrapolated value of V when c = 0. Computer techniques can be useful in selecting (or fitting) appropriate values of k and n to give a least-squares best fit.

Sedimentation Class IV — compression settling

Very high particle concentrations can arise as the settling particles approach the floor of the sedimentation tanks and adjacent particles are actually in contact. Further settling can occur only by adjustments within the matrix, and so it takes place at a reducing rate. This is known as *compression settling* or *consolidation* and is illustrated by the lower region of the zone-settling diagram (Fig 8.6). Compression settling occurs as the settled solids are compressed under the weight of overlying solids, the void spaces are gradually diminished, and water is squeezed out of the matrix.

Compression settling is important in gravity thickening processes. It is also particularly important in activated-sludge final settling tanks, where the activated sludge must be thickened for recycling to the aeration tanks.

Design of sedimentation tanks

From a consideration of sedimentation theory it has been shown above that, in the case of ideal settling, the main design parameter to be considered is surface loading rate, Q/A, because it represents the critical particle settling velocity for complete removal. Practical Class II settling likewise was shown to require that adequate depth, H, or detention time, t, be provided in order to allow flocculation to take place. It was also noted that some data on these effects could be obtained from the quiescent settling column test. Apart from the difficulties associated with sampling, such data must also be modified to account for differences between batch-settling column tests and practical continuous-flow sedimentation tanks. Uniform flow distribution cannot always be assumed in practice owing to density currents, inadequate dissipation of momentum at the tank inlet and drawdown effects at the effluent weirs. As a result of all these effects, surface loadings and detention times derived from quiescent settling column tests should be multiplied by a suitable safety factor, typically 1.7 to 2.5, for practical design.

These considerations apply to all three types of tank commonly used for Class II sedimentation, namely rectangular horizontal flow tanks, circular radial flow tanks and square upflow tanks.

In the case of Class III sedimentation, it was also shown that the surface loading rate is the major parameter to be considered in design. Most of the following development therefore applies to the design of both Class II and Class. III sedimentation tanks. Further details on the application of the various types of sedimentation behaviour and tank designs are given in Chapters 13 and 14.

The design of sedimentation tanks for a given flow rate, Q, involves the selection of the surface loading rate, Q/A, from which the required tank surface area may be calculated, and either tank depth, H, or detention time, t. The relationships between the various parameters concerned can be expressed as shown below.

For Q in m³/d (kL/d) and Q/A in m³/m².d, the particle settling velocity, V_s (mm/s), is given by

$$V_p = \frac{Q/A}{86.4} \qquad (8.11)$$

Tank surface area (m²), $A = Q/(Q/A)$ $\qquad (8.12)$

Tank length or diameter (m), $L = \sqrt{\alpha A}$ $\qquad (8.13)$

where $\alpha = L/W$ for rectangular tanks, and $4/\pi$ for circular ones; and W is the width of the tank. Detention time (hours) is

$$t = \frac{24H}{Q/A} \qquad (8.14)$$

The task of proportioning the tank once values of the major parameters are chosen can be simplified by using a simple design chart (Fig 8.7) based on the above equations. Alternative designs may be quickly compared using this diagram, and effects of flow variations on critical loading parameters be determined.

The forward velocity must also be considered in *rectangular tanks*, as excessive velocity may result in the scouring and resuspension of settled sludge. This requirement influences the choice of length-to-width ratio for such tanks.

Forward velocity, V_h (m/d), is given by

$$V_h = \frac{Q}{WH}$$

or, in terms of the parameters used in preparing Fig 8.7, V_h (mm/s) becomes

$$V_h = \frac{L}{3.6\,t} \qquad (8.15)$$

for L in metres and t in hours.

This expression is represented in the upper left-hand quadrant of Fig 8.7 and, when read in conjunction with the lower left-hand quadrant, it gives the relationship between V_h and L/W ratio for rectangular tanks. Values of L/W in practice range from 3 to 6, with a value of 4 being common.

Weir loading rate, Q/L_w, is important in *rectangular tanks*. A single weir across the end of these tanks is considered too short to prevent the influence of the approach current generated by the weir from extending upstream into the settling zone, with possible disruption of the flow pattern through the tank. This effect is usually overcome by providing multiple suspended weir troughs, designed to limit the maximum weir loading rate to about 300 m³/m.d.

In *circular radial flow tanks*, the weir loading rate which results from a single perimeter weir is usually within the normally-quoted range of values,

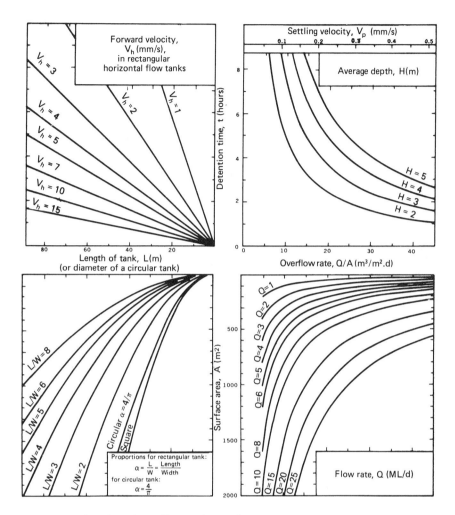

Fig 8.7 Design chart for sedimentation tanks

so that suspended weirs are not usually necessary for circular outward flow tanks. On the contrary, precautions must be taken with outlet weirs in such tanks because the very small depth of flow over the weir under low flow conditions makes the tank flow pattern very sensitive to slight errors in the levelling of the weir. Disruptions to the flow pattern may also result from wind action. These problems are usually effectively overcome by employing saw-toothed weirs to increase the depth of flow.

Inlets should be designed to dissipate the momentum and accurately distribute the incoming flow in such a way as to establish the required flow pattern in the tank.

The diverging flow which occurs in circular outward flow tanks is inherently less stable than the uniform forward flow in rectangular tanks, so that the design of the inlet stilling box is important in circular tanks. Excessive turbulence must be avoided in the inlet region since the sludge collecting hopper in most types of tank is located immediately beneath the inlet.

Sludge scrapers must be provided in modern rectangular and large circular sedimentation tanks, since it is not practicable to slope the floor sufficiently steeply for gravitational self-cleaning.

One of the distinctive features of square hopper-bottomed tanks is that their sides are steeply sloped so that they are self-cleaning. Sludge moves down the walls by gravity to collect at the bottom of the hopper, from where it can be drawn off under hydrostatic head. The operating simplicity and lack of mechanical parts which are features of these tanks have led to their widespread use in small treatment plants. They are not generally economical for larger plants, however, because of the rapid increase in hopper depth and the corresponding cost increases which large tanks entail.

Shallow depth sedimentation

It has just been shown that particles will be completely removed from a rectangular sedimentation tank if their settling velocity, V_p, is equal to, or greater than, the surface loading rate on the tank, Q/A, independently of the depth of the tank (provided that the forward velocity is not so high that settled material is scoured from the sludge zone). Any particles having a lower settling velocity than $V_p = Q/A$, say $V_p{}^1$, will be removed only in the proportion $V_p{}^1/V_p$. For example, if a particle follows the settling path AB_1 in Fig 8.8, corresponding to a settling velocity of $V_p{}^1 = V_p/n$, the proportion of such particles removed will be $1/n$. If, however, a tray were inserted in the settling zone at B_1, B_2 and B_3, that is, at depth intervals of H_o/n, all such

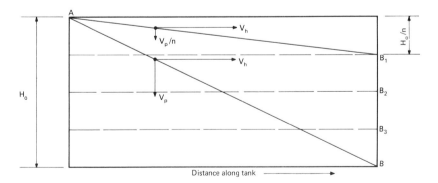

Fig 8.8 Definition sketch for horizontal shallow depth sedimentation

particles would be removed and hence the efficiency of the sedimentation tank would be greatly increased.

Alternatively, if only particles having a settling velocity of V_p were required to be removed, the forward velocity, and hence the flow rate through the tank, could be increased by the factor n. This is the principle of *shallow depth sedimentation*, which was recognised as early as 1904.

Up to the 1960s, however, shallow depth sedimentation found few applications, largely because suitably simple and economic methods of removing sludge from the multiple horizontal trays had not been devised.

In the late 1960s, it was found that sludge removal could be facilitated by sloping the shallow trays at an angle of about 5° upwards in the direction of flow. Cleaning could then be carried out by periodically taking the tank out of service and draining it; sufficient backflow velocity could be generated to remove the accumulated sludge by gravity from the trays. This type of inter-mittent operation, however, is unsuitable for many applications, although it may be acceptable in conjunction with filter backwashing.

Many of the practical problems of shallow depth sedimentation have now been overcome by steepening the angle of inclination of the plates (to about 60° to the horizontal in upflow units). At this slope, the flow pattern between the plates resembles that of an upflow clarifier rather than that of a hori-zontal flow system. These units are self-cleaning — sludge which settles on the upper face of the plates slides down them; particles collide and tend to stick together, with the result that sludge particles leaving the bottom of the plates are large enough to settle against the velocity of the inflowing water.

A similar principle to that of the *inclined plate settler*, which has been independently developed, is the *tube settler*, made by dividing the spaces between the plates by vertical baffles to form tubes of square cross-section.

A definition sketch for inclined plate settling is shown in Fig 8.9. The principles of the following analysis, however, apply generally to both inclined plate and inclined tube settling.

From Fig 8.9, it is apparent that the critical particle for design will be one which enters a plate settler at a point, X, with a velocity component, V_L, parallel to the plates and a settling velocity V_p, so that it reaches the bottom plate at point Y. The theoretical detention time, t_o, for such a particle will be given by

$$t_o = \frac{XZ}{V_L} = \frac{ZY}{V_p}$$

From the geometry of Fig 8.9, $XZ = L + S/(\sin \theta \cos \theta)$ and $ZY = S/\cos \theta$. Therefore,

$$t_o = \frac{S/\cos \theta}{V_p} = \frac{L + S/(\sin \theta \cos \theta)}{V_L}$$

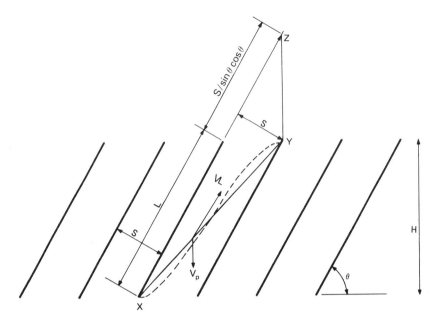

Fig 8.9 Idealised inclined plate settler

whence

$$V_L = V_p \left[\frac{L \cos \theta}{S} + \frac{1}{\sin \theta} \right] \tag{8.16}$$

It is of interest to compare the equivalent upflow velocity in this case with the critical velocity, $V_u = V_p = Q/A$, in a conventional upflow clarifier (Fig 8.3(c)).

The vertical component of the velocity V_L in the plate settler is given by $V_u = V_L \sin \theta$. Substitution into Eq. 8.16 gives

$$V_u = V_p \left[\frac{L \sin \theta \cos \theta}{S} + 1 \right] \tag{8.17}$$

$$= \frac{V_p}{2} \left[\frac{L}{S} \sin 2\theta + 2 \right] \tag{8.18}$$

For vertical plates ($\theta = 90°$), $V_u = V_p$. The maximum value of V_u is obtained by differentiating Eq 8.18 with respect to θ and setting $dV_u/d\theta = 0$, which gives $\theta = 45°$. It is usual, in practice, to increase θ to about 60°, to ensure relative freedom from clogging.

In the term $(L \sin \theta \cos \theta)/S$ in Eq 8.17, it may be observed that $L \sin \theta$ is the vertical projection, H, of the plate length, L, while $S/\cos \theta$ is the intercept of the plate spacing, S, on a vertical plane. Therefore, (L $\sin \theta$)/ (S/$\cos \theta$) = n, the number of spaces intersected by a vertical plane through the plate settler. Substitution into Eq 8.17 then gives

$$V_u = V_p(n + 1) \tag{8.19}$$

According to Eq 8.19, the equivalent upflow rate, V_u, in an inclined plate settler can be up to (n + 1) times the critical particle settling velocity V_p or, since $V_u = V_p = Q/A$, the surface loading rate can be multiplied by the factor (n + 1). The practical flow variations over the area of a clarifier, however, are such that, although substantial increases in upflow rate can be attained by using shallow depth sedimentation, it is not practicable to achieve the full estimated theoretical increases.

Most practical inclined tube or plate settlers have only quite small spacings between the inclined surfaces — about 50 mm is common. At these spacings, the Reynolds number is usually less than 500, so that flow is laminar. The path taken by the settling particles is therefore not a straight line, as represented by XY in Fig 8.9, but a curve, as shown by the broken line. This does not, however, affect the time taken by the particle in travelling from X to Y.

Shallow depth sedimentation has found its most frequent applications in water treatment. Accordingly, further discussion about practical aspects of this process may be found in Chapter 13.

8.3 Filtration

Applications

Filtration is used in both water treatment and wastewater treatment as a separation process which removes fine inorganic and organic particles from the water. Sand filters are often used in treatment of water to remove fine particles which cannot be economically removed by sedimentation; but they are seldom used in wastewater treatment, except in circumstances where an effluent of very good quality is required.

There are several different filtering processes used for the separation of particles from a stream of water or sludge. *Vacuum filters* and *filter presses* are used for removing water from sludges by the use of a filter cloth, which retains a layer of sludge from which water is sucked or pressed by an induced pressure difference. *Diatomaceous earth* filters are described in section 13.4. These units operate mainly through the use of a mechanical straining process.

This section, however, deals mainly with the operation of the more common type of filter, in which the filtering medium consists of granular material such as sand, anthracite, activated carbon or other grains.

Mechanical straining

When sand filters were first used, they were regarded primarily as mechanical straining devices. It has been found, however, that granular filters remove particles which are very much smaller than the dimensions of the interstices between their grains. Some of this effect may be accounted for by postulating that when the larger particles of impurities become lodged in a space between two grains, the portion of the opening not occupied by the particles will present smaller openings which are capable of trapping still smaller particles. If this were, in fact, a major component of filtration, the surface layers of the grains would rapidly become clogged, and fine material dislodged by the resulting hydraulic drag as the water was forced through the very fine remaining apertures would be likely to pass right through the remaining depth of filter bed without being caught. Although there must be some *mechanical straining* effect, it accounts for only a *minor part* of the action of a filter. A granular filter is capable of capturing very fine particles, even in the absence of particles large enough to bridge the interstices.

Adsorption

There are three essential parts of the filtration process in a granular material. They are: (a) the bed of fixed solids (consisting of the filter medium together with previously deposited impurities), (b) the water passing through the interstices between the fixed solids, and (c) the solid impurities suspended in that water.

Adsorption of particles of impurities onto the fixed bed (that is, the fine particles stick either to a grain of filter material or to previously deposited and adsorbed impurities) is a major factor in successful filtration through porous media. Adsorption is a process whose efficiency depends on the surface properties of both the adsorbing matrix and the small particles which are adsorbed. There are two factors in the adsorption of a particle: its ability to *stick* to the matrix when it is brought into contact and its *transport* to a position where it either contacts the surface or comes close enough to be attracted to it.

The method of attachment of particles is similar to the process of coagulation (Chapter 9). A small particle in close proximity to a solid surface is subject to either electrical attraction or repulsion (depending on the surface charges developed by both the particle and the surface when in contact with the water) and to the attraction caused by van der Waals forces (see Fig 9.1). It is also subject to the hydraulic forces resulting from the movement of the water. The effective range of the surface forces has been estimated to be up to about 0.2 microns in distilled water, but the addition of a small amount of dissolved salts can cause a tenfold reduction of this range to about 0.02 microns. The electrical forces can either inhibit or enhance the removal of fine particles from the water as it passes through a filter. For most of a filtering period, the grains of filter material are coated with a layer of impurities and, therefore, the surface charge produced on the impurities is important in ensuring a prolonged effective filter operation before cleaning is required. The requirement is the same as that for the destabilisation of colloids (Chapter 9). If the water has been treated to give optimum destabilisation of colloids for effective flocculation and sedimentation, it is likely that the remaining particles will be suitably destabilised for effective filtering. In filtration, the physico-chemical surface activity of the filter grains (as it affects adsorption) is possibly more important than particle size and shape, which affect the mechanical straining of impurities. The addition of certain *polyelectrolytes* to the water as it enters a filter can improve the effectiveness of adsorption. Addition of suitable polyelectrolytes to the backwash water has been used in a large treatment works to precondition the filter medium grains and thus improve adsorption in the early stages of a filter run, giving more efficient filtration.

If the forces of adhesion between the deposited impurities and the filter grains are so strong that the impurities are not readily removed during backwashing, the impurities and filter grains may lump together to form *mudballs*, which are very resistant to being cleaned by backwashing; their hydraulic behaviour makes them settle in a fluidised bed of sand. Care must therefore be exercised to ensure that although the adhesion surface forces are strong enough to trap and hold impurities, they are weak enough to allow their release during backwashing.

Transport

For adsorption to occur, particles must be carried close enough to the matrix surface to become attracted and attached to it. They are carried through the interstices in the filter matrix by the water flow, which, under normal conditions, is laminar.

There are three main mechanisms by which particles are transported into contact with the filter matrix: interception, sedimentation and diffusion (see Fig 8.10). *Interception* is the process whereby a particle being carried along a streamline chances to come close enough to a surface for its attachment. If a particle of effective diameter d_p is moving along a streamline which passes within a distance of $\frac{1}{2} d_p$ from a solid surface, there is an opportunity for adsorption. *Sedimentation* is the process in which a particle is deflected from the streamline path by the gravitational effect, resulting from the difference between its weight and its buoyancy. A granular filter has an action which can be considered as an irregular shallow depth sedimentation unit. In laminar flow conditions, *diffusion* is the process whereby particles are randomly deflected by buffeting resulting from molecular activity (Brownian motion).

The effectiveness of interception and sedimentation in a filter increases

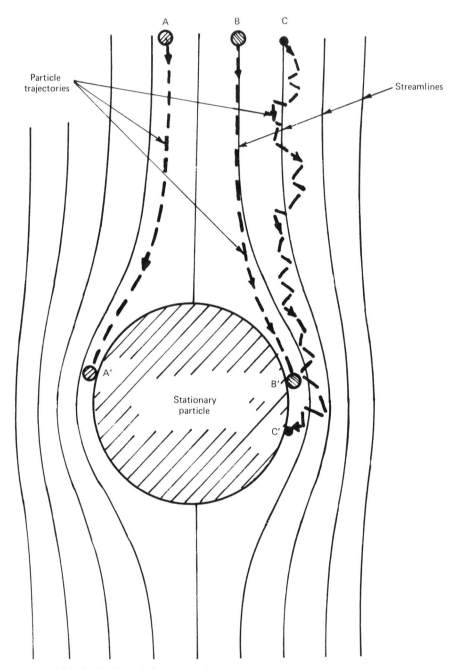

Particle A follows streamline from A to A' (*interception*)
Particle B is deflected from streamline by gravity (*sedimentation*)
Particle C is buffeted about by Brownian motion (*diffusion*)

Fig 8.10 Methods of particle transport

with an increase in particle size, but the effectiveness of diffusion increases with a decrease in size. Thus, although a filter may remove large particles efficiently by interception and sedimentation, and very small particles by diffusion, there is an intermediate size of particle for which the removal efficiency is relatively low. For practical filters, this is about 1 micron.

Flocculation is another process which takes place in a granular filter. The water passing through the filter interstices develops hydraulic velocity gradients which assist in making small particles come together to form larger particles (see Chapter 9), thus increasing the efficiency of interception and sedimentation.

Impingement, in which particles are deflected from streamlines by inertial forces, plays only a negligible part in water filter operations, mainly because of the small density differences between the water and the particles, and the low velocities.

Removal efficiency

Except with very dirty water, the removal efficiency of a filter is independent of the applied concentration, because each particle with a given size and surface condition has an equal probability of passing through the maze of passages without becoming attached to the matrix. This can be expressed mathematically by

$$-\frac{\partial C}{\partial L} = \lambda C \tag{8.20}$$

where C is the concentration of impurities; L is the distance through the filter bed; and λ is the rate factor, a parameter whose value depends on, among other things, grain size and nature, impurity size and nature, water velocity and degree of clogging.

The value λ, as a function of the deposition of impurities, has been empirically found to approximate

$$\lambda = \lambda_0 + c\sigma - \frac{\phi\sigma^2}{f_0 - \sigma} \tag{8.21}$$

where λ_0 is the initial rate factor (for a clean filter); σ is the volume of deposits per unit volume of filter; f_0 is the initial porosity of the filter bed; c and ϕ are rate factor parameters.

An equation which Ives has shown to be more generally applicable, though more complex, is

$$\lambda = \lambda_0\left(1 + \frac{\beta\sigma}{f_0}\right)^x \left(1 - \frac{\sigma}{f_0}\right)^y \left(1 - \frac{\sigma}{\sigma_n}\right)^z \tag{8.21a}$$

where x, y and z are empirical indices; β is the bulking factor of impurities; σ_n

is the ultimate accumulation of impurities; and f_o is the initial porosity of the filter bed.

Examination of the expressions shows that, when clogging starts (σ small), the efficiency of removal increases as material is first deposited. With further deposition, the value of λ increases slowly for a time, then it decreases until it approaches zero, at which stage the deposition stops. This is related to the stronger hydraulic forces needed to force the water through the remaining interstices, thus inhibiting deposition of impurities.

The rate of increase of σ at any depth, L, can be estimated by equating the increase in deposits to the impurities removed from the stream. This gives

$$\frac{\partial \sigma}{\partial t} = \lambda V_w C \qquad (8.22)$$

where t is the time, and V_w is the face velocity of water (that is, the flow rate divided by the area of the bed).

The course of deposition in a filter may be estimated by a numerical finite difference solution of the three equations, 8.20, 8.21 and 8.22, on a computer, to calculate σ for successive values of L and t.

Example 8.1

After some time of operation, a layer in a filter is receiving water at a rate of $1.5 L/m^2.s$ with a concentration of suspended impurities of 60 mg/L (density 1003 kg/m³). The concentration of deposited impurities at the time was 0.02 m³/m³ of sand bed, and the rate parameters were λ_o = 10 m⁻¹, C = 1.2 mm⁻¹, ϕ = 22 mm⁻¹, and the initial porosity was 0.4.

Make an estimate of the volumetric proportion of deposited impurities one hour later, at that position in the filter, assuming that Eq 8.21 sufficiently describes the particular conditions.

Solution
First estimate rate factor by substituting in Eq 8.21

$$\lambda = 10 + (0.02 \times 1200) - \frac{22\,000 \times (0.02)^2}{0.4 - 0.02} = 10.84 \text{ m}^{-1}$$

From Eq 8.22

$$\frac{\partial \sigma}{\partial t} = \lambda V_w C = 10.84 \times \frac{1.5}{1000} \times \frac{60 \times 10^{-6}}{1.003} = 9.72 \times 10^{-7} \text{ s}^{-1}$$

If δt = 3600 seconds,

$$\delta \sigma = \frac{\partial \sigma}{\partial t} \delta t = 9.72 \times 10^{-7} \times 3600 = 3.5 \times 10^{-3} \text{ m}^3/\text{m}^3$$

Therefore, σ at end of one hour = 0.02 + 0.0035 = 0.0235 m³/m³

Head loss in operating filter

For filter flow rates in the range of 1 to 4 L/s.m², and sand with an effective size of 0.5 to 1.0 mm, the error in assuming that the head loss is proportional to the flow rate is practically negligible. Thus Darcy's law

$$V = K \frac{h}{L} \tag{8.23}$$

can be used to estimate the head loss in a filter, where h is the head loss; L is the depth of filter bed over which the loss occurs; V is the the velocity of the water at the filter surface (1 L/s.m² = 1 mm/s); and K is Darcy's coefficient of permeability.

The coefficient of permeability is a function of the density, ρ, and viscosity, μ, of the water, the size and shape of the grains in the bed, and their porosity, f.

Kozeny's equation gives an estimate of the head gradient in a clean bed of sand filtering clean water as

$$\frac{h}{L} = \frac{k}{g} \frac{\mu}{\rho} V \frac{(1 - f)^2}{f^3} \frac{A^2}{\Psi} \tag{8.24}$$

where k is a dimensionless coefficient with a value of about 5 for most filtering conditions; A is the grain surface area; and Ψ is the grain volume.

For spherical grains, $\dfrac{A}{\Psi} = \dfrac{6}{d}$, where d is the diameter of sphere but

for other shapes, $\dfrac{A}{\Psi} = \dfrac{6}{\psi d}$, where ψ is a shape coefficient — about 0.9 for

waterworn sand, 0.7 for angular sand, and 0.65 for well-shaped crushed material. If k is assumed to be 5, the head loss through a clean bed of depth L is given approximately by

$$h = \frac{180}{g} \frac{\mu}{\rho} V \frac{(1 - f)^2}{f^3} \frac{L}{\psi^2 d^2} \tag{8.25}$$

The two parameters relating to the bed which have the most effect on head loss are d, the grain diameter, and f, the porosity. A decrease in either will cause an increase in head loss.

In a practical filter there is a mixture of particle sizes, the water is not clean and, for most of the time, many of the grains of filter medium are coated with impurities. The calculation of head loss is useful only to estimate the minimum head loss in a filter for a given flow. Because of the difference between practical and ideal conditions, only a moderate degree of agreement between actual and estimated head losses can be expected.

Example 8.2

A clean filter has a bed consisting of uniform, waterworn sand grains 0.6 mm in diameter. The porosity of the bed is 0.4 and the bed is 0.6 m thick. If the flow rate is 1.5 L/s.m², estimate the head loss if the viscosity of the water is 1×10^{-3} N.s/m².

Solution
Substituting in Eq 8.25 (converting to basic SI units),

$$h = \frac{180}{9.81} \times \frac{1 \times 10^{-3}}{[1000]} \times \frac{1.5}{1000} \times \frac{(1 - 0.4)^2}{0.4^3} \times \frac{0.6}{0.9^2 \times 0.0006^2} = 0.32 \text{ m}$$

It has been found from experience that, as a filter bed collects impurities, the increase in the head loss is approximately directly proportional to the amount of impurities collected. With a uniform quality of feed, the head loss in a filter during operation can then be written as

$$h = V(a + b\,\forall) \tag{8.26}$$

where V is the approach velocity of the water; $\forall$ is the volume of water filtered through unit area of bed since the last backwash; and a and b are parameters depending on the size and shape of the material, and the quality of the applied water.

Example 8.3

A filter has a head loss of 0.3 m when newly washed, and 1.3 m after 24 hours, when operating at a rate of 1.5 L/s.m². Estimate the head loss both immediately after backwash and 10 hours later, if the same water is applied at a rate of 2 L/s.m².

Solution
Substitution of the data in the formula gives two simultaneous equations

$$0.3 = \frac{1.5}{1000}[a + (0 \times b)]$$

$$1.3 = \frac{1.5}{1000}[a + (\frac{1.5}{1000} \times 24 \times 3600 \text{ b})]$$

Solution of these gives a = 200, b = 5.14

For the new condition, substitution gives

$$h_0 = \frac{2}{1000}[200 + (0 \times b)] = 0.4 \text{ m}$$

and

$$h_{10} = \frac{2}{1000}[200 + (\frac{2}{1000} \times 10 \times 3600 \times 5.14)] = 1.88 \text{ m}$$

Head loss when backwashing

The total head loss during a backwash is equal to the sum of head losses in the sand bed, gravel bed and distribution system.

In the *sand bed*, the head loss follows Darcy's law for low flows. Water flowing upwards through a granular bed creates hydraulic drag forces on the grains. As long as a grain is in contact with other grains, the resultant of the intergranular forces and drag forces on the grain is equal to the buoyant weight of the grain; but, if the grain is freely suspended in the water, the intergranular forces must be zero and the drag force is then equal to its buoyant weight.

The drag force acts on the grains and there is an equal and opposite reaction on the water. This gives rise to a pressure loss as the water passes through the granular bed. It follows that the pressure loss is given by

$$\delta P = (W_b - F_f)/A$$

where δP is the pressure loss in the bed; W_b is the buoyant weight of bed material; F_f is the total of granular forces acting on the floor of the bed; and A is the horizontal area of the bed.

As F_f cannot be negative, the maximum value of δP is W_b/A. When the flow exceeds that at which the Darcy pressure loss ($\rho g \times$ head loss) is equal to the buoyant weight of the grains in unit area, the sand bed expands and thus increases the porosity. Hence, the pressure loss remains equal to, or less than, the buoyant weight of the grains per unit area. When the porosity has increased so that the grains in the bed are free to move while suspended by the hydraulic forces, the bed is said to be *fluidised*. Fluidisation is a special case of hindered settling (Section 8.2).

The total head loss in a fully fluidised sand bed is approximately equal to the original depth of the bed. This is coincidental, because the apparent relative density of sand is about 1.65 (that is, $2.65 - 1$) and, with a porosity of about 0.4, the volume of the sand grains is about 0.6 times the volume of the bed.

The pressure corresponding to the buoyant weight of the grains per unit area therefore corresponds to that caused by a head of water about 0.6×1.65 times the depth of the bed.

The empirical Richardson–Zaki formula relates the porosity and upflow velocity in a fluidised bed:

$$V_s = V_p (1 - C)^n \tag{8.27}$$

where V_s is the hindered settling velocity (which, in a fluidised bed, is equal to the upflow velocity); V_p is the settling velocity of a single particle (of mean size); C is the volumetric concentration (1 − porosity); and n is an index which depends on the nature and grading of the grains.

The value of n varies from about 2.5 for particles which settle with a turbulent wake to 4.65 for spherical particles around which the flow of water is laminar. For filter sand, the value is usually in the range 3.6 to 4.5.

As the magnitude of the upflow velocity, V_s, in the fluidised condition increases, so the porosity increases and the concentration decreases. If the initial bed depth and concentration are L and C_o respectively, the depth of the fluidised bed is LC_o/C. The percentage expansion of the bed is equal to $100 (C_o − C)/C$.

The upflow through a bed is inherently *unstable*. The head loss over a given depth is proportional to the concentration, and therefore *decreases* as the flow increases. Any local increase in flow reduces the local concentration. Therefore, the resistance to flow is reduced and this tends to cause a further increase of flow. Uneven backwashing of filters results from this phenomenon, and controls external to the bed must be provided.

The external control of flow is provided by the head loss in the finer layers of gravel in the sand support or by the distributing orifices in the filter floor, or both. The head loss through these must be large enough to control the flow, despite the unstable nature of the granular bed.

The viscosity of water varies with temperature. Therefore, lower flow rates are required with very cold waters, and higher flow rates with warm waters (as found in hot climates), to produce the same sand expansion and washing efficiency.

Example 8.4

A filter bed of uniform sand has an operating depth of 0.6 m at a porosity of 0.41. When backwashed at a rate of 7.2 L/s.m² at 15°C, the bed expands to a depth of 0.72 m and, at 16.1 L/s.m², it expands to a depth of 0.906 m. Estimate the backwash rate required at the same temperature to cause 30 per cent expansion.

Solution
Substitution of the data in the Richardson–Zaki equation, $V_s = V_p (1 − C)^n$, gives

$$7.2 = V_p \left[1 - \left(0.59 \times \frac{0.6}{0.72} \right) \right]^n$$

$$16.1 = V_p \left[1 - \left(0.59 \times \frac{0.6}{0.906} \right) \right]^n$$

Divide LHS by LHS and RHS by RHS, which gives

$$0.447 = \left(\frac{0.508}{0.609}\right)^n$$

Therefore, n = 4.44.
Substitution of this value in one of the above equations gives

$$7.2 = V_p \left[1 - \left(0.59 \times \frac{0.6}{0.72}\right)\right]^{4.44} = V_p(0.508)^{4.44}$$

from which $V_p = 145.6$ mm/s.
Now, for 30 per cent expansion,

$$V_s = 145.6 \left[1 - \left(0.59 \times \frac{100}{130}\right)\right]^{4.44} = 9.93 \text{ mm/s}$$

8.4 Aeration

Applications

Aeration is a process whereby oxygen may be dissolved in wastewater during aerobic biological treatment (Chapters 11 and 14) to provide for the respiration of micro-organisms and to prevent malodourous anaerobic conditions. It is also used for the re-oxygenation of water supplies which have been taken from sources in which the oxygen concentration may be very low. Examples of these are groundwater, the hypolimnion of lakes or reservoirs, and polluted rivers (Chapter 13).

The turbulence and increased surface area which encourage the solution of oxygen in water also encourage the dissolution of gases which are not normally present in air. Thus, aeration can be used not only to dissolve oxygen from the air but also to remove unwanted volatile gases such as hydrogen sulphide, carbon dioxide and ammonia from waters undergoing treatment.

Gas solubility and equilibrium

Where there is an interface between a gas and a liquid, gas molecules from the gaseous side of the gas-liquid interface hit it and dissolve in the liquid; the number of these is proportional to the partial pressure of the particular gas and other minor factors. At the same time, molecules of dissolved gases escape from the liquid; the number of these is proportional to the concentration of the dissolved gas in the liquid surface and to a factor dependent on the temperature of the water, the composition and concentration of impurities and the nature of the gas.

The net transfer of a gas from the gas phase to the liquid phase is the difference between these two sets of migrating molecules. When the two opposing streams of molecules are equal, the system is said to be in *equilibrium* and the solution is said to be *saturated*.

Henry's law provides that, at low concentrations, the *saturation concentration* of a gas is proportional to the *partial pressure* of that gas at the liquid-gas interface.

This can be expressed by the formula

$$C_{si} = k \, p_i \tag{8.28}$$

where C_{si} is the saturation concentration of gas 'i'; k is the Henry's law constant; and p_i is the partial pressure of gas 'i' (absolute).

The proportionality constant in Henry's law is a function of the kind of gas, the temperature, the liquid and the impurities in the liquid.

The solubility of oxygen is of particular interest in studies of the biological treatment of wastes and of river quality. The effect of temperature between 5° and 25°C and salinity on its solubility in clean water from air at sea level (total pressure = 101.325 kPa, or oxygen partial pressure = 21.24 kPa) is given by the following approximate empirical equation

$$C_s = \frac{482.5 - S[0.003 - (2.6T \times 10^{-5})]}{[32.6 + T]} \tag{8.29}$$

where C_s is the saturation concentration of oxygen (mg/L); S is the salinity (mg/L); and T is the temperature (°C).

Although this equation applies to pure water and sea water, it is reasonably correct for wastewater if S is taken as total dissolved solids. The solubility of oxygen in sewage is about 95 per cent of that in pure water. In some industrial wastes, it may be even less. The total pressure used in this equation is approximately that at sea level and a correction must be made for altitude. The saturation concentration should be reduced by one per cent for every 88 metres of elevation:

$$C_{sh} = C_{so}(0.99)^{h/88} \tag{8.30}$$

where C_{so} is the saturation concentration at sea level and C_{sh} is the saturation concentration at an elevation of h metres. At an elevation of 1520 m, the saturation concentration is reduced by about 16 per cent.

Basically, the equilibrium of dissolving gases relates to the interchange between free gas molecules and molecules of the gas in the water. There are, however, some gases which *react* with the water, so that in some cases only a small proportion of gas molecules entering the water may remain there in simple solution, while others combine chemically with the water, and may take part in a series of reactions, each with its own *equilibrium condition*.

Examples are carbon dioxide, hydrogen sulphide and ammonia (see Table 8.1).

Table 8.1 Some reactions of gases with water

$$CO_2 \rightleftharpoons CO_2 \quad \overset{+H_2O}{\underset{-H_2O}{\rightleftharpoons}} H_2CO_3 \rightleftharpoons H^+ + HCO_3^- \rightleftharpoons 2H^+ + CO_3^{2-}$$
(gas) (dissolved)

$$H_2S \rightleftharpoons H_2S \rightleftharpoons H^+ + HS^- \rightleftharpoons 2H^+ + S^-$$
(gas) (dissolved)

$$NH_3 \rightleftharpoons NH_3 \quad \overset{+H_2O}{\underset{-H_2O}{\rightleftharpoons}} NH_4OH \rightleftharpoons NH_4^+ + OH^-$$
(gas) (dissolved)

When some of the dissolved gas leaves the solution to become free gas, the equilibrium is upset. To restore equilibrium, some of the compounds formed by the combination of the gas with water are decomposed to form water plus some dissolved gas, which replaces some of the gas which has left the solution. These reactions with carbon dioxide and hydrogen sulphide are driven to the right by alkaline conditions, and to the left by acid conditions (note the formation of H^+ ions). Therefore, under alkaline conditions, there may be quite considerable amounts of carbonate ion and sulphide ion present, but the amounts of *dissolved molecular* carbon dioxide and hydrogen sulphide present may be negligible. To facilitate removal of these gases by aeration, *acid* conditions are needed to readjust the equilibrium condition, reduce the proportion of carbonate and sulphides and increase the proportion of the volatile molecular forms of dissolved carbon dioxide and hydrogen sulphide, so that it may escape from the solution. Likewise, *alkaline* conditions are required to convert *ammonium* ions to *ammonia* molecules, to allow them to be removed.

If it were desired to dissolve these gases from a stream of gas, the opposite would apply. Alkaline solutions would be used to dissolve hydrogen sulphide and carbon dioxide, but an acid solution would be used to capture ammonia.

Factors in gas transfer

The transfer rate of a gas, per unit area of surface, is proportional to the *difference* between the *actual* concentration of that gas at the liquid surface and its *saturation* concentration. This relationship holds because (a) the rate at which molecules *leave* the water is proportional to the actual concentration at the surface, and (b) the rate at which they *enter* is proportional to the partial pressure and that, in turn, is proportional to the saturation concentration. The net number of migrating molecules being dissolved is given by the difference between the numbers of those entering and those leaving the surface.

The coefficient of proportionality for this relationship depends on the microscopic conditions occurring at the gas-liquid interface. Gases arrive at, and leave, the interface by diffusion. On the gas side, where molecules are in rapid motion with reasonably long free paths between collisions, diffusion is rapid, but on the liquid side of the interface, it is very slow. A jar of water standing on a bench will dissolve oxygen only very slowly because the surface layer rapidly becomes practically saturated and the uptake of oxygen from the air slows down; at that stage, the rate of solution of oxygen depends on the rate of diffusion away from the surface in the liquid. Molecular diffusion in liquids is very slow.

In an aerator, the space in the vicinity of the surface may be considered as consisting of four main regions: the turbulent gas region, the laminar gas region in the boundary layer on the gas side of the interface, the laminar liquid region in the boundary layer on the liquid side of the interface, and the turbulent liquid region.

The main resistance to gas transfer occurs on the liquid side of the interface, where there are two stages: (a) molecular diffusion through the 'boundary layer', and (b) eddy diffusion by turbulence once the boundary layer is passed. The molecular diffusion stage is the main limiting feature. An increase in general turbulence will decrease the thickness of the boundary layer and, hence, less resistance will be offered to the passage of gas.

Some surface active impurities (such as detergents) can affect the properties of the boundary layer, generally reducing the rate of gas transfer. Films of grease and oils can also interfere with the transfer of gases by creating an extra interface through which they have to pass.

A variation in temperature can affect the transfer rate. Increased temperature speeds up molecular motion, transfer rates being increased by about 2 per cent for each degree Celsius increase. The saturation concentration, however, is generally reduced by a temperature increase, thus causing a decrease in solution rates but an increase in dissolution rates.

The rate of transfer of a gas, and its effect on concentration, can be expressed by

$$\frac{dm}{dt} = K_\ell \, A \, (C_s - C_\ell) \qquad\qquad (8.31(a))$$

and

$$\frac{dC_\ell}{dt} = \frac{dm}{dt} \frac{1}{V} \times 10^3 \qquad\qquad (8.31(b))$$

where K_ℓ is the transfer coefficient for unit area (kg/s.m²); A is the area of air-water interface (m^2); dm/dt is the rate of gas transfer (kg/s); $\forall$ is the volume of water (m^3); C_s is the saturation concentration of the gas (mg/L); C_ℓ is the actual concentration of the gas in the water (mg/L); and dC_ℓ/dt is the rate of change of concentration (mg/L.s).

In a practical case, neither K_ℓ nor A can be measured, but the value of the composite transfer coefficient K_ℓ A can be inferred from the behaviour of equipment (by test). The value then applies only to the particular aeration system in which the measurements were made.

The objective of aerator design is therefore an increase in the value of K_ℓ or A, or (usually) both. K_ℓ can be affected by the turbulence in the vicinity of the air-water interface; increase in turbulence reduces the thickness of the laminar boundary layer and thus increases K_ℓ. Methods of increasing the surface area are bubbling air through water, creating droplets of water in air, spreading the water in a film over a large solid surface, or cascading.

In oxygenation aerators for sewage treatment, the value of $(C_s - C_\ell)$ can be increased by increasing C_s. This can be accomplished by either the use of molecular oxygen to increase the oxygen partial pressure, or increasing the total pressure, or both. The value of C_ℓ is kept as low as practicable, consistent with the efficiency of the process.

In aerators for removal of unwanted gases, the value of C_s is kept as near to zero as practicable by the provision of good ventilation to remove the gases as soon as they are released from droplets of liquid. Because the concentration of dissolved gas approaches the saturation concentration exponentially, it is impracticable to completely remove any unwanted gases. A compromise between cost and performance is therefore necessary.

In all cases of engineered aeration, the establishment and maintenance of both turbulence and a high surface area requires the expenditure of energy. The energy consumption required to provide a desired degree of treatment is a measure of the efficiency of the process.

Examples of the application of aeration principles in water and wastewater treatment are given in Chapters 13 and 14.

Comparison of sewage aerators

There is no standard basis for comparison of oxygen transfer apparatus. In the literature, there are many ways of expressing oxygen transfer efficiency. They include

a Percentage transfer of oxygen (from diffusers)
b Power consumption per volume of aerator capacity
c Power consumption per kg of BOD removed
d Kilograms of oxygen per kilowatt-hour under various base conditions.

The rate of oxygen transfer for a particular transfer system is

$$W = K_{\ell\,20}A(C_s - C_\ell)\theta^{(T-20)}\alpha \tag{8.32}$$

where W is the rate of oxygen transfer (kg/h); $K_{\ell\,20}$ is the transfer coefficient at 20°C in clean water (kg/h.m²); A is the interface area (m²); C_s is the saturation concentration of oxygen in sewage (mg/L); C_ℓ is the actual concentration of oxygen in sewage (mg/L); T is the sewage temperature (°C); α is the ratio of transfer coefficient in the sewage to transfer coefficient in clean water (about 0.9 to 0.95), to allow for effects of surface impurities; and θ is the temperature coefficient. A typical value of θ is 1.02, but it may vary from about 1.017 to about 1.024, depending on the type of gas and the type of aerator.

Therefore, any basis used for evaluating the capacity of aeration equipment should include

a The power consumption per unit of oxygen transferred
b The liquid to which the oxygen is being transferred during the test
c The difference between C_s and C_ℓ (called the 'driving force') during the test.

With this information, it is possible to estimate the value of $K_\ell A$ for a particular equipment. The method used by some manufacturers is to quote kilograms of oxygen transferred per kilowatt-hour to clean water (or tap water) devoid of oxygen at a given temperature, under a pressure of one standard atmosphere (101.325 kPa). Some manufacturers use 20°C as the standard temperature; others, with parent companies in colder Europe, use 10°C.

Mixing ability This is often an important factor to consider when choosing a wastewater aerator. Although the obvious primary function of an aeration device in sewage treatment is to induce an oxygen transfer into the liquid, other important functions in activated sludge systems or aerated lagoon systems are to keep the waste solids and biological flocs in suspension and to provide for mixing of the contents of the aeration tank, thus blending the feed with the aeration mixture. These other functions sometimes influence the layout of the device and, sometimes, they are the critical features of the design. Generally, the turbulence required for increasing $K_\ell A$ values also holds solids in suspension and ensures proper mixing if the devices are effectively deployed but there are cases, especially when the power input per unit volume is low (as when treating weak wastes in a liquor with low MLSS), when the mixing becomes the basis of the design.

A system in which large solids occur — such as sewage aeration without primary sedimentation — will require a greater mixing effort than would be required for treating previously settled sewage.

Example 8.5

An aerator for use at a sewage treatment installation for a ski resort is tested at sea level with clean water devoid of oxygen at 15°C. It is found to be possible to transfer 10 kg of oxygen an hour under these conditions.

In operation, it will be installed at an elevation of 1500 m above sea level, to dissolve oxygen in sewage at 10°C. Estimate the oxygen transfer, if the sewage saturation concentration is only 90 per cent that of water at the same temperature, and the operating oxygen concentration is 3 mg/L.

Solution

To find the saturation concentrations for clean water under the two conditions, use Eqs 8.29 and 8.30.

For clean water at sea level and 15°C

$$C_s = \frac{482.5}{32.6 + T} = \frac{482.5}{47.6} = 10.14 \text{ mg/L}$$

For clean water at 1500 m and 10°C

$$C_s = \frac{482.5}{42.6} (0.99)^{(1500/88)} = 9.54 \text{ mg/L}$$

For sewage under these conditions

$$C_s = 9.54 \times 0.9 = 8.59 \text{ mg/L}$$

To find $K_{\ell\, 15}$ A for test conditions (Eq 8.30)

$$10 = K_{\ell\, 15} A (C_s - C_\ell) = K_{\ell\, 15} A \times 10.14$$

Therefore, $K_{\ell\, 15} A = 10/10.14 = 0.99$

For operating conditions (from Eq 8.32)

$$W = 0.99(8.59 - 3)(1.02)^{(10 - 15)} \times 0.95 = 4.76 \text{ kg/h}$$

Note the difference between *test* performance and the transfer rate under *operating conditions*.

Example 8.6

Water is trickled over a stack of identical, well-ventilated trays to remove hydrogen sulphide, and the pH is kept constant. The concentration at the first tray is 3.0 mg/L, and at the third tray it is 1.0 mg/L. Estimate the concentration at the sixth tray.

Solution

The ventilation insures that there is negligible concentration in the atmosphere and that the saturation concentration is therefore almost zero. The loss of gas is then proportional to the concentration. At each tray, a fixed *proportion* of gas is removed. Let the proportion be x. Then, from the data,

$$3 \times x^2 = 1$$
$$x = (1/3)^{1/2} = 0.57$$

From the third tray to the sixth tray is 3 steps, therefore the concentration at tray 6 is

$$1.0 \times (0.57)^3 = 0.19 \text{ mg/L}$$

Note that 2 mg/L is removed in 2 steps but that the following 3 steps remove only 0.81 mg/L.

8.5 Flotation

Particles of impurities can be separated from water by sedimentation if their weight is sufficiently greater than their buoyancy; but when the density of the particles is very close to that of the water in which they are suspended, the velocity of settling can be very low, and the time required for settling is then impracticably long. In such circumstances, the separation can be speeded up by attaching tiny gas bubbles to the particles so that the density of the composite particle (impurity plus gas) is appreciably less than that of the water. The particle will then float to the surface. Thus, air flotation methods can be used in water treatment and wastewater treatment for separation of particles which are too light to settle effectively but too heavy to float unaided.

Stability of composite particles

In the simplest case in which an air bubble becomes attached to a solid particle the stability of the composite particle depends on the surface properties of the water and the particle, as they affect the various surface tensions. Fig 8.11 shows the surface tension components acting at the junction of the gas-liquid interface and the surface of the solid particle. The parameters σ_{GL}, σ_{SL} and σ_{GS} represent the surface tensions in the gas-liquid, solid-liquid and gas-solid interfaces, respectively.

If the stresses are resolved in the direction of the surface of the solid, the following equilibrium condition is derived:

$$\sigma_{SL} = \sigma_{GS} + \sigma_{GL} \cos \theta \tag{8.33}$$

The values of the surface tensions depend on the type of solid and the impurities in the water. For example, wetting agents will increase σ_{GS} or decrease σ_{GL}, or both.

If σ_{GS} becomes equal to the sum of σ_{SL} and σ_{GL}, θ becomes 180° and the bubble will become detached from the solid. Air flotation then becomes impossible. In mineral separation by flotation, the difference in surface properties between the unwanted rock and the wanted mineral is used to

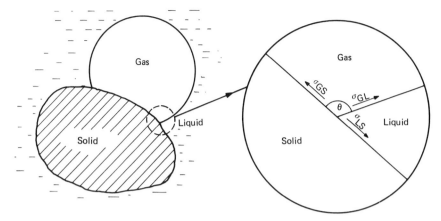

Fig 8.11 Surface tension relationships — definition diagram

make some particles float while others sink. Usually the flocculent particles formed by the precipitation of aluminium or ferric hydroxides will allow bubbles to become attached.

In addition to the simple bubble attachment mechanism described above, there are two other methods of composite particle formation: bubbles may be caught in the surface irregularities of the solid particles, and small bubbles may become trapped or enmeshed in floc matrices during flocculation.

The formation of flocs and composite particles is dependent on the destabilisation of colloidal particles (see Chapter 9). The formation of flocs requires destabilisation between particles, and attachment of bubbles requires destabilisation between particles and bubbles. Both bubble-particle attachment and flocculation have optimum pH values, which are not usually the same. Experiments have indicated that efficient bubble-particle attachment is more important than flocculation.

Bubble formation

Bubbles for flotation can be generated either by blowing compressed air through diffusers into the water, thus creating many small bubbles *(dispersed air flotation)*, or by supersaturating the water with air so that small air bubbles will be generated as the excess air comes out of solution *(dissolved air flotation)*. Dispersed air flotation is used widely for mineral treatment. The bubbles generated are usually much larger than those which can be obtained with dissolved air flotation and they cause turbulence which would break up fragile floc particles. Dissolved air flotation is, therefore, the usual method adopted for effluent and water treatment. This process can provide bubbles with diameters of between 20 and 100 μm.

One method used to attain the supersaturated condition required for dissolved air flotation is to first expose the water to air under pressure (thus temporarily increasing the saturation concentration and encouraging solution of air) so that the amount of dissolved air will increase. Then the pressure is reduced to near atmospheric pressure so that the excess air which has been forced into solution can escape as fine bubbles that can adhere to the floc particles.

The other method is to reduce the pressure (that is, create a vacuum) so that the saturation concentration will be reduced and the water will be super-saturated at the new low pressure. Under these conditions, the air will come out of solution as fine bubbles. Dissolved air flotation by the vacuum method is seldom practised on a large scale because it requires the construction and maintenance of an elevated airtight vessel which can be kept under vacuum.

Small bubbles do not form spontaneously from a super-saturated solution of gases in clean water. The pressure of gas within a bubble is equal to the sum of the ambient liquid pressure and the pressure increment induced by the surface tension in the bubble boundary. Therefore, when the diameter of a bubble is near zero, the surface tension-induced pressure increment is very large and so are the partial pressures of the predominant gases contained in it; the liquid around a bubble can be undersaturated with respect to the gas in the bubble, although it is supersaturated with respect to the atmosphere. In clean water, therefore, bubbles of less than a particular critical size will shrink and disappear. Bubbles can form on particles which act as nuclei and in surface imperfections of the vessel (as can be seen in a glass of lemonade), or on solid (greasy) surfaces.

Particle rise rate

The rise of composite particles is analogous to the settling of particles, which has already been discussed in Section 8.2, but both the difference between particle weight and particle buoyancy and the velocities of the particles are in the opposite direction from those considered in sedimentation theory. The rise rate of a particular particle may be calculated from Stokes's law or Newton's law or a transitional function, depending on whether the hydraulic flow around the particle is fully laminar, fully turbulent, or in between. In practice, it is difficult to assess the exact proportions of gas and solid which will make up a particular particle, and rise rates are obtained from experience.

The total volume of composite particles in a flotation unit depends on the ratio of gas bubbles to impurities. The concentration of composite particles is usually high enough for *hindered* rising to occur (analogous to hindered settling described in Section 8.2). There is an optimum concentration of bubbles which will give the maximum particle rise rate. An excessive concentration will reduce the rise rate of the composite particles as the hindering effects become large; and if there is an insufficient concentration of bubbles, the bulk density of the composite particles will not be low enough to achieve the maximum rising velocity. The optimum amount of air to use in each circumstance should be determined from pilot studies. Rise rates of from 1.0 to 1.5 mm/s can usually be attained with attention to the amount of gas released.

Common system configurations

The three main ways of achieving pressure dissolved air flotation are shown in Fig 8.12. The essential components are

a A *pressure vessel* constituting a pressure aerator in which air under pressure is dissolved in water

b A *pressure-sustaining valve* to maintain a near-constant pressure in the pressure vessel

c An *air pump* to supply air for solution under pressure. This pump may be controlled from the water level in the pressure vessel

d A *pump* to force water into the pressure vessel

e A *flotation unit* with provision for separation of the impurities and the clarified effluent.

Facilities for chemical coagulation are often included so that colloidal particles may be destabilised to improve particle growth and bubble attachment. Many different designs are used for the pressure aerator. The choice of design often depends on the amount of impurities which could cause clogging, and the importance of having a unit which requires a minimum amount of maintenance; these considerations often outweigh those of aeration efficiency and power conservation.

The *full-flow* flotation unit (Fig 8.12(a)) has the advantage that all of the waste (or water) is exposed to the air pressure, and bubble formation, when the pressure is released, should be uniform. The disadvantage is that any flocculation which may have occurred is destroyed in the turbulence as the water passes through the pressure-sustaining valve. A moderate pressure of 200 to 300 kPa is adequate for the pressure vessel in this configuration.

With the *split-flow* flotation (Fig 8.12(b)), only part of the flow is subjected to the pressure in the pressure vessel, and the resulting turbulence as it passes out through the pressure-sustaining valve. Water with coagulated and flocculated particles from the stream which bypasses the pressure vessel is mixed with freshly-depressurised waste as it enters the flotation unit. The pressure required in the pressure vessel is several times greater than that required in a full-flow configuration.

Recycle flotation (Fig 8.12(c)) has some advantages. Between 10 and 25 per cent of the clarified effluent is recycled through the pressure vessel to provide the dissolved air for supersaturating the main flow. Not only can all of the waste flow be coagulated and flocculated, but relatively clean water is used in the pump and pressure vessel, so that blockages and wear are reduced and efficiency increased. The size of the flotation unit, however, must be

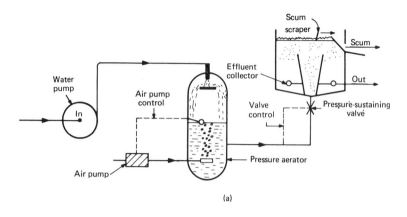

(a)

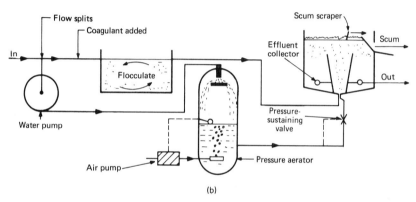

(b)

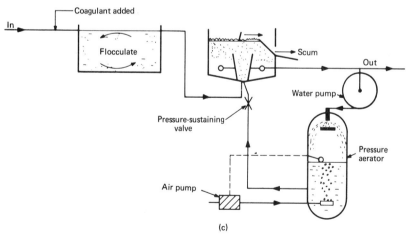

(c)

Fig 8.12 Diagrams showing common configurations for flotation systems: (a) full flow, (b) split flow, (c) recycle

larger than in other configurations because the flow through it is the sum of the main waste flow and the recycle.

In both split flow and recycle flotation, the mixing of the depressurised stream with the main flow should be rapid, so that all the particles in the main flow have an opportunity to collect bubbles, but not violent enough to break up unduly the flocs which may have formed.

Example 8.7

Clean water has been saturated with air at a pressure of 200 kPa gauge. A bubble 2 microns in diameter has been formed and is at a depth of 2 metres below the water surface after release of the pressure. If the surface tension of the water at the prevailing temperature is 0.074 N/m, will the bubble grow or shrink?

Solution

The pressure increment caused by surface tension is equal to the total surface tension around the circumference of the bubble in a diametral plane, divided by the area of the bubble in that plane. If the diameter is d metres,

$$\Delta p = (\sigma_{GL} \times \pi d)/(\pi d^2/4)$$
$$= 4\sigma_{GL}/d = 4 \times 0.074/(2 \times 10^{-6}) \text{ Pa} = 148 \text{ kPa}$$

The absolute ambient pressure is atmospheric pressure plus the hydrostatic gauge pressure at a depth of 2 metres of water. If the atmospheric pressure is A kPa; the absolute ambient pressure is

$$A + (2.0 \times 9.81) = A + 19.62 \text{ kPa}$$

The total pressure in the bubble is then equal to

$$A + 19.62 + 148 \text{ kPa} = A + 167.6 \text{ kPa}$$

The pressure corresponding to the saturation pressure is 200 kPa gauge; the water is therefore supersaturated with respect to the pressure in the bubble, and the bubble will grow.

Review questions

8.1 Discuss the main factors to be considered by the designer of a screen installation
   a On a water supply intake
   b At the entrance to a sewage treatment plant.

8.2 In what ways does practical sedimentation differ from ideal conditions, and how do these differences affect design?

8.3 Describe the main differences between conventional sedimentation and shallow depth sedimentation.

8.4 Discuss the process in which very small particles are removed from water passing through a granular filter.

8.5 Describe the conditions which render it difficult to obtain uniform flow over the area of a filter during backwash, and suggest methods of coping with these difficulties.

8.6 Comment on the uses of aeration in the treatment of water and wastewater. Under what conditions is aeration of water undertaken?

8.7 Describe the principles of dissolved air flotation, and explain how they are applied in the removal of particles of neutral buoyancy from a stream of water.

9 Coagulation and Flocculation

9.1 Introduction

Sedimentation plays an important part in the separation of unwanted solids from water and wastewater. In Chapter 8 it was shown that the velocity of settling under quiescent conditions depends not only on the difference between the density of the particles and the density of the suspending liquid but also on particle size. Other factors affecting the settling velocity are the shape of the particles and the viscosity of the liquid, but these factors are not readily controllable in most practical situations.

In laminar settling, the settling velocity of a particle is proportional to the square of its diameter (other factors being the same). For very small particles, other influences may be important. Colloidal-sized (less than 1 μm) particles are subject to Brownian motion and this can prevent settling indefinitely in a stable colloidal suspension.

A knowledge of the behaviour of colloids is necessary for the under-standing of many water and wastewater treatment processes. The particles which produce *turbidity* in natural waters commonly consist of colloidal clay. Natural *colour* in water is believed to be due to large molecules of complex organic acids, which are almost of colloidal size and come from decaying vegetation. Some dissolved materials (like calcium) can be removed by *precipitation*; the particles are extremely small when first precipitated, before flocculation occurs.

Important features of treatment to remove such very small suspended particles from water or wastewater are the processes by which these particles are induced to come together to form larger particles, which will settle rapidly enough to be removed by a practicable sedimentation process. *Coagulation* and *flocculation* are the processes used to achieve this goal.

In normal English usage the term 'coagulate' means to 'change from fluid to more or less solid state, clot, curdle, set, solidify'; and 'floccule' is a 'small portion of matter like a flock of wool'. However, when these terms are used in the context of water and wastewater technology, they have rather specialised meanings:

Coagulation is the process in which colloidal suspensions are destabilised and particles start to agglomerate

Flocculation is the process in which small particles are brought together by gentle stirring or agitation; this results in the formation of larger particles of adequate size to settle with a velocity acceptable for separation. The term is also used to mean the growth process of the particles.

9.2 Colloids and colloidal suspensions

When a material is truly dissolved in water, it is dispersed as either molecules or ions. The 'particle' sizes of a dissolved material are usually in the range of 2×10^{-4} to $10 \times 10^{-4} \mu$m. The particles cannot settle and cannot be removed by ordinary filtration.

Formerly, colloids were classed as substances which apparently go into solution but, in fact, remain dispersed as discrete particles. True colloidal suspensions and true solutions are readily distinguished, but there is no sharp line of demarcation. Colloidal particles are now defined as those particles in the size range 10^{-3} to 1μm.

Colloidal systems are not confined to the dispersion of solids in a liquid but include, inter alia, aerosols, fog, smoke, emulsions and solid sols (like opal). Water and wastewater applications are confined generally to two types of colloidal system, both of which have water as the disperse phase — *colloidal suspensions*, in which solids are suspended in water, and *emulsions*, in which insoluble liquids (such as oils) are suspended in water.

Features of colloidal suspensions are

a Colloids cannot be removed from a suspension by ordinary filtration; they can be removed by ultrafiltration or by dialysis through the pores of some animal and artificial membranes

b Colloidal particles are not visible under an ordinary microscope but they can be seen as specks of light with an ultramicroscope when a beam of light is passed through the suspension. (This is caused by the Tyndall effect, which is the scattering of light by colloidal particles.)

c Brownian motion prevents the settlement of particles under gravity. Some colloids can be removed by a centrifuge

d There is a natural tendency for colloids to coagulate and precipitate. Sometimes this tendency is countered either by mutual repulsion of the particles or by the strong attraction between the particles and the medium in which they are dispersed (usually water in cases of interest here). If these effects are strong and coagulation does not occur, the suspension is said to be 'stable'.

Colloidal particles may be either aggregates of molecules or single large molecules (such as proteins and starches). Many substances of interest to water and wastewater engineers occur as colloids

a Colloidal clay, which causes turbidity
b Large organic molecules, some of which cause colour
c Proteins, carbohydrates (like starch) and fats in sewage
d Oxides of iron, manganese, and silica
e Precipitated aluminium hydroxide and other 'coagulants'.

When the main factor causing stability of a colloidal suspension is the attraction between the particles and water, the colloids are said to be *hydrophilic*; but when there is no great attraction between particles and the water, and stability depends on mutual repulsion, the colloids are said to be *hydrophobic*. On the one hand, the hydrates of iron and aluminium (often used as coagulants) form hydrophobic colloids in water; the stability then occurs as a result of mutual electrostatic repulsion. On the other hand, hydrophilic colloids (like proteins, starches, or fats in water) become stable as a result of the attraction between the water and the particles; stable suspensions of hydrophilic colloids are more difficult to coagulate than are suspensions of hydrophobic colloids. Much of the following discussion relates to the behaviour of hydrophobic colloids such as are found in water treatment and in physico-chemical treatment of wastewaters.

Colloids have a large surface area per unit volume. (For example, if a 10 mm cube were broken into cubical particles with a side of $10^{-2} \, \mu m$, the surface area would be increased a millionfold to 600 m².) Surface effects are therefore of significance. Of these, two are important: (a) the tendency for substances to concentrate on surfaces (adsorption), and (b) the tendency for surfaces of substances in contact with water to acquire electrical charges, which give them electro-kinetic properties.

The surface electrical charges result either from the colloidal material's affinity for some ions in the water, or from the ionisation of some of the atoms or groups of atoms which leave the colloid. This surface charge attracts ions carrying a charge of opposite sign and thus creates a cloud of 'counter-ions' in which the concentration decreases as the distance from the particle increases.

The overall situation is complex. The colloids which carry similar charges will *repel* each other but, because of the presence of counter-ions, the situation cannot be directly likened to that of charged particles in air, where an inverse square law applies. In particular, the presence of the counter-ions complicates the law relating the degree of repulsion between colloidal particles, causing a more rapid fall-off in repulsive force as distance increases.

In addition to the forces related to the electrical charges, colloidal particles, when close together, are subject to van der Waals forces. These originate in the behaviour of electrons which are part of the atomic or molecular system. They are always forces of attraction, and become significant only at small distances (e.g. 1 μm or less).

The forces between charged colloidal particles can be represented by a graph (Fig 9.1).

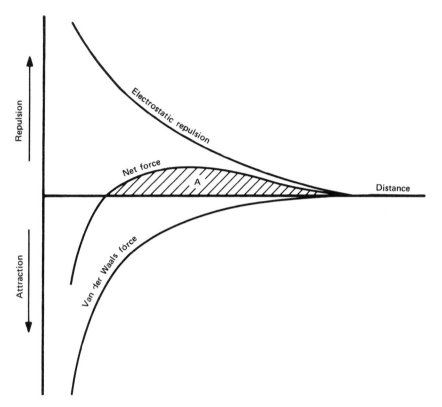

Fig 9.1 Forces between charged colloidal particles

The hatched area A represents the energy required to bring two particles close enough so that there is a net attraction between them so that they may be expected to be drawn together. The source of this energy may be either impacts from molecules (Brownian motion) or relative movement in the water. If the energy of an impact is inadequate, the remaining repulsion will again force the particles apart, resulting in a stable suspension.

9.3 Coagulation

To destabilise a hydrophobic colloidal suspension to permit coagulation to occur, it is necessary to reduce the energy requirement, A, shown in Fig 9.1.

The van der Waals forces cannot be manipulated but the electrical forces can be; the two principal methods are

a Reduce or neutralise the charges on the colloids
b Increase the density of the counter-ion field, and thus reduce the range of the repulsive effect.

Adjustment of pH

The charge on colloidal surfaces is usually a function of the type of material and the pH. At high values of pH, colloids tend to be negatively charged, while at low values they tend to be positively charged. This could be related to exchange of H^+ and OH^- ions to establish equilibrium with the water at different pH values.

At a certain pH value (which depends on material of the colloid and the concentrations of other materials present), the colloidal charge is zero. This pH value is known as the *iso-electric point* for that particular colloid. Therefore, adjustment of pH is a method by which destabilisation can be attained but, for common colloids (like clay) in water, the necessary pH reduction would require large amounts of acid and then, later, pH adjustment by the addition of correspondingly large amounts of alkali before discharge.

Neutralising charges

Neutralising charges on colloids may be accomplished by the addition of either multivalent ions or colloids, or both, having an opposite charge. These are frequently added as a chemical coagulant. The Schultz-Hardy rule indicates that the coagulating power of a chemical rises rapidly with its valence. For example, Al^{3+} and SO_4^{2-} ions are several hundred times more effective than Na^+ and Cl^- ions.

Chemicals commonly used as coagulants in water treatment are aluminium and ferric salts, which hydrolyse to produce a number of insoluble hydrates (their composition depending on pH, temperature, other materials present and age). At pH values between 6 and 7, these hydrates form positively-charged colloids which will neutralise the naturally-occurring negatively-charged colloids and, hence, destabilisation is possible.

In addition, destabilisation of the coagulant colloids produces a hydrous oxide binder, which can form a matrix for the resulting floccules.

Other impurities, some of which are responsible for tastes and odours, can be adsorbed onto the colloids or can be enmeshed in the floccules which form.

Reduction of electrical field

In water which is almost pure (with a low concentration of ions), the cloud of counter-ions is widely dispersed. With increase in ionic strength of the solution, the counter-ion cloud becomes more concentrated near the colloidal particles, more nearly counteracting the charge, and the field of influence of the colloidal charge becomes more restricted. Therefore, an increase in the ionic strength of a colloidal suspension will tend to cause destabilisation, with consequent coagulation. This phenomenon has been observed in nature where turbid rivers run into brackish estuaries and coagulation and sedimentation occur. However, the required increase in salinity makes this phenomenon unsuitable for use as the principal method of destabilisation in water treatment.

9.4 Coagulation chemicals

Chemicals used for coagulation in water treatment not only should be cost-effective for coagulating impurities but should not leave any toxic or other undesirable residues in the water.

Aluminium compounds

The common aluminium salt used is *aluminium sulphate*. As *filter alum*, it is available either in lump, granular or powdered form (depending on the local supplier). Filter alum contains a variable amount of water of crystallisation, depending on the local method of manufacture ($Al_2(SO_4)_3.nH_2O$, where n is usually in the range 12 to 16). As *liquid alum*, it can be trucked or piped to suitable storages if a treatment plant is near an alum-producing plant. Liquid alum is often cheaper than crystalline alum but it requires acid-proof tanks and piping for storage and transport. It usually contains the equivalent of about 6 to 8 per cent soluble alumina, compared with about 17 per cent for crystallised alum.

There is a limited pH range in which the insoluble aluminium hydrates, such as aluminium hydroxide, will form from a dilute alum solution. If the pH is too low, a soluble compound ($Al.OH.SO_4$) will form. If it is too high, the aluminium becomes complexed into soluble aluminate ions (AlO_2^-).

The optimum pH range in a particular case depends on the nature and concentration of the impurities in the water. For a soft water containing a considerable amount of colour, the optimum pH is likely to be in the range 5.0 to 6.3, but for a turbid water with moderate alkalinity, it is likely to be 6.0 to 7.0.

As the pH goes above 7, the charge on colloidal aluminium hydroxide reverses from positive to negative. The presence of positive ions of calcium can help in neutralising this charge and achieving precipitation of aluminium at pH values above 7.

When hydrolysed, alum produces sulphuric acid as well as the hydrate; for example, when forming the simplest hydrate ($Al(OH)_3$) the hydrolysis reaction is

$$Al_2(SO_4)_3 + 6H_2O \rightleftharpoons Al(OH)_3 \downarrow + 3H_2SO_4$$

It is therefore regarded as an acid salt and the water must contain enough of either natural or added alkalinity to react with the acid as it forms, thus keeping the resultant pH within the desired range for good flocculation. Added alkalinity is usually in the form of lime (calcium hydroxide), soda ash (sodium carbonate) or caustic soda (sodium hydroxide)

$$Ca(OH)_2 + H_2SO_4 \longrightarrow CaSO_4 + 2H_2O$$
$$2Na_2CO_3 + H_2SO_4 \longrightarrow Na_2SO_4 + 2NaHCO_3$$
$$2NaOH + H_2SO_4 \longrightarrow Na_2SO_4 + 2H_2O$$

It sometimes happens with water having a high alkalinity that large amounts of alum would be required to reduce the pH to that required for optimum precipitation. In such a case, economy may be obtained by the use of some sulphuric acid for pH control, in conjunction with an adequate amount of alum to form a suitable floc.

Sodium aluminate

Sodium aluminate is an alkaline salt manufactured by treating aluminium oxide with caustic soda. The simple hydrolysis reaction is

$$NaAlO_2 + 2H_2O \rightleftharpoons Al(OH)_3 \downarrow + NaOH$$

It can be used either in conjunction with alum or on its own, in waters which do not have enough natural alkalinity (that is, where it would be necessary otherwise to correct the coagulation pH by adding an alkali). However, the resulting coagulation may not be as good as when alum is used with an alkali, because the divalent sulphate ions introduced with the alum have a favourable influence on coagulation.

Iron salts

Ferric ions can be hydrolysed and precipitated as ferric hydroxide in a number of different forms, at pH values generally above about 4.5. Poor coagulation occurs in the pH range 7 to 8.5.

The ferric ion, like the aluminium ion, hydrolyses to form a range of hydrates and an acid. Enough alkalinity (natural or added) must be present to combine with the acid and maintain a suitable pH value for good coagulation, but, unlike aluminium hydroxide, ferric hydroxide does *not* re-dissolve in alkaline solutions, and so there is no particular upper pH limit for ferric coagulation. In addition, ferric hydroxide floc is usually heavier, and hence faster settling, than aluminium hydroxide floc.

In the coagulation of coloured acid waters, the presence of the divalent sulphate ion assists coagulation to a greater degree than that of the monovalent chloride ion.

The commonest ferric salt used for coagulation in water treatment is *ferric chloride* ($FeCl_3$). It is available variously as a liquid containing about 35 per cent $FeCl_3$ by weight, a crystalline form containing 60 per cent $FeCl_3$ by weight, and as an anhydrous powder. Ferric chloride is very corrosive in the presence of water and, therefore, it must be transported in rubber-lined tanks or glass containers.

Ferric sulphate ($Fe_2(SO_4)_3$) is available commercially in some areas as an anhydrous material which may be transported and stored in wooden barrels.

Sometimes *ferrous salts* are used. To be effective, the ferrous ion should be oxidised to the ferric form when in solution. At pH values above 8.5, dissolved oxygen in the water will cause oxidation but, at lower pH values, chlorine can be used as an oxidising agent. *Ferrous sulphate* ($FeSO_4.7H_2O$), also known as *copperas*, is a granular material which can be purchased in bags or in bulk. Because it requires a pH of more than 8.5 to be oxidised by dissolved oxygen, it cannot be used on its own in natural waters. When used in conjunction with lime, it is useful in coagulating the precipitate obtained in lime-softening of water and in removal of excessive iron and manganese from certain groundwaters.

Chlorinated copperas can be used for waters with a lower pH. It is made by mixing solutions of copperas and chlorine:

$$6\ FeSO_4 + 3\ Cl_2 \longrightarrow 2\ Fe_2(SO_4)_3 + 2\ FeCl_3$$

An excess of chlorine can provide for disinfection of the water.

Copperas can be more readily used than the ferric salts, because it is not so corrosive and can be fed through ordinary chemical feeding equipment.

Lime

Lime can be used to destabilise colloidal suspensions and emulsions of organic substances or oils present in sewage, or effluents from food and engineering industries. Also, by raising the pH, it can assist in the precipitation of some radioactive and toxic metals as hydroxides. Lime is also used in softening water, to convert soluble calcium bicarbonates to insoluble calcium carbonate. It is available in powder form as either burnt lime (calcium oxide, CaO) or slaked lime (calcium hydroxide, $Ca(OH)_2$).

Because commercial lime contains insoluble impurities and lime is only sparingly soluble in water, lime solution chambers must be continually stirred and provision must be made for cleaning out scale which may form in dosing pipelines.

The calcium introduced by the lime dose is precipitated mostly as calcium carbonate. If phosphates are present they are precipitated as insoluble calcium phosphate. The discrete particles of precipitated calcium carbonate grow slowly, mainly by direct deposition from a super-saturated solution. Sludge recycling or some other form of 'solids contact' is therefore necessary for effective coagulation and settlement of lime precipitates.

Ferric chloride, copperas or alum are sometimes used in conjunction with lime to improve the flocculation of the particles which are precipitated.

Coagulant aids

In some waters or effluents, coagulation is poor, even with the best dose of coagulant. Sometimes, an improvement in coagulation — and, conse-quently, in settling velocity — is desired so that either a plant may carry peak loads in excess of the original design or there may be a reduction in the size of the original construction.

The addition of extra substances known as *coagulant aids* can often result in considerable improvement in coagulation and an increase in the settling velocity of the resulting floc.

Clay

Clay (bentonite, fuller's earth, or other clay) is useful in some waters which are deficient in negatively-charged colloids. The clay colloids provide nuclei for the formation and growth of flocs, as well as a medium to add some weight to the particles. It could be useful to experiment with the addition of clay when comparatively clear waters prove difficult to coagulate. The adsorptive qualities of clay may be useful in removing some odours and tastes from polluted waters.

Polyelectrolytes

These consist of long-chain macromolecules, having electrical charges or ionisable groupings. Various compounds are available. The performance of each varies with the nature of both the raw water or effluent and the primary coagulant used. All of them must be well dispersed by thorough, rapid mixing.

The general effect of a polyelectrolyte, when properly chosen and applied, is to produce a tougher and denser floc, which grows to a larger size and settles more rapidly than is possible using a primary coagulant alone. This is brought about by the action of the long-chain molecules which form bridges or cross-links between colloidal particles.

When polyelectrolytes are applied in water treatment, the dose should be selected to optimise the overall performance of the plant — not merely the coagulation and settling. Small pieces of tough floc caused by polyelectrolyte over-dosing can rapidly block filters, necessitating frequent washing.

In some countries (such as France) polyelectrolytes are not used for treating potable water because of the dangers which are considered to be associated with monomer impurities which may be present. Other countries (such as the United Kingdom) have lists of polyelectrolytes which are approved for use in treating drinking water supplies.

Activated silica

This is a colloidal silica formed by neutralisation of an aqueous solution of sodium silicate (water-glass). The neutralisation can be effected by addition of either sulphuric acid, chlorine, alum, ammonium sulphate, hydrochloric acid, sodium bicarbonate or carbon dioxide. Careful control of pH is necessary, as is thorough agitation during the mixing, to prevent the formation of silica gel, which forms at pH < 7 and can block pipelines and mixing equipment.

When the mixture has been made and been 'aged' for up to two hours to allow for the formation of the desired silica colloids, it can be fed into the water at, or just downstream of, the point of application of the primary coagulant. Coagulation is usually improved by quite small doses (up to 1 mg SiO_2/L). The effect is particularly useful with low water temperatures.

The use of activated silica, as well as other coagulant aids, usually requires skilled supervision.

Other coagulant aids

These include starch-based material, tannin-based material, and alginates.

Chemicals for pH adjustment

On some occasions, it is necessary to increase or decrease the pH of a water or waste, either to obtain improved coagulation and flocculation or to make the pH of treated water acceptable for discharge. Apart from the coagulants which vary the pH of the water, the chemicals commonly used for pH adjustment are *sulphuric acid* or *carbon dioxide* to decrease pH, and *soda ash* (sodium carbonate), *lime* (calcium oxide or hydroxide), or *caustic soda* (sodium hydroxide) to increase it.

To reduce pH for coagulation, sulphuric acid is more commonly used than carbon dioxide. Carbon dioxide is used to reduce pH after lime-soda softening.

Of the alkalis, *lime* ($Ca(OH)_2$) is frequently used because of its low price when compared with the other alkalis. However, powdered commercial lime usually contains some insoluble impurities, and special care is therefore required in mixing and dosing it.

Caustic soda (NaOH) is the next cheapest alkali, and its hygroscopic crystals readily dissolve to form a strongly alkaline solution. Accidental overdosage can readily cause unacceptably high pH values unless the water is very well buffered.

Soda ash (Na_2CO_3), which is more expensive than lime and caustic soda, is supplied as crystals which dissolve readily in water. Accidental overdoses would seldom take the pH above 9. For final pH adjustment after coagulation, the carbonate ion assists in achieving calcium carbonate stability to reduce the amount of corrosion (Chapter 5), and there is no insoluble residue to settle out in the distribution system.

9.5 Rapid mixing

It is desirable that coagulants, when added to the water, should be thoroughly and intimately dispersed throughout the volume of water before a colloidal precipitate is formed. The amount of reagent solution added is very small in comparison with the main flow of water. The flow of reagents is not always uniform and continuous, as some metering pumps deliver the solution in intermittent pulses.

The essential features of a good mixing device are

a Adequate turbulence
b Adequate backmixing
c Rapid dispersion of chemicals.

The turbulence is required to spread the reagent normal to the general direction of flow, and the backmixing is required to spread the reagent in the direction of flow, and thus to compensate for any irregularity in its rate of delivery. The amount of backmixing in a pipe or channel is only small. Both turbulence and backmixing can be increased by the insertion of orifices, valves, bends or baffles which increase energy loss, and the resulting flow separation and eddies aid in backmixing.

Where a separate mixing chamber is used, the detention time of the main flow through it should be several times the maximum time between pulses. Mixing chambers are often designed to have a detention time of between 30 and 60 seconds at maximum flow, thus giving adequate backmixing. The reagents should be added to the main flow either at the inlet to the mixing chamber, or just upstream from the inlet.

Turbulence dissipates energy and, therefore, energy must be expended to achieve efficient mixing. If the energy is properly applied, the amount consumed is an approximate measure of mixing efficiency. The power required for good mixing is in the range of 3 to 15 watts for each litre per second of flow (W.s/L or joules per litre).

Sometimes, a *hydraulic jump* is used for mixing. This is often associated with a Parshall flume used for flow measurement. Much of the energy is dissipated in the 'roller'; but because this is out of the main stream, it is not used efficiently for mixing (Fig 9.2).

Hydraulic jets are used as mixing devices. Unobstructed jets are not efficient, but plate obstructions can generate local turbulence and improve the mixing efficiency (Fig 9.3).

Mechanical devices such as paddles rotating at from 2 to 15 revolutions per

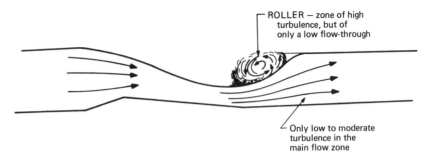

ROLLER — zone of high
turbulence, but of
only a low flow-through

Only low to moderate
turbulence in the
main flow zone

Fig 9.2 Hydraulic jumps do not provide efficient mixing

minute, turbine blades, or propellors like ship screws, can be used. The formation of local vortices can reduce the useful input, but they can be controlled by the installation of suitable baffles.

Air has been used as a mixing device. Air under pressure, introduced through submerged outlets, causes turbulence as it rises to the surface. The degree of turbulence and general mixing can be controlled by the placement and the type of outlets, and by the pressure applied. However, if tiny air bubbles become entrained in, or attached to, floc particles, they can upset subsequent sedimentation because the bulk density of a floc particle containing air could be equal to, or even less than, the density of water.

Example 9.1

Calculate the size required and the approximate power input needed for a mixing chamber treating a maximum flow of 20 ML/d.

Solution
i   Size required

$$\text{Flow conversion: } 20 \text{ ML/d} = \frac{20 \times 10^6}{86\ 400} \text{ L/s} = 231.5 \text{ L/s}$$

For 30 seconds' detention, capacity required $= 30 \times 231.5\text{L} \cong 6.9 \text{ m}^3$.
A chamber 1.6 m $\times$ 1.6 m $\times$ 3 m deep would allow about 0.3 m freeboard.

ii Power input

Assume 5 watts for each litre per second
Power $= Q \times 5 = 231.5 \times 5 = 1158$ watts

Example 9.2

A pipeline with several bends is used for mixing a continuous stream of

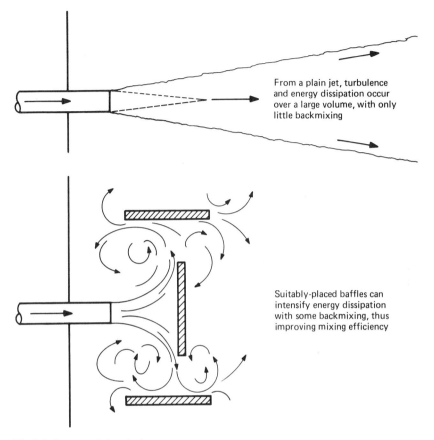

From a plain jet, turbulence and energy dissipation occur over a large volume, with only little backmixing

Suitably-placed baffles can intensify energy dissipation with some backmixing, thus improving mixing efficiency

Fig 9.3 Jets as mixing devices

coagulant with a stream of water. At maximum flow, the total head loss, h, in the mixing portion of the pipe is 0.6 m. Assuming that head loss is proportional to the square of the rate of flow, estimate the energy dissipation in joules per litre (i) at maximum flow, and (ii) at half maximum flow.

Solution

i   Energy dissipation at maximum flow

The energy loss is given by
$$\Delta E = gh \text{ J/kg}$$

Therefore, assuming that one litre has a mass of one kilogram, the energy loss in the pipeline is

$$0.6 \times 9.81 = 5.89 \text{ J/L}$$

ii At half flow

The head loss will be reduced in proportion to the square of the flow

Therefore h $= 0.6 \times (0.5)^2 = 0.15$ m

and the corresponding energy loss is

$0.15 \times 9.81 = 1.47$ J/L

Note the substantial reduction in energy per unit volume. Under low flow conditions, the mixing efficiency of fixed hydraulic devices is substantially reduced.

9.6 Optimum coagulant dose

The factor to be optimised is made up of two main components: cost and performance. In general, the optimum dose will be the lowest (least cost) dose which will produce a *readily settleable* floc to remove turbidity efficiently in a *reasonably short* time, remove excess *colour* from the water, and have suitable filterability properties. The speed of *settling* of the floc is reflected in the sedimentation design — slower settling means larger tanks with correspondingly increased capital costs. The speed of *formation* of the floc is reflected in the flocculation chamber design. A floc which forms only slowly requires a large flocculation tank to provide adequate detention time.

When colour removal is important, the adsorption or combination of the colour colloids or ions into the floc is a factor to be considered.

Any floc not settled out before filtration should be strong enough to be retained in the filter, but not so strong that it rapidly clogs the surface layers of the filter. In addition, comparative floc strengths and the tendency for reflocculation of broken floccules may be taken into account when deciding on the optimum dose. In theory, it should be possible to estimate the correct dose from an analysis of the water. However, the errors of analysis, together with errors of ignorance (because we are not yet aware of all the complex ionic interactions) and the skilled, time-consuming work involved in obtaining an analysis, make this method of dose estimation entirely inappropriate when dealing with natural waters or with wastewaters in day-to-day treatment.

The jar test

In initial tests of water from a particular source, tests should be carried out to determine the best combination of coagulant and pH adjustment, and the optimum pH for coagulation. Although a single coagulant may be adequate for coagulation in water from some sources, water from other sources may require pH correction or even addition of coagulant aids to achieve satisfactory performance. These factors need to be known before a design is prepared for chemical storage and chemical feeding apparatus.

In the jar test, different doses of coagulant, and of other chemicals if necessary, are added simultaneously to several (often six) samples of the water to be treated. Each sample undergoes the same rapid mixing and slow stirring, until a suitable floc is formed.

Samples for jar tests should be tested *as soon as practicable* after collection, so that the change in the properties of the colloids will be minimal. The jars used for transport should be completely filled (without any air space), because changes in the amounts of dissolved carbon dioxide, oxygen or nitrogen, can affect the results of the test.

Samples should not be transported by air unless they are fully pressurised, because reduced pressures can cause degasification which sometimes greatly affects the settling rate or the pH. For example, at one location, the water was super-saturated with air admitted to rising mains to control water hammer following pump stoppages. After the samples were transported on a two-hour flight, the tests indicated a rapidly settling floc. Later tests on the site showed that tiny air bubbles coming out of solution and becoming attached to the flocs made settling almost impossible.

Neither the jar test equipment nor the procedure nor the method of reporting results has been standardised. The description given here is similar to methods used by some authorities.

Before the test is started, the turbidity, colour, pH and alkalinity of the raw

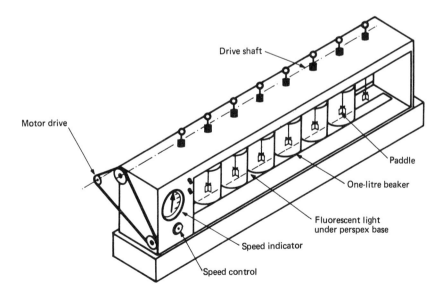

Fig 9.4 Jar test apparatus

water should be determined. These can be compared later with those of the settled water or filtered water or both.

The jar test apparatus shown in Fig 9.4 consists of a set of vertical paddles in a row, so arranged that litre beakers can be conveniently placed under each paddle. The paddle height can be adjusted. The driving motor has a variable speed control, and a tachometer indicates the rotational speed of the paddles.

A well-diffused light, either above or below the samples, provides uniform light conditions for observing the floc. A black background (such as a piece of wallboard coated with matt black paint) helps to provide the necessary contrast for convenient observation of the floc.

Simultaneous dosing can be accomplished by means of a simple rack to which test-tubes are attached. After the test-tubes with appropriate doses are loaded, the rack is placed on the jar test machine so that all test-tubes can be inverted over their corresponding beakers simultaneously.

Steps in the method

1 Place 1 L of water in each of six one-litre beakers, and place them in position under the paddles on the jar test machine.

2 Place appropriate quantities of coagulant in each of six test-tubes on the rack (2 mL, 4 mL, 6 mL, 8 mL, 10 mL, and 12 mL of 5 g/L alum solution).

3 Place the rack in position in readiness for dosing, and adjust the speed of the paddles for an initial rapid mix (say 100 rev/min).

4 Tip the coagulant from the test–tubes into the beakers by tipping the rack. Quickly add about 5 mL of distilled water to each test-tube and tip again to rinse out the remaining coagulant.

   If two or more chemicals are to be used, they should be added separately. There should be a separate rack for each chemical, so that all measurements may be made before starting the stirring paddles, and the second, and possibly third, chemicals may be added rapidly if required by simply changing racks and tipping.

5 After about 30 seconds from the first addition of coagulant, reduce speed to that used for flocculation, for example 20 to 50 rev/min.

6 Observe the time from the addition of coagulant to the first appearance of visible, discrete floc particles in each beaker. (This time will depend not only on the behaviour in the beaker but also on the visual acuity of the observer — but provided that the same observer makes all the observations, the *relative* times will indicate the relative reaction rates in the various beakers.)

7 After a suitable period for flocculation (usually in the range of 15 to 30 minutes depending on the flocculation time provided in the treatment plant), the motion should be stopped.

8 Observe the appearance, size and quantity of floc at the end of the

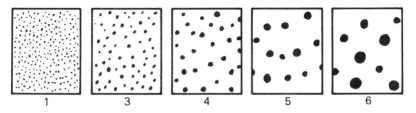

Fig 9.5 A typical floc comparator

flocculating period. A floc-size chart (Fig 9.5) is useful for obtaining uniform reporting of floc size from different operators.

9 Estimate the settling velocity of the majority of the flocs from the depth of the water and the time taken to settle.
10 After 30 minutes (or more if desired), observe the quantity and character of any unsettled floc.
11 Carefully decant a small amount (about 100 mL) of the settled water from the top of each beaker and determine colour, turbidity, pH and alkalinity.

This completes the usual observations which are made for a jar test. However, further comparative information may be obtained about floc toughness and ability to re-form after rupture by the following steps.

1 With the beakers and settled samples back in position, start the motor and adjust the speed to progressively higher values at thirty-second intervals until floc is broken up. Observe speeds at which visible break-up occurs in each beaker.
2 Run the stirrers at the speed used for the initial rapid mix for a period of about one minute.
3 Reduce speed to that used for the initial flocculation, and observe the time for re-formation of visible floc.
4 After ten minutes, observe the floc size in each beaker.

Example 9.3

Tests show that optimum coagulation with a particular water occurred when a litre of it was dosed with 4 mL of a 10 g/L alum solution and 1.6 mL of a 5 g/L suspension of lime ($Ca(OH)_2$). Calculate the daily requirements of alum and lime to coagulate a flow of 350 L/s.

Solution
First convert the doses to mg/L. Because each litre of the alum stock solution contained 10 g of alum, each millilitre contained 10 mg.

The optimum dose of 4 mL contained 40 (i.e. 4 × 10) mg of alum. This was

Table 9.1 Coagulation test report

Sample no	Source . . . .
Date collected	Conditions . . . .
Date delivered	. . . .
Date tested	. . . .
Tested at	Transported by . . . .

Raw water tests:

pH	Turbidity . . . . TU
Alkalinity . . . . mg/L CaCO₃	Colour . . . . Hazen units
Hardness . . . . mg/L CaCO₃	Total iron . . . . mg/L Fe

Jar no		1	2	3	4	5	6
Coagulant doses mg/L	A.						
	B.						
Time for floc to form (min)							
°Size of floc							
Time for floc to settle (min)							
Depth of jar (mm)							
Settling velocity (mm/s)							
pH*							
Turbidity* (TU)							
Colour* (Hazen)							
Alkalinity* (mg/L CaCO₃)							

* Of settled water in   Flocculation test for . . . . min
'near-optimum' jars   at speed of . . . . rev/min

Comments . . . .

. . . .

Adopted optimum dose: . . . . mg/L of . . . . (A)
                            . . . . mg/L of . . . . (B)

OR
Recommend further tests | YES | | NO |

added to a one-litre sample. The alum dose was therefore 40 mg/L. By similar reasoning, the lime dose was 8 mg/L.

Conversion from dose in mg/L to daily requirements is simple if the following conversion is memorised:

$$1 \text{ mg/L} = 1 \text{ g/kL} = 1 \text{ kg/ML} \ (= 1 \text{ ppm approx})$$

The daily volume, $\maltese$, for a flow rate of Q L/s is

$$\frac{Q \times 60 \times 60 \times 24}{10^6} \text{ ML/d}$$

Therefore, $\maltese = \dfrac{350 \times 60 \times 60 \times 24}{10^6} = 30.24 \text{ ML/d}$

Therefore, daily chemical requirements are

Alum	$30.24 \times 40 =$	1210 kg
Lime ($Ca(OH)_2$)	$30.24 \times 8 =$	242 kg

9.7 Flocculation

When a colloid has been destabilised, the growth of flocs due to the agglomeration of the colloidal particles occurs mainly in two stages, known as *perikinetic* and *orthokinetic* flocculation.

Perikinetic flocculation

In the first stage, particles collide and stick together as they move randomly about under the influence of Brownian motion. This stage is called perikinetic flocculation. The time taken for particles to grow so large that they are no longer significantly affected by Brownian motion depends on the frequency of collisions. The opportunity for collision afforded to any single particle is proportional to the concentration of the particles, so that perikinetic flocculation is more rapid in concentrated suspensions than in dilute ones.

The time taken for effective completion of the perikinetic phase of flocculation is usually less than a minute.

Orthokinetic flocculation

In the second stage, known as orthokinetic flocculation, particles are moved together by gentle motion of the water. The rate of flocculation depends on particle nature, size and concentration, and the velocity shear gradient of water. Mathematical models have been used to investigate the effects of some of these factors. Although some of the parameters cannot, in practice, be quantified and some of the assumptions are idealistic, the resulting solution does indicate, in general terms, the trends obtained by adjusting operating conditions.

One such model assumes that if two particles come sufficiently close together, they will collide to form one larger particle. The closeness which is required to bring about a collision is specified by defining a *zone of influence* of a size such that if the zones of influence of two particles touch or overlap, the particles will agglomerate.

This model further assumes that the particles are small enough to have negligible settling velocity, and will travel at the same velocity as the water. If the water is either stationary or moving with a uniform velocity, there will be no relative motion of particles, which will therefore maintain the existing interparticle distances without any further flocculation. If, however, there is a velocity shear gradient, there will be relative motion between the particles, and some collisions can occur.

Consider a particle P (Fig 9.6) in a zone of uniform velocity shear gradient $(dV/dy = G)$, with a velocity of V_0, in the horizontal plane $(y = 0)$ containing the particle. If this particle has a zone of influence of diameter d_1, and the other particles in suspension in the water have a zone of influence of diameter d_2, then any other particle whose centre passes within $(d_1 + d_2)/2$ of the centre of particle P can be expected to become attached to it, that is, a collision will occur.

The volume rate at which water *passes through* the sphere of radius

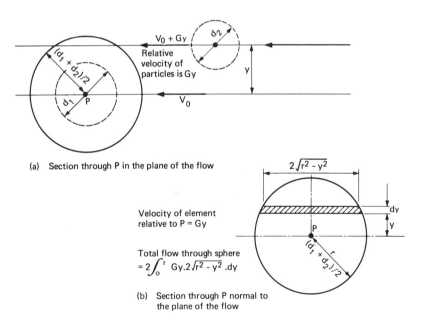

(a) Section through P in the plane of the flow

Velocity of element
relative to P = Gy

Total flow through sphere
$$= 2 \int_0^r Gy . 2\sqrt{r^2 - y^2} \, . dy$$

(b) Section through P normal to
the plane of the flow

Fig 9.6 Assumed mechanism of particle collision

$(d_1 + d_2)/2$ about particle P can be estimated by integration. If there are n particles per unit volume, the expected number of collisions with a particular particle in unit time is given by

$$\frac{nG}{6} (d_1 + d_2)^3 \qquad (9.1)$$

In a well-mixed flocculation zone, every particle has the same probability of collision. If each collision involves two particles only and the particles are uniform, the total number of collisions per unit volume in unit time can be given as

$$n \times \frac{nG}{6} (2d)^3 \times \frac{1}{2}$$

$$= \frac{2}{3} n^2Gd^3 \qquad (9.2)$$

In a practical situation, it is difficult to assign values to n and d. Also, because spatial and temporal variations of G are large in turbulent flow conditions, it is not possible to specify local values of G, although the root mean square value can be estimated from the power dissipation.

In addition, each successful collision results in the formation of other larger particles, which can then collide either with the remaining original particles, or with the other particles of varying sizes. The whole situation rather quickly becomes extremely complex, so that Eq. 9.2 cannot be applied directly because of the changes in the value of n and of d.

However, useful basic trends can be deduced from the theory. Within limits, the rate of flocculation is proportional to

a The velocity shear gradient
b The volume of the particle zone of influence
c The square of the numerical concentration of particles.

Differential settling

A third type of flocculation occurs where there are particles of varying sizes present, as in either a sludge blanket or a solids contact clarifier.

Relative motion between particles occurs because the larger particles settle faster than smaller particles. In a uniform upflow with the interparticle upflow velocity similar to the settling velocity of an average particle, the larger particles with higher settling velocities will move downwards to meet the smaller particles which are being carried upwards. Here, too, the flocculation rate is increased by the concentration of particles.

The jostling motion of the larger particles could also result in local velocity shear gradients which could be effective in speeding up orthokinetic flocculation of very small particles in their vicinity.

Estimation of RMS velocity shear gradient

The rate of viscous dissipation of energy in a velocity shear gradient field can be readily estimated by consideration of an element of height, h, and plan area, A, with the upper surface being moved at a velocity Gh, relative to the lower surface. The horizontal viscous stress is equal to μG, and the viscous shear force is $A\mu G$.

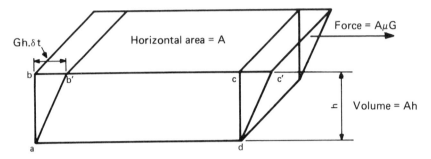

Fig 9.7 Definition diagram for energy dissipation

The external work per second is the product of force and velocity difference and is equal to $A\mu G \times Gh$, and this must be equal to the internal dissipation of energy in the same time. Hence the power consumed is

$$P = \mu G^2 V \tag{9.3}$$

If the shear gradient is uniform

$$G = \sqrt{\frac{P}{\mu V}} \tag{9.4}$$

where G is the velocity gradient (s^{-1}); P is the power dissipation (W); V is the volume (m^3); and μ is the absolute viscosity (N.s/m^2) ($\cong 10^{-3}$ for water at 20°C).

In non-uniform, unsteady and turbulent flow conditions, the value of G calculated from power input is the root-mean-square value.

Floc rupture

Although the initial rate of floc formation is proportional to the velocity shear gradients, high-velocity shear gradients can cause large flocs to be ripped apart as a result of either internal tension, or surface shear stress erosion, or both.

Fig 9.8(a) shows the velocities at the upper and lower edges of a particle relative to the centre of the particle. The tangential velocities of magnitude

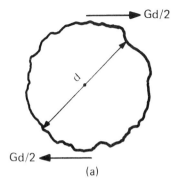 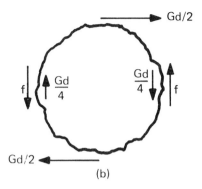

Fig 9.8 Possible floc rupture mechanism

Gd/2 produce a couple which will tend to make the particle rotate with a peripheral velocity of the order of Gd/4. This induces additional shear stresses at both the leading and trailing edges of the particle (Fig 9.8(b)).

If the principal tensile stress induced by the shear forces on the particle exceeds the tensile floc strength, the particles will break apart. The tensile stress is proportional to Gd and the floc tensile strength, U, is a function of the properties of the colloids and other matter which have come together to form the floc. The value of U can also be a function of floc size.

As long as θGd $\leq$ U (θ is a proportionality constant depending on water temperature and particle shape), the floc does not rupture but, if θGd > U, floc rupture will occur.

Although the rate of particle growth can be accelerated by having large values of G when the particles are small, large particles coming into a zone where G is high can be eroded or ruptured, or both. This effect limits the size to which floccules will grow — the higher the local maximum G values, the smaller is the attainable maximum floc size.

Taper flocculation

The time taken for growth of floc particles is reflected in the size of flocculation basins necessary to provide adequate detention time. Rapid initial flocculation rates can be attained at moderately high G values, with progressively decreasing G values as it becomes necessary to provide further particle growth without disruption.

The arrangement by which the floc is subjected to progressively lower G values as floc size increases is called *taper flocculation*.

Values of G and t

The optimum values of G, the average shear gradient, and t, the flocculation time, depend on the chemical composition of the water and the nature and amount of colloids present. The optimum G tends to decrease with increasing turbidity. Mean G values of between 20 and 100 s⁻¹ and flocculation times of 20 to 40 minutes are commonly used.

For any water, there is an optimum combination of G and t, and a range of G and t values near the optimum which will give adequate performance (shown hatched in Fig 9.9).

Camp proposed the product of G and t as a dimensionless number which could be used to judge the adequacy of flocculation. Camp numbers, Gt, of between 2×10^4 and 2×10^5 were considered to achieve a satisfactory flocculation. Other workers have suggested that the effect of floc concentration should be included in any assessment of flocculation adequacy. The number GtC (where C is the floc volume concentration) has been suggested as a useful parameter, and it should be used where sludge recycling or sludge blanket conditions occur, because these result in a large increase in the concentration of sludge in suspension.

Fig 9.9 shows the typical zones in the G-t plane. Combinations of G and t falling in the hatched area give satisfactory performance. Excessive velocity gradients cause floc rupture and excessive flocculation times allow floc erosion to occur. If the Camp number is too small, the amount of flocculation is not adequate.

The zones of satisfactory performance are different for waters from different sources. In extreme cases, the zones for two different waters may

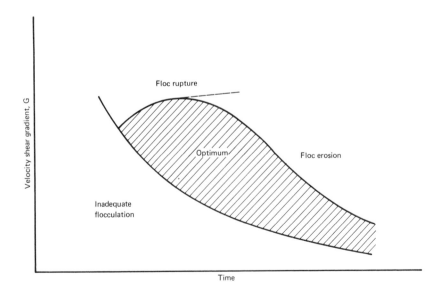

Fig 9.9 Typical zones in G-t plane

not overlap. An indication of the flocculation characteristics of a particular water may be obtained from jar tests with varying flocculation periods and paddle rotational velocities.

Sludge recycling
Flocculation rate is increased by increased concentration of floc and by differential settling. Recycling of settled floc is often used to improve the rate of floc formation. In some waters, old floc can provide denser nuclei than can be obtained with newly-precipitated floc, thus increasing the settling velocity of the resulting composite floc. Recycling of sludge is particularly beneficial in cold, low-alkalinity, coloured waters with little turbidity. Recycling is automatic in both sludge blanket clarifiers and solids contact clarifiers, where existing suspended solids precipitated from the water are mixed with the inflow.

9.8 Flocculation equipment

The agitation necessary to induce flocculation is created in several ways:

Hydraulic	–	jets
		baffled channels
Air injection	–	rising bubbles
Mechanical	–	paddles and reel
		turbine
		propeller
Solids contact	–	(sludge blanket)

Hydraulic flocculator

This is a flocculator in which shear velocity gradients are achieved either by dissipation of energy as water flows through a channel with fixed baffles, or by dissipation of energy from jets or inlet orifices. The rate of energy dissipation is given by the mass flow rate and head loss:

$$P = (Q\rho)(gh) \tag{9.5}$$

The mean velocity shear gradient (G) is given by

$$G = \sqrt{\frac{P}{\Psi\mu}} = \sqrt{\frac{Q\rho gh}{\Psi\mu}} \tag{9.6}$$

where Ψ is the volume of flocculator and, if the head loss is proportional to the square of the flow ($h = KQ^2$), this becomes

$$G = \sqrt{\frac{KQ^3\rho g}{\Psi\mu}} \tag{9.7}$$

The time of flocculation, t, is $\forall/Q$

The Camp number, Gt, $= \sqrt{\dfrac{KQ^3 \rho g}{\forall \mu}\left(\dfrac{\forall}{Q}\right)} = \sqrt{\dfrac{KQ \rho g \forall}{\mu}}$ (9.8)

The Camp number is, therefore, proportional to the square root of the flow rate. Flocculation becomes less efficient as flow rate decreases. This can be tolerated where the variations in flow rates are limited, as for industrial supplies and domestic supplies in some areas where the ratios of maximum to minimum daily demands are not more than about 1.5. Hydraulic agitation provides a simple system of flocculation. At times of low flow, slower rates of flow through clarifiers will partially compensate for reduced flocculation efficiency, because the settling velocity of floc need not be so great.

Baffled channels are also used for flocculation. Sometimes baffles are used to direct water from side to side of a channel, and at other times they may be installed so that the water flows over and under the baffles or past fixed posts.

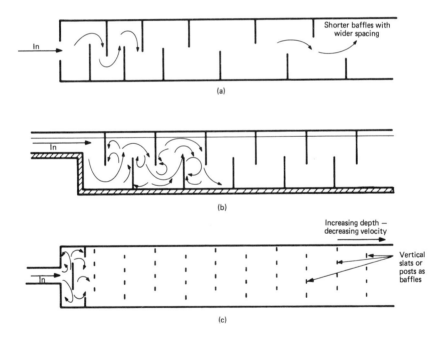

Fig 9.10 Types of baffled channel flocculator: (a) plan of side-to-side baffled channel flocculation, (b) longitudinal section of under-and-over baffled channel flocculation, (c) plan of channel flocculation with posts. Note the methods of providing tapered flocculation in (a) and (c).

Jets into basins can be used to provide flocculation. As the water enters the first basin, high G values can be tolerated and the jet opening may be adjusted to maintain flocculation energy. However, problems with floc disruption can occur at the entry to subsequent basins.

A sewer can act as a flocculation channel, flocculating colloidal sewage solids. Primary sedimentation efficiency can be detrimentally affected if this floc is badly ruptured during its passage into the sedimentation tank.

Air injection

This is a possible way of inducing agitation. Air is admitted through nozzles or diffusers arranged near the bottom of the tank. With large bubbles, the maximum shear velocity gradients in the vicinity of the bubbles can be relatively high. With small bubbles, there is a danger of some bubbles becoming entrained in the floc. Air injection is not used much in water treatment, but in sewage treatment an aerated grit removal chamber acts also as a flocculator to assist in removal of small solids by later sedimentation.

Mechanical flocculators

These use agitators made up as reels, turbines or propellers to cause turbulence and consequent velocity shear gradients in the water (see Fig 9.11). In many cases, the energy input can be estimated from the characteristics of the agitator and the basin geometry.

For ideal flocculation, the G value should be as nearly uniform as practicable. If a tank is considered as consisting of the impeller zone and the remaining, or tank zone, the four characteristic velocity shear gradients of interest are

a Maximum impeller zone shear gradient
b Mean impeller zone shear gradient
c Mean tank zone shear gradient
d Minimum tank zone shear gradient.

In some practical situations, the mean shear gradient in the tank zone can be as low as 10 per cent of the mean shear gradient in the impeller zone, and the tank zone minimum can be 20 to 30 per cent of the tank zone mean. Very low minimum shear gradients in portions of the tank remote from the agitators indicate useless dead space which is not being used effectively for flocculation.

The maximum shear gradients in the impeller zone can cause floc break-up. They occur adjacent to the solid surfaces of the agitators and in the more violent eddies which form in the immediate vicinity of the agitator blades. The magnitude of these maximum shear gradients is related to the relative velocity between the water and the agitators.

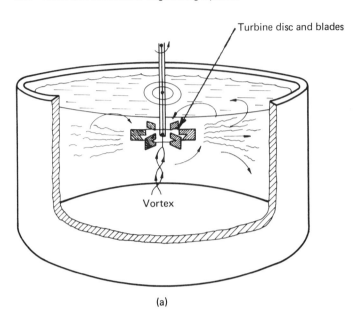

(a)

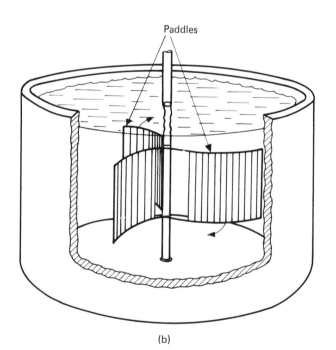

(b)

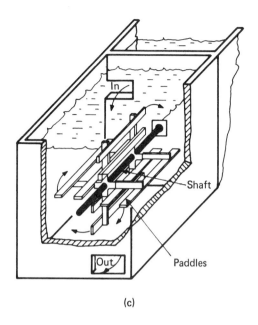

(c)

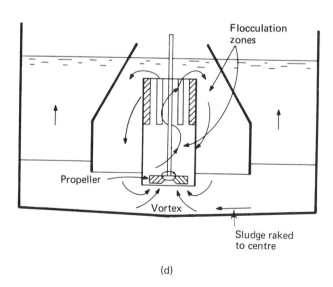

(d)

Fig 9.11 Types of mechanical flocculator agitator: (a) small turbine, (b) large turbine, (c) reel flocculator, (d) propellor flocculator

Good flocculator design will reduce maximum shear gradients in the impeller zone and maintain a reasonable degree of turbulence throughout the tank zone to ensure useful shear gradients — even at minimum values.

With *paddle and reel flocculators*, the relative velocity between the agitator blade and the water is not equal to the blade velocity because the water as a whole develops a rotational velocity in the same direction as the blades. The torque transmitted from the agitator blades to the water is a function of their geometry and their velocities relative to the water.

The restraining torque tending to prevent motion of the water is produced by skin friction drag on the walls of the container, and by the flow of water past any fixed baffling. It is a function of the rate of water movement. As the Reynolds numbers are such that the flow is almost invariably turbulent, both the blade drag and the wall drag are approximately proportional to the square of the appropriate relative velocities.

For a constant rotational momentum, the torque transmitted to the water from the agitator is equal and opposite to that induced by the drag friction and reactions from the walls (neglecting inlet and outlet effects). If the torque produced by blades on *one* arm of a reel-type rotor is given by

$$T_1 = A[\omega(1 - a)]^2 \tag{9.9}$$

where A is the drag coefficient for a particular blade configuration; ω is the angular velocity of the blades; and $a\omega$ is the angular velocity of water, a being a proportionality coefficient such that $\omega(1 - a)$ equals the angular velocity of the blades with respect to the water, with $0 < a < 1$; and if the torque produced by the basin resistance to rotation is given by

$$T_b = B(\omega a)^2 \tag{9.10}$$

(B = basin torque factor) then for a rotor with n arms,

$$T_n = n A[\omega(1 - a)]^2 = T_b = B(\omega a)^2 \tag{9.11}$$

Therefore

$$n A(1 - a)^2 = Ba^2$$

and

$$a = (n A \pm \sqrt{nAB})/(nA - B) \tag{9.12}$$

For a few arms A in constant, but where the number of arms is so large that the wake of one affects the hydraulic performance of another, A is no longer so.

For fixed values of A and B, a increases as n increases, thus reducing the relative velocity between the blades and the water. This decrease in relative velocity results in a decrease in the maximum value of velocity shear gradients near the blades. Also, the larger number of blades means that the combined turbulent wakes of the multiple blades will more fully occupy the space in the flocculator. That is, maximum shear rates near the blades are reduced and average shear rates are increased by the reduction in 'dead' space.

The basin drag is a function of basin shape. A circular basin has a minimum drag; a square basin has a greater drag and this can be further increased by the addition of fixed baffles, or stators.

Turbine flocculators are used to cause small-scale eddy turbulence in the water in the agitator zone, and to cause a large circulation rate so that the water will return to the agitator zone before the eddies have died out.

Propellers are often used for mixing, but only rarely for flocculation.

Short-circuiting can be troublesome in a system in which slow chemical and physico-chemical reactions are occurring. Chemically-dosed water should be retained for a period sufficiently long to give both reaction time and time for some flocculation opportunity. Flocculation agitators cause fairly good mixing of the contents of a tank.

With one well-mixed tank, it can be shown mathematically that about 40 per cent of the inflow will pass through in less than half the theoretical detention time. With three tanks in series, only 20 per cent passes through in less than half the theoretical time. It is common practice to construct flocculation tanks as a number of compartments in series (usually three or four) to reduce the effects of short-circuiting.

Example 9.4

A flocculator to treat a flow of 90 L/s has been constructed with three compartments in series, each 3 m deep, 3 m wide and 6 m long. It has been equipped with a reel-type agitator, with six narrow radial arms in each compartment, spaced 60 degrees apart. Each arm carries two blades which are parallel to the main horizontal shaft. Each blade is 150 mm wide and 4 m long. The distance from the centre of the shaft to the centre of the inner blade is 0.5 m, and 1.0 m to the outer one. When operating with a velocity of 0.575 m/s at the outer edge of the outer blade, the electrical energy being used is 675 W.

If the efficiency of the motor and gearbox is 60 per cent, and the water temperature is 20°C, calculate

a The mean shear velocity gradient

b The Camp number

c i   The hydraulic torque and power input required when first starting the reel in still water, and ii The rotational velocity of the water as a fraction of the agitator rotational velocity.

Solution

a The mean shear velocity gradient is given by $G = \sqrt{P/\forall\mu}$. Since motor and gearbox efficiency is 60 per cent, then

$$P = 675 \times 60/100 = 405 \text{ W}$$
$$\forall = 3 \times (3 \times 3 \times 6) = 162 \text{ m}^3$$

If μ is taken as 10^{-3} Pa.s

Then, $G = \sqrt{405/(162 \times 10^{-3})} = 50.0 \text{ s}^{-1}$

b The Camp number is the product of G and the detention time, t (t = $\forall/Q$).

The total volume is 162 m³ and the flow is 90 L/s or 0.09 m³/s

Therefore, $t = 162/0.09 = 1800 \text{ s}$ (30 min)

Camp number $= Gt = 50 \times 1800 = 9 \times 10^4$

c Estimation of the rotational velocity of the water requires an estimate of the torque and drag characteristics of the agitator reel.

i Peripheral velocity of reel = 0.575 m/s

Radius of periphery $= 1 + 0.15/2 = 1.075$ m

Rotational velocity of reel $= 0.575/1.075 = 0.535$ rad/s

To obtain the torque which would be induced at this rate of rotation in stationary water (when starting, for instance):

Velocity of outer blade $= 0.535 \times 1 = 0.535$ m/s

Blade length-width ratio, $L/W = 4.0/0.15 = 26.7$

For values of L/W greater than 10, the coefficient of drag can be approximated by $C_D = 1.9 - (W/L)(9.8 - 40 \, W/L)$

Force on outer blade, $F = C_D \rho A V^2/2$

Therefore, $F = 1.59 \times 1000 \times (0.15 \times 4) \times 0.535^2/2 = 136.5$ N

Torque from one outer blade $= 136.5 \times 1$ N.m

The drag coefficient, size and angular velocity of the inner blade are the same as those of the outer blade, but velocity and moment arm are only half those of the outer blade.

Torque from one inner blade is $136.5 \times (0.5)^2 \times 0.5 = 17.1$ N.m

Therefore, torque from one arm with two blades $= 136.5 + 17.1 = 153.6$ N.m

In three tanks, there are 18 arms, and the total torque in still water $=$ 153.6 $\times$ 18 $=$ 2765 N.m

The power input at an angular velocity of 0.535 rad/s would then be 0.535 $\times$ 2765 $=$ 1479 W

ii If the water has an angular velocity a times that of the blades, then the forces, and consequently the power input, would be reduced in proportion to the square of the relative velocity.

The power input when under steady operation has been estimated as 405 W. Therefore, $(1 - a)^2 = 405/1479$; whence, $a = 0.48$

It is estimated that the average angular velocity of the water is 0.48 *times* the angular velocity of the blades on the reel.

Example 9.5

a Calculate the mean velocity and the RMS value of the velocity shear gradient in a pipe with an internal diameter of 300 mm carrying a flow of 14 L/s at 20°C. The roughness of the pipe is such that the head loss gradient is 0.0144 per cent.

b Comment on the suitability of this pipe to transfer flocculated water to a settling tank.

Solution

a The mean velocity, $V = Q/A = 0.20$ m/s

The RMS value of velocity shear gradient, $G = \sqrt{P/\forall_\mu}$

$h = 0.0144L/100$, where L is the length of the pipe section

$$G = \sqrt{\frac{Q \rho g \times 0.0144L/100}{\mu L \pi D^2/4}}$$

$$= \sqrt{\frac{0.014 \times 1000 \times 9.81 \times 0.000144}{[10^{-3} \times \pi \times (0.3)^2] \div 4}} = 16.7 \text{ s}^{-1}$$

b This value of G is of a similar magnitude to that often found in the later stages of tapered flocculation systems. The straight sections of the pipeline would therefore be satisfactory for transfer of floc. Particular care would need to be exercised in designing pipe inlet, outlet and bends to ensure that excessive local shear gradients did not occur.

Review questions

9.1 Describe the main features of colloids and colloidal suspensions, and explain the conditions which result in a stable suspension.

9.2 In what ways can a colloidal suspension be de-stabilised to permit coagulation to occur?

9.3 What are the common features of chemicals used for coagulation of colloidal suspensions?

9.4 Explain the objectives of flocculation, and the methods used to achieve them.

9.5 Outline the various constraints which must be considered when designing a mechanical flocculator.

9.6 In what circumstances would the use of coagulant aids be desirable?

10 Disinfection

10.1 Introduction

Disinfection is carried out to destroy the microbiological agents which cause disease. It differs from sterilisation, which implies the destruction of all micro-organisms. For water and wastewater, sterilisation may be appropriate, but economic considerations prohibit its use. Several types of micro-organism are pathogenic (see Sections 4.5 and 4.6). Typhoid, cholera and gastroenteritis are bacterial diseases which are commonly waterborne. Similarly, viral diseases such as hepatitis, parasitic worms such as bilharzia and some tapeworms, together with protozoan diseases such as amoebic dysentery, are waterborne. The wide range of pathogens and their extremely low number preclude routine testing for particular pathogens. Instead, the requirements for disinfection refer to indicator organisms, usually *E coli* (see Section 4.5). Water entering the distribution system should be free of *E coli* in 100 mL of sample. The standards for effluents usually reflect the use of the receiving water. For example, if it is used for non-contact recreational purposes, standards like a mean of less than 1000 faecal coliforms/100 mL may suffice, while, for body-contact recreational purposes, the mean would be less than 100 faecal coliforms/100 mL. Turbidity measurements can be used as an indirect control of pathogen numbers. A correlation has been shown between turbidity removal and virus removal in water treatment. A standard of 0.5 of a turbidity unit implies that the water will contain few pathogens. Such a low figure has little meaning in terms of the appearance of the water.

Water supplies are usually disinfected. The widespread adoption of disinfection was a major factor in reducing waterborne diseases, and this has been interpreted as the major single factor in increasing average human life expectancy. Effluents can be disinfected prior to discharge from treatment plants to receiving waters, to reduce the concentration of pathogens. This practice is not universally adopted.

10.2 Requirements of a disinfectant

A disinfectant must be able to destroy particular pathogens at the concentrations likely to occur, and it should be effective in the normal range of environmental conditions. Disinfectants which require extremes of temperature or pH, or which are effective only for waters with a very low turbidity, are unsuitable for large-scale use.

While the disinfectant should destroy pathogens, it must not be toxic to man or other higher animals, such as fish, in a receiving water. Ideally, some residual disinfecting capacity should be provided for a water supply to provide protection against re-infection while the water is in a distribution system. The residual which passes to the consumer should be neither unpalatable nor obnoxious.

A disinfectant should be safe and easy to handle, both during storage and during addition. The availability of simple or automatic analytical procedures ensures a reliable and consistent dosing system, which can be accurately controlled. The other major consideration is that of cost, which is particularly important for municipal plants where large volumes must be disinfected continuously.

These factors severely restrict the number of reliable disinfectants. The requirements of effectiveness in destroying pathogens, facility and safety of handling, and non-toxicity to man in normal use, provide a major problem. For example, the addition of certain toxic metals can provide effective destruction of pathogens but the residual toxicity is harmful to humans. Chlorine is the most widely used disinfectant. It fulfils many of these conditions but it is a dangerous chemical and requires rigorous safety precautions. The other disinfectants which have found large-scale use are ozone and chlorine dioxide. Others, such as heat, ultraviolet radiation, ultrasonic vibration, ultrafiltration, silver, bromine and iodine, are used only in restricted applications.

10.3 Chlorine as a disinfectant

Under normal conditions, chlorine is a green-yellow, corrosive gas with a density 2.5 times that of air. It can be liquified under a relatively small pressure (3.7 atmospheres). The gas is very soluble in water and is a potent disinfectant even at low concentrations. When dissolved in water, chlorine forms two acids by reaction with molecules of water (Eq 10.1)

$$Cl_2 + H_2O \rightleftharpoons HCl + HOCl \tag{10.1}$$

Hydrochloric acid (HCl) is a common mineral acid and plays no significant role in disinfection. Hypochlorous acid (HOCl) is a disinfecting agent and is referred to as *free available chlorine*. Both the acids can dissociate to produce their respective anions and protons. For hypochlorous acid, this dissociation (Eq 10.2) is important, since the hypochlorite ion (OCl⁻) is not a disinfectant

$$HOCl \rightleftharpoons H^+ + OCl^- \qquad (10.2)$$

The hypochlorous acid is 50 per cent dissociated at approximately pH 7.5 (Fig 10.1). To ensure effective disinfection, the pH must be maintained below pH 7.0 so that at least 90 per cent is in the undissociated, active disinfectant form.

Chlorine rapidly penetrates microbial cells and kills the micro-organism. However, the effectiveness of chlorine is influenced greatly by the physical and chemical characteristics of the water or wastewater. The presence of suspended solids or the clustering of micro-organisms may protect pathogens and so reduce the disinfecting ability. Chlorine is a strong oxidising agent and any reducing agents, such as nitrites, ferrous ions and hydrogen sulphide, rapidly react with it, reducing the concentration available to destroy pathogens.

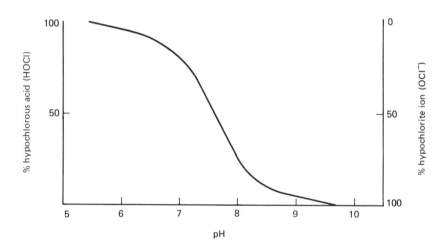

Fig 10.1 Variation of hypochlorous acid/hypochlorite ion system with pH

Ammonia is present in both water supplies and effluents. It reacts with chlorine in water to form, sequentially, monochloramine, dichloramine and trichloramine. The reactions can be considered as successive replacements of hydrogen atoms in ammonia by chlorine atoms (Eqs 10.3, 10.4 and 10.5).

$$NH_3 + HOCl \rightleftharpoons H_2O + NH_2Cl \text{ (monochloramine)} \qquad (10.3)$$

$$NH_2Cl + HOCl \rightleftharpoons H_2O + NHCl_2 \text{ (dichloramine)} \qquad (10.4)$$

$$NHCl_2 + HOCl \rightleftharpoons H_2O + NCl_3 \text{ (trichloramine)} \qquad (10.5)$$

In addition, several other reactions may occur. The monochloramine and dichloramine may react further to give nitrogen gas (N_2) and/or nitrous oxide (N_2O). The proportions of any of these products depends upon the reaction conditions, notably concentrations, temperature and pH. The general reaction scheme can be represented as in Fig 10.2, in which the chlorine dose is plotted against the chlorine available to kill pathogens.

For the region A-B, the chlorine added reacts rapidly with any reducing agents in the sample. This reduces the chlorine to chloride (Cl^-), which is not a disinfectant. The residual chlorine is low and, for a small chlorine dose, there will be no disinfecting properties. The addition of more chlorine is represented by region B-C. The chlorine has completely oxidised the reducing agents and has formed monochloramine and dichloramine by reaction with ammonia. The chloramines are disinfectants and are detected as a chlorine residual. Monochloramine and dichloramine are much less powerful disinfectants than is free chlorine. If they are present in high concentrations or if a long reaction time is permitted, these chloramines will destroy pathogens. Monochloramine and dichloramine are referred to as *combined available chlorine*. In this region (B-C) the addition of chlorine produces an approximately proportional increase of combined chlorine residual.

Further addition of chlorine produces trichloramine (Eq 10.5), nitrogen, nitrous oxide and other products which are not disinfectants. Thus, in the region C-D, the addition of further chlorine reduces the available chlorine and, hence, the ability of the solution to destroy pathogens. On further

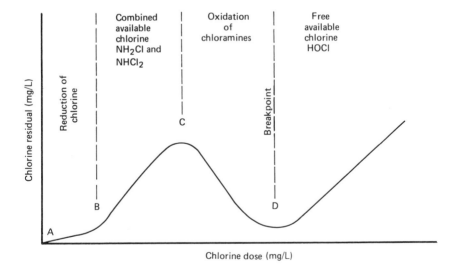

Fig 10.2 Products of the reaction between ammonia and chlorine in water

chlorine addition these reactions are complete (point D) and the ammonia is completely oxidised. Any subsequent addition of chlorine will remain as free available chlorine (HOCl) and will act as a strong chlorine residual. Point D is referred to as the *breakpoint*. Chlorination is commonly carried out beyond the breakpoint to ensure a free chlorine residual. The chlorine dose required to reach the breakpoint is several times the ammonia concentration. If effluents contain so much ammonia that breakpoint chlorination would be prohibitively expensive, chlorination is taken to region B-C to form a combined chlorine residual.

The chlorine-ammonia reaction as set out in Fig 10.2 should be regarded only as a simplified representation. The free and combined residual concentrations depend upon the reaction conditions for any particular sample. The relative concentrations of free and combined chlorine residual can be monitored by simple colorimetric or instrumental means. The methods rely upon the greater reactivity of the free chlorine (HOCl) which rapidly gives a reading, while the combined residual (NH_2Cl and $NHCl_2$) reacts relatively slowly. For example, the reagent diethyl-p-phenylene-diamine sulphate (DPD sulphate) gives a red colour by reaction with free chlorine. The addition of varying amounts of potassium iodide induces the production of colour by monochloramine and dichloramine. A complexing agent is incorporated with DPD sulphate to prevent interference by trace metals. The reagent is available in tablet form; No 1 DPD will determine free available chlorine, No 2 DPD the free chlorine plus monochloramine, and No 3 DPD the total chlorine.

Kinetics of chlorination

The ability of a reagent to destroy pathogens is related to the concentration of the disinfectant and the contact time between the pathogens and disinfectant. One general relationship is known as Chick's law (Eq 10.6), which assumes that the distribution of micro-organisms is controlled by processes of diffusion:

$$\frac{dN}{dt} = -kN \tag{10.6}$$

where N is the number of viable micro-organisms of one type at time t, and k is a constant (dimensions t^{-1}). Integrating for $N = N_0$ at $t = 0$ gives

$$\log_e \frac{N}{N_0} = -kt \tag{10.7}$$

Therefore

$$\frac{N}{N_0} = e^{-kt} \tag{10.8}$$

The 'rate of kill' depends upon the number of micro-organisms which were present originally. If the micro-organisms all possess the same resistance, the kills follow an exponential pattern (Eq 10.8). A complete kill is not feasible. The efficiency of disinfection is reported in terms of the ratio of micro-organisms killed to the original number of micro-organisms present, such as 99 per cent, 99.9 per cent or 99.99 per cent kills.

Chick's law is not followed by all disinfectants for all micro-organisms. The kill rate depends upon such factors as the penetration of the cell wall, the time to penetrate vital centres within the cell, and the distribution of disinfectant and micro-organisms. Each species of micro-organism therefore will have a different sensitivity to each disinfectant. This is accounted for by manipulating k or t in Eq 10.8 to linearise plots of N/N_o. The simplest form of such equations is

$$C^n t_p = \text{constant} \tag{10.9}$$

where C^n is the concentration of disinfectant; t_p is the contact time between disinfectant and micro-organism to achieve the desired kill; and n is a constant for one system of disinfectant and micro-organism at one kill rate. For example, with chlorine as disinfectant and a 99 per cent kill, the forms of Eq 10.9 for the following micro-organisms are

E coli $C^{0.86} t_p = 0.24$

Poliomyelitis virus $C^{0.86} t_p = 1.2$

Coxsackie virus A2 $C^{0.86} t_p = 6.3$

For disinfectants such as chlorine, which have $n < 1$, the contact time is usually the most important single factor to ensure adequate pathogen destruction. A contact time of 30 minutes is used in many applications.

Applications of chlorine

Chlorine can be used directly as a disinfectant, in which case the active reagent is hypochlorous acid; alternatively, combined chlorine residuals can be formed and they act as the disinfectant.

For waters of satisfactory purity, without excessive colour or turbidity, not subject to wide variations of quality, and free from phenolic substances and algal products, a dose of 0.1 to 0.2 mg/L with a contact time of 30 minutes provides adequate disinfection at a pH of 6 to 7. Waters of poorer quality require a higher chlorine dose. The contact time of 30 minutes is needed before the water reaches the consumer. The contact time can be provided within the treatment plant or partly within the plant and partly within the post-chlorination storage and distribution systems.

Chloramines are weaker disinfectants, and they require contact times of the order of one hour. They may be used for waters which contain a high concentration of ammonia or in situations where a chlorine residual is to be maintained for a long time.

When chlorine is added to a particular water, the residual is a function of both the dose and the time elapsed after the dose (Fig 10.3). Routine tests are carried out after a nominated time (such as 30 minutes). This ensures that the pathogens have been exposed to a concentration at least equal to (but usually greater than) the measured residual for the nominated time. The necessary conditions for an adequate kill of pathogens are incorporated in dosing requirements which are often in the form: the total free residual after x minutes shall be not less than y mg/L.

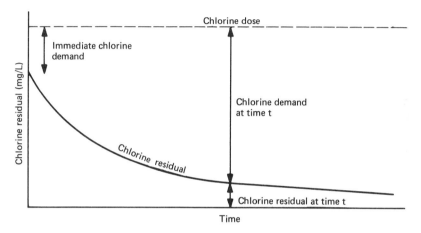

Fig 10.3 Chlorine residual variation with time

Chlorine has some beneficial uses for water supply in addition to disinfection. It is a strong oxidant, capable of oxidising some materials in the water. Colour, taste and odour in water supplies are often of biological origin and are caused by the presence of organic molecules. Iron and manganese salts may be present, particularly in groundwater supplies. They are usually in reduced form and they precipitate in the distribution system. Chlorine will oxidise some of these materials, reducing colour, taste and odour and converting ferrous ions to ferric ions, which can be precipitated. The presence of phenolic compounds in water supplies is a particular problem. Phenols (C_6H_5OH) react with chlorine to form chlorinated phenols which have a very penetrating taste and odour. Conventional chlorination will produce the chlorophenols, and so it is unsuitable if phenols are present. The use of chloramines sometimes avoids chlorophenolic taste and odours.

A high concentration of chlorine can be added, such treatment being termed *superchlorination*. Large doses of chlorine completely oxidise ammonia and the colour, taste and odour-producing compounds in the water. Chlorophenols are further oxidised, thus correcting taste and odour formation. The high dose of chlorine which remains after these chemical reactions can carry out effective disinfection. The excess chlorine must be removed prior to distribution, otherwise the water will be corrosive and have a distinct chlorine taste and odour. Dechlorination is conveniently carried out with sodium bisulphate, sulphur dioxide or activated carbon. These reactions are rapid (10 to 15 minutes contact) and they effectively remove excess chlorine. For example, the reaction between sulphur dioxide and chlorine to give sulphuric acid and hydrochloric acid is

$$Cl_2 + SO_2 + 2H_2O \rightleftharpoons H_2SO_4 + 2HCl \qquad (10.10)$$

The other use of chlorine in water supply is as a prechlorination stage prior to rapid sand filtration. This reduces the bacterial load on filters and enables longer filter runs before backwashing is needed. It provides additional safety, in that a lower number of pathogens will be present for the final disinfection, and growths within the treatment system are controlled. There are some adverse effects from adding chlorine to water which contains a high organic concentration. The organic material and chlorine can react to form compounds which are not removed in subsequent processes and produce water of poor quality with regard to tastes and odours.

Chlorine is widely used as a disinfectant in swimming pools. The general principles outlined in the preceding sections apply to swimming pool disinfection except that higher chlorine residuals are required to reduce the possibility of pathogen transmission. In open-air pools, chlorine can be added with a chemical protector (sodium dichloroisocyanurate) which reduces the photochemical decomposition of chlorine. The disinfection can be carried out with chlorine or with sodium or calcium hypochlorite. The solid disinfectant is usually preferred for small pools.

Effluents are chlorinated to reduce the release of pathogens either to the receiving water or for effluent re-use. The disinfection is usually carried out with a 30 minute retention time, the chlorine dose depending upon the treatment given to the wastewater. Raw sewage may require 30 mg/L of chlorine or more, settled sewage less than 20 mg/L, secondary treated sewage less than 10 mg/L, and effluents which have been filtered, less than 6 mg/L. The aim is to produce a stable residual of approximately 0.5 mg/L.

Technology of chlorine addition

Chlorine may be purchased as solid calcium hypochlorite, as liquid sodium hypochlorite or as liquid chlorine. Liquefied chlorine, available in drums or cylinders, is used at large plants. The rate of removal of chlorine from a drum or cylinder is a function of temperature. The vapour pressure of chlorine is temperature dependent and, as liquid chlorine vaporises, latent heat of vaporisation must be supplied. The temperature of a cylinder will be less than the average air temperature as the latent heat is absorbed. If chlorine is withdrawn too rapidly from a cylinder or drum, frosting or excessive sweating due to condensation occurs. In very damp climates, the rates of removal should be reduced. Therefore with a high air temperature it is possible to withdraw chlorine relatively quickly, whereas for a low air temperature, slow withdrawal is needed. For example, it may be possible to use an entire cylinder in four days at an air temperature of 21°C, while one month would be needed at 2°C. At high temperatures, frothing of gas while boiling causes a carry-over of impurities. Condensation of chlorine in gas lines should be avoided. A pressure-reducing valve attached near the cylinder or drum should keep the pressure in the pipes below the vapour pressure associated with the pipe temperature.

Chlorine is dissolved in a small part of the flow to be disinfected. This produces a strong solution of hypochlorous acid, which can then be added to the main stream to provide the required chlorine dose. The mechanism for dosing chlorine into the service water to produce the strong hypochlorous acid requires careful control. Chlorine gas is safe only when it is handled correctly. Instruction sheets containing simple rules for use by engineers and operatives can usually be obtained from chlorine suppliers.

A schematic representation of a chlorinator is given in Fig 10.4. The chlorinator includes a pressure-reducing valve, vacuum and pressure-relief valve and an anti-suction valve. The high solubility of chlorine in water, combined with the hydraulic design of the injector, ensures that chlorine is drawn into the water under vacuum. This reduces the possibility of release of chlorine to the atmosphere if the equipment develops a leak. The hypo-

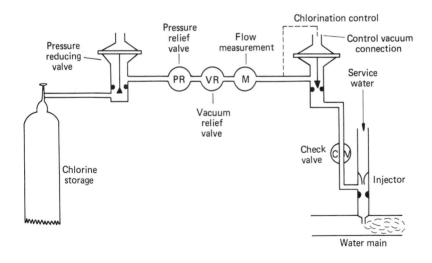

Fig 10.4 Schematic representation of a chlorinator

chlorous acid solution can be released into a water main by turbulent diffusion. For example, at a Reynolds number of 4000 or greater, the chlorine will be dispersed within ten pipe diameters. The chlorine can be dispersed at points of hydraulic discontinuity — for example, near a submerged weir.

In practice, it is most convenient to control chlorination by adjustment of the chlorine concentration. Other possible variables, such as the contact time and form of chlorine residual, are fixed by the design of the plant and the quality of the water. The chlorine dosed to the water or effluent is most commonly controlled by adjusting the chlorine added to the service water (Fig 10.5). The control vacuum is varied manually or automatically on the basis of the measured flow-rate and the determination of chlorine residual. Fig 10.5 illustrates a control system of this type.

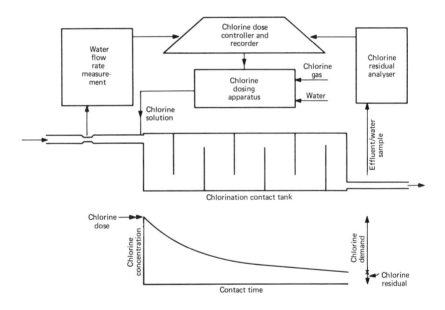

Fig 10.5 Chlorination control

Chlorination with sodium or calcium hypochlorite uses principles similar to those outlined for liquid/gaseous chlorine. The hypochlorite can be drip-fed into the service water, and tablet chlorinators are available.

Advantages and disadvantages of chlorine

Chlorine is the most widely-used chemical disinfectant. It fulfils many of the requirements outlined in Section 10.2. It has found widespread use not only for large and small water supply systems, but also for the treatment of swimming pool waters and for effluent disinfection. Chlorine is a powerful disinfectant at low concentrations. Its ability to destroy pathogens without adversely affecting the future use of a water or effluent is a major advantage. Analytical methods have been developed which provide a simple, direct and accurate measurement of chlorine residuals. The control of chlorine dose can be accurately maintained from the analytical data. It is a dangerous chemical which requires careful handling. However, the widespread and long-standing use of chlorine has resulted in the establishment of well-documented controls for safe operation. It is produced during the manufacture of sodium hydroxide from sodium chloride (common or rock salt). As sodium hydroxide is a major industrial chemical and is produced in large volumes, the associated large-scale production of chlorine makes it a relatively inexpensive disinfectant.

There are some disadvantages in the use of chlorine. Its reaction with phenolic compounds can make simple chlorination unsuitable for some waters and effluents. Both free chlorine and chloramines have been shown to have some adverse effect upon some higher animals, notably fish, which can be significant for receiving waters with viable fish populations. Chlorination has been shown to produce trihalomethane compounds such as chloroform ($CHCl_3$) by reaction with organic material in waters and wastewaters. The organic material can be either naturally occurring (such as humic and fulvic acids) or of human origin. The amount of trihalomethanes produced is approximately proportional to the concentration of organic matter in the water. Trihalomethanes have been shown to be carcinogenic, and so there is some concern about the generation and release of such compounds. Chlorine is not notably effective in removing certain taste, odour and colour constituents from waters.

It is evident that, although chlorine is widely used and will continue to be widely used, there are conditions in which it is not an ideal disinfectant. Other disinfectants should be considered, and their performance and use compared with that of chlorine.

10.4 Ozone

Ozone is an allotrope of oxygen. It is composed of three oxygen atoms, bound together (O_3), rather than two oxygen atoms as in the common form of molecular oxygen (O_2).

It can be produced by passing a silent electrical discharge through dry filtered air. Ozone is a pungent, irritating gas which attacks the nose, eyes and throat and is toxic at low concentrations. Its corrosive nature means that only resistant materials like stainless steel and polyvinyl chloride can be used to handle it. Like oxygen, ozone is only slightly soluble in water. It is unstable, breaking down to give molecular oxygen (O_2). Its low solubility and its instability require that it be generated on site and introduced into the water as fine bubbles. A retention time of 5 to 10 minutes is usually sufficient to destroy pathogens.

Ozone is an effective method of destroying pathogens in clear water. It is a strong oxidant, and is effective for removing taste, odour, iron, manganese and colour constituents from waters. Its ability to completely oxidise organic material minimises the organic content of waters and so it inhibits the growth of low life forms in water. It is not known to produce dangerous or objectionable compounds, as chlorine does in yielding chlorophenols and trihalomethanes. The only product from the addition of excess ozone is the breakdown product, oxygen, and so nothing 'foreign' is added. The breakdown of ozone does mean that there is no lasting residual disinfectant in the water or effluent. If a residual is required, it may be necessary to add chlorine or chlorine dioxide to act as a residual in the distribution system, while the ozone is used as the primary disinfectant and for its other effects such as taste and odour suppression.

Ozone acts through the destruction of all protoplasm. Disinfection by ozone depends mainly upon the concentration of the gas added. In Eq 10.9, the term n is greater than one:

$$C^n t_p = \text{constant} \tag{10.9}$$

Ozone is usually more expensive than chlorine; it requires a high energy input during production — approximately 10 to 15 times that of chlorine. It is only slightly soluble in water and provides no residual. However, for waters which have a taste, odour or colour problem, it has a major advantage over chlorine. The difficulties associated with the production of toxic or noxious compounds by reaction with chlorine have led to a renewed interest in ozone as a disinfectant for waters and effluents. To date, it has found most use in continental Europe.

10.5 Chlorine dioxide

Chlorine dioxide (ClO_2) is an unstable gas, which can be generated by the addition of acid or chlorine to sodium chlorite. For example, with excess chlorine at pH < 5,

$$Cl_2 + 2NaClO_2 \rightleftharpoons 2NaCl + 2ClO_2 \tag{10.11}$$

In water, chlorine dioxide reacts to produce two unstable acids, chlorous acid and chloric acid, which can act as disinfectants:

$$2ClO_2 + H_2O \rightleftharpoons HClO_2 + HClO_3 \tag{10.12}$$

Chlorine dioxide is a highly reactive gas and particular care is required to ensure its safe handling. Its instability requires it to be generated on site and to be used immediately. Although chlorine dioxide is relatively expensive as a disinfectant, its strong oxidising characteristics make it valuable in the control of taste, odour, iron, manganese and colour. Chlorine dioxide is not affected by ammonia compounds; it oxidises compounds to form tasteless products and provides a persistent residual in the distribution system. To date it has found most use in the US, particularly for taste and odour control in water supplies.

10.6 Other disinfectants

Several other methods of disinfection have specific uses.

Simple retention

A disinfectant provides only a percentage kill; a small fraction of the pathogens can survive. For instance, when a disinfected effluent is discharged, it is to be expected that some regrowth of micro-organisms will occur in the receiving water. The relative magnitude of the regrowth compared with natural decay of micro-organisms varies for each location. Simple retention provides a significant die-off of pathogens. They are sensitive to environmental conditions and they require the protected environment of mammalian metabolism to reproduce rapidly. Under normal surface water conditions (particularly, limited nutrients and low temperature), pathogens tend to die off. Storage of waters or wastewaters in a reservoir or stabilisation pond encourages this die-off, together with the settlement of pathogens. The impoundment of effluents in a stabilisation pond for 10 to 20 days can provide effective pathogen removal without the addition of chemicals.

Iodine and bromine

Iodine and bromine have disinfecting properties similar to those of chlorine; they are less hazardous to use and they do not give troublesome odours. They are not available in large volumes and so they are more expensive than chlorine for large-scale use. Both bromine and iodine are used for small-scale, emergency or portable disinfection. Bromine is used for disinfection in some swimming pools where it causes less eye irritation than does chlorine.

Colloidal suspensions of silver

Metallic ions can be used as disinfectants. Colloidal suspensions of silver are used at low concentrations (0.01 to 0.05 mg/L Ag). The dilute silver suspensions require contact times of several hours to provide reliable destruction of pathogens, and this long contact time makes the method expensive for large-scale use. Several materials, such as iron oxides and vegetable matter, interfere with the disinfection. Water disinfected with silver contains no taste, odour or colour caused by the metallic ions and it provides a stable long-term residual. Its major use is as a portable or small-scale disinfectant.

Heat

Heat is a traditional method of disinfecting. Boiling water for approximately 15 minutes (depending upon altitude) destroys pathogens. Pasteurisation, that is heating to a temperature of greater than 60°C, is effective at destroying many pathogens. Autoclaving, which raises the temperature to greater than 100°C (typically 121°C) at increased pressure, can be used for small scale water disinfection. Heat is uneconomical for large-scale use, but it is widely used as an emergency method. The water contains no residual and care must be taken to prevent recontamination before use.

Ultraviolet radiation

High-intensity ultraviolet radiation breaks down organic molecules, including those present in pathogens. Water also absorbs ultraviolet light, so the supply must be irradiated over a shallow depth (< 120 mm). Other materials in the water, such as suspended solids, colour and organic compounds, also absorb the radiation and reduce its disinfecting properties. The method is suitable for very small-scale disinfection. Again no residual is provided. Ultraviolet radiation is used for effluent disinfection, but only works well for high-quality effluents with low suspended solids concentrations.

Ultrasonic radiation

Ultrasonics can break down the chemical structure of molecules, including those in pathogens. This is an effective method of disinfection, but it is expensive for large-scale use.

Ultrafiltration

Pathogens can be removed by filtration. Ultrafiltration through a very fine filter medium removes solids, including pathogens, and provides a disinfected water but leaves no residual. The water must not contain large amounts of suspended solids which would block the filters too readily. This method has specific small-scale uses, but is too expensive for large-scale use.

10.7 Conclusions

Disinfection of water supplies is almost universally practised or approved. For effluents, the difficulties of residual toxicity, aftergrowth in receiving waters, and reactions during disinfection make the case for disinfection complicated. The most widely-used disinfectant is chlorine, which fulfils most requirements of an effective disinfectant. There are some waters and effluents which are less suited to the use of chlorine, particularly those which contain soluble colour, taste or odour components. For these waters, ozone and chlorine dioxide have merit. The small-scale, emergency, specialist or portable treatment of water may rely upon other equally effective disinfectants which, while more expensive for large-scale use, are suited to small or particular applications.

Disinfection should be regarded as a final insurance to prevent the release of pathogens. The other unit processes in both water and wastewater treatment which remove pathogens include impoundment, settlement and filtration. The final addition of a disinfectant serves only to ensure the hygienic quality of the water or effluent. It is not the sole operation responsible for pathogen destruction. In fact, the effectiveness of a disinfectant is improved by prior removal of materials from the water. Therefore, efficient operation of the preceding processes optimises disinfection.

Review questions

10.1   What properties of chlorine have made it a widely-used disinfectant?

10.2   Why is disinfection not usually carried out below pH 6 or above pH 8?

10.3   Why is ammonia sometimes added to water prior to chlorine addition in hot climates?

10.4   What are the advantages of superchlorination?

10.5   What are the disadvantages of effluent chlorination?

10.6   What precautions should be taken when dosing and handling chlorine?

10.7   Which types of water are most suited to the use of ozone as a disinfectant?

10.8   Why would water disinfected only by boiling be unsuitable for use in a swimming pool?

Review questions

10.1   What properties of chlorine have made it a widely-used disinfectant?

10.2   Why is disinfection not usually carried out below pH 6 or above pH 8?

10.3   Why is ammonia sometimes added to water prior to chlorine addition in hot climates?

10.4   What are the advantages of superchlorination?

10.5   What are the disadvantages of effluent chlorination?

10.6   What precautions should be taken when dosing and handling chlorine?

10.7   Which types of water are most suited to the use of ozone as a disinfectant?

10.8   Why would water disinfected only by boiling be unsuitable for use in a swimming pool?

11 Biological Treatment Processes

11.1 Introduction

Conventional sedimentation, the major process in primary wastewater treatment, normally removes 60 to 70 per cent of the suspended matter containing 30 to 40 per cent of the BOD present in municipal wastewaters, leaving 150 to 200 mg/L BOD and about 100 mg/L SS in the primary effluent. Discharge of effluent of this quality without exceeding the assimilative capacity of the receiving environment is only possible where very large volumes of water are available for dilution, or where the effluent may be irrigated over a large land area. For discharge to inland streams or lakes, a considerably higher quality is necessary.

It is possible to remove most of the remaining non-settleable suspended matter, with some accompanying reduction in BOD, by providing a chemical coagulation process ahead of primary sedimentation. Dissolved organic matter is not effectively removed in this process, however, so that while the resulting effluent may be low in SS, the overall BOD removal may be only 60 to 80 per cent, leaving some 50 to 100 mg/L BOD in the effluent. Further treatment is therefore necessary prior to discharge to inland streams. Chemical processes also have the disadvantage of producing large quantities of chemical sludge, in addition to the organic sludge normally produced.

Conventional physical and chemical processes are therefore not usually capable of meeting effluent discharge criteria for inland waters.

One of the major polluting effects of wastewater on streams, as noted in Chapters 4 and 7, results from depletion of dissolved oxygen by the action of aerobic organisms in degrading the organic content of the waste. This suggests that one method of removing organic matter from wastewaters would be to concentrate the natural aerobic biodegradation process into an engineered system under controlled conditions. Practical *aerobic biological treatment processes* seek to do this, within the constraints of available land area and economic resources available to construct and operate treatment works.

Where the concentration of organic waste matter is very high, however, it often becomes either physically difficult or economically impracticable to transfer sufficient oxygen into the wastewater to sustain aerobic action. The most economical method of treating such concentrated wastes is usually by *anaerobic biological processes*. Such processes are widely used in treating the concentrated organic sludges produced at most conventional wastewater treatment plants.

The design of efficient, economical biological wastewater treatment systems of either type requires an understanding of the biological principles on which they are based.

11.2 Biodegradation and biological growth

Successful biological treatment depends on the development and maintenance of an appropriate, active, mixed microbial population in the system. This microbial population may be present as either a fixed film attached to some form of support medium, as in the trickling filter and rotating biological filter processes, or a suspended growth, as in activated sludge processes and anaerobic digestion. In each of these treatment systems, organic waste matter is used as a food source by the microbial population. In their life processes, these micro-organisms use some of the organic matter in order to synthesise new cell material, and they obtain the energy for their synthesis and cell maintenance functions by degrading some of the organic matter to simple compounds. Thus, biological growth involves both *cell synthesis* and *biodegradation* processes.

Characteristics of the main constituents of organic waste matter (food) — proteins, carbohydrates and lipids — and the main types of organism involved in removing them in wastewater treatment — bacteria, protozoa and algae — are discussed in Chapter 4. Also discussed in that chapter are some aspects of organism classification in terms of their food, energy and oxygen requirements. Other aspects of classification relevant to subsequent discussions on biological wastewater treatment processes also concern food and energy requirements of micro-organisms.

Organisms which require a complex source of organic carbon for growth are called *heterotrophic*, while those organisms which are able to synthesise their organic requirements from inorganic carbon sources such as CO_2 are called *autotrophic*.

Heterotrophic organisms obtain the energy necessary for their growth and maintenance functions by breaking down some of the organic food supply. Autotrophic organisms are able to obtain their energy requirements either by oxidising inorganic ions, in which case they are *chemosynthetic*, or by utilising sunlight, when they are *photosynthetic* organisms. *Aerobic heterotrophic bacteria* are the organisms responsible for the primary breakdown of organic matter in wastewater treatment. Autotrophic organisms of importance in special cases include the bacteria responsible for nitrification, and algae which fulfil an important role in contributing oxygen in oxidation ponds.

Anaerobic and facultative heterotrophic bacteria are important in the stabilisation of the concentrated organic sludges produced in wastewater treatment and also in the treatment of concentrated organic industrial wastes.

Simplified representations of the overall aerobic and anaerobic biological growth processes are given in Eqs 4.2 and 4.3 respectively, while nutrient and mineral requirements of these processes are dealt with in Section 4.3.

Environmental factors which influence biological growth include *temperature, pH, mixing intensity* and the presence of *toxic agents.* Temperature may affect the reaction rate of micro-organisms to the extent of doubling it for each 10°C increase. Different organisms predominate at different temperature ranges, however, so that there is little difficulty in developing a suitable micro-organism population in all but the coldest climatic conditions. For optimum biological growth the pH should generally be in the range of 6.5 to 7.5, although growth will occur over the range of pH 4.0 to 9.5. Toxic materials should not be present in toxic concentrations, although it is often possible to develop a microbial population which is acclimatised to quite high concentrations of some toxic materials. Mixing is important, especially in suspended growth systems, to ensure effective contact between the active micro-organisms and the organic matter, to prevent accumulation of products of microbial decomposition, and to preserve a uniform environment throughout the volume of the reactor.

Any deficiency in nutrient or environmental factors will inhibit biological growth, and will lead to loss of process efficiency. In any case, process efficiency can be maximised by keeping all conditions of operation as constant as possible.

The biological growth curve

The growth of a *batch* culture of micro-organisms utilising a single growth-limiting nutrient (substrate), such as organic carbon, is illustrated in Fig 11.1, where it is assumed that all other nutrient and environmental requirements as discussed above are satisfied. Initially, when the food supply is present in excess, the organisms grow at a rate controlled by their inherent metabolic rate, and organism numbers increase logarithmically.

This phase is followed by a declining growth phase during which shortage of available food begins to limit the rate of organism growth until at some point, approaching exhaustion of the food supply, the mass of organisms present reaches a maximum. Thereafter, as cells die and are used as a food source by those which remain, the total cell mass declines, in the process of endogenous respiration.

One implication of the growth curve in Fig 11.1 is that, in the declining growth phase, the rate of organism growth at any time is a function of the food concentration. It should be noted, however, that practical biological wastewater treatment processes are *continuous* rather than batch operations, and may be represented, on average, as a single point on the batch growth curve. Each of these operating points is evidently characterised by a particular value of both micro-organism concentration and food concentration. A convenient measure of the organic loading rate in a biological process can be expressed as a ratio, known as the *food-to-micro-organism ratio — F/M*.

Another very important observation, not readily apparent from Fig 11.1, is that not only does the rate of organism growth decline as food supply becomes growth limiting, but the *net yield of organism mass per unit mass of substrate utilised* also declines. Hence the lower the F/M ratio, the greater will be the proportion of the substrate degraded to supply the energy requirements of the cell, and the lower the rate of accumulation of biological solids in the system. It is not feasible to operate practical biological processes to produce zero net growth of biological solids, because a certain proportion of cell material is always relatively resistant to further degradation. This means that as cells grow and in turn die and are used as food by other organisms, these poorly-degradable cell residues will accumulate. Consequently, practical biological treatment systems must be provided with means for withdrawing and disposing of the net mass increase in biological solids.

From these observations, it is possible to develop another process parameter which is of value in the design and operation of many biological treatment systems — *mean cell residence time*, θ_c (also known as the solids retention time or sludge age). This may be defined as the average time a mass of cells remains in a biological treatment system before being withdrawn in the waste solids stream. If the total mass of biological solids in the system is represented by $[X]_T$, and the daily increase in solids mass which occurs as a result of growth by $[\Delta X]_T$, then θ_c is given by

$$\theta_c = \frac{[X]_T}{[\Delta X]_T} \text{ days}$$

if $[X]_T$ is in kg and $[\Delta X]_T$ is in kg/d.

It will be shown in Chapter 14 that θ_c can be correlated with a modified form of the F/M ratio to give a relationship which is useful for process design and operation.

Application to practical aerobic biological treatment systems

The batch biological growth curve (Fig 11.1) was developed for pure cultures of micro-organisms using a single growth-limiting nutrient. Practical

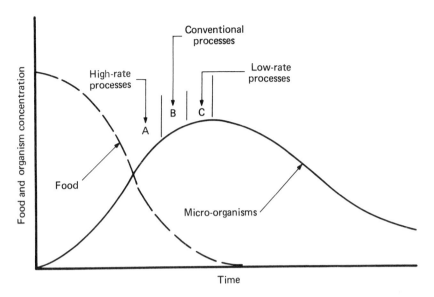

Fig 11.1 The batch biological growth curve showing typical ranges of operating points for continuous biological treatment processes

biological treatment systems, however, are usually continuous processes which employ mixed populations of micro-organisms to treat highly complex and variable wastes. Nevertheless, the general considerations outlined above provide a useful basis for understanding the requirements of practical systems.

Nutrients, trace elements and other growth factors required for balanced biological growth are usually present in adequate amounts in normal domestic wastewaters, while toxic materials are not usually present in toxic concentrations. Environmental requirements are also satisfied by domestic wastewaters and most habitable climates, although extremes of temperature may reduce the efficiency of biological processes. Difficulties may arise with any of these factors as a result of industrial wastes discharged to the system. In such cases, it is necessary either to control the quality of industrial wastes entering the sewers or to make allowance in the design of the treatment works to accommodate the particular combination of wastes to be treated.

Oxygen requirements for aerobic processes must be satisfied by ensuring an adequate rate of oxygen transfer by natural or artificial means. Sufficient oxygen should be available to satisfy the oxygen demand in aerobic biological oxidation while maintaining a minimum of 1 to 2 mg/L of DO in the wastewater; otherwise, the reaction rate may be oxygen-limited.

The food-to-micro-organism ratio is an excellent measure of process loading rate in aerobic treatment systems. There are practical difficulties, however, in measuring and characterising food and micro-organism mass in the system; in both cases, it is necessary to use indirect measures. *Waste strength* is usually measured in terms of BOD or COD. Micro-organism mass is much more difficult to determine accurately, and it is often necessary to use gross parameters such as the area of surfaces in, or the gross volume of, the support media on which the micro-organisms grow.

In *suspended growth systems*, such as activated sludge, the organism concentration is usually related to the 'mixed liquor suspended solids concentration' (MLSS) or its volatile fraction (MLVSS). Thus, a practical definition of food-to-micro-organism ratio for such systems becomes

$$F = \frac{\text{Mass of BOD added to system each day}}{\text{Total mass of MLVSS in the system}} \qquad (11.1)$$

Because MLSS is simpler to measure than MLVSS, and because the ratio of MLVSS to MLSS tends to be relatively constant (typically equivalent to about 75 to 80 per cent) for a given system, F is often defined in terms of MLSS concentration. There is evidence that active organisms comprise only a relatively small percentage of the total biological solids in conventional suspended growth systems. Measurements of gross organic content in the suspended activated sludge solids, such as the MLVSS determination, therefore give an exaggerated measure of active organism content in the system. Nevertheless, it has been found that there is usually a good correlation between total mass of MLVSS and other process parameters such as effluent BOD, rate of increase of biological solids and oxygen consumption.

For *fixed film systems*, such as the rotating biological filter, the active mass of organisms in the system is more difficult to determine. Although the total mass of organisms growing on the disc surfaces may be very much higher than the total mass of MLSS in a corresponding activated sludge system, it is probable that only the surface layers of biological film are directly active in the waste treatment process. Hence, the most practical measure of the total organism activity in a rotating disc filter is the surface area of the discs.

Practical biological treatment processes are often conveniently divided into high-rate, conventional and low-rate processes on the basis of their F/M ratio, shown qualitatively on the batch growth curve in Fig 11.1 as regions A, B and C respectively. High rate processes are characterised by high growth rates and high values of F (1.0 or more) and also, from the earlier discussion on the batch growth curve, by high rates of accumulation of biological solids per unit of organic matter removed. Conversely, low rate processes have low values of F (less than 0.1), low growth rates and relatively low rates of solids accumulation, since more of the organic matter is broken down in respiration processes. Conventional processes usually fall in the range of F = 0.2 to 0.5 and have moderate rates of growth and solids accumulation.

The mean cell residence time can be most readily applied to processes in which it is possible to estimate the total mass of micro-organisms in the system. Suspended growth systems are therefore better able to be described in terms of θ_c than fixed film processes. In spite of the difficulties of measuring microbial mass in fixed film processes, however, it is likely that it is higher than in suspended growth systems, and is retained in the biological reactor for a much longer time. It is probable that θ_c is greater in fixed film processes.

For maximum overall efficiency of biological processes in removing organic impurities, it is necessary to separate the net growth of biological solids from the effluent. It is therefore important that most practical biological treatment systems generally produce biological solids in a form which may be readily removed in a *final sedimentation* process. Settling characteristics of the excess biological solids are related to process loading rate (F/M ratio), nutrient and oxygen availability and whether or not toxic materials are present in the wastewater. Shortages of nutrients or oxygen, excessive organic loading rates and shock loads of toxic materials all tend to adversely affect settling characteristics as well as biological reaction rates. If biological solids are permitted to remain in the plant effluent they will result in high turbidity and suspended solids concentrations. Escaping biological solids will also exert an oxygen demand on the receiving stream, either because of their continued respiration or because they die and are used as an organic food source by other organisms.

Once removed from the effluent, biological solids require further treatment before they can be returned to the environment.

Application to practical anaerobic biological treatment systems

The active agents in anaerobic processes are many forms of anaerobic and facultative heterotrophic bacteria found naturally in soil, mud and water as well as in domestic and animal wastes. These organisms fall generally into two functional groups, which operate in sequence. Thus, the anaerobic reaction, summarised in Eq 4.3, is better represented as a two-stage reaction:

Complex organic matter	+	Facultative and anaerobic bacteria	→	Organic acids Aldehydes Alcohols Carbon dioxide Hydrogen	+	Methane-forming bacteria	→	Methane Carbon dioxide Small amounts of other gases

In the first stage — liquefaction — complex organic materials are broken down by one group of organisms to form simple, short-chain, fatty acids and similar intermediate products. These simple products are then further oxidised in the second stage — gasification — by the methane formers, which produce mainly carbon dioxide and methane.

Successful performance of anaerobic processes depends on maintaining the correct balance between the two stages of the reaction.

An important feature of the anaerobic reaction is that the ultimate hydrogen acceptor in the energy transformations of the bacterial cells is some form of inorganic chemical rather than molecular oxygen as in the case of aerobic processes. Furthermore, because of the limited oxidation achieved by anaerobic processes, the energy yield per unit mass of substrate utilised is much lower than that of aerobic processes, so that net cell growth is much lower in anaerobic processes. Growth rate is also much slower in anaerobic processes. The overall result is that much of the energy in the influent organic matter is transformed into the combustible gas, methane, rather than into unstable bacterial cells, so reducing the amount of unstable solids in the process effluent and, at the same time, producing a useful by-product.

Since the growth rate of anaerobic organisms is generally almost an order of magnitude slower than that of aerobic organisms, it is usually necessary to provide larger reactors than might be required for equivalent aerobic processes.

Most of the problems occurring in the anaerobic process are associated with the second, or methane fermentation, stage of the reaction. The methane-forming bacteria are highly sensitive to environmental factors so that process efficiency depends upon the success with which the design and operation of anaerobic systems permits uniform physical and chemical environmental conditions to be maintained.

Hydraulically, most anaerobic processes are continuous or semi-continuous systems, operated more or less as completely mixed, no re-cycle reactors. As such, the mean cell residence time, θ_c, is equal to the mean hydraulic detention time, t. This means that, unless the value of θ_c (= t) is at least equal to the reciprocal of the net growth rate of the anaerobic bacteria, these organisms will be washed out of the reactor and the process will fail. Critical minimum values of θ_c under optimum steady-state conditions are of the order of three days. Practical systems, however, operate under conditions so far from ideal that anaerobic reactors must be designed with detention periods 5 to 20 times the critical value.

The *mixing* intensity must be sufficient to approach the assumed completely-mixed flow pattern, otherwise the reactor volume must be increased accordingly. Mixing ensures effective distribution of incoming food materials and active micro-organisms throughout the whole of the reactor volume and prevents local accumulations of possibly inhibitory reaction products. It also assists in keeping the physical and chemical environment uniform throughout the reactor.

The *temperatures* at which anaerobic processes have been found to reach optimum efficiency occur in two ranges: 32 to 38°C (mesophilic) and 45° to 55°C (thermophilic). The lower of the two ranges (about 35°C) is generally considered to be the economic optimum for most anaerobic processes. Departures from the optimum temperature require adjustments to process design to allow for a reduced reaction rate.

More important than operating at the optimum temperature in practice is the maintenance of a constant temperature (within $\pm 1\,^{\circ}$C) in the reactor. This requires both efficient heating apparatus and efficient mixing.

Continuous feeding into anaerobic processes has a considerable advantage over intermittent feeding, since it promotes uniformity of reaction and helps to avoid imbalance between the two stages of the reaction.

Nutrient and trace element requirements of anaerobic processes are similar to those outlined above for aerobic processes. Since net cell yield in anaerobic processes is very low, the total requirement for nutrients per unit mass of organic matter stabilised is much lower than in the case of aerobic processes. Accordingly, nutrients and trace elements are usually greatly in excess of process requirements.

Toxic material sensitivity of anaerobic processes may generally be greater than that of aerobic processes. Some heavy metals, however, may actually be less toxic under the reducing conditions in anaerobic processes. Acclimatisation of anaerobic processes to gradual build-ups of some toxic materials is also possible. It is important to note that methane-forming bacteria are obligate anaerobes, so that oxygen is highly toxic to them.

Optimum pH for methane-forming bacteria is only 6.8 to 7.2, although the organisms are able to operate over the slightly wider range of pH 6.6 to 7.6. *Buffering* is important to prevent pH depression which could result from products of various phases of the anaerobic process such as carbon dioxide and organic acids.

11.3 Methods of aerobic biological treatment

In the foregoing discussion, it was noted that conventional methods of biological treatment can be classified as either fixed film or suspended growth processes. In recent years, a number of hybrid systems, which incorporate elements of both fixed film and suspended growth systems, have also been developed. An outline of the main processes of each of these classifications is given below. Within each classification, the processes are discussed in their approximate order of development.

Fixed film processes

Land treatment

In land treatment systems (Fig 11.2(a)), the active biological content includes many forms of soil bacteria, mainly aerobic and facultative forms, and many other higher organisms and vegetation species. Oxygen is transferred by natural processes from the atmosphere. Net growth of biomass in land treatment is usually in the form of vegetation, which must be harvested either as crops or by grazing animals or even by simply mowing the grass.

Land treatment is probably the oldest method of disposing of human and other household wastes and, in rural areas and small communities, is still the accepted method in many countries. For modern cities, with their abundant piped supplies of fresh water and consequently large discharges of wastewaters, enormous areas of land would be required for land treatment. In addition, there is always a risk of heavy stream pollution by storm runoff from land disposal areas, unless provision is made to collect and treat stormflows prior to discharge to surface water bodies. Land treatment is therefore generally considered to be impracticable for most modern cities.

In recent years, however, widespread interest in environmental and resources problems has led to a re-examination of the possibilities of land treatment of wastewaters in some countries, notably the US, especially for regions with limited water resources. Apart from the value of the water for irrigation purposes, land treatment is attractive because it offers the possibility of using the nutrient content of the wastewater, reducing the need for artificial fertilisers. Although the matter is still a subject of controversy, it seems unlikely that land treatment of raw wastewaters will again be competitive with more modern forms of wastewater treatment and disposal, except in unusual circumstances. Apart from the problems of land requirements and stream pollution mentioned above, many authorities are concerned that heavy metals and other toxic materials, which are present in wastewaters from large industrial cities, may accumulate in the soil of land disposal areas and eventually render the soil sterile. Thus, there are many problems requiring careful investigation before a decision is made to use land treatment for disposal of wastewaters in any particular location.

Because of the difficulty in measuring the active biomass in land treatment, the best available unit of loading is in terms of *application rate per unit of land area* (kg/ha.d). Design and management of land irrigation treatment systems should take into account such factors as

a Climate — rainfall, evaporation, temperature and humidity
b Soil — type, depth and texture
c Application rates — water, organic matter, plant nutrients (especially nitrogen) and total dissolved solids.

Example 11.1

A flow of 2.5 ML/d of settled sewage with 200 mg/L BOD and 40 mg/L organic and ammonia nitrogen is to be applied to a land irrigation area. If the limiting nitrogen loading is 300 kg/ha.yr, what is the area of land required, the total annual equivalent depth of effluent applied and the BOD areal loading rate?

Solution

Note that 1 mg/L = 1 g/m^3 = 1 kg/ML

Then, total daily nitrogen loading $= 2.5 \text{ ML/d} \times 40 \text{ kg/ML} = 100 \text{ kg/d}$

$$\text{Land area required} = \frac{\text{Total annual nitrogen load}}{\text{Annual application rate}}$$

$$= \frac{100 \text{ kg/d} \times 365 \text{ d/yr}}{300 \text{ kg/ha.yr}}$$

$$= 122 \text{ ha}$$

$$\text{Annual effluent application rate} = \frac{2500 \text{ m}^3/\text{d} \times 365 \text{ d/yr}}{122 \text{ ha}}$$

$$= 7480 \text{ m}^3/\text{ha.yr}$$

$$= 0.75 \text{ m/yr}$$

$$\text{Areal BOD loading rate} = \frac{(2.5 \times 200) \text{ kg/d} \times 365 \text{ d/yr}}{122 \text{ ha}}$$

$$= 1500 \text{ kg/ha.yr}$$

Trickling filter

The trickling filter (c 1900) — also called a percolating filter and bacteria bed — consists of a bed of suitable coarse porous media on which grows a biological slime consisting mainly of bacteria, and on which graze various forms of worms and larvae which help to keep the slime active (Fig 11.2(b)). Settled sewage is distributed over the surface of the medium and, as it flows down through the bed, the fine, suspended and dissolved organic matter is absorbed by the slime bacteria. Oxygen to sustain aerobic biological oxidation is provided by air which circulates through the bed. Clogging of the interstices within the filter bed as the bacteria grow is usually prevented by portions of the bacterial slime being washed out of the bed by the wastewater flow. This material, which constitutes the net increase in biomass in the system and which would otherwise contribute high BOD and SS concentrations to the effluent, is then removed in final sedimentation tanks (known as 'humus tanks') for further treatment prior to disposal.

It is difficult to obtain an adequate measure of the active mass of biological solids in a trickling filter. Although the total surface area of the medium gives some indication of the possible areas on which the biomass could grow, both the actual thickness of the biomass and the percentage of it which is active cannot be practically determined. Therefore, it is customary to take the *volume of the medium* as the most practical measure of micro-organism activity in a trickling filter and so to express *organic loading rate* in terms of the daily mass of *BOD applied per unit volume of filter medium* (kg $\text{BOD/m}^3.\text{d}$). The *hydraulic loading rate per unit surface area of filter* $(\text{m}^3/\text{m}^2.\text{d}$ or $\text{kL/m}^2.\text{d})$ is also important since it affects distribution of the flow over the surfaces of the medium, and hence the quality of contact between the applied organic matter and the active biomass.

Example 11.2

A settled sewage flow of 2.5 ML/d with 200 mg/L BOD is applied to 2 trickling filters, each 40 m diameter and 2 m deep. Calculate the organic and hydraulic loading rates.

Solution

$$\text{Organic loading rate} = \frac{\text{Total daily BOD load}}{\text{Total filter volume}}$$

$$= \frac{(2.5 \times 200) \text{ kg BOD/d}}{2 \times \pi/4(40)^2 \times 2 \text{ m}^3}$$

$$= 0.10 \text{ kg BOD/m}^3.\text{d}$$

$$\text{Hydraulic loading rate} = \frac{\text{Total daily flow}}{\text{Filter surface area}}$$

$$= \frac{(2.5 \times 10^3) \text{ m}^3/\text{d}}{2 \times \pi/4(40)^2 \text{ m}^2}$$

$$= 1.0 \text{ m}^3/\text{m}^2.\text{d} \ (= 10 \text{ ML/ha.d})$$

Rotating biological filter

The rotating biological filter (c 1960) or RBF process is a recently-developed method of biological treatment which resembles the trickling filter process in that it uses a biological film grown on solid surfaces, but these are on a large number of closely spaced discs mounted on a shaft which rotates above a shallow basin profiled to the perimeter of the discs (Fig 11.2(c)). Approximately 40 per cent of the surface of each disc is submerged in the settled sewage flowing through the trough at any time. The shaft slowly rotates, alternately exposing the biological growth on the discs to the atmosphere and submerging it in the flow. During the period of contact with the sewage, the biological film absorbs organic matter and then, during contact with the atmosphere, it absorbs oxygen, so enabling aerobic oxidation to proceed. The net growth of biomass is washed off the surfaces of the discs and must be removed in final sedimentation tanks before discharge. Organic loading, as noted earlier, in this case is measured in terms of *daily mass of BOD applied per unit surface area of discs* (g BOD/m².d).

Example 11.3

A flow of 60 000 L/d of settled sewage with 220 mg/L BOD is treated in a two-stage rotating biological filter plant, each stage comprising one shaft 4 m long and bearing 30 × 2 m diameter discs per metre. Calculate the average organic loading rate on the discs.

Solution

Total BOD load = (60 000 × 220) × 10^{-3} g/d = 13 200 g/d

Total disc area = 2 × 4 × $\pi/4(2)^2$ × 2 × 30 = 1508 m²

Therefore, organic loading rate $= \dfrac{\text{BOD load}}{\text{Disc area}}$

$$= \frac{13\ 200}{1508} = 8.75 \text{ g BOD/m}^2.\text{d}$$

Suspended growth processes

Waste stabilisation ponds

These are intermediate between land treatment and the other more controlled forms of biological treatment in terms of their requirement for land (Fig 11.2(f)).

Biological reactions occurring in waste stabilisation ponds, however, are more complex than those which occur in the other aerobic treatment processes. In the pond liquid, aerobic heterotrophic bacteria break down the organic matter. Algae then utilise these breakdown products, together with sunlight energy, to photosynthesise new algal cells, releasing oxygen which helps to sustain the aerobic breakdown process. This process, in which the activity of bacteria and algae is mutually beneficial, is called *algal-bacterial symbiosis*. In the sludge layer which develops in the bottom of the pond, anaerobic biological processes occur and contribute significantly to the treatment efficiency of most ponds.

The waste matter applied in the pond influent is thus partly stored on the floor of the pond, partly lost as biodegradation products and partly discharged as biomass, notably algae, in the effluent. Hence, in the degree of effluent quality control they can achieve, ponds are probably somewhat inferior to more complex systems, because of the variable concentration of algae escaping in the effluent.

Estimation of active biomass in stabilisation ponds is again impracticable, so that gross areal or volumetric loading rate is often used. Most ponds have much the same depth, however, and many of the important phenomena, such as solar energy entering the pond to promote algal photosynthesis and wind action for mixing pond contents, are related to pond surface area. Therefore, the most widely quoted measure of organic loading rate is the daily *mass of BOD applied per unit surface area of pond* (either kg BOD/ha.d or g BOD/m².d), although both *depth* and *detention time* are usually quoted as well. Difficulties associated with using such factors for design of ponds and some improved methods of pond design are discussed in Chapter 14.

Example 11.4

Raw sewage at a flow rate of 1.0 ML/d, with 300 mg/L BOD, is treated in a series of 4 ponds, with nominal dimensions 300 m $\times$ 100 m, 200 m $\times$ 75 m, 100 m $\times$ 75 m and 100 m $\times$ 75 m, and each 1 m deep. Calculate the mean detention time for each pond, the average areal organic loading for the pond system and the organic loading on the leading pond.

Solution
For illustrative purposes, slopes of the pond banks are neglected and the calculations are based on the nominal dimensions.
Nominal pond surface areas are

$$A_1 = 300 \times 100 = 30\ 000\ m^2,\ A_2 = 15\ 000\ m^2\ and$$
$$A_3 = A_4 = 7500\ m^2$$

and since ponds are 1 m deep, nominal volumes are

$$V_1 = 30\ 000\ m^3,\ V_2 = 15\ 000\ m^3\ and\ V_3 = V_4 = 7500\ m^3$$

Detention time in ponds, $t = V(m^3)/Q(m^3/d)$ and since $Q = 1000\ m^3/d$

$$t_1 = \frac{30\ 000}{1000} = 30\ d,\ t_2 = 15\ d\ and\ t_3 = t_4 = 7.5\ d$$

$$Average\ areal\ BOD\ loading = \frac{Total\ BOD\ load\ (kg/d)}{Total\ surface\ area\ (ha)}$$

$$= \frac{300 \times 1}{6} = 50\ kg/ha.d$$

$$= 5\ g/m^2.d$$

$$Areal\ BOD\ loading\ on\ first\ pond = \frac{300}{3} = 100\ kg/ha.d = 10\ g/m^2.d$$

Aerated lagoons
Aerated lagoons (Fig 11.2(e)) are intermediate between waste stabilisation ponds and the activated sludge process, resembling the former in their general form, their construction in earth and also in their flow sheet, since there is no solids recycle. Aerated lagoons also resemble activated sludge processes, however, in that oxygen is supplied by artificial means rather than by algal photosynthesis. The rate of mixing provided by the aeration system is much more intense in aerated lagoons than the natural mixing which occurs in oxidation ponds, so that a higher solids concentration is kept in suspension, and hence is present in the lagoon effluent. In fact, the mass of biological solids leaving in the effluent each day is equal to the day's net growth of biomass. Thus, final sedimentation of effluent is necessary to achieve a high degree of effluent quality control.

Organic loading rates for aerated lagoons may be expressed in terms of areal or volumetric loading, as in the case of waste stabilisation ponds.

Because of the greater control of the mixing intensity in aerated lagoons, however, they admit of a more mathematically adequate analysis of the equilibrium concentration of biological solids in the system for a given applied organic load. It is possible, therefore, to express loading rate as an F/M ratio, in terms of kg BOD/kg MLVSS.d.

Example 11.5

An aerated lagoon 50 m square at the water surface and 3 m deep (with banks sloped at 2 horizontal to 1 vertical) receives a wastewater flow of 2.5 ML/d with 600 mg/L BOD. Calculate the detention time, volumetric organic loading rate and F/M ratio (assuming that equilibrium volatile SS concentration in the lagoon is 400 mg/L $\equiv$ 0.4 kg/m^3).

Solution

BOD load to lagoon = 600 kg/ML $\times$ 2.5 ML/d

$$= 1500 \text{ kg/d}$$

Lagoon volume $\cong$ (Average side length)^2 $\times$ depth

$$= [50 - (2 \times 3)]^2 \times 3 = 5808 \text{ m}^3$$

Therefore, detention time $= \dfrac{V}{Q} = \dfrac{5808 \text{ m}^3}{2500 \text{ m}^3/\text{d}} = 2.32$ days

Volumetric organic loading $= \dfrac{1500 \text{ kg BOD/d}}{5808 \text{ m}^3}$

$$= 0.26 \text{ kg BOD/m}^3.\text{d}$$

F/M ratio $= \dfrac{\text{BOD loading}}{\text{Mass of Volatile SS in lagoon}}$

$$= \dfrac{1500 \text{ kg BOD/d}}{5808 \text{ m}^3 \times 0.4 \text{ kg Vol SS/m}^3}$$

$$= 0.65 \text{ kg BOD/kg Vol SS.d}$$

Activated sludge process

The activated sludge process (1914) is an aerobic, biological oxidation process in which sewage is aerated in the presence of a flocculant, mixed microbial culture known as *activated sludge*.

Essential elements in the process (Fig 11.2(d)) are the aeration tank, in which the activated sludge and incoming wastewater are thoroughly mixed (the mixture is known as *mixed liquor*) and an abundant supply of dissolved oxygen is provided, a final settling tank for separating the activated sludge from the treated effluent, a return sludge system to recycle settled activated sludge solids back to the influent to the aeration tanks, and a means for with-

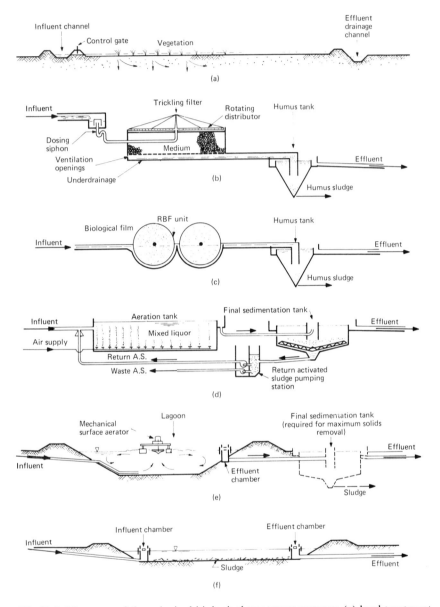

Fig 11.2 Diagrams of the principal biological treatment systems: (a) land treatment (flood irrigation), (b) trickling filter, (c) rotating biological filter, (d) activated sludge, (e) aerated lagoon, (d) waste stabilisation (oxidation) pond

drawing each day's net growth of biological solids from the system. The unique feature of activated sludge processes, compared with the other processes discussed above, lies in the fact that there is separate and positive control of the retention time of activated sludge solids and the liquid effluent. Hence, it is amenable to much closer control than are other processes.

The organic loading rate in the activated sludge process is given by the F/M ratio, as defined in Section 11.3 above — kg BOD/kg MLVSS.d.

Many modifications of the basic activated sludge process have been developed since it was introduced. Some of these are simple variations aimed at improving the load capacity of the process, others are aimed at varying the quality of effluent produced, while still others are aimed at simplifying operation and maintenance. Some modifications employ flow patterns which differ markedly from those of the basic activated sludge process.

Example 11.6

Settled sewage at a flow rate of 2.5 ML/d and 200 mg/L BOD is treated in an activated sludge plant which is equipped with two aeration tanks each 25 m long × 5 m wide × 4 m deep, and with a mixed liquor volatile SS (MLVSS) concentration of 2000 mg/L. Calculate the detention time, the volumetric organic loading rate and the F/M ratio.

Solution

$$\text{Detention time, } t = \frac{V}{Q} = \frac{2 \times 25 \times 5 \times 4}{2500} = 0.4 \text{ days}$$

$$= 9.6 \text{ hours}$$

$$\text{Volumetric organic loading} = \frac{\text{Mass BOD load/day}}{\text{Aeration tank volume}}$$

$$= \frac{2.5 \text{ ML/d} \times 200 \text{ kg BOD/ML}}{1000 \text{ m}^3}$$

$$= 0.5 \text{ kg BOD/m}^3.\text{d}$$

$$\text{F/M ratio} = \frac{\text{Mass BOD load/day}}{\text{Mass MLVSS in aeration tanks}}$$

$$= \frac{500 \text{ kg BOD/day}}{1000 \text{ m}^3 \times (2000/1000) \text{ kg/m}^3}$$

$$= 0.25 \text{ kg BOD/kg MLVSS.d}$$

Recent developments — hybrid systems

A number of systems which involve elements of both fixed film and suspended growth processes have recently been developed. Two systems which have been applied to full-scale waste treatment and show promise of being of wider application are discussed below.

Activated biofiltration process

The process (Fig 11.3(a)) consists of a tower of carefully-spaced timber slats which act as support media for a biological film, and a wet well which contains a suspended biological growth. Settled sewage enters the wet well and the mixture of sewage and biological solids is pumped to the top of the tower where it is distributed over the surfaces of the timber media. As the wastewater trickles from layer to layer of slats in the tower, organic matter is removed by both the fixed film and the suspended biological solids. Because of its open construction, air circulation through the tower is very efficient and oxygen transfer is facilitated by the splashing which occurs as the wastewater flows from one layer of slats to the next. Thus, the tower acts not only as a biological reactor but also as an aeration tower and the aeration rate can be adjusted by varying the pumping rate from the wet well. The normal pumping rate is about ten times the settled sewage flow rate. The equivalent of the net sewage inflow to the wet well is displaced as mixed liquor over the effluent weirs. From here, it may flow directly to the final sedimentation tank where the biological solids are settled for return to the wet well, while the effluent is removed for discharge — or further treatment if necessary. Where a higher quality effluent or nitrification is required, an additional short-term aeration tank may be provided between the wet well and the final sedimentation tank.

The activated biofiltration system offers the benefits of a fixed film process in its ability to handle shock loads, while offering some of the advantages of suspended growth systems in terms of process control, with considerable reduction in the area required.

Because of the introduction of the fixed film tower, however, it is difficult to obtain a simple measure of total biological solids in the system. It is therefore not possible to define the loading rate in terms of F/M ratio, or to estimate mean cell residence time, for direct comparison with other systems. Instead, loadings have to be expressed separately, in terms of BOD loading per unit volume of medium for the tower (kg BOD/m³.d), and in terms of F = kg BOD/kg MLVSS.d for the aeration basin, after allowing for the BOD removed by the tower.

Fluidised bed process

A fluidised bed system (Fig 11.3(b)) consists of a bed of relatively fine medium, such as sand or crushed clinker, on the surfaces of which an active biological film is developed (analogous to the trickling filter). Wastewater flows upwards through the bed at a rate sufficient to expand and fluidise the medium, and hence the process also resembles a suspended growth process such as activated sludge.

The behaviour of the fluidised medium is similar to that in a granular medium filter during backwash. Provided the upflow rate is carefully controlled, the medium will expand only enough to attain a hindered settling

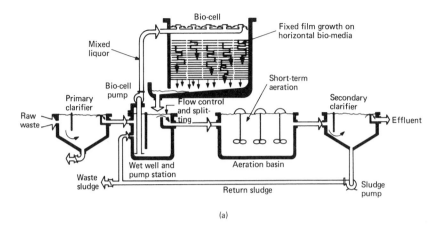

(a)

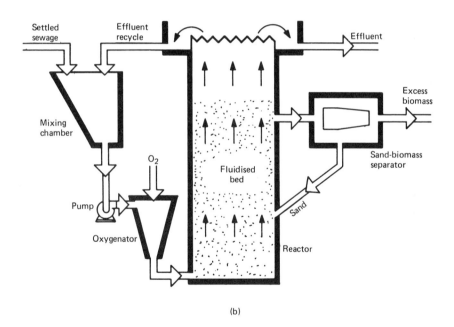

(b)

Fig 11.3 Hybrid aerobic biological treatment systems: (a) activated biofiltration process (*Courtesy: Neptune Microfloc*), (b) fluidised bed process (*Courtesy: Dorr-Oliver*)

velocity equal to the upflow velocity of the wastewater.

The biomass concentration in fluidised beds used for carbonaceous oxidation has been found to be about 14 000 mg/L (as volatile solids). Thus, it is possible to maintain a very much higher solids concentration than is usually possible in activated sludge processes. To supply sufficient oxygen to ensure aerobic conditions, pure oxygen is dissolved under pressure in the incoming wastewater to give a DO concentration of 40 to 100 mg/L. Because of the high microbial mass retained in the system, and the ready supply of oxygen, the reaction rate in fluidised bed systems is very fast. Treatment to full secondary standard, about 20 mg/L BOD and 30 mg/L SS, has been achieved in less than 15 minutes. Excess biomass can be removed from the system by daily removal of some of the medium from the bed, separation of the biomass from the medium surfaces and the return of the clean medium to the bed. If this system is used, it effectively takes the place of a secondary clarifier. Because the biomass can be reasonably well sampled, it is possible to estimate the total mass of the biological solids in the fluidised bed system, to give values equivalent to MLSS and MLVSS in activated sludge processes. Therefore, loading rate can similarly be defined in terms of F/M ratio. It is also possible to calculate the mean cell residence time.

It has been claimed that fluidised bed systems offer the best features of both fixed film and suspended growth processes, but require only 5 per cent of the land area to produce the same degree of treatment.

Fluidised bed systems have also been developed for carrying out biological nitrification. Additionally, they may be used for denitrification (the reduction of nitrate to nitrogen gas) under anaerobic conditions.

11.4 Methods of anaerobic biological treatment

Anaerobic processes in wastewater treatment are used mainly for treating the organic sludges removed from the wastewater in primary sedimentation and in final sedimentation following aerobic biological treatment. Simple forms of anaerobic treatment, such as anaerobic ponds and septic tanks, however, are used for treating wastewater (rather than sludge) although, even in these cases, the most intense anaerobic action takes place in the layer of concentrated sludge which settles to the bottom. Although the poor level of mixing, especially in the simpler processes, makes classification a little difficult, most conventional anaerobic processes are essentially *suspended growth systems*.

Among the more recent developments in anaerobic treatment methods are *fixed film processes* such as the anaerobic filter.

Suspended growth processes

Anaerobic ponds
Anaerobic ponds (Fig 11.4(a)) are heavily-loaded open ponds, usually 2 to 4 m deep, used as pretreatment ponds in municipal wastewater treatment or in industrial waste treatment. In either case they serve to reduce the organic load

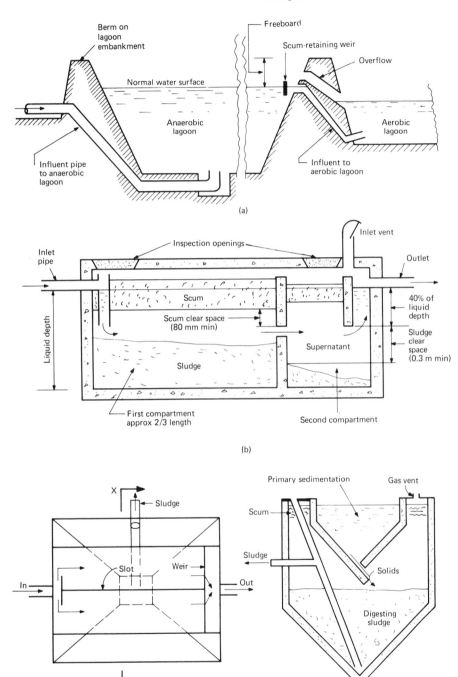

Fig 11.4 Simple anaerobic treatment systems: (a) anaerobic-aerobic lagoon system, (b) septic tank, (c) Imhoff tank

applied to a series of facultative or aerobic ponds which are invariably required to further treat the wastewater prior to its discharge into the environment. Odour problems are common with this type of pond, especially during start-up, and in systems having seasonally variable loading patterns. Thus, they should be located well away and down-wind from developed areas.

Septic tanks

These are single-storey tanks used for treating wastewaters from single households or institutions in areas where piped sewerage is not available. They operate essentially as combined sedimentation and anaerobic digestion tanks. A well-designed tank should provide a chamber in which reasonably quiescent settling is allowed to occur. Solids settle to the bottom of the chamber, forming a sludge layer, while fats and floatables rise to the surface to form a scum layer, which helps to prevent access of oxygen through the liquid surface and also helps to control escape of odours. These three zones (see Fig 11.4(b)) are characteristic of well-operating septic tanks.

Anaerobic digestion takes place mainly in the sludge layer, although some liquefaction of the scum layer also occurs. The rate of digestion is very slow at the low temperatures which prevail during winter in cooler climates. Sufficient volume must therefore be available to store solids during the period when digestion is poor. In any case, inert and slowly-degradable material accumulates and, unless removed, eventually reduces the liquid volume between sludge and scum layers to the extent that no treatment may occur.

In common with effluents from other anaerobic processes, septic tank effluent requires further treatment before it is suitable for discharge to surface waters. Sub-surface disposal through absorption trenches is therefore the most commonly adopted method for on-site disposal.

Imhoff tanks

Imhoff tanks are two-storey tanks (Fig 11.4(c)) which represent an advance on the septic tank in that, although they perform the same functions of sedimentation and anaerobic digestion of sludge, these are done in separate compartments. The incoming wastewater flows through the upper compartment, allowing solids to settle to the bottom of the chamber, which is in the shape of a hopper. At the bottom of the hopper, the solids pass through a baffled outlet into the lower chamber in which anaerobic digestion takes place.

The lower chamber incorporates capacity to store solids during periods of poor digestion or between desludging operations. Gas vents are provided in the top of the outer chamber, while the baffles at the bottom of the settling chamber prevent gases from entering the settling chamber itself. The digestion chamber is also provided with collection hoppers and sludge withdrawal pipes for periodic removal of digested sludge for disposal.

Imhoff tanks, because of the cost of constructing the very deep tanks required, are generally considered economical only for relatively small communities, where their operating simplicity offers some advantages over separate sedimentation and digestion tanks.

Cold digestion

Cold digestion is the simplest type of digestion used for stabilising organic sludges produced in conventional primary and secondary treatment. It is operated without temperature control and hence is only suitable for warm climates where the ground temperature remains well above freezing point throughout the year.

Cold digesters are characterised by stratification into four distinct layers (Fig 11.5(a)):

a Scum zone, where floating materials tend to accumulate
b Supernatant liquor zone, where water released from the digesting solids accumulates
c Active digestion zone, where the anaerobic degradation process takes place
d Digested sludge zone, where stabilised solids settle for removal.

Since the zone of active digestion occupies less than half the volume of cold digesters, and the operating temperature is far from the optimum, permissible loading rates are very low.

Many small trickling filter plants are equipped with cold digesters, usually arranged in pairs and operated in series. In small digesters of this type, the methane gas produced is usually vented to the atmosphere.

Two-stage digestion systems

These have two digestion tanks in series (Fig 11.5(b)). To increase process efficiency, the sludge in the leading, or primary, digester is heated to control temperature, and mixed to ensure effective distribution of the feed sludge and active organisms through the whole of the digester volume. The secondary digester is not heated or mixed, and is used mainly to allow separation of digested sludge and supernatant liquor. Digested sludge is drawn from the secondary digester for dewatering and disposal, while the supernatant, which has a very high BOD, is returned to the aerobic biological phase of the plant for further treatment.

Because conditions in two-stage digesters are far better controlled and nearer the optimum, much higher loading rates are possible than is the case with cold digesters. In some cases, methane is collected and used as a fuel to assist in heating the sludge in the primary digester.

High-rate digestion This operates at a much higher loading rate than conventional two-stage digestion, and hence it requires very close control if it is

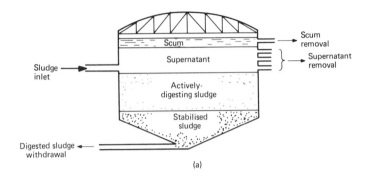

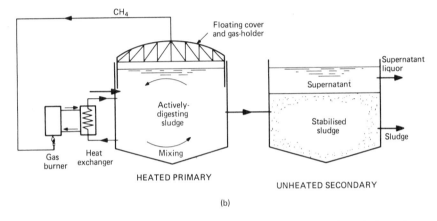

Fig 11.5 Conventional anaerobic digestion systems: (a) cold digestion, (b) heated two-stage digestion

to perform efficiently. Conditions for optimum high-rate digestion are

a Optimum temperature control
b Efficient mixing
c Thickening of feed sludge (especially if treating excess activated sludges) to increase solids concentration
d Continuous feeding of raw sludges.

Recirculation of some of the digested sludge solids is sometimes provided.

The *anaerobic contact process* is a further development of the high-rate digestion process which provides for separation and recycling of digested sludge solids. It is thus analogous to the activated sludge process and allows separate control of the hydraulic detention time, t, and the mean cell residence time, θ_c. Because the digested sludge produces gas, some form of degassing system should be provided upstream of the solids separation (settling) tank, otherwise settling efficiency is impaired. The main application of this type of process is in the treatment of strong industrial wastes.

Fixed film processes

The *anaerobic filter* is a recently-developed process, which comprises a bed of 35 to 50 mm stones through which wastewater is passed upwards. Hence the filter is kept submerged and a film of anaerobic bacteria builds up on the surfaces of the filter stones. Because of the low cell yield of the anaerobic process, bacteria are retained in the bed for a very long time before being scoured from the filter. Hence, it is possible to maintain a long mean cell residence time (of the order of 100 days) at a mean hydraulic detention time of only a few hours. The anaerobic filter is reported to achieve effective treatment of both dilute and concentrated wastes, even at normal temperatures.

Review questions

11.1 What is the main objective in using biological processes to improve the quality of wastewaters? What alternatives are availabe for removal of dissolved and fine suspended organic material?

11.2 Explain the concept of food-to-micro-organism ratio, and its importance in biological treatment of wastes.

11.3 Discuss the relative advantages and disadvantages of fixed film and suspended growth processes in biological treatment of wastewaters.

11.4 In what circumstances is preference given to anaerobic processes for waste treatment?

12 Sludge Treatment and Disposal

12.1 Introduction

The main objective of water treatment is to produce a safe drinking water supply, while in wastewater treatment it is to reduce the pollutional load on a receiving water. A necessary implication of the treatment process is that the solid materials present in the raw water and raw wastewater must accumulate in a sludge. The treatment and disposal of this sludge should be considered as an integral part of the treatment process and not as an 'add-on' unit of little importance. The treatment processes should be regarded therefore as concentration or separation processes which produce a low-solids stream (effluent or potable water) and a high-solids stream (sludge).

The cost of treating the sludges, particularly for wastewaters, is a major component of the total cost of treatment, and the effects of the final disposal methods and return flows from sludge treatment can have significant implications for the preceding processes.

It is convenient to discuss the treatment and disposal of water and wastewater sludges in separate sections. The nature and mass of solids in these two types of sludge are different.

12.2 Characterisation, treatment and disposal of sludges from water treatment

Water treatment produces sludges from the processes of coagulation, settlement, clarification and filtration. Raw water supplies are usually chosen to contain very low solids concentrations and therefore, even after the addition of coagulants, the total amount of solids involved in water treatment is relatively small. As a first approximation, it can be assumed that each $1.0 \, m^3$ of raw water will produce $1 \times 10^{-3} \, m^3$ of dry sludge solids from conventional treatment processes. The sludge will contain coagulant (probably aluminium hydroxide) and it will de-water relatively easily. Sludges from water treatment will contain a low percentage of organic material. The sludge does not present significant hygiene, odour or rodent infestation problems.

The processes for treatment and disposal of these sludges are summarised in Table 12.1.

Table 12.1 Treatment and disposal of water treatment sludges

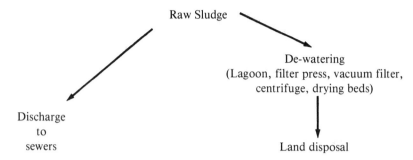

The simplest and often the most convenient method of sludge disposal for small to medium-sized water treatment works is discharge to the sewers. Provided that the sewers have sufficient capacity, such a procedure transfers the problem from the water treatment plant to the wastewater treatment plant. The presence of the additional load at the wastewater treatment plant is usually insignificant; in fact, the presence of the coagulant improves settlement in the primary tank. If discharge to the sewers is not feasible, on-site treatment is required. Impoundment in a lagoon — or preferably a series of lagoons — produces a consolidated sludge. Any supernatant liquid can be returned to the treatment plant to be blended with the raw supply. Alum (or iron) sludges can be reclaimed by treatment with sulphuric acid to reform aluminium sulphate. The method is applicable only in plants which use high coagulant doses and produce sludges from which the impurities can be removed.

Several other types of residue are produced during water treatment; these can include screenings, spent activated carbon, brines from the regeneration of ion exchange resins, and the sludges which result from iron and manganese removal, softening, presedimentation of raw waters, filter backwashing and from the use of coagulant aids. The sludges from lime-soda water-softening processes are likely to be the most voluminous of these residues. Water-softening sludges will contain mixtures of calcium carbonate, magnesium hydroxide and lime, and may contain coagulants. The sludges are stable with a low organic content; they can be treated and disposed of as for alum sludges, or can be reclaimed. The reclamation of lime sludges is carried out by dewatering and drying the sludges then incinerating the residue. Incineration at approximately 1200°C converts calcium carbonate to calcium oxide (quick lime), and converts magnesium hydroxide to magnesium oxide. The product can be reused as lime; however, an accumulation of magnesium will occur which reduces the effectiveness of the reused lime as a softening agent. Reclamation is most appropriate for low magnesium concentration sludges. Alternatively, additional separation stages are required to minimise the magnesium content in the recycled lime.

Mechanical dewatering and thickening equipment can be employed to reduce the volume of water treatment sludges. The machines used — for example, presses, centrifuges and filters — are similar to those discussed in the section on wastewater sludges.

12.3 Characteristics of wastewater sludges

The main objective of all forms of wastewater treatment is the production of an effluent suitable either for disposal into the environment, or for some form of re-use. This means that the impurities present in the wastewater must either be transformed into innocuous end-products or be effectively separated from the effluent stream. Impurities which are removed are either drawn off as side-streams to the main flow or converted into gaseous products. Treatment and disposal of side-streams is an essential part of the overall treatment process, and frequently they contribute significantly to the total cost of treatment.

In conventional wastewater treatment works, the main sidestream products, apart from screenings and grit, are the various forms of sludge, comprising the underflow from sedimentation tanks which effect separation of the greater proportion of the removed impurities. Treatment and disposal of these sludges is dependent on the volume and characteristics of the sludges produced, which in turn are related to the type of treatment giving rise to the sludge.

The simplest classification of wastewater sludges is based on the process from which they are produced.

Raw or primary sludge This is drawn from the primary sedimentation tanks. It contains all the readily settleable matter from the wastewater; it has a high organic content — mainly faecal matter and food scraps — and is thus highly putrescible. In its fresh state, raw sludge is grey in colour with a heavy faecal odour. Both colour and odour intensify on prolonged storage under anoxic conditions, leading rapidly to onset of putrefaction and extremely unpleasant odours. This is often evident in small works when sludge is drawn from the sedimentation tanks into open pits for transfer to the digestion tanks.

Humus sludge This comprises the underflow from the humus tanks which follow trickling filters. It consists of biological solids sloughed or scoured from the surface of the filter media and thus represents the net growth of biomass in the filters. Sloughing rate varies through the year, but is usually most intense during spring. Again, being largely organic in content, humus sludges exhibit problems similar to those of primary sludges under anoxic or anaerobic conditions.

Excess activated sludge This is usually drawn off the return sludge system from the underflow of the final sedimentation tanks in the activated sludge process. It consists of light flocculent biological solids with a significant demand for oxygen, largely owing to the respiration of the sludge micro-organisms. The mass of excess sludge produced each day represents the net growth in biomass and is related to the loading rate of the process. Activated sludges typically have a much higher moisture content than other organic wastewater sludges and they present greater de-watering problems.

Chemical sludge This is produced by processes involving chemical coagulation or chemical precipitation. In conventional wastewater treatment such processes are seldom used, but they appear to offer the most economical means of removing phosphorus in wastewaters and effluents and for the treatment of intermittent flows such as storm sewage overflows. Such sludges comprise mainly the reaction products of the added chemical and the impurity to be removed. Where chemicals are applied to raw sewage, the sludge produced is a mixture of chemical sludge and organic raw sludge. If the chemical is dosed following full secondary treatment, there will be relatively little organic contamination of the sludge.

Digested sludge This is the product of either aerobic or anaerobic digestion and is a well-stabilised material capable of being de-watered on open drying beds without severe odour problems. Well-stabilised, anaerobically-digested sludge has a black appearance with a tarry odour; it is non-putrescible and is no longer attractive to flies and other insects.

Characterisation of wastewater sludges

Rational selection of unit processes for sludge treatment and disposal requires definition of both the volume and the characteristics of the sludge to be treated. The operations involved may be categorised under the general headings of conditioning, thickening, stabilisation and de-watering with associated processes of storage, transport and ultimate disposal.

The following discussion is concerned with the definition of the parameters used in measuring sludge characteristics, and some typical ranges of values encountered in practice are presented.

Composition of sludges

The overall effect of municipal wastewater treatment is to concentrate the solids, which comprise less than 0.05 per cent of the mass of the raw wastewater, into sludges having gross solids contents generally in the range 1 to 10 per cent.

Total solids residue (TSR) is the usual method of measuring the gross solids content. It is determined by evaporating to constant weight a measured amount of sludge, weighing the residue and expressing this as a percentage of the original wet sludge weight.

Sludge moisture content (P_M), equal to $(100 - TSR)$ per cent, is an alternative parameter, commonly quoted as a measure of gross sludge composition.

Volatile solids content (VS), measured as the weight loss on ignition of the dried sludge solids from the TSR test at a standard temperature (usually $600°C$), is a measure of the organic content of the sludge. It is thus related to the possible reduction in the sludge mass by incineration processes and it gives an indication of the degree of stabilisation which could be achieved by biological processes. Volatile solids content is usually quoted as a percentage of the total solids residue.

Solids content remaining after ignition (ash) is termed the *fixed residue* (FR) and defines the weight of inorganic matter in the sludge and thus the minimum weight of solids which would remain for ultimate disposal after incineration.

More detailed chemical analyses of the solids component may be required where disposal methods such as composting and land application are contemplated. Such analyses may involve determination of nutrients such as *carbon, nitrogen, phosphorus* and *potassium*. In some cases it may be

Table 12.2 Typical composition of sludge solids

Nutrient	Primary			Anaerobically-digested sludge		
Carbon solids (volatile)	40.0	(65.0)	80.0	30.0	(40.0)	60.0
Nitrogen	1.5	(2.5)	4.0	1.6	(3.0)	6.0
Phosphorus	0.8	(1.6)	2.8	1.5	(2.5)	4.0
Potassium	0.0	(0.4)	1.0	0.0	(3.0)	4.0

Note: Figures quoted are percentages by weight of total solids residue. Bracketed numbers represent typical values in normal ranges

necessary to check the amounts and types of *heavy metals* present. Some typical results quoted for the content of plant nutrients are given in Table 12.2. It should be stressed that the values are only representative, and all sludges reflect the wastewater treatment processes and practices at particular plants.

The most important characteristics of sludges are the organic content and the moisture content. A high organic content in an unstabilised sludge indicates that the sludge will continue to degrade and is therefore likely to present health, odour and rodent problems. The ability of sludges to retain moisture and the implications of this for sludge treatment are discussed in the next section. Table 12.3 summarises the moisture and organic content of several sludges. The figures are typical; the values for a particular sludge may be outside the ranges quoted.

Table 12.3 Moisture and organic content of sludges

Sludge type	Range of moisture content (% by weight)	Organic content (% dry weight)
Primary sludge	93 – 97	40 – 80
Activated sludge	98 – 99.5	65 – 75
Digested sludge	96 – 99	30 – 60
Humus sludge	94 – 99	65 – 75
High rate plastic media sludge	92 – 97	65 – 75

12.4 Volume of sludge

Since sludges commonly contain only between 1 and 10 per cent solids by weight, their major component is water. Furthermore, since sludge solids are of similar density to water, the water content accounts for most of the volume of wet sludges. Sludge moisture content is therefore the single parameter which has the greatest effect on the volume of sludge to be processed at a given plant. It is therefore useful to examine sludge moisture-weight-volume relationships.

For the sludge which contains 1 per cent dry solids (moisture content, P_M = 99 per cent) 1 g of dry solids is associated with 99 g of water, or 10 kg of dry solids is associated with 990 kg of water. The average density of wastewater sludge solids is 1400 kg/m^3 and the density of water is 1000 kg/m^3. Therefore $10/1.4 = 7$ L of dry solids are associated with 990 L of water; or, for 10 kg of dry solids in a 1 per cent solids content sludge, the total volume occupied is 997 L. Similarly, for a 2 per cent solids content sludge, the volume occupied, with 20 kg of dry solids, is 994 L. In both cases the amount of dry solids has only a small influence upon the total volume of the sludge. If the total volume is assumed to be 1000 L (or one cubic metre), the error is less than 1 per cent.

For any sludge, the volume, $\forall$, is given by

$$\forall = \frac{\text{Mass}}{\text{Density}} \qquad (12.1)$$

If the sludge has a dry solids content less than 20 per cent (that is $P_M > 80$ per cent), then

Density of wet sludge $\simeq$ Density of water

$$= 1000 \text{ kg/m}^3$$

Sludge volume, $\forall$ (m³)

$$= \frac{\text{Total mass of wet sludge}}{\text{Mass of dry solids}} \times \frac{\text{Mass of dry solids}}{1000}$$

$$= \frac{100}{100 - P_M} \times \frac{\text{Mass of dry solids (kg)}}{1000} \qquad (12.2)$$

For example, for a sludge of 2 per cent solids content, 10 kg of dry solids would have a sludge volume given by

$$\forall = \frac{100}{100 - 98} \times \frac{10}{1000} \qquad (12.2)$$

$$= 0.5 \text{ m}^3$$

If a sludge is concentrated so that the mass of dry solids, S_s, remains constant, but the moisture content is decreased from P_{M_1} to P_{M_2}, the ratio between the initial volume, $\forall_1$, and the final volume, $\forall_2$, is given by

$$\frac{\forall_1}{\forall_2} = \frac{100}{100 - P_{M_1}} \times \frac{S_s}{1000} \times \frac{100 - P_{M_2}}{100} \times \frac{1000}{S_s}$$

$$= \frac{100 - P_{M_2}}{100 - P_{M_1}} \qquad (12.3)$$

Thus, removing water from a sludge of low solids content affords a dramatic reduction in volume. Doubling the solids content from 1 to 2 per cent halves the volume of wet sludge. In Table 12.4 the density of dry solids has been assumed to be 1400 kg/m³ for sludges of greater than 10 per cent solids content and the liquid is assumed to be water (density 1000 kg/m³).

12.5 Tests for de-watering of sludges

Wherever sludges have to be disposed of in restricted land areas or transported over long distances for ultimate disposal, some form of volume reduction is usually necessary. From the above discussion, it is apparent that sludge de-watering is an effective method of volume reduction in such cases. It is also an essential pretreatment where incineration is required. De-watering processes in common use, such as pressure filters, vacuum filters

Table 12.4 Weight and volume of sludges

Sludge solids content %	kg sludge per kg dry solids	m³ sludge per tonne dry solids
1	100	100
2	50	50
5	20	20
10	10	9.7
15	6.7	6.4
20	5.0	4.7
30	3.3	3.0
40	2.5	2.2

and centrifuges, require for their design some measure of the sludge de-watering characteristics. Two alternative methods are used to measure the ease of de-watering — specific resistance and capillary suction time.

Specific resistance to filtration, r, is the most commonly-used measure of sludge de-watering characteristics. It is determined by means of a laboratory apparatus for filtering a sample of sludge under an applied vacuum (Fig 12.1). During the test, the volume, V, of filtrate is noted at regular time intervals. These data are then plotted in the form t/V against V. The slope of the straight line of best fit to the data is then used to calculate the value of specific resistance to filtration, as described in the following development.

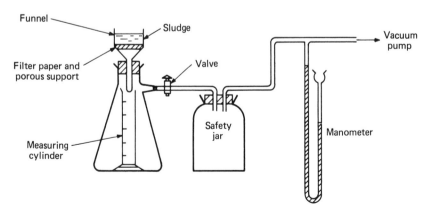

Fig 12.1 Apparatus for the determination of specific resistance to filtration

Sludge filtration rate has been described by the following relationship

$$\frac{d\Psi}{dt} = \frac{PA^2}{\mu(rC\Psi + R_M A)} \qquad (12.4)$$

where Ψ is the volume of filtrate (m³); t is time (s); P is the vacuum (Pa); A is the filtration area (m²); μ is the filtrate viscosity (Pa.s); r is the specific resistance to filtration (m/kg); C is the suspended solids concentration (kg/m³); and R_M is the initial resistance of filter medium.

Integration of Eq 12.4 and rearrangement gives

$$\frac{t}{\Psi} = \frac{\mu rC}{2PA^2}\Psi + \frac{\mu R_M}{PA} \qquad (12.5)$$

Hence, from a plot t/Ψ against Ψ, the slope, b, of the line of best fit is given by

$$b = \frac{\mu rC}{2PA^2} \qquad (12.6)$$

and hence

$$r = \frac{2PA^2b}{\mu C} \qquad (12.7)$$

which can be calculated from the measured applied vacuum (49 kPa is recommended), the filter area, filtrate viscosity and the suspended solids concentration of the sludge. The value of $\bar{r}$ obtained by using sludge suspended solids is sometimes referred to as the apparent specific resistance, r, rather than true specific resistance calculated from the suspended solids in the filter cake.

Typical values of specific resistance are given in Table 12.5. A sludge of high specific resistance is more difficult to de-water than one of low specific resistance. Sludges with a specific resistance of $> 10^{14}$ m/kg are difficult to de-water. Conventional de-watering by methods such as filter pressing is feasible for $r \sim 2 \times 10^{12}$ m/kg. It should be noted, however, that the value of

Table 12.5 Typical specific resistance of wastewater sludges

Sludge type	Specific resistance m/kg
Primary sludge	$1 - 3 \times 10^{14}$
Coagulated primary sludge	$3 - 10 \times 10^{11}$
Activated sludge	$4 - 12 \times 10^{13}$
Digested sludge	$3 - 30 \times 10^{13}$
Coagulated digested sludge	$2 - 20 \times 10^{11}$

r depends so closely on the nature of the sludge solids and the mechanism by which water is retained within the solids matrix that, for designing de-watering facilities, it is necessary to determine the value of r for the particular sludge concerned.

Capillary suction time (cst)

Sludge filterability can be determined by timing the movement of water from a sludge sample longitudinally through filter paper. The apparatus is shown schematically in Fig 12.2. Sludge is placed in the sludge well and the water moves radially outwards from the sludge. The rate of advance of the solvent front is timed manually or electronically as it moves between two pre-set points on the filter paper. This method provides a simple technique for estimating de-waterability and, on a comparative basis, can be very useful. The method relies upon the varying pressure applied by the movement of water through filter paper, so that a theoretically complete mathematical treatment of cst is not possible.

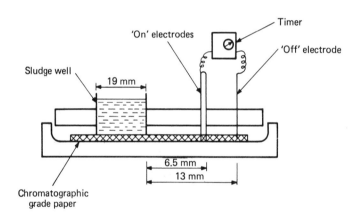

Fig 12.2 Apparatus for the determination of capillary suction time

Table 12.6 gives some typical results of cst measurements for a range of sludges. The cst values usually correlate well with r determinations. However, it is best if such correlation is confirmed experimentally. The cst values do not allow for the solids content and therefore it is necessary to specify the solids content of the sludge. It is possible for a sludge with a low cst value and a high solids content to be easily de-watered.

Table 12.6 Capillary suction times for wastewater sludges

Sludge type		Capillary suction time cst (s)	
		Range	*Average*
Primary sludge	(1% solids)	9 – 100	70
	(3% solids)	9 – 300	200
	(5% solids)	10 – 500	300
	(7% solids)	10 – 700	400
Activated sludge	(2% solids)	20 – 3000	400
Digested sludge	(3% solids)	10 – 1000	150

12.6 Objectives and methods in sludge treatment and disposal

Objectives

The main objectives of sludge treatment are

a Stabilisation of the organic matter contained in the sludge
b Reduction in the volume of sludge for disposal by removing some of the water
c Destruction of pathogenic organisms
d Collection of by-products which may be used or sold to off-set some of the costs of sludge treatment. Unfortunately, this is an ideal rarely achieved in practice except in the case of methane gas, which is produced in anaerobic digestion. The methane is often collected and used as a fuel to provide heat for controlling the temperature of the digesting sludge and, occasionally, for driving dual fuel engines which may be used to generate power for the treatment plant. The production of a compost and the use of sludges for agricultural purposes can be viewed as a use
e Disposal of the sludge in a safe and aesthetically acceptable manner.

Methods

Sludge treatment and disposal at any particular location may comprise any or all of the following steps:

a Concentration — reduction in the volume of sludge to be treated by encouraging the sludge to compact to a higher solids content
b Treatment — to stabilise organic matter, destroy pathogens and/or yield by-products
c De-watering and drying — removal of water, thus reducing sludge volume. Sludges with less than 80 per cent moisture content are usually spadeable
d Disposal — the only places where sludge can be disposed of are into the air, onto land or into water. Whether or not the impact on the receiving

environment is legally, aesthetically and ecologically acceptable depends on both the degree of treatment provided and the method of dispersing the sludge into the environment.

In comparing the various alternative methods of sludge treatment and disposal, it is important to consider all steps necessary for the *final* disposal of the treated sludge.

A scheme which includes the majority of available processes is given in Table 12.7. Not all these methods or types of method would be practised at any one site and not all of the methods are necessarily compatible. For each site, the range of options requires consideration.

Table 12.7 Treatment and disposal options for wastewater sludges

Thickening	Stabilisation	De-watering	Partial disposal	Ultimate disposal
Gravity	Anaerobic digestion	Drying beds	Incineration	Sanitary landfill
Flotation	Aerobic digestion	Filter press	Pyrolysis	Crop land
Centrifuge	Lagooning	Centrifuge	Wet air oxidation	Ocean
Elutriation	Heat treatment	Vacuum filter Belt press Lagooning	Composting	

The most commonly-used method of sludge stabilisation is anaerobic digestion. Digested sludges are suitable for direct disposal or they can be further treated and handled without odour or hygiene problems. The principles of anaerobic digestion are set out in Chapter 11 and should be incorporated within a sludge treatment scheme. The sludge produced is amenable to de-watering; it has a reduced and stabilised organic content (Table 12.2) and it is hygienic; but it still requires disposal.

Digested sludges are often further treated and de-watered in drying beds or in lagoons. Mechanical de-watering further reduces sludge volumes and is a necessity for incineration. Ultimate disposal of any residue or sludge is to land or sea. If non-digested sludges are being handled, particular attention has to be paid to odour, insects and rodent infestation and hygiene. Subsequent sections deal in greater detail with particular processes.

12.7 Treatment processes

The most common treatment process is anaerobic digestion (see Chapters 11)

and 14) and the digested sludge can be further treated in a lagoon. Aerobic digestion is employed particularly at small treatment plants.

Lagoons

This process includes a mixture of cold digestion, air drying and gravity thickening. Sludge lagoons are usually designed on a simple 'volume per capita' basis (0.2 to 0.5 m³/person) for an expected service of 7 to 15 years before desludging is required. A water depth of 3 to 5 m is provided, and free-board of at least a metre is required.

Internal side-slopes should be 3:1 and the sides should be lined with impervious material above, and to about 1 m below, top water level in the lagoon. Inlet arrangements should ensure even distribution of the digested sludge flow over the whole area of the lagoon floor. An outlet weir should be provided to draw off the displaced water, which should then be returned to the treatment plant inlet. It is usual to construct two lagoons; one is filled first and can be emptied while the next is filling. The lagoons should not pollute ground waters and, therefore, they require lining in some locations.

The sludges removed from a lagoon vary in solids content. Depending on the influent sludge, the lower compacted layers can be of 20 per cent solids content, while surface layers contain only a few per cent of solids. The sludges removed from the lagoon require final disposal.

Aerobic digestion

Sludges can be stabilised by an aerobic process. They are maintained in an aerobic condition by external aeration, through which organic material is oxidised. This process is widely used for sludges from small extended aeration activated sludge plants. An aerobic digester has modest construction requirements when compared with an anaerobic digester, for it does not require gas collection. The supernatant is well oxidised, so that any return flows do not impose heavy loads on the rest of the treatment plant. The loss of methane when compared with anaerobic digestion is not always significant when the capital investment and running costs for using the methane are taken into account.

Other treatment methods

Several other treatment methods have been proposed, or are used in restricted circumstances. These include freezing and thawing the sludge, which improves de-watering. A low-pressure coolant such as butane can be employed, but it tends to dissolve greases and oils from the sludge, reducing the useful life of the butane. (Waterworks sludges may be a more appropriate application for this method.) The fragile nature of the frozen and thawed sludge particles, together with the cost, has prevented widespread use of the technique. Where freezing and thawing can be provided naturally, such as by storage through several very cold winters, the method is effective.

Heat treatment processes and composting can be considered as treatment processes, but are dealt with as partial disposal methods. Other processes, such as ultrasonics, have only restricted use owing to cost or operational problems.

12.8 Thickening and de-watering methods

The difference between a thickening and a de-watering method is arbitrary. Thickening can be considered to produce a sludge of less than 10 per cent solids content and tends to precede a sludge treatment process. De-watering produces a sludge of greater than 10 per cent solids content and is used after a sludge treatment process. Similar techniques can be used for thickening and de-watering. A centrifuge operated with a high throughput produces a thickened sludge but can be used to produce sludges of 20 per cent solids content. Both thickening and de-watering methods can be improved by the addition of coagulants or conditioning agents.

Chemical conditioning

The addition of certain chemicals increases the rate of water loss by sludge. Chemical conditioning is sometimes used in conjunction with drying beds and gravity thickening, and is a prerequisite for other processes such as filter presses, vacuum filters and centrifuges. The common conditioners are iron salts ($FeCl_3$, $FeSO_4Cl$, $Fe_2(SO_4)_3$), alum ($Al_2(SO_4)_3.18H_2O$), lime (CaO, $Ca(OH)_2$) and polyelectrolytes. All these conditioners act by binding sludge particles together and permitting water to run out. Combinations of inorganic salts and polyelectrolytes can be effective.

Lime is used to condition primary and digested sludges prior to filter pressing or vacuum filtration; it is added as 10 to 25 per cent of the dry sludge solids. Lime has an advantage with primary sludges because it suppresses odour formation. Iron salts can be expensive and difficult to obtain. Alum is also used prior to vacuum and pressure filtration and drying beds. Polyelectrolytes appear to make the sludge floc stronger and less prone to collapse during mechanical treatment. Polyelectrolytes are widely used in association with centrifuging.

Air drying

Sludges can be air dried in drained drying beds, but the constraints imposed by odour control limit this method to digested sludges. Rectangular beds are usually constructed in brick or concrete with a suitable underdrainage system overlaid with sand or clinker or both. The beds should have a gradient of approximately 1 in 200 to facilitate drainage. Design should facilitate access by foot or mechanical plant and provide adequate underflow (Fig 12.3). At least four drying beds, and preferably more, are required to allow a suitable drying interval between sludge applications to each bed.

Sludge is run in to a depth of approximately 300 mm. After a few days, excess liquor can be removed and returned to the treatment plant. The sludge can be lifted at approximately 70 to 75 per cent moisture content when it is spadeable, or preferably at 55 to 60 per cent moisture content, when it appears to be solid.

The size of a drying bed depends upon local climate and sludge characteristics, since water is lost by evaporation and percolation. Design figures of 0.1 to 0.5 m^2/cap provide a suitable guide.

Gravity thickening

Waste sludge can be thickened by allowing it to resettle. The general principles of settlement apply to this method, with the particles undergoing hindered settlement while the bottom sludges are compressed.

Surface loadings for this process are usually 300 to 500 m^3/m^2.d. Primary sludges can be thickened at 150 kg/m^2.d and give thickened sludge of 10 per cent solids content. Activated sludges are loaded at 25 kg/m^2.d to yield sludges with 2 to 5 per cent solids. The process is a useful pretreatment prior to other mechanical methods of de-watering. The effectiveness of gravity thickening can be increased by the addition of chemical conditioners. Care has to be taken during the operation of gravity thickening to minimise odours. If an undigested sludge is held for several hours, it becomes anaerobic and hence very offensive.

Elutriation

Washing sludge with water or effluent is known as *elutriation*. It removes ammonia compounds which interfere with coagulants as well as very fine suspended matter which is difficult to de-water. It is most effective if carried out as several sequential washings, and it is often used on primary and digested sludges prior to chemical conditioning and filtration.

Filter pressing

Pressure filtration is a batch process in which conditioned sludge is pumped slowly with increasing pressure between filter plates which support cloths to retain the solids and permit the passage of liquid. The pressure applied reaches approximately 700 kPa, the resultant cake is 20 to 40 mm thick, and 40 per cent dry solids are achieved. The process is intermittent. Modern presses have minimised the labour requirements.

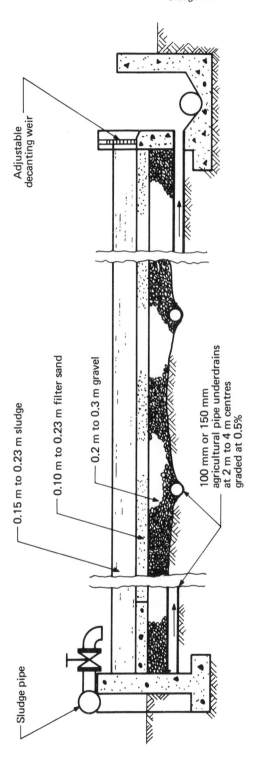

Adjustable decanting weir

0.15 m to 0.23 m sludge

0.10 m to 0.23 m filter sand

0.2 m to 0.3 m gravel

100 mm or 150 mm agricultural pipe underdrains at 2 m to 4 m centres graded at 0.5%

Sludge pipe

Fig 12.3 Sludge drying bed

Vacuum filtration

In the vacuum filtration process, a continuous filter septum is partially immersed in the conditioned sludge and is slowly rotated through it (Fig 12.4). A vacuum of approximately 85 kPa is applied inside the drum and so liquid (water) is drawn into the drum. A cake of de-watered sludge accumulates on the outside of the drum to a thickness of approximately 50 mm. The cake is removed by a scraper. By this method, primary and digested sludges can be concentrated to 32 per cent solids and activated sludges to 25 per cent solids.

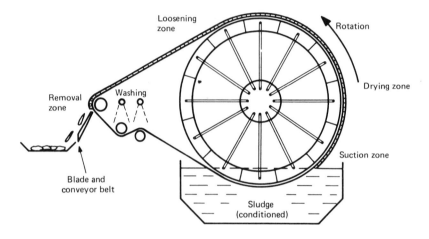

Fig 12.4 Diagrammatic representation of a vacuum filter

Centrifuge

With the centrifuge method, conditioned sludge is added to a rapidly rotating bowl (> 30 rev/s). The rotation separates the sludge solids to the outer side of the bowl and they are removed by a screw conveyor or scroll (Fig 12.5). The sludge solids are removed at one end of the bowl and the liquid at the opposite end. The method is compact, but it requires careful control of process variables. Centrifuges will concentrate sludges to 20 per cent solids, but they are more commonly employed to achieve solids concentrations of approximately 10 per cent.

Other methods

Several other methods are employed to de-water sludges:

a Air flotation, which uses fine air bubbles to carry sludge solids to the surface

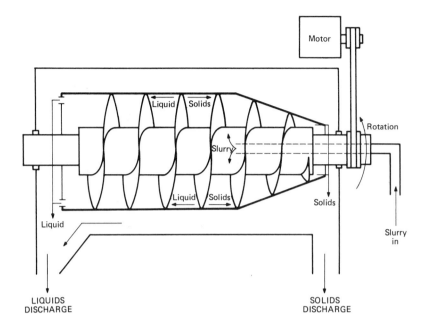

Fig 12.5 Solid bowl centrifuge

b Filter belts, which compress sludge between two endless belts
c Heat treatment processes, in which the sludge is heated to a high
temperature (180° to 250°C) under pressure
d Several hybrid methods are available; they include various combinations
of the above methods.

12.9 Partial disposal

The following methods produce significant reductions in sludge volumes or
improve the acceptability of the sludge.

Incineration

Sludges can be burnt to produce an ash which contains very little water and
very little organic content. The sludge is therefore reduced to the non-volatile
fraction. A sludge containing 30 per cent solids, of which 50 per cent are
volatile, would be reduced to approximately 15 per cent of the original wet-
sludge volume. Stringent controls to prevent secondary pollution are
required on any gaseous or liquid discharge from the incinerators.

Sludge solids have calorific values similar to conventional fossil fuels

(20 000 to 50 000 kJ/kg). Thus, dry sludges can be burnt with no additional fuel consumption. In practice, the fuel value is reduced considerably by the water in the sludge, so that effective de-watering is necessary prior to incineration. Designs are usually based on the production of sufficient heat to drive off the associated water from the sludge. Sludges can be incinerated with municipal refuse.

The two types of furnace employed are the multiple hearth and the fluidised bed. Multiple hearth furnaces consist of a series of floors in a cylindrical tower; the cake is introduced at the top of the tower and it gradually falls to the lower floors. The material is moved over the floors by rabble arms. The major combustion occurs at the lower levels, and heat from these levels dries out sludges at the upper levels. Fluidised bed furnaces have a cylindrical chamber which contains approximately 1.0 m of sand on a heat-resistant steel grid. The bed is fluidised by injection of compressed air, and as the sludge is injected into the sand bed under pressure through an air-cooled lance, water evaporates and the organic material burns.

Pyrolysis

Pyrolysis is combustion under conditions of reduced oxygen; complete oxidation is not possible. The partially-combusted gaseous products from the low-temperature (600°C) pyrolysis unit are passed to a high-temperature furnace (2000°C) where complete oxidation is carried out. This sequence reduces the formation of large solids (clinker) during combustion, and ensures that the gases released to the atmosphere are fully oxidised. As with incineration, the low energy value of wet sludges makes it necessary to de-water the sludges before pyrolysis and, usually, to provide additional fuel. An economic source of fuel is provided by municipal refuse, which can be classified to separate non-combustible materials (such as metals and glass) from the combustible fraction (such as paper and plastic) and shredded to give a high energy material, often referred to as *refuse-derived fuel*. Pyrolysis of municipal refuse-derived fuel and de-watered municipal wastewater sludge therefore can provide a system which uses the properties of these two waste products, and facilitates their disposal.

Composting

De-watered sludge can be composted with household refuse to produce an agricultural or horticultural compost. Non-degradeable materials such as rags, metals and glass are removed from the refuse before composting. The method produces a saleable product which has been well accepted in some communities. The process appears to be most suitable for communities in which the industrial input into garbage and wastewater is not significant.

12.10 Ultimate disposal

All sludges or their residues require some form of ultimate disposal; the methods can be classified as *land dumping, land treatment* and *sea dumping*.

Land dumping

Sludges can be disposed of at a sanitary landfill site, provided that this does not cause contamination of surface and ground waters. The high water content of sludges usually makes it uneconomic to transport wet sludge to a landfill site, so the sludges are de-watered before disposal. At small works the sludge can be buried at, or near, the works. This disposal practice is labour intensive in that a trench is dug, sludge added and the area re-covered with topsoil.

Land treatment

Wastewater sludges contain some elements required for plant growth. A digested sludge contains approximately 3 per cent nitrogen, 2 per cent phosphorus and 0.4 per cent potassium in the dry sludge solids. By comparison, a commercial fertiliser contains approximately 20 per cent nitrogen, 20 per cent phosphorus and 2 per cent potassium. The sludge does contain a high organic content (see Table 12.3), which is valuable in maintaining soil structure. Sludge should therefore be regarded more as a soil conditioner than as a fertiliser. Sludges also contain pathogenic organisms and can be a source of odours; therefore, it is most common to use them only after digestion and, in some cases, pasteurisation or disinfection is required before the sludge can be used on agricultural land. The requirements for the pretreatment of sludges before land application also depend on the crop to be grown. If the sludge is applied in a forest without any direct agricultural value, the hygiene requirements would be less rigorous than for application to a market garden, where the produce would be for direct human consumption.

In the agricultural use of sludge, approximately 1.0 ha is required for each 1000 of population. Most sludge is produced in large urban areas, and the logistics of transporting it to agricultural land can present problems. Additionally, there is usually a significant industrial component in municipal wastewaters; certain toxic metals, for example, concentrate in the sludge and can restrict its land application. Land treatment is widely practised and does represent a recycling of organic materials back into the food chain.

Sea dumping

Sludges have been disposed of into the sea for many years. The sludge should be discharged into deep water so that the processes of dispersion and degradation can occur. This method of disposal is suitable only for coastal sites. The mode of disposal is usually controlled by local factors — some cities transport the sludge by boat, others use a pipeline.

12.11 Conclusions

The treatment and disposal of sludges is often considered as an unimportant additional operation added to the end of a treatment system. In fact, the treatment and disposal of municipal wastewater sludges usually represents a large proportion of the total cost of wastewater treatment. For water treatment, the disposal of sludges is usually less important. The sludge handling streams of a treatment system should be carefully integrated so that the total treatment is optimised. It is also important to realise that sludge treatment and sludge de-watering processes include a return 'filtrate' flow. This flow can represent a significant SS and BOD load to a treatment works. The impact of the preceding settlement and biological processes on the sludge treatment processes is equally important; for example, excessive production of aerobic sludges, which are difficult to treat and dispose of, adversely affects sludge treatment.

The high organic content of sludges together with the presence of pathogens means that aesthetic and hygiene requirements are often a major consideration. This applies particularly in hot climates, where anaerobic conditions are established very rapidly. In these conditions, the sludges should be well stabilised and a high priority should be given to odour and pathogen control.

This brief discussion of sludge treatment and disposal methods can serve only as an introduction to the problem of sludge handling. Each sludge and each location require a separate assessment of treatment and disposal requirements.

Review questions

12.1 Why can waterworks sludges be lagooned without additional treatment, while wastewater sludges require treatment prior to lagooning?

12.2 What are the advantages of de-watering sludges?

12.3 Why is the value of specific resistance independent of sludge solids concentration, while capillary suction time varies with sludge solids concentrations?

12.4 Which methods of treatment and disposal as outlined in Table 12.7 are mutually compatible?

12.5   On the basis of the values given in Tables 12.2, 12.3 and 12.4, what would be a suitable sludge lagoon design loading for a conventional activated sludge plant with an anaerobic digester?

12.6   Why are air-drying beds unsuitable for primary sludges?

12.7   What are some problems associated with spreading most wastewater sludges on agricultural land?

12.8   What reduction in sludge volume is achieved by incineration of primary, secondary and digested sludges?

13 Water Treatment

13.1 Introduction

Frequently, water sources which are conveniently located with respect to the place of intended use do not possess all the necessary qualities as indicated in Chapter 5. The purpose of water treatment is to upgrade the quality of the water so that it becomes suitable for its intended use, or to protect consumers against possible contamination of the water source.

The type and extent of treatment required depends on the nature and degree of the quality deficiencies to be corrected. For example, if the water generally conforms to the desired standards for both chemical content and appearance but may be subject to occasional minor bacterial contamination, it may require only disinfection. But if the raw water is frequently either turbid or coloured, it will require more extensive treatment, such as coagulation followed by sedimentation, filtration and disinfection (see Table 13.1).

Waters which contain excessive amounts of either dissolved salts or toxic materials will require relatively expensive treatment before they become acceptable. Such highly saline or potentially toxic waters would not be used if other water sources could be developed at reasonable cost.

Table 13.1 Typical methods used for correcting quality deficiencies

Property	Treatment processes used
Colour	a Coagulation and filtration (with activated carbon) b Sometimes oxidation by chlorine or ozone
Turbidity	Coagulation and filtration (coagulation may be omitted if raw water has a relatively low turbidity)
Tastes and odours	a Activated carbon adsorption e Aeration b Coagulation and filtration f Catchment and stream control c Chlorination g Chlorine dioxide d Ozonation
Copper and zinc	Removal methods for dissolved copper and zinc vary with the nature of other impurities present

Property	Treatment processes used
Calcium and magnesium (hardness)	a Precipitation as magnesium hydroxide and calcium carbonate on addition of lime and soda b Ion exchange processes
Iron and manganese	Treatment methods depend on other impurities present. In general, removal is effected by oxidation and precipitation as hydroxide, but precipitation of iron as ferrous carbonate and removal by ion exchange are sometimes used
Sodium Potassium Sulphate Chloride Nitrate	These anions and cations cannot be removed from water supplies by moderately-priced processes. Expensive desalination is required
pH	pH can be corrected by addition of acid or alkali (usually H_2SO_4, HCl, CO_2, $Ca(OH)_2$, Na_2CO_3 or NaOH)
Phenolic substances	a Chlorine dioxide b Ozone c Activated carbon
Sulphuretted hydrogen	a Aeration under acid conditions b Chlorination or ozonation c Precipitation with ferrous salts, forming ferrous sulphide
Carbon dioxide	a Aeration b Conversion to bicarbonate by addition of alkali
Toxic materials (general)	It is difficult to reduce most toxic materials reliably to the very low concentrations required by the standards
Lead	Can be precipitated under alkaline conditions
Arsenic	a Coagulation and filtration may remove up to 50 per cent b Ion exchange with a bed of activated alumina can reduce arsenic concentration to an acceptable level
Fluoride	a Some fluoride precipitates *with magnesium* in excess lime softening b Desalination
Bacteria	Coliform less than 50/100 mL: disinfection with chlorine or ozone. Coliform 50-5000/100 mL: coagulation, filtration and disinfection. Heavy pollution with coliform more than 5000/100 mL (or *E coli* > 2000/100 mL): extensive treatment needed
Radioactivity	Special ion exchange processes, and carefully controlled coagulation and filtration, with activated carbon adsorption has been shown to remove some radio-nuclides
Trace organics, herbicides, oils, Insecticides	Adsorption on flocs during flocculation, and on activated carbon

A *common treatment sequence* is followed to remove moderate turbidity or colour, or both, from water, together with treatment to counteract bacteriological contamination of up to about 5000 MPN total coliforms per 100 mL (or up to 2000 *E coli* per 100 mL). The sequence is illustrated in Fig 13.1. Some types of unit which could be used for each stage in this sequence will be discussed in turn.

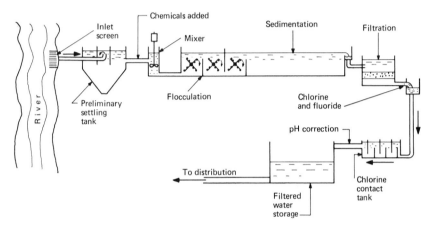

Fig 13.1 A common sequence of processes in water treatment

13.2 Preliminary treatment

Screens

The inlet screen on a water treatment plant prevents entry of debris such as leaves, twigs and other floating and suspended rubbish, as well as fish and eels. The rubbish removed from a water intake screen is seldom of a putrescible nature, and it may not cause problems if it is returned to the stream. The arrangement shown in Fig 13.2(a) consists of a perforated screen which is cleaned by a rotating brush. The debris is swept back into the stream and the mechanism is protected from large floating debris by a coarse bar screen. Fig 13.2(b) shows a travelling belt screen with sections of screen mesh attached to endless chains so that debris which attaches to the screen is raised to be flushed away by jets of water.

Preliminary settling tank

In areas subject to monsoonal rains or floods, the water is likely to carry, at times, enough heavy sediment to cause problems in sludge handling. In such places, a preliminary settling tank, or presedimentation basin, may be installed. The surface loading rate of such a presedimentation basin may be in

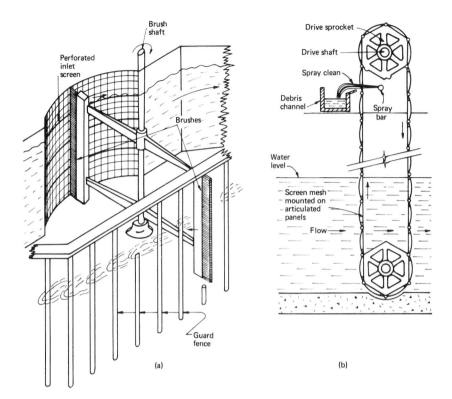

Fig 13.2 Two types of intake screen: (a) a swept perforated plate with debris returned to stream, (b) a travelling belt screen

the range 1.0 to 5.0 L/s.m², depending on the size of the particles to be separated. If its area is large, the basin may be rectangular or circular with mechanical scrapers for sediment collection, but if the tank area is small enough, a Dortmund-type horizontal flow tank with hopper-shaped bottom may be used (Fig 13.3). The maximum surface area of such a tank is limited by the practicable depth.

13.3 Flocculation and sedimentation

The theory of mixing, coagulation and flocculation was discussed in Chapter 9, and the theory of sedimentation in Chapter 8. In this chapter, the discussion centres on the ways in which these theories are applied in water treatment practice.

   In the last decade of the nineteenth century, American engineers introduced rapid sand filtration. In most installations, it was necessary to carry

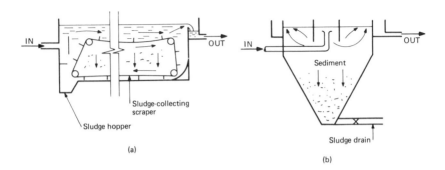

Fig 13.3 (a) A horizontal flow presedimentation tank with sediment scrapers, (b) a Dortmund-type tank for smaller installations (Note — no scraper required)

out some preliminary treatment of the turbidity and colour by coagulation before application of the water to the filter. With turbid or highly-coloured waters, the filters clogged rapidly unless some of the coagulated material was first removed. This led to the use of sedimentation to remove readily settleable material from the water before it was passed through filters. Studies of flocculation processes were aimed at improving the settling characteristics of coagulated material so that, with more efficient settling, less floc would be carried into the filters.

Inefficient sedimentation results in the rapid clogging of filters and effluent quality deterioration. The frequent filter washing which results from these conditions means that more process time is lost and the water loss for filter washing is increased. Therefore, when water which requires removal of a considerable amount of turbidity is to be treated, careful attention should be given to the design and operation of the flocculation and sedimentation processes.

In the early years of rapid sand filtration, the main forms of chemical mixing, flocculation and sedimentation were those effected by separate mechanical or hydraulic flocculation, followed by settling in rectangular or circular tanks in which the flow was predominantly in a horizontal direction.

Horizontal flow sedimentation

Fig 13.4 is a longitudinal section diagram of an early type of hydraulic flocculator and rectangular horizontal flow tank. Such a tank may still be appropriate in countries where there is no labour shortage; the tank may be emptied and cleaned at suitable time intervals.

The later incorporation of mechanical rakes for sludge collection made possible the continuous processing of water, without interruptions for emptying the tank to remove accumulated sludge.

Circular horizontal flow tanks were usually provided with a central inlet

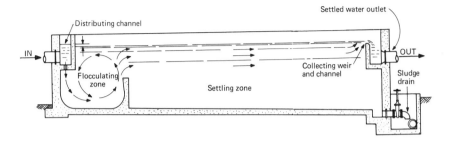

Fig 13.4 An early type of rectangular flocculation and settling unit featuring hydraulic flocculation, horizontal flow sedimentation and intermittent sludge removal from an emptied tank

chamber, with the water passing out radially to a peripheral collecting weir. A development from this type of tank was the enlargement of the central inlet chamber to form a flocculation chamber. Settlement then took place in an annular space between the wall of the flocculation chamber and the outer wall. Rotating arms fitted with angled blades to plough sludge to a central collection point were mounted on a central shaft.

Horizontal flow sedimentation tanks, although generally more expensive than the upflow sludge blanket clarifiers and other solids contact clarifiers (to be discussed later), still have some applications. They are of value treating water which forms a good rapid settling floc on the addition of the coagulant, and also in cases where temperature variations of incoming water could cause troublesome convection currents in a vertical flow clarifier (a temperature difference as small as 0.1°C could be troublesome). Thermal convection currents have been known to create trouble in cold temperate, warm temperate and tropical climates.

In addition, horizontal flow sedimentation tanks are more suitable for fluctuating and intermittent flows than are sludge blanket and solids contact clarifiers.

Sludge blanket clarifiers

The upflow *sludge blanket* clarifier, developed about 1940, had some success because

a In many waters, the settleability of sludge improves with age. Retained and recycled sludge within a clarifier forms good nuclei for the growth of new flocs and increases the settling velocity

b The high concentration of particles of varied sizes provides relative movement and collision opportunity to improve flocculation

c The density difference between the slurry zone, or slurry pool, and the clear water above it, enhanced the hydraulic stability of the flow through the clear water, or final settling zone

d The amount of sludge sliding down the sloping sides of the hoppers into the incoming water is sufficient to form a mixture having the same concentration and density as that of the slurry already in the slurry pool, thus avoiding unstable density conditions.

The sludge blanket clarifier is an upflow device in which the slurry or sludge in suspension is itself suspended by the upflow velocity of the water. Sludge is removed through a suitable sludge concentrator at a rate sufficient to prevent excessive accumulation. Concentrator areas in different clarifiers vary in size from about 4 per cent up to 25 per cent of the water surface. A large concentrator improves flexibility of operation, especially when the flow has to be increased rapidly.

Not only sludge blanket clarifiers, but also solids contact clarifiers, operate with a slurry zone in which the sludge concentration is related to the water upflow velocity at the separation surface at the top of the slurry pool when in equilibrium. The empirical hindered settling relationship (see Chapter 8) is $V_s = V_p(1 - kc')^n$. If a clarifier is operating in a steady state condition with an upflow velocity of V_{s1} at the slurry pool surface, and the flow is increased so that the upflow velocity at the slurry pool surface increases to V_{s2} without either accumulation or loss of total sludge, then the volume occupied by the slurry pool at equilibrium will increase in the ratio

$$[V_p^{(1/n)} - V_{s1}^{(1/n)}]/[V_p^{(1/n)} - V_{s2}^{(1/n)}]$$

This sludge bulking with an increase of flow can cause the slurry pool level to rise too high, and sometimes to reach the settled water channel; either the

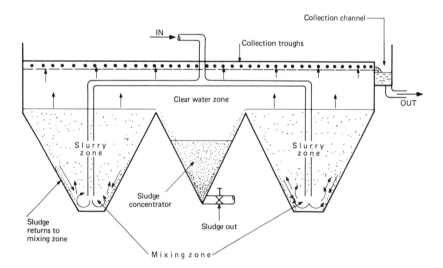

Fig 13.5 Arrangement of hopper-bottomed 'sludge blanket' clarifier with separate sludge concentrator

increases should be made sufficiently slowly to permit excess sludge to be withdrawn through the sludge concentrator as bulking occurs, or some sludge should be removed before the flow increase in anticipation of the change.

When there is substantial organic pollution of the raw water and the temperature is above 25°C, as in *hot climates*, there is a possibility that the sludge will become putrid, giving objectionable tastes and odours to the water. The putrefaction of sludge can be minimised by control of bacteria with prechlorination.

The size of *hopper-bottomed* units is limited by the necessity to maintain adequate slope to ensure that the sludge will slide down (about 60° from horizontal), and by the practicable depths which can be constructed. A *flat-bottomed sludge blanket clarifier* of French design is shown in Fig 13.6. It is known as a *Pulsator*, a name derived from its method of operation. The water enters the clarifier at the bottom and is withdrawn through collecting

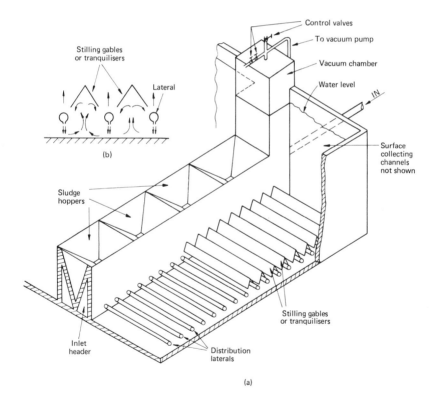

Fig 13.6 (a) A flat-bottomed sludge blanket clarifier without sludge rakes *(Courtesy: Degremont Pulsator)*, (b) Section through laterals and stilling gables, showing probable flow pattern

troughs at the top of the water, the main flow being almost vertically upwards.

With a flat-bottomed clarifier, the sludge tends to settle evenly over the whole of the floor. To keep the sludge in suspension and to mix it with the incoming water, it is necessary to distribute the inflow over the clarifier floor with sufficient turbulence to cause mixing (even at low rates of inflow). The distribution of inflow is achieved by the use of horizontal pipe laterals leading from a main inlet header. Holes at intervals in the bottom of the laterals cause jets of influent to be directed onto the floor.

Pulsations induced in the inflow ensure that the turbulence is intermittently adequate to pick up and re-suspend any settled sludge and to mix the influent with a reasonable volume of slurry to reduce convection effects. In small units the pulsations can be induced by an automatic dosing siphon, which gives intermittent flow. In larger units, there is a possibility of air entrainment in the operation of a siphon and, therefore, a pulse is usually

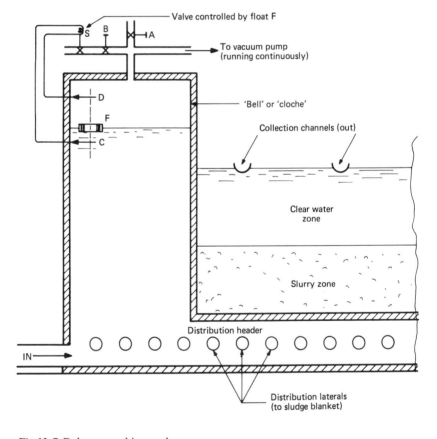

Fig 13.7 Pulse control in a pulsator

induced by withdrawal of some of the influent water into a 'bell' or 'cloche' connected with the main inlet header, followed by rapid release of the withdrawn water back into the header. The pulse is controlled by a vacuum pump and air valves. The solenoid-operated valve, S (see Fig 13.7) opens when float F rises to level D, thus allowing air to enter and the water to flow out as a pulse; it closes when the water drops to level C, thus causing water to be sucked up from the influent header to the bell.

To increase or decrease the duration of a pulsation cycle, valve A is adjusted to vary the air leakage and thus control the rate of rise of the water in the bell. The setting of valve B controls the rate of ingress of air into the bell when valve S is open. It thus controls the fall rate of the water, and consequently the strength of the pulse.

The turbulence from the pulse is prevented from forming troublesome eddies through the whole of the sludge blanket by the presence of stilling gables (see Fig 13.6).

Flocculation takes place within the sludge blanket layer, and excess sludge overflows into the sludge concentrator from where it is removed. If too much sludge is present, it continues to spill into the concentrator until the slurry pool concentration is such that the hindered settling velocity (see Chapter 8) is equal to the upflow velocity of the water. If the amount of sludge present is not enough to provide a slurry pool which reaches up to the edge of the sludge concentrator, no sludge will be collected or discharged. The appropriate sludge quantity and level are therefore automatically maintained.

A recent modification consists of sloping plates in the upper portion of the slurry zone. These extend into the clear water zone and greatly improve the flocculation of the particles in the slurry. This increases the settling velocity of the sludge and results in a decrease in the size of clarifier necessary to treat a given flow.

Solids contact clarifiers

Some clarifiers with slurry zones are equipped to give more positive stirring and mixing than is common in the simpler sludge blanket clarifiers. In these clarifiers, the inflow is mechanically mixed with probably five to ten times its own volume of slurry and return sludge and impelled into a flocculation zone before release into the separation or settling zone. Mechanical mixing and flocculation ensure that the effectiveness of these processes is almost independent of the flow-through rate. The three main types to be discussed here are

a Mechanical circulation with sludge scraper
b Mechanical circulation with gravity sludge return
c Hydraulic circulation with gravity sludge return.

Fig 13.8 shows a clarifier with a *propeller to recirculate the sludge* and to

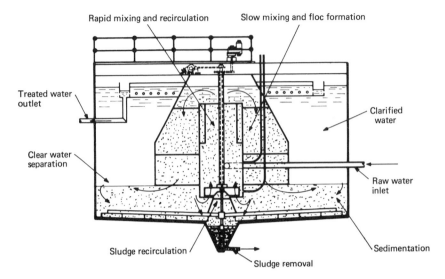

Fig 13.8 Solids contact clarifier with mechanical circulation and sludge scraper, with central sludge withdrawal *(Courtesy: William Boby — Reactivator)*

provide turbulence to assist in flocculation, and a *scraper to collect the sludge* to the centre for both discharge and recirculation. Raw water dosed with chemicals enters the central duct in the wake of the recirculation propeller, thus giving rapid initial mixing with sludge and slurry. Some turbulence

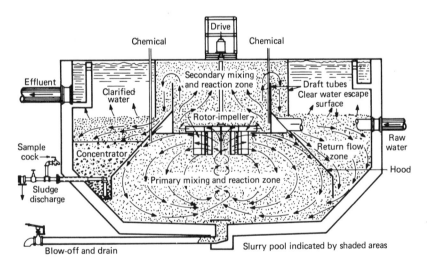

Fig 13.9 Solids contact clarifier with mechanical circulation, gravity sludge return and peripheral sludge concentrator *(Courtesy: Degremont)*

persists through the slow mixing and floc formation zone, and the floc-laden water passes down to the sedimentation zone.

The clear water separation surface is held in position by the upflowing water, while some sludge settles to the bottom and is scraped back to the centre. The settled water is collected in a channel near the top of the tank.

Both the Infilco Accelator and the Paterson-Candy Accentrifloc are solids contact clarifiers with *gravity sludge return and mechanical circulation* (Fig 13.9). The raw water in these clarifiers is introduced into a triangular-shaped ring which distributes the inflow around the upper perimeter of the primary mixing and reaction zone. Large rotating paddles keep the contents of this zone in motion and maintain the sludge in suspension. A turbine transfers the slurry, after primary mixing, to the secondary mixing and flocculation zone from which it is discharged at the clear water escape surface of the settlement zone. Settling sludge and recirculated slurry return to the primary mixing zone, while the separated clear water is collected in peripheral or radial channels at the top of the tank. A concentrator hopper near the perimeter of the tank collects excess sludge for discharge.

Hydraulic recirculation is used in the clarifier shown in Fig 13.10. It is induced by the momentum of the inflow which is directed up the central inverted cone. The jet pump effect draws in the sludge which has settled on the walls and moved down to the bottom of the clarifier. Turbulence induced in the central cone results in mixing and flocculation. Some of the settling sludge is intercepted by the concentrator hopper, C, and discharged to waste. Clear water is collected over a peripheral weir at the top of the tank. Hydraulic circulation is suitable for an installation where the variability of flow is expected to be low.

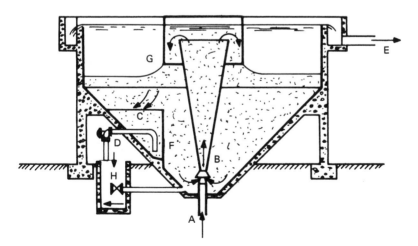

Fig 13.10 Solids contact clarifier with hydraulic jet pump circulation and gravity return in sludge *(Courtesy: Degremont)*

Shallow depth sedimentation

The theory of shallow depth sedimentation has been discussed in Chapter 8. Tube and plate settlers are gaining some favour in water treatment processes and, to a lesser extent, in sewage treatment processes. There are three main configurations for shallow depth sedimentation:

a Steeply-inclined, with upflow
b Nearly horizontal flow
c Steeply-inclined, with downflow.

Several companies supply tubes manufactured for installation in conditions of *steeply-inclined upflow*. Fig 13.11 illustrates the type of tube module supplied by Neptune Microfloc. The tubes are 50 mm square, with a slope length of 600 mm. They are set at an angle of 60° to the horizontal. For structural strength, the tubes are sloped in alternate directions in successive rows. The inclination of the tubes is such that they are self-cleaning as the sludge slides down and drops out of the bottom of the module. As settled sludge slides down the tubes, a snow-balling effect occurs, with the result that sludge particles falling from the bottom of the module are much bigger and faster-settling than those particles carried up into it by the water. If it were not for this effect, the settled sludge would not be able to drop through the rising water about to enter the tubes. Steeply-inclined upflow tubes are therefore not suitable for settling non-flocculent material such as mineral particles or fine grit.

Steeply-inclined tubes are used in new installations,'for uprating existing plants and for improving effluent quality in existing plants. Although the installation of tubes can improve the operation of a good clarifier, they do not necessarily make a bad clarifier good; general flow patterns should be checked as satisfactory before a conversion to tube settlement uprating is undertaken.

Nearly horizontal tubes are used in small water treatment plants. The sludge which settles in them remains where it falls until the time for the intermittent clean-out. The length of the tubes is proportioned to give an appropriate amount of storage capacity so that cleaning does not have to be too frequent. The sedimentation unit is usually placed in series with a filter; when it becomes overloaded, the excess of sludge is carried through to the filter, which quickly blocks and requires a backwash. The tubes are constructed with sufficient slope so that the sludge will run out of them when they are drained for a filter backwash (between 5° and 7°).

The Lamella separator is a *steeply-inclined downflow* multi-plate settler. The slope is between 30° and 45°, and it is continuously self-cleaning. The slope can be less than in an upflow unit because the sludge movement is in the same direction as the water movement and the water assists in transporting the sludge. The layout is shown in Fig 13.12. It is necessary to extract the

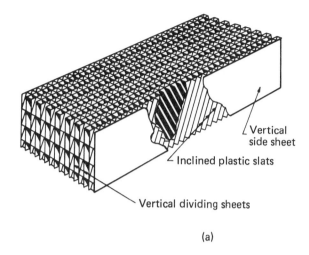

(a)

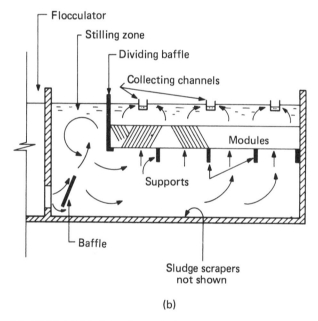

(b)

Fig 13.11 (a) Module of steeply-inclined tubes *(Courtesy: Neptune Microfloc)*, (b) Steeply-inclined modules installed in a clarifier

clean water from the module before both clean water and sludge mix underneath the module; for this purpose a small clean water collection header is placed under each plate near its lower end; the water is conducted from there back to the outlet channel by a series of pipes. This type of unit is not

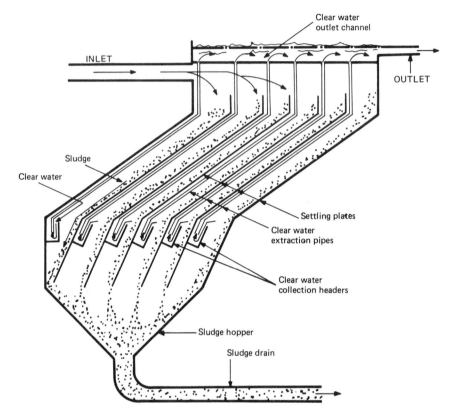

Fig 13.12 Lamella separator — inclined downflow, shallow depth sedimentation

particularly adaptable for uprating existing plants, but it can be used effectively for separation of non-flocculent sediments and in new installations.

A typical plate size for this type of sedimentation unit is 1.5 × 2.5 m. The clearance between plates is 25 to 50 mm. In common with other shallow-depth sedimentation units, the water passing through it has a low detention time in the unit. Accordingly, effective preflocculation is required so that the water is already conditioned for efficient separation. Also, the detention of sludge is minimal so that, in hot climates, there is very little opportunity for the sludge to become putrescent before discharge.

Convection currents in clarifiers

Convection currents which result from density differences can cause problems in clarifier operation. The density differences are usually caused by variations in either temperature or suspension concentration. Water at 15°C has a density of 999.126 kg/m³ and at 16°C, 998.970 kg/m³, a difference of

0.156 kg/m³. With a temperature difference of only 0.1°C, the density difference would be 1.56 × 10⁻² kg/m³, and the buoyant force on a cubic metre of water 0.1°C warmer than the ambient temperature could be 1.56 × 10⁻² × 9.81 N. The acceleration would be such that in 10 seconds the velocity would change by 1.5 mm/s (neglecting friction) — during which time the distance moved would be as little as 7.5 mm. Although a velocity of 1.5 mm/s is very small, the usual upflow operating velocity for a clarifier is only one-half to two-thirds of this velocity and, therefore, convection currents resulting from very small temperature differences can give trouble.

The same magnitude of acceleration can be produced by a volumetric concentration difference of less than 0.01 in an alum floc suspension, where the particle density is about 2 kg/m³ greater than that of water. This concentration effect has its use in maintaining a stable slurry pool surface in solids contact or sludge blanket clarifiers. It is important, however, that the sludge flow patterns and mixing characteristics of clarifiers ensure that in regular operation the incoming water mixes evenly with the sludge to produce a suspension of the same density as that of the ambient suspension; this would avoid concentration convection currents which could disrupt the process. During flow increases, some sludge blanket disruption is inevitable. During periods of decreasing flow, sludge blankets are usually very stable.

Flotation

In some installations, the influent water is supersaturated with air or oxygen; one cause of this is the intermittent ingress of air to pumping mains, where it later dissolves under pressure; another cause is photosynthesis, which produces oxygen. In hot climates, the increase of temperature in exposed pipelines can reduce the solubility of air, causing supersaturation. When floc starts to form it provides nuclei for the release of tiny gas bubbles, which become enmeshed in it; or photosynthesis in algae enmeshed in floc can release oxygen. The addition of gas bubbles can reduce the effective bulk density of the flocs so that they will settle very slowly or, in some cases, even float. Under these conditions, efficient normal sedimentation is practically impossible.

Research has recently been carried out to adapt dissolved air flotation methods to the treatment of these problem waters which are supersaturated or algae-laden. The water is first flocculated in the normal way and then a secondary stream of water, which has been near-saturated with air under pressure, is mixed with the main flow of water through a specially-designed nozzle after the flocculation is finished. The air bubbles which form as the excess air comes out of solution become attached to the floc particles, and make the bulk density of the composite floc-air particles lower than that of water.

The water then passes into a flotation unit, where the floc floats to the surface to form a scum; this is scraped off, while the clarified water is removed from the bottom of the unit (see Fig 13.13). It has been found that efficient flotation can be attained with a secondary flow equal to about 5 per cent of the main flow, and saturated with air at a pressure of about 350 kPa.

Surface loading rates of flotation units are in the range 1.4 to 3.5 L/s.m². Flotation units are normally smaller than the corresponding normal clarifier, and produce a scum which contains less water than does a settled sludge. Total detention time for the flocculation and flotation of Thames water at an experimental plant is reported as 16 minutes. However, flotation units need air and water pumps which create a continual energy demand and a maintenance requirement. Initially, flotation in water treatment can be expected to be confined to the treatment of water which otherwise would pose difficult problems.

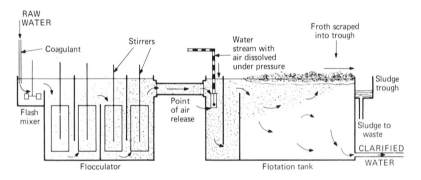

Fig 13.13 Diagram of experimental water treatment flotation plant *(After Water Research Centre, UK)*

Selection of clarifier type

The type of clarifier most suitable for service depends on the characteristics of the water to be treated as well as on the variability pattern of water demand. In general, the appropriate type of clarifier is the one which will meet the performance requirements at the lowest total cost.

Low-alkalinity water with low turbidity and high colour often produces a light, slowly-settling floc — especially when cold. With this type of water, the floc settling velocity often increases if the floc is aged for several days. It is therefore necessary, in the interests of reasonable performance, to adopt a system which includes the re-use of old floc such as a sludge blanket clarifier, or a solids contact clarifier, with a sufficiently large slurry pool for sludge ageing. Alternatively, a system of sludge reclamation and recycling could be used; the old flocs make good nuclei on which the new precipitates can be deposited.

Turbid water usually forms a good floc which settles readily — even when fresh — although its settling qualities may improve with age. The clay particles responsible for the turbidity provide weight for the floc, and their colloidal properties assist the flocculation process. In these conditions, a wider choice of clarifier types is possible and this choice may include horizontal flow and shallow depth clarifiers. These types perform better in stop-start conditions and rapidly varying flow than do sludge blanket types. Sludge blanket and solids contact clarifiers operate best when the flow is almost constant and within a critical range: if the flow is too high, the concentration drops and the stability of the slurry pool surface is destroyed, but if the flow is too low, there would be problems in obtaining good mixing of the influent in a sludge blanket clarifier.

If shallow depth sedimentation is used, there must be good flocculation because the water does not remain in the unit long enough for flocculation of suspended solids to occur. Shallow depth sedimentation also requires very good flow control because small variations in approach velocity near the lower ends of the ducts can cause uneven flow through them.

For situations where temperature fluctuations can give trouble, the best type of clarifier is difficult to determine. There are two factors which could aid in achieving desirable conditions in a solids contact clarifier. First, good mixing in the slurry pool will assist in maintaining uniformity of temperature in that zone. Secondly, a shallow clear water zone will limit the potential energy released as the warmer water rises through the ambient cold water, and this energy reduction will limit the size and velocities of the resultant convection cells.

When the raw water usually has a low turbidity, or is cold or super-saturated with air and a settleable floc is formed only with difficulty, the process of *direct filtration* may be used. In this process, the water is dosed with coagulant and, sometimes, coagulant aids; then it is allowed a reaction time and applied direct to the filters without prior flocculation and sedimentation. When this system is used, the savings resulting from the omission of a clarifier should offset the extra costs of more frequent filter cleaning.

13.4 Filtration

The three main filtration methods for public water supplies are *slow sand* filtration, *rapid sand* filtration, and *diatomaceous earth* filtration. Table 13.2 compares the operating characteristics of these three types.

Slow sand filters

The first filter to supply water to the public of a whole town was a slow sand

Table 13.2 Comparison between diatomaceous earth, rapid sand, and slow sand filters
(Table shows typical values only — see text for fuller details)

	Diatomaceous earth		Rapid sand	Slow sand
Filter medium	Fossilised diatom skeletons		Silica sand	Silica sand
Thickness of filter bed	Initial: 2-3 mm Final: about 12 mm (Built up by 'body feed')		0.45-0.75 m	Initial: about 1 m reduced to 0.5 m by successive cleaning
Grain size	0.01 mm to 0.2 mm		Effective size 0.4 to 1.0 mm	Effective size 0.2 to 0.4 mm
Filtration rate $(L/s.m^2)$	0.7 to 1.4		1.3 to 4.0	0.035 to 0.07
Head loss (m)	Vacuum	Pressure		
Initial	0.35	1.4	0.3	0.06
Final	5	21	2.0-2.5	1.2
Support for medium	Usually fine mesh metal 'septum', and a layer of diatomite applied as a precoat		0.3 to 0.5 m of graded gravel. Sand sometimes applied directly over concrete floor and distribution nozzles	0.3 to 0.45 m of graded gravel
Method of cleaning	Used filter media discarded and replaced by new material. Spent material removed by reverse flow		Sand washed in place by reverse flow and sometimes air, or surface rakes, or surface jets	Surface layers of medium scraped up and removed — later returned to filter bed after having been washed
Length of operation between cleanings	6 to 40 hours		12 to 72 hours	20 to 60 days
Penetration of impurities	Slight		Almost through total thickness of filter bed	30 to 60 mm
Major process	Physical straining		Interception and inter-particle settling	Entrapment in biological films of active layer
Pretreatment Usual	None		Coagulation, flocculation and sedimentation	None

	Diatomaceous earth	Rapid sand	Slow sand
Sometimes	Aeration, pre-settling, or microstraining	Coagulation only, occasionally none	Aeration or presettling or both
Tolerable raw water quality Turbidity	Low (< 10 units)	High	Moderate (< 40 units)
Colour	Low	High (up to 300 units)	Low
Algae	Low	Moderate	Moderate
Construction costs	Low	Medium	High
Running and maintenance costs	High	Medium	Low

filter built at Paisley, Scotland, in 1804, but it was not until 1829 that James Simpson commissioned the first slow sand filter for the Chelsea Water Company in London. Slow sand filtration became popular for water treatment during the nineteenth century. A series of experiments carried out at Louisville, Kentucky, during the period 1895 to 1897 led to the development of the rapid sand filter for treating public water supplies. Very few slow sand filters have been constructed in the US since about 1915. However, a large slow sand filter was constructed in London in 1972, because some industrial users in the area required water with a low silica, iron and aluminium concentration, and this requirement could not be met by rapid sand filtration.

Although the general trend is towards the use of rapid sand filtration in new installations, there are still many slow sand filters in use and giving satisfactory service. A slow sand filter is essentially a bed of sand through which the water passes, together with the necessary structures and controls to apply the water, to control the flow, and to remove the water after filtration.

Fig 13.14 is a diagrammatic section through a slow sand filter. The basic structure is the filter basin, which is normally made of concrete, though in some circumstances it could be an earthen basin lined with rubber or other waterproof material. Large installations have a number of basins. Small installations usually have at least three, so that one can be taken out of service for cleaning and maintenance at intervals. The size of individual basins is usually between 0.1 and 0.5 ha. The sand under-drainage system consists of pipes and channels to collect the water and convey it to the outlet, and of gravel layers so graded that they prevent the filter sand from entering the drainage pipes. These layers consists of gravel which varies in size from 30 to

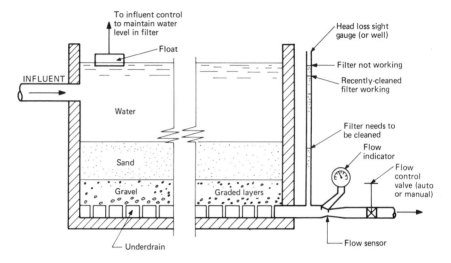

Fig 13.14 Diagrammatic section of slow sand filter

50 mm in the lower layers down to about 3 mm in the upper layer. Their total thickness is from 0.3 to 0.45 m. The sand used has an effective size* of between 0.2 and 0.4 mm. It is installed on top of gravel to a depth of between 0.7 and 1.2 m. The depth of water over the sand when the filter is in operation is usually about 1 m.

The flow and level of water are controlled by the inlet and outlet valves. The outlet valve can be adjusted at intervals to maintain an almost constant flow out of the filter, while the inlet valve can be a float-operated valve which maintains the water level in the filter. Rates of flow vary from about 167 to 1000 L/s.ha, but are usually in the range 350 to 700 L/s.ha.

When water is first applied to a clean filter, there is very little purification. The effectiveness of the slow sand filter depends on the establishment of a biologically active surface mat of gelatinous biomass, which assists in retention of turbidity and bacteria and provides predators for the pathogens. After some time, this mat becomes so dense that it creates too much of a barrier to the passage of the water and the head loss increases beyond acceptable limits. The filter must then be cleaned. This happens at intervals of between one and three months. Traditionally, to clean slow sand filters, the water is drained away and men with scrapers or shovels remove the top 50 to 80 mm of soiled sand; the filter is then put back into service. The removed sand is washed and stored for later use. This cleaning process requires a considerable amount of manpower. When the thickness of the sand which remains has been reduced by successive cleanings to less than 600 mm, the

* See footnote on p 319

sand previously removed and washed is replaced in the filter to restore the original thickness. In most new slow sand filters, arrangements are made for mechanical cleaning, to eliminate much of the labour costs associated with the manual cleaning of older filters.

The *advantages* of slow sand filtration are

a No pretreatment, perhaps other than preliminary sedimentation, is needed
b No chemicals are required
c Less skilled supervision is required than for rapid sand filtration
d It has a good bacterial removal efficiency
e The effluent is less corrosive than that from rapid sand filtration
f There is a long period of satisfactory operation between cleanings.

The *disadvantages* are

a A large area is required, and the structures are extensive — capital cost is high
b It has poor colour removal efficiency
c Turbidity removal is poor if the raw water turbidity is more than about 40 turbidity units.

Conditions which could favour the installation of a slow sand filter are

a A source of water which is moderately polluted, but has a low turbidity
b A location where supplies of chemicals are unreliable
c A shortage of skilled persons to operate a rapid sand filter
d A plentiful labour force for construction and cleaning.

These conditions indicate that slow sand filters may be appropriate for some remote areas in developing countries, provided that the raw water turbidity is within reasonable limits. They may also be used in circumstances where the treated water is required to have qualities not attainable in water from rapid sand filters.

Recent research has demonstrated the effectiveness of burnt rice husks as a filter medium. The natural protective coverings of rice grains have a framework of silica. If the carbonaceous material is burnt away, the remaining silica can be used in a slow-rate filter, in the same way as sand is used. If burning is not complete, some of the carbonaceous material may be available as activated carbon to adsorb small quantities of organic material and colour. The scrapings from filter cleaning are discarded and replaced by a fresh layer of burnt husks. This provides a cheap, effective filter medium for use in hot climates where disposal of rice husks otherwise presents a problem.

Rapid sand filters

When rapid sand filters were introduced for treating public water supplies, the loading rates were about 1.2 to 1.5 $L/s.m^2$. For slow sand filters, the rates had been only 0.035 to 0.07 L/s.m². At the higher rates of filtration.

a Coagulation was required in most cases to prevent the impurities from being drawn through the filter bed
b Impurities were drawn deeper into the sand bed, so that surface cleaning was no longer adequate
c Clogging occurred much more rapidly — filters required cleaning at intervals of 24 to 72 hours instead of at intervals of 1 to 2 months as with slow sand filters.

For rapid sand filtration to be acceptable it was necessary, therefore, to develop a means of cleaning the full depth of the filters rapidly and economically. The method adopted was to remove the impurities from the sand bed by a reverse flow of water, either preceded, or accompanied, by some form of agitation to loosen the impurities from the sand grains. A rapid sand filter therefore comprises

a A sand bed in which the filtration occurs
b A support for the sand bed
c An underdrainage system to carry away filtered water and to admit backwash water (and air for agitation, if used)
d An inlet for water
e An outlet for used washwater
f Means for controlling the flows through the filter.

Fig 13.15 shows the general arrangement of the elements of a typical rapid sand filter. In *normal operation*, the inlet valve and the filtered water valve are open and other valves are closed. Water enters through the inlet valve, passes down through the sand and underdrain system, and out through the filtered water valve.

To start a *backwash cycle* using air scour followed by water scour, the inlet valve is closed but filtering is allowed to continue for a time to avoid excessive loss of settled water. After a reasonable 'drawdown' period (during which some of the settled water in the filter chamber is filtered instead of wasted), the filtered water valve is closed and the waste valve opened, thus dumping into the drain that portion of the settled water which was above the level of the backwash collection trough. The air valve is then opened to admit air under pressure into the underdrainage system where the apparatus distributes it evenly underneath the filter. The air, bubbling up through the sand bed, causes agitation which loosens the impurities from the sand grains. At the end of the air scour, the air valve is closed and the backwash valve opened to admit water to the underdrain system at a rate sufficient to wash the sand. The water passes upwards through the sand and carries with it the impurities into the backwash collection troughs and thence into the gullet and drain.

To finish the backwash cycle, the backwash and waste valves are closed

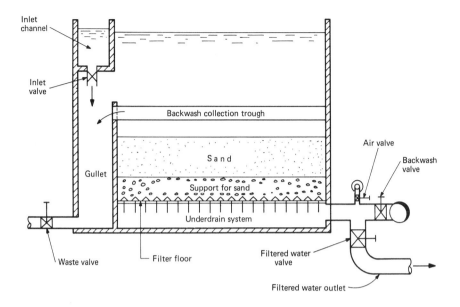

Fig 13.15 General arrangement of a typical rapid sand filter

and the inlet valve is opened. When the water has reached a satisfactory level in the filter basin, the filtered water valve is again opened and filtering is resumed.

The *sand bed* in a conventional rapid sand filter consists of clean silica sand to a depth of 0.6 to 0.75 m, having an effective size* of between 0.4 mm and 0.7 mm and a uniformity coefficient** of less than about 1.7. In some European countries, the effective size of sand used in rapid sand filters is 0.9 to 1.0 mm. In many cases in Europe, it is necessary to use coagulant aids because the water is so cold in the winter. This provides a tougher floc, which makes the larger sand satisfactory as a filter. In the United States, crushed anthracite is sometimes used as a substitute for sand. Anthracite has a density of about 1400 kg/m³ (compared with the sand value of 2650 kg/m³) and it does not require such high backwash rates to achieve fluidisation of the filter bed.

When a sand bed is washed, there is a tendency for stratification to occur, with the larger particles migrating to the bottom of the bed and the smaller particles migrating to the top. In normal operation, the water is, therefore,

---

* *Effective size* of a filter sand is that size of sieve opening which would permit the passage of 10 per cent by weight of the sand (D_{10})

** *Uniformity coefficient* is the ratio of the size of a sieve which would permit the passage of 60 per cent by weight (D_{60}) to the effective size (D_{10}). UC $= D_{60}/D_{10}$

filtered firstly through the fine sand and later through the coarse sand. The length of a filter run depends on the amount of storage voids available in the sand bed for retention of the impurities. If the fine sand layers become clogged before the storage space in the coarse layers deeper in the filter is used, the length of run must be shorter than ideal.

Dual media filters aim to overcome this problem. If anthracite with an effective size of about 1.0 mm is placed over sand with an effective size of 0.6 mm (for example), the anthracite, being lighter, will form a surface layer after backwashing so that the water will be filtered through the coarse anthracite and then through the finer sand, and ideal conditions are more nearly approached.

Mixed media filters use three different materials. The bottom layer of the filter bed consists of fine garnet (density = 4200 kg/m³), the middle layer consists of silica sand (density = 2650 kg/m³) and the upper layer consists of coarser anthracite (density = 1400 to 1700 kg/m³). The three materials are not so closely graded that they form separate layers, but mixing takes place, giving a gradual gradation of void sizes from large near the surface to fine near the bottom. The sand support bed requires a layer of coarse garnet sand to prevent the fine garnet sand from penetrating the gravel bed and distributors.

Upflow rapid sand filters (also known as Immedium filters) operate with the water passing upwards through a sand bed; thus, coarse-to-fine filtration is achieved without the use of a variety of media. Washing is in the same direction as in normal filtration, so that the backwash water contaminates the filtered water zone. The use of this type of filter is therefore not wholly satisfactory for public water supplies — particularly if the raw water is significantly polluted. It can, however, be used for industrial water supplies.

The *filtration loading rate* of the sand bed in rapid sand filters is traditionally between 1.3 and 1.4 L/s.m². However, the allowable loading for satisfactory performance depends on the type of water, the extent and type of pretreatment and other factors in the design and operation of the filter. Higher rates are practicable with coarse-to-fine filtering systems and with coarser sand when coagulant aids are used at the coagulation and settling stage. Low rates are required with weak floc, and with fine-to-coarse filtration. Rates used nowadays are generally in the range of 1.3 to 4.0 L/s.m².

The *sand support* commonly consists of layers of gravel placed over the filter compartment floor. The purpose of this support is threefold: to provide uniform drainage conditions for removing filtered water from the sand bed, to prevent sand from entering the underdrainage system, and to assist in the even distribution of backwash water. In early filters, the bottom layers of gravel consisted of material with a diameter of 50 to 70 mm, but the trend nowadays is towards smaller gravel in the bottom layers — a maximum size of between 15 and 25 mm is often used. The total thickness of gravel is about

300 to 450 mm in many installations. The uppermost layer of the gravel must prevent the intrusion of the sand; it can consist of a coarse sand with an effective size of about 1.0 to 2.0 mm. With mixed media filters, the uppermost layers of the support consist of special high-density coarse sand.

Much attention has been given to the design of the gravel layers to ensure even backwash flow, effective cleaning of sand and freedom from gravel displacement, but the problems are still only partially solved. A good designer will be careful about improvisation without previous trial on a pilot scale; he will copy systems which have proved satisfactory, while he will shun designs which are known to have given trouble. Some equipment suppliers who recommend the use of coarse sand (effective size of about 1.0 mm) recommend the complete abolition of the gravel layers, the sand being placed directly in contact with slotted plastic nozzles set in the filter floor.

The *underdrainage* system is hydraulically designed to carry the backwash water; backwash water flow rates through sand beds in different systems range from about 6 to 16 L/s.m², whereas filtering rates are only 1.3 to 4.1 L/s.m². The objective of underdrainage system design is to distribute both the backwash water and the air for scouring the sand as evenly as practicable over the full extent of the sand bed. The three main configurations of filter underdrain are shown in Fig 13.16.

Where the distribution nozzles are used as controls, the flow distribution will be uneven unless the combined head loss through the nozzles, the gravel bed and fluidised sand to a depth equal to the original depth of sand bed is a monotonic increasing function of upflow rate. In the case of the arrangement in Fig 13.16, the total head loss in the distribution channel and a lateral should be less than about 10 per cent of the nozzle head loss, so that the backwash flow rates through·the nozzles should not vary by more than 5 per cent as a result of friction losses in the underdrains. Too much coarse gravel in a gravel bed will permit free horizontal movement of backwash water in the space between the nozzles and the sand bed, and therefore partially negate the distribution value of the nozzles.

Where *air scour* is used in conjunction with a drainage system which uses nozzles, the nozzles are specially designed to distribute the air evenly. These nozzles are fitted with hollow stems which project down into the laterals or into the plenum as shown in Fig 13.17. A small air control orifice is drilled in the stem of each nozzle just below the filter floor. The pressure difference which can be sustained across this orifice is dictated by the length of the stem below the hole. The greater the allowable pressure difference, the less is the effect of extraneous disturbing influences on the air flow rate. A hood over the top of the nozzle can help to prevent water from entering the top of the stem and interfering with the air distribution. During the air scour cycle, air is introduced into the underdrain system; it escapes through the nozzles into the filter.

If *water* and *air* are to be used *simultaneously* for filter cleaning, care must

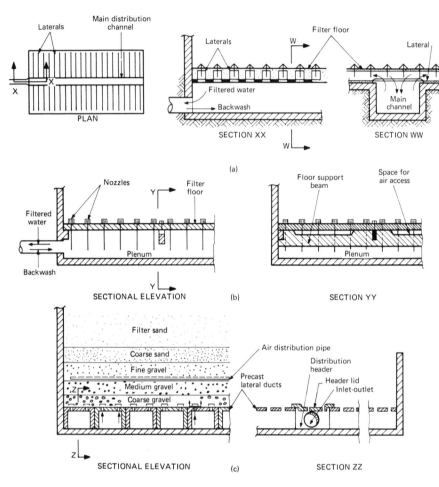

Fig 13.16 Filter underdrain systems: (a) a main distribution channel conveying the water to laterals, which feed the nozzles set in the filter floor; the head loss in the nozzles controls the flow distribution, (b) an open space, or plenum, beneath the filter floor, serving the nozzles which are set in the floor; the head loss in the nozzles controls the flow distribution, (c) a system which provides for easy access of the water into the lower gravel layers; the head loss in the upper portion of the gravel bed controls the distribution of flow

be taken to ensure that the necessary water can be distributed to the various parts of the filter in such a way that the height of the waves in the water surface is small in comparison with the head used for forcing the air through the control orifice — otherwise uneven air scour will result. This condition can best be attained in a plenum distribution system, particular care being

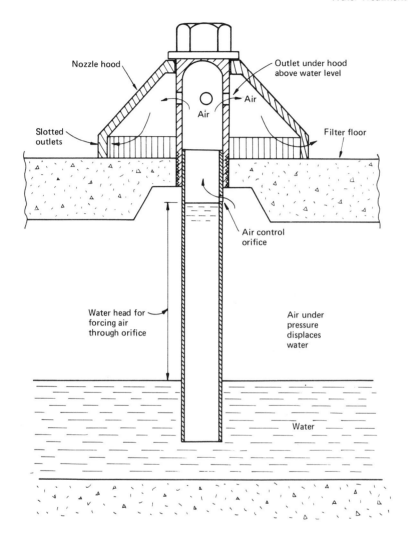

Fig 13.17 Diagram showing nozzle for air scour

taken to dissipate the energy of the incoming water, which could cause excessive waves and turbulence.

In the low head loss arrangement shown in Fig 13.16(c), backwash water can freely enter the lower gravel layers; the head loss which controls the flow distribution is that which occurs in the upper gravel layers. If air scour is required, air is supplied through a separate layer of perforated air pipes set in one of the gravel layers.

A typical *washwater collection and disposal* system is shown in Fig 13.18. The washwater is forced up through the filter bed and emerges laden with impurities removed from the sand. The troughs to collect the dirty water are placed as low as practicable, in view of the need to avoid excessive disturbance of the hydraulic flow pattern in the expanded sand bed. The troughs discharge the water into the gullet, which forms a main collecting channel, whence it passes through the waste discharge valve.

If it is expected that some of the displaced impurities may be too heavy or may settle too rapidly to be carried up into washwater collection troughs, the gullet wall may be used as a weir, and the depth of water over the sand during the backwash is kept to a minimum so that the horizontal velocity thus induced may carry the impurities over into the gullet. This is known as a 'cross-wash' system. In order to intensify the horizontal velocity, water is sometimes introduced at the surface of the sand on the side opposite the gullet.

Backwash procedures are equally as important as the design of the underdrain, sand support and sand bed in planning a system in which the sand is thoroughly and evenly washed, without the occurrence of mud balls and gravel movement.

A filter backwash is started in response to one of three conditions: excessive head loss, excessive effluent turbidity, or excessive run time. In most installations, the head loss criterion is the most frequent reason for backwash initiation; the usual head loss limit is set at about 2 m. If the floc in the water is too weak, it sometimes happens that it is not retained in the filter bed until the desired maximum head is attained and a 'turbidity breakthrough' occurs. In conditions where the pretreatment by clarification is very good, or the flowthrough rates are low, the floc trapped in the sand bed may become so well gelled with time that thorough washing would be difficult if the operator were to wait until the usual maximum head loss were reached; in such a case, the time limitation would control the initiation of backwash.

Until recently, the general American practice for backwashing a filter was to use a high-rate backwash of from 12 to 16 L/s.m² to lift the sand grains into suspension; the dirt was removed by the resulting shearing and rubbing action. This action of the water was, in some cases, enhanced by surface rakes or high-pressure water jets to break up lumps of packed impurities and sand.

The European practice has been to use an air scour in which air is bubbled through the sand bed at a rate of 5 to 15 L/s.m² for a period of about five minutes (to let friction dislodge the impurities from the sand grains), followed by a low to medium-rate water backwash at 7 to 10 L/s.m² until the water becomes clear (about 10 minutes).

A recent trend both in Europe and the USA is to use a period of combined water and air scour during which the air loosens the impurities, while a low-rate water backwash of about 6 L/s.m² carries them to the surface and prevents their penetration which sometimes occurs with air scour only. This period is then followed by a medium-rate water backwash at a rate of 9 to 12 L/s.m² to clear out the loosened impurities. A satisfactory combined

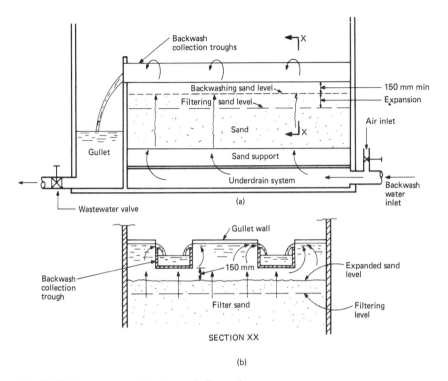

Fig 13.18 Wastewater collection and disposal system

water-air scour can be achieved only if particular attention has been paid to the design of the water and air distribution systems.

In hot climates, where the raw water may be polluted with nutrients, the growth of algae in the sedimentation and filter basins may be a problem. This can be overcome by chlorination of the water before sedimentation.

The viscosity of the warmer water found in hot climates is lower than that in temperate climates, and therefore the backwash rate needed for efficient filter cleaning is greater than that with cooler water.

The *flow control* for rapid sand filters is achieved in a number of ways. The following descriptions cover only three of them, and they are illustrated in Fig 13.19. Most systems include some means of automatic flow control (control valves operated by signals from level-sensing or flow-sensing elements) and care should be taken to avoid control conditions which lead to controller instability, such as *hunting* caused by continual over-correction.

Flow control systems in water treatment plants are usually operated hydraulically or pneumatically. The damp conditions often occurring in filter control galleries are not conducive to the reliable long-term operation of electrical equipment.

In a treatment plant equipped with *downstream flow control* as shown in

Fig 13.19(a), a flow measuring device (venturi, orifice, weir or other type) is used to provide a signal which operates the flow control valve. The control system adjustment may be set by hand so that the rate of flow is kept close to a predetermined rate. The plant inflow control valve is then operated by a device which senses the level in the channel feeding the filters. The efficiency of turbidity removal in a filter is greatly reduced by sudden changes in flow. The total head loss across the filter and filter control valve is equal to the difference between the water level in the filter chamber and the hydraulic grade level downstream of the control valve. This is almost constant during normal operation. The flow is controlled by motion of the filter control valve, which automatically adjusts to compensate for changes in the resistance to flow in the filter bed and, because the filter bed clogs slowly, only a relatively slow movement is required. This allows the valve action to be well damped so that hunting will not occur, and sudden flow variations may be avoided.

With this control system, there is a sudden change in the flow through the pretreatment portion of the plant when a filter is taken out of service for backwashing, and an even greater change as the filter chamber is refilled after backwashing. These sudden changes can cause a marked deterioration in the settlement efficiency of any clarifier.

The system of *upstream flow control* with flow splitting, as shown in Fig 13.19(b), avoids shock loadings on the pretreatment units. The plant inflow can be either set to a given flow rate, or automatically controlled by the demand for water (perhaps from the level in the filtered water storage). The flow to each filter is controlled by a flow-splitting device, through which the flow rate is a function of the level in the distribution channel. In this way, the flow from the pretreatment section is split equally among all operating filters. Each filter flow control valve is operated by the level in its particular filter chamber, thus the level above the filters is kept almost constant.

The control system with *common head loss* on all filters can be effected with less automatic control equipment than is used for either of the other two methods already described. It is also known as a *declining flow rate* system. A filter which is relatively clean can filter water efficiently at a higher flow rate than one in which clogging with impurities is well advanced. A filter which is starting to pass turbid water can continue to produce acceptable water for a time if the flow rate is reduced. It would appear that, in some installations, the best use could be made of a filter if a high flow rate could be used while it is relatively clean, with the rates of flow being gradually reduced as the filter becomes clogged. This is what happens if all filters are subjected to a common head loss. In Fig 13.19(c) the total head loss through each filter, together with its underdrain and flow-limiting orifice, is equal to the difference in head between the influent header and the common effluent weir.

Filters are backwashed in a fixed sequence. The time for backwashing the

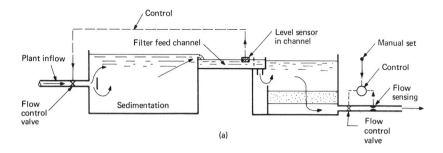

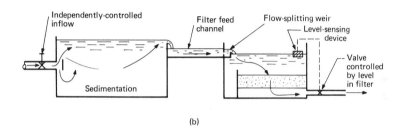

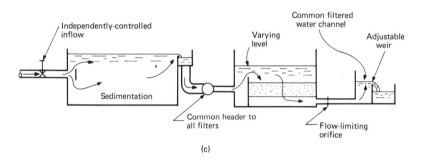

Fig 13.19 Diagrams of three methods of flow control through rapid sand filters (valves for filter isolation and backwash operations are not shown): (a) downstream flow control, (b) upstream flow control with flow splitting, (c) upstream flow control with common head loss on all filters

next filter in the sequence is judged from the rising level of the water in all the filter basins.

The improvement in performance, coupled with absence of automatic control equipment, makes this common head-loss filtration control ideal for use in countries with limited technology.

Diatomaceous earth filters

Diatomaceous earth (diatomite) consists of the fossilised skeletons of single-celled microscopic marine plants, allied to algae, which extract silica from the water and use it to construct hard skeletons. The particles vary in size from about 0.01 mm up to about 0.2 mm; consisting of silica, they are rigid and strong. The bulk density of processed diatomaceous earth is from 150 to 200 kg/m³. Naturally occurring deposits of diatomaceous earth are mined; the material is graded according to size and marketed as a filter medium.

Since about 1930, many manufacturers have used filtration through diatomaceous earth to achieve clarity and purity of process liquors, but it was only during the Second World War that the process was developed for treating potable water. The army needed lightweight portable equipment for removing amoebic dysentery cysts from water to be used by the troops. Since then, the process of diatomite filtration has been further developed for treatment of municipal water supplies.

During the 1950s and 1960s, experience with the operation of diatomite filters greatly increased the knowledge of process and design requirements. Generally, diatomite filters are used for the removal of low turbidity from waters in which the bacteriological quality is fairly good. In these cases, the coagulation, flocculation and sedimentation which normally precede rapid sand filtration (as shown in Fig 13.1) are omitted. Developments in the application of diatomite filtration include pretreatment processes for waters which contain iron and manganese, and its use for final filtering following lime-soda softening (see Section 13.6).

Fig 13.20(a) shows a possible arrangement for a diatomaceous earth filter. There are two main types of configuration for diatomite filters: pressure filters and vacuum filters. The one shown in the figure is a pressure filter; the pump is on the inlet side of the filter elements, raising the pressure to force the water through them. With a vacuum filter, the pressure of the water on the inlet side is near atmospheric, and a pump on the outlet side reduces the pressure there to establish a pressure gradient through the filter elements. Although vacuum filters cause some problems, such as air binding, which are not found in pressure filters, they are easier to operate and maintain, and are used in small plants for treating relatively clear waters (such as that from swimming pools).

There are three distinct phases in the *operation* of a diatomite filter: precoating, filtering and septum cleaning (or backwashing). At the end of each run, the material used for filtering is all lost and the preparation of a suitable layer of filtering material for the start of the next filtering operation consists of *precoating* the septum with a layer of diatomite two to three millimetres thick. To form a precoat, filtered water is pumped through the filter, together with a slurry of diatomite, the particles of which bridge the gaps in the septum of each element and build up to form a suitable mat; the water used for precoating can be recycled until it is clear on leaving the treated water outlet. The *filtering cycle* starts as soon as the precoat is completed. During the filtering cycle, raw water dosed with body feed is pumped at a controlled rate through the filter elements. The *body feed* is diatomite added at such a rate to ensure that the permeability of the mixture of impurities and body feed making up the filter cake on the elements remains low enough for operation over a reasonable time. Without body feed, the impurities would rapidly clog the surface of the mat of filter medium. As well as controlling permeability, the body feed will repair any cracks which may develop in the precoat layer during a run. Filtering must be continuous in order to hold the filter cake together, because it may break if the hydraulic pressure from the flow were removed. At times when there is no demand for water, the filtered water can be recycled to maintain continuous flow. When the thickness of the

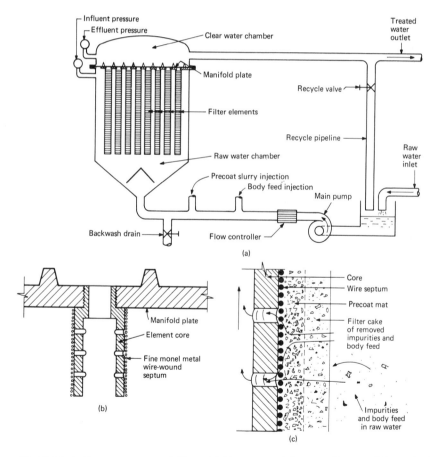

Fig 13.20 A diatomaceous earth filter: (a) diagrammatic layout, (b) a possible method of septum support, (c) section through filter element during filter operation

filter cake becomes excessive, or the pressure loss through the filter reaches the operational maximum, the filter elements must be cleaned. In the *cleaning cycle*, the accumulated filter cake, consisting of the precoat, the body feed and the accumulated impurities, is removed. Several different methods have been devised to ensure complete removal of the filter cake and to flush it completely out of the housing. The filter cake should not be sent to a sewer or a stream, but should be disposed of in a land-fill — it is not practical to re-use it.

The main cost item in the operation of a diatomite filter is the diatomite itself. When a proposal for an installation is considered, two important factors are the local cost of the material and its continued long-term availability. Factors which favour the use of diatomite filters are the need for a lightweight, portable, effective method of filtration (as in military field conditions), the need for a filtration system at a particular location for a limited period (as for a construction camp or village), the treatment of waters of low turbidity (as for swimming pools and supplies from clean streams) and where a low capital cost augmentation is required to meet seasonal or occasional high demands (as in a tourist camp or town). In some instances, the total estimated cost of constructing, maintaining and operating diatomite filters for public water supply has been less than that for conventional rapid sand filters and slow sand filters. Their use has declined since the introduction of dual media and mixed media rapid sand filters, which treat water with added filter aids and process at higher than conventional rates of flow.

13.5 Post-filtration treatment

By the time water has undergone filtration and any pretreatment which has been considered necessary, the most obviously unwanted properties will have been removed (Fig 13.1 and Table 13.1). There still remain, however, several adjustments or chemical additions which may be desirable before the water is fit to be discharged to the distribution system and the consumer. These are: disinfection, pH correction and, if it is required, fluoridation.

Disinfection

Chlorination is the commonest form of disinfection used (see Chapter 10). Sometimes chlorine may be added to the water at some stage before filtration; this is primarily as an agent for the oxidation of iron or manganese, the bleaching of colour, or the removal of tastes and odours. The effectiveness of disinfection increases as the number and size of solid particles decreases (see Chapter 10); therefore, disinfection is more efficient *after* filtration.

A minimum contact time is required between the addition of the chlorine and the delivery of the water to the consumer. The reason for this is twofold: to allow time for an effective kill of pathogens and to permit dissipation of the chlorine to reduce the incidence of chlorinous tastes. This contact time may be provided in a special chlorine contact tank which is baffled to prevent short circuiting, in a pipeline of sufficient length or in a reservoir. Because of the long detention time in a reservoir, residual chlorine concentrations may be relatively low. Thus, although there will be some residual protection against bacterial recontamination, there will be only a slow kill rate for the more virulent pathogens such as some types of virus.

Because the chlorine is more active at lower pH values, the most effective chlorination method is a chlorine contact tank before pH correction (Fig 13.1). When chlorine contact takes place in a pipeline it usually follows pH correction, so that even though the chlorine residual may be relatively high, the activity is decreased because the hypochlorous acid (HOCl) has a higher degree of ionisation at the higher pH values.

Ozone, too, is more effective as a disinfectant if added after filtration. Air with ozone is bubbled through tanks in which the water is detained for sufficient time to achieve an adequate kill of pathogens. The excess ozone in the gas leaving the contact tanks has to be led away and heated to convert it back to oxygen before it is discharged to the atmosphere (see Chapter 10).

pH correction

When water has undergone coagulation with alum or iron salts, the pH is reduced. The pH of the filtered water depends on the optimum pH for coagulation with aluminium salts, or on the amount of iron salts added. In either case, it is likely that the filtered water will become acid in reaction and corrosive. Correction of pH at this stage is usually effected by adding a solution of either sodium carbonate or sodium hydroxide. Lime, although cheaper, can contain insoluble residues which either cause turbidity or settle out in reservoirs and distribution systems. Lime has, however, some value in reducing the corrosivity of the water (Chapter 5), and some authorities may be prepared to accept a small amount of turbidity from lime addition because of other benefits which accrue from its use.

If the pH correction were carried out before filtration, some of the fine floc could be redissolved and pass through the filters in solution, with a possibility of its later reprecipitation in the distribution system.

All that is required for effective pH correction is to add the appropriate amount of chemical to the effluent stream, ensuring that it becomes mixed within a reasonable distance of flow.

Fluoridation

Fluoride is sometimes added to water supplies to provide the necessary fluoride content to permit the development of strong tooth enamel in children. It is usually added after filtration but before the water goes into the clear water reservoir. Mixing in the clear water reservoir, as a consequence of the momentum of the incoming water, can not only even out minor variations in the dose rate, but also act as a buffer between the dosing point and the distribution system if there is any malfunction in the dosing system.

The three most commonly used chemicals for fluoridation are sodium fluosilicate (Na_2SiF_6), sodium fluoride (NaF) and hydrofluosilicic acid (H_2SiF_6). Sodium fluosilicate is sometimes known as sodium silicofluoride. All these chemicals hydrolyse completely so that the fluoride ion results from the use of any of them or from naturally occurring fluoride.

$$SiF_6{}^{2-} + 2H_2O \longrightarrow 4H^+ + 6F^- + SiO_2$$

Sodium fluosilicate is a white, non-hygroscopic powder available commercially in a form which is about 98 per cent pure (containing about 59.7 per cent fluoride). It is only sparingly soluble in water (0.43-0.77 per cent at 0° to 25°C), and a dry feeder and agitated mixing tank are required to prepare a slurry or solution for feeding. The material is dusty, corrosive to metals and harmful to the skin, so that great care is needed when handling it. It is reasonably priced and can be used for large water supplies (flow > 100 L/s).

Hydrofluosilicic acid (also known as fluosilicic acid) is always supplied in aqueous solution, usually between 15 and 35 per cent. It is a colourless, fuming, clear free-flowing liquid; it is very corrosive and must be stored in plastic or rubber-lined tanks. It is dosed by a positive displacement ram pump or diaphragm pump.

Sodium fluoride is a white free-flowing powder, available commercially with a purity of 95 to 98 per cent. The most useful property of this chemical is that its solubility is almost constant at 4.05 per cent over a wide range of ambient temperatures. This permits the use of a saturator, in which a saturated solution can be prepared and fed to the water by a positive displacement metering pump. Because of this convenience it is often used in small plants, although the cost of the chemical is relatively high. For large plants, the equipment required becomes bulky if the fluoride is fed in solution, and dusty conditions are created if the fluoride is fed from a dry feeder.

With all three sources of fluoride, care must be taken in handling. The chemicals are harmful if they come into contact with the skin, or are inhaled or ingested. Either the water used for diluting the solution should be free of hardness, or polyphosphates should be added to prevent the precipitation of insoluble calcium fluoride (CaF_2) or magnesium fluoride (MgF_2) in the dosing pipelines. Care must be taken with maintenance of equipment, because health authorities demand accuracy of dose; the corrosive nature of the solutions can cause equipment malfunction. It is recommended that chemical tests for fluoride concentration should be carried out at least once a day.

Example 13.1

A solution of hydrofluosilicic acid which contains 170 g of H_2SiF_6 per litre is to be used to dose a flow of 200 L/s. The water naturally contains 0.3 mg/L of F^-, but it is required that the treated water have a fluoride content of 1.0 mg/L. Calculate the rate of feed of hydrofluosilicic acid required.

Solution
The difference between the target concentration and natural concentration is $1.0 - 0.3 = 0.7$ mg/L.

Therefore, the rate of dose, as F^-, needed is 200×0.7 mg/s $= 140$ mg/s

The molecular weight of the acid (H_2SiF_6) is $2 + 28 + (6 \times 19) = 144$, of which 114 is F.

Therefore, the rate of feeding H_2SiF_6 is $140 \times 144/114 = 176.8$ mg/s, which corresponds to $176.8/170 = 1.04$ mL/s [Note 1 g/L $\equiv$ 1 mg/mL] or 89.9 L/d

13.6 Softening

Softening is practised when the hardness of water is not acceptable; the degree of softening depends on the use to which the water will be put. In a domestic supply, hardness creates nuisance scums, wastes soap when used for laundry or ablution, and deposits scale in hot water services. Softening is seldom applied to municipal water supplies if the hardness is less than about 3 milli-equivalents per litre (me/L) (150 mg/L as $CaCO_3$), and a reasonable target hardness after treatment is about 1.6 me/L (80 mg/L as $CaCO_3$). Feedwater for boilers has to be soft to prevent the formation of scales and sludges which interfere with the heat transfer, resulting in overheating the metal and possible failure under pressure. The permissible hardness depends on the operating pressure of the boiler. For general treatment of municipal supplies, a process of precipitating the calcium and magnesium by adding lime and soda is usually adequate, but for boiler feedwater and other uses demanding a very soft water, it is necessary to use ion exchange methods. If water for boiler feed is very hard, both types of softening may be used (the ion exchange after the lime and soda).

As already stated (Chapter 5), hardness is caused by calcium and magnesium ions in the water. The presence of bicarbonate ions affects the dose of chemicals required to precipitate the calcium and magnesium, and therefore hardness is classified in two ways: first, as calcium or magnesium hardness; and secondly, as carbonate or non-carbonate hardness. Carbonate hardness is caused by calcium or magnesium ions associated with bicarbonate ions, and non-carbonate hardness is caused by calcium or magnesium ions associated with chloride, sulphate or other ions.

Lime-soda processes

The sequence of processes in simple lime-soda softening is shown in Fig 13.21. The similarities to the sequence for treating river water should be noted (Fig 13.1). The amounts of soda ash (Na_2CO_3) and lime ($Ca(OH)_2$) are estimated from a chemical analysis of the water and are added to the influent stream. Sometimes, a small amount of iron salts or alum is added as a flocculation aid. The dosed water passes to a solids contact or sludge blanket-type clarifier, where the chemicals precipitate onto the suspended particles.

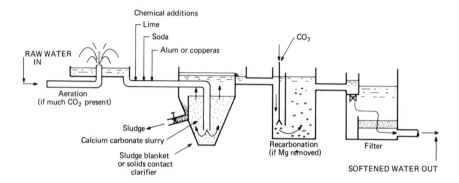

Fig 13.21 Sequence of operations in simple lime-soda softening

Lime is used as a cheap form of alkali which will raise the pH to between 9.5 and 10, so that bicarbonates will be converted to carbonates and the calcium precipitated as calcium carbonate. Further raising the pH will cause the magnesium to be precipitated as magnesium hydroxide. The solubility product for magnesium hydroxide is such that the pH has to be raised to between 10.5 and 11 to get good magnesium removal. This is achieved by adding an excess of lime over that indicated as needed by the chemical equations, and of sufficient soda to precipitate the calcium, leaving sodium hydroxide in the water. The amount of excess lime added is often 0.8 to 1.3 me/L, depending on the desired efficiency of magnesium removal. As the pH is increased any carbon dioxide present will be converted to carbonate and will be available for the precipitation of calcium. Water with a high carbon dioxide concentration can be aerated before lime treatment to reduce chemical requirements by eliminating some of the carbon dioxide. The chemical reactions are as given below.

For carbonate hardness with calcium:

$$Ca(HCO_3)_2 + Ca(OH)_2 \longrightarrow 2CaCO_3 + 2H_2O$$

For non-carbonate hardness with calcium:

$$CaSO_4 + Na_2CO_3 \longrightarrow CaCO_3 + Na_2SO_4$$

For carbonate hardness with magnesium:

$$Mg(HCO_3)_2 + 2Ca(OH)_2 \longrightarrow Mg(OH)_2 + 2CaCO_3 + 2H_2O$$

For non-carbonate hardness with magnesium:

$$MgSO_4 + Ca(OH)_2 + Na_2CO_3 \longrightarrow Mg(OH)_2 + CaCO_3 + Na_2SO_4$$

For excess lime removal:

$$Ca(OH)_2 + Na_2CO_3 \longrightarrow CaCO_3 + 2NaOH$$

For carbon dioxide removal:

$$CO_2 + Ca(OH)_2 \longrightarrow CaCO_3 + H_2O$$

Inspection of the chemical equations will show that the dose may be estimated as follows

Equivalents of lime = equivalents of carbonate hardness
+ equivalents of magnesium hardness
+ equivalents of carbon dioxide
+ excess lime to raise pH

Equivalents of soda = equivalents of non-carbonate hardness
+ equivalents of excess lime

Example 13.2

Analysis of a hard water gave the following results:

Total hardness = 5 me/L; calcium hardness = 2.6 me/L;
alkalinity = 4.0 me/L; acidity = 0.2 me/L

Calculate the required doses of lime $(Ca(OH)_2)$ and soda (Na_2CO_3) for softening.

Solution

Carbonate hardness is equal to either the alkalinity or the total hardness, whichever is the lesser. In this case, the alkalinity is the lesser, at 4 me/L. Magnesium hardness is the difference between the total hardness and the calcium hardness = 5.0 – 2.6 = 2.4 me/L. The carbon dioxide is equivalent to the acidity = 0.2 me/L (or 4.4 mg/L as CO_2). Non-carbonate hardness is the difference between total hardness and carbonate hardness = 5.0 – 4.0 = 1.0 me/L. Assume excess lime equivalent to 1.0 me/L.

Then, from the relationship above, the amount of lime needed is

$$4.0 + 2.4 + 0.2 + 1.0 = 7.6 \text{ me/L}$$
$$= 7.6 \times 74/2 = 281 \text{ mg/L as } Ca(OH)_2$$

and the soda needed is

$$1.0 + 1.0 = 2 \text{ me/L}$$
$$= 2 \times 106/2$$
$$= 106 \text{ mg/L as Na}_2\text{CO}_3$$

The coagulation and flocculation to remove hardness by the lime soda process is also reasonably effective for reducing turbidity, colour, bacteria and viruses.

Before filtration, the water must be *stabilised.* The water leaving the clarifier has a fairly high pH (in the range 9.5 to 11) and is saturated (if not supersaturated) with calcium carbonate. If it were applied to the filter with the high pH which results from excess lime treatment, calcium carbonate would precipitate in the filters and cement the sand grains together. In any case, it is necessary to reduce the pH before the water is sent to the consumers. The usual method of reducing the pH and bringing the water to a stable condition in which it will not precipitate calcium carbonate is to add carbon dioxide, which is generated by burning gas, oil or coke. The products of combustion are bubbled through the water in a *recarbonation tank.* If too little carbon dioxide dissolves, the tendency to precipitate calcium carbonate is increased; if too much, the water can become corrosive. Some manufacturers of recarbonation equipment offer submerged combustion recarbonators (Fig 13.22).

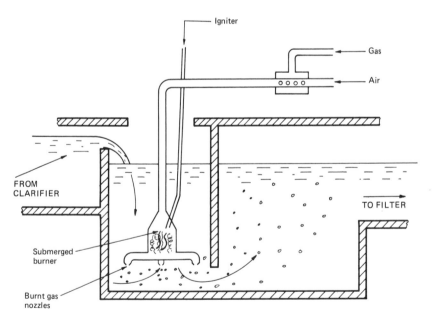

Fig 13.22 Schematic flow arrangement for submerged combustion recarbonation

In these units, the gas or oil is ignited in a burner at a depth of about 3 m below the water surface and the products of combustion are discharged as small, hot bubbles. This increases the rate of solution.

The *filter* generally used in lime-soda softening plants is a rapid sand filter of design similar to those already described in Section 13.4.

The high pH in the clarifier is an effective disinfectant, but a residual disinfectant may be added at the plant outlet in the distribution system. Fluoride may also be added to the plant effluent.

In a case where the target hardness and raw water quality are suitable, *split treatment* can eliminate the need for recarbonation and result in saving chemicals; but an extra reaction and separation tank is needed, thus increasing the capital cost.

In split treatment (Fig 13.23), the flow is split into two streams. One stream is dosed with lime and softened by the excess lime process; some of the calcium and most of the magnesium in that stream are removed in a solids contact clarifier. The effluent from this clarifier then rejoins the second stream which, so far, has not been softened. The combined stream is dosed with soda ash, if necessary, and passed through a solids contact clarifier.

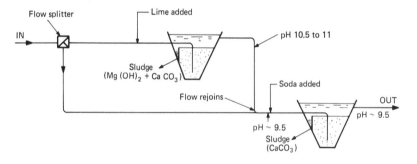

Fig 13.23 Schematic flow diagram for split treatment

The caustic alkalinity of the water which has been treated with excess lime reacts with the bicarbonates in the untreated stream to form carbonates. These carbonates, together with any extra which may have to be added, then react with the remaining calcium to form calcium carbonate, most of which will precipitate. Split treatment removes practically all the magnesium from the first stream, but practically none from the second stream.

Caustic soda precipitation

In some smaller softening installations, there is some interest in using caustic soda for replacing all or part of the lime and soda requirements. When lime and soda together are added to water, the reaction may be considered as

$$Ca(OH)_2 + Na_2CO_3 \rightleftharpoons CaCO_3 \downarrow + 2NaOH$$

Caustic soda may be used as a replacement for lime and soda ash, the replacement ratio being one equivalent of caustic soda for the combination of one equivalent of lime plus one equivalent of soda ash. Although caustic soda is more expensive than lime, its use reduces the amount of soda ash needed and the amount of sludge for disposal. The chemical reactions for the use of caustic soda are

For carbon dioxide

$$CO_2 + 2NaOH \longrightarrow Na_2CO_3 + H_2O$$

For carbonate hardness

$$Ca(HCO_3)_2 + 2NaOH \longrightarrow CaCO_3 \downarrow + Na_2CO_3 + 2H_2O$$
$$Mg(HCO_3)_2 + 4NaOH \longrightarrow Mg(OH)_2 \downarrow + 2Na_2CO_3 + 2H_2O$$

For non-carbonate hardness

$$CaSO_4 + Na_2CO_3 \longrightarrow CaCO_3 \downarrow + Na_2SO_4$$
$$MgSO_4 + 2NaOH \longrightarrow Mg(OH)_2 \downarrow + Na_2SO_4$$

The removal of carbon dioxide and carbonate hardness with caustic soda produces sodium carbonate, which is available for reaction with the calcium non-carbonate hardness. If the calcium hardness is greater than the sum of the acidity (CO_2 as $CaCO_3$) and twice the alkalinity (HCO_3^- as $CaCO_3$), it will be necessary to add soda ash to make up the amount of carbonate needed to precipitate the calcium. If a treated water is required to have a minimum amount of dissolved solids, and the calcium hardness is less than the sum of the acidity and twice the alkalinity, the lime should be only partially replaced so that the caustic soda used is limited to the amount needed to produce only enough sodium carbonate to react with the non-carbonate calcium hardness. In this way, sufficient calcium will be available to precipitate the alkalinity as $CaCO_3$.

Ion exchange

Some naturally-occurring zeolites (insoluble sodium aluminosilicates, $Na_2O.Al_2O_3.xSiO_2.yH_2O$) are able to exchange the sodium ions for other ions, particularly Ca^{2+} and Mg^{2+}. In 1906, an artificial zeolite (with the trade name *Permutit*) was developed in Berlin by the fusing of quartz, kaolin and sodium carbonate. Since that time, synthesised insoluble resins with superior exchange properties have been developed and are generally used in modern ion exchange softening.

If a cation exchange sodium resin is represented by Na_2R, the R being the complex resin base, the *ion exchange reactions* for water softening may be written.

$$Mg^{2+} + Na_2R \rightleftharpoons MgR + 2Na^+$$
$$Ca^{2+} + Na_2R \rightleftharpoons CaR + 2Na^+$$

These reactions are reversible. The direction of reaction depends on the equilibrium constants of the resin for the reaction, the concentrations of sodium, magnesium and calcium ions, and the degree of 'saturation' of the exchange capability of the resin.

For the *softening cycle*, the concentration of sodium ions is low and the reaction proceeds from left to right. The magnesium and calcium ions are 'trapped' by the insoluble solids and the sodium ions are released from the solids into the water stream. When all the available exchange sites on the resins have been occupied by calcium or magnesium, no further removal can occur. In practice, an increase in effluent hardness occurs before complete exhaustion of a resin bed, and the softening cycle then ends.

To achieve *regeneration* of the resin, the sodium ion concentration is increased by the use of a sodium chloride brine (about 10 per cent) to soak the solids. The reaction is then forced to go from right to left and, after the excess brine has been rinsed away, the Na_2R is in readiness for another softening cycle.

The softening *capacity* of exchange materials varies from 140 to 280 equivalents per cubic metre (e/m^3) for some natural greensands, from 230 to 800 e/m^3 for synthetic zeolites, and from 800 to 1400 e/m^3 for high-capacity styrene resins.

A softening *unit* consists of a bed of exchange medium (0.6 to 1.8 m deep) in a container, with facilities for: (a) the control of the flow rate, (b) the introduction and removal of regenerant brines, and (c) occasional washing of the exchange medium. The desirable flow rate is a function of the required quality of effluent and the type of medium, but it should be between 2 and 5.5 $L/s.m^2$.

Preliminary treatment is sometimes required to remove organic matter, iron and other impurities, which may either permanently occupy exchange sites (thus reducing the exchange capacity — known as *fouling* the media) or cause clogging. This occasionally requires full coagulation, flocculation, sedimentation and filtration to prepare the water so that the ion exchange medium will be protected.

The advantage of ion exchange softening is that the hardness may be reduced to any desired degree by suitable regeneration and operation techniques and choice of exchange medium. For reducing the hardness of very hard waters, the cost is more than that of the lime-soda process, so that for special purposes ion exchange is sometimes used to further reduce the hardness of lime-soda softened water.

Example 13.3

A medium-capacity styrene with an exchange capacity of 750 e/m^3 and a recommended areal loading rate of 4 L/s.m² is to be used for softening a stream of water with a maximum flow rate of 7.1 L/s. The water contains 2 me/L of hardness. Assuming a bed depth of 1.2 m, and a 90 per cent utilisation of exchange capacity before breakthrough, calculate

a The diameter of the bed
b The quantity of water passed before regeneration is needed
c The time of a run, assuming that average flow rate is 75 per cent of maximum.

Solution

$$\text{Area} = \frac{\text{Max flow rate}}{\text{Areal loading}} = \frac{7.1}{4} = \quad 1.78 \text{ m}^2$$

Diameter of vessel $= 2\sqrt{A/\pi} = 1.5\text{m}$

Volume of bed $= A \times \text{depth} = 1.78 \times 1.2 = 2.14 \text{ m}^3$

Total exchange capacity $= 2.14 \times 750 = 1602$ equivalents

Available exchange capacity $= 1602 \times 90/100 = 1442$ equivalents

Water contains 2 me/L hardness

Therefore *amount passed* $= 1442/0.002 \text{ L} = 721 \text{ kL}$

Time taken $= (721 \times 10^3/7.1) \times (100/75)/3600 \text{ hr}$
$\qquad\qquad = 37.6 \text{ hr.}$

13.7 Aeration

The fundamentals of aeration have been described in Chapter 8. In water treatment practice, aeration is used both to reduce the concentrations of volatile unwanted impurities such as hydrogen sulphide, volatile malodourous oils and carbon dioxide, and to increase the concentration of oxygen for oxidation of readily oxidisable impurities such as ferrous iron, manganese and some simple odour-producing substances.

In some areas water, when entering the ground, takes with it some organic impurities. The decomposition uses up dissolved oxygen and produces carbon dioxide. In the resulting chemically reducing environment, ferric iron in the aquifers may be reduced to the soluble ferrous state and go into solution. Aeration of such water as a preliminary treatment step can remove much of the carbon dioxide, and provide oxygen for oxidation of the iron to the insoluble ferric state.

River water of doubtful quality, with low dissolved oxygen and containing gases from organic decomposition, can be improved by aeration prior to conventional treatment. The oxygen which dissolves in the water can prevent or minimise putrefaction of sludges in the sedimentation tanks and filters, and some of the undesirable gases can be volatilised and removed.

Removal of carbon dioxide by aeration before lime-soda softening will reduce both the chemical requirements and the volume of sludge for disposal.

In waterworks practice, aeration is usually aimed primarily at removing dissolved substances. This is helped by ventilation of the air-water interfaces to blow away removed substances as soon as they are released from the water. The main type of aeration used is, therefore, spray aeration. Cascade aerators and diffused air aerators are not as efficient for dispersing released substances, but they may be used occasionally to dissolve oxygen.

Spray aerators have a number of nozzles which throw the water into the air in the form of droplets. At some locations they are purely functional (as in Fig 13.24(a)) while, at others, they may be designed as fountains, thus constituting architectural features as well as treatment processes.

Cascade aerators consist of a series of horizontal channels (Fig 13.24(b)) in which the water falls through the air from channel to channel and entrains air as bubbles on entering each successive channel.

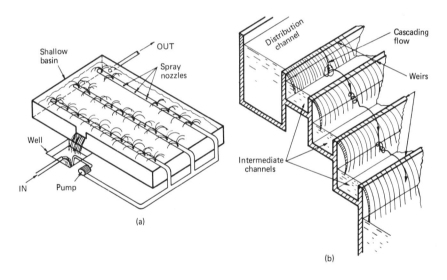

Fig 13.24 (a) Spray aerator, (b) cascade aerator

13.8 Iron and manganese

Selecting an appropriate process sequence for the removal of iron and manganese from water supplies is made complex by the variety of reactions which can occur with these elements. The choice depends on the presence or absence of manganese, carbon dioxide, organic acids, turbidity, dissolved oxygen, hardness and bicarbonates. It also depends on whether or not the iron and manganese are bound to organic material, and on the pH.

In general, a small pilot study can be used to find out the degree of treatment needed for the desired quality goals (see Chapter 5). In some cases, simple aeration followed by sedimentation and filtration may be adequate, but in other cases, the pH, carbon dioxide and organic content may be such that pH adjustment and catalytic action or other processes may be required.

Basic processes

There are five basic processes for removing or sequestering iron and manganese in water treatment:

Oxidation by aeration followed by sedimentation and filtration, or by filtration alone if the concentration is low. Iron and manganese in raw water supplies occur in the soluble ferrous (Fe^{2+}) and manganous (Mn^{2+}) forms. Oxidation converts them, respectively, to the almost insoluble ferric (Fe^{3+}) and manganic (Mn^{4+}) forms. Lime is sometimes added to raise the pH so as to facilitate the precipitation of ferric and manganic hydroxides. Chlorine, ozone or potassium permanganate may be used as an oxidising agent to supplement or replace the aeration, to convert the manganese to an easily deposited oxide, and to assist in breaking down the organic material to which the iron may be bound. If the iron is bound to organic material and does not readily coagulate, alum, ferric chloride or copperas may be added to act as a coagulant.

Catalytic action may be required for the oxidation of manganese. This occurs in beds of either pyrolusite ore or zeolite regenerated with potassium permanganate. In some cases, potassium permanganate is fed continuously into the water before it enters a filter. A bed of coke, coated with deposits of ferric hydroxide, also acts as a catalyst.

Lime softening, with the high pH which results, and preliminary aeration to remove carbon dioxide and add oxygen, will result in the conversion of the iron to the ferric state and its precipitation as ferric hydroxide.

Ion exchange, with either zeolites or ion exchange resins, can remove ferrous and manganous ions if they are associated with bicarbonate. These occur in groundwater devoid of oxygen. Care must be taken to avoid aeration or oxidation, which would produce ferric or manganic ions that would precipitate and clog the ion exchange bed. This process is practicable when used as incidental to softening only, when the amount of iron and manganese combined is less than about 0.03 times the hardness.

Sequestering the iron and manganese may be satisfactory in some circumstances. This involves the use of complex molecules which can encase (or combine with) the ions of iron and manganese so that, although they are still in solution, they are no longer in a position to take part in further reactions. Usual sequestering agents are polyphosphates or organic compounds; a common polyphosphate used for this purpose is sodium hexametaphosphate (known by the trade name *Calgon* in some countries). Subsequent heating of water treated in this way may destroy the effectiveness of the treatment.

13.9 Tastes and odours

The greatest number of consumer complaints about a water service refer to aesthetic deficiencies, such as odour and taste. The parameters which define odour and taste are difficult to measure, and the treatment to correct deficiencies depends on the nature and origin of the impurities causing the trouble.

Origins and treatment options

Tastes and odours may result from

a Release of substances from micro-organisms growing in the water. These micro-organisms can be algae, fungi, actinomycetes, protozoa or bacteria
b Decomposition of these micro-organisms, if killed
c Decomposition of vegetable matter — weeds, leaves, grasses and aquatic vegetation — in the water
d Reduction of sulphates and sulphur-containing organic matter to sulphides and mercaptans, under anaerobic conditions
e Discharge of sewage effluents and industrial wastes into water. These may carry phenols, metals and various organics which produce chloro-organic compounds with chlorination
f Discharge of the storm run-off from urban areas and roadways. Hydrocarbons, decomposing organic matter and traces of bitumen and tar may be present
g Drainage of leachate from sanitary landfills. This carries offensive, dissolved, organic substances.

The options for the treatment of taste and odour problems fall into three categories: prevention of the development of tastes and odours; conversion of the tastes and odours into non-offensive safe products; and removal of the taste and odour-producing substances.

Prevention

Sometimes, tastes and odours develop seasonally in a reservoir as a result of growths of algae or other micro-organisms. Regular monitoring of the micro-biological status of a reservoir can often indicate the onset of microbiological proliferation in time for preventive measures to be undertaken. Algal growths, for example, can be controlled by the addition of small quantities of copper sulphate to a reservoir; the dose should be carefully proportioned to avoid damage to fish life or to other aspects of ecology.

Discharges of sewage effluents and industrial wastes should be studied to ascertain whether any improvement in the taste and odour of the water supply could be effected by other treatment or by diversion of wastes which discharge into the supply stream.

Weed control along the banks of a reservoir and along streams and drains leading into a reservoir may effectively reduce some taste and odour problems.

Conversion to non-offensive products

Except for metallic tastes resulting from metallic ions, most of the objection-able tastes in water are caused by the presence of malodourous substances. In general, molecules of these substances have functional groups such as amines, ammonia, sulphides, thiols, phenols, and carbon-carbon unsatu-rated bonds. These functional groups are all electron-rich (or reducing) and, as well as producing unpleasant odours, they impart a degree of toxicity to the compounds. Reaction with an electron deficient (oxidising) molecule will reduce both the odour and the toxicity. For example, sulphides can be oxidised to elemental sulphur, sulphite and sulphate; amines ($R–NH_2$) to amine oxides; thiols (such as $CH_3–SH$) to sulphonic acids (such as $CH_3.SO H$); and unsaturated carbon compounds can become saturated.

The oxidising agents readily available for use in water odour control are the same ones that can be used for disinfection: chlorine, chlorine dioxide and ozone. While each of these agents is effective in removing a range of odours and accompanying tastes, each also has its limitations.

Neither chlorine nor chlorine dioxide in moderate doses will oxidise the malodourous compounds produced from decaying vegetable matter by actinomycetes, but these compounds are readily oxidised by ozone. Either chlorine dioxide or ozone will rapidly oxidise phenol and phenol-like compounds, which are oxidised only with difficulty when chlorine is used.

Marginal chlorination (less than breakpoint — see Chapter 10), in the presence of organic material, produces a range of organo-chlorine products which give a 'chlorinous' taste and odour to the water. Addition of further chlorine, so that there is a *free chlorine residual* after a period of *at least two hours*, will oxidise most of these organo-chlorine compounds and convert them into inoffensive ones. It will also oxidise sulphides to elemental sulphur or to sulphates.

Ozone at practicable concentrations is ineffective against odours from acetic acids, sulphites or saturated hydrocarbons, but it is effective in destroying a wider range of odours than is chlorine; it leaves no residual taste or odour in the water. In Europe, waters carrying industrial wastes are frequently used as sources for water supply, and ozone is used at many European water treatment plants for disinfection, taste and odour control. Ozone is more expensive than chlorine as a disinfectant, but its effectiveness against malodorous compounds may justify its trial or use in cases where there are difficult taste and odour problems.

Because of the probable complexity of the chemistry of unknown odours, together with the known limitations of available oxidants, it is necessary to perform pilot-scale tests for odour control proposals before installations are planned. The choice of oxidant for odour control will also affect the method of disinfection to be used.

Removal of offensive material

Some offensive substances can be removed either by aeration or by adsorption onto solid particles.

Effective and practical removal by *aeration* (see Chapter 8) requires that the substances be reasonably volatile. Spray aeration is an effective way of removing sulphides from an acid solution as H_2S and some of the volatile oils produced by algae. There are, however, many substances which cause tastes and odour which are insufficiently volatile for effective removal in this way.

Some of the offensive substances can be *adsorbed* onto colloids such as clay and the particles of floc which are produced by a coagulant. In this way, much taste and odour may be removed by coagulation, flocculation and filtration, but in bad cases this removal may not be adequate. *Activated carbon*, however, is a very effective agent for the adsorption of organic molecules from solution onto its finely convoluted surfaces; it may be used in either powdered or granular form.

Powdered activated carbon is fed into the water stream during treatment. Sometimes it is added with the coagulant before flocculation and sedimentation, and sometimes it is added between sedimentation and filtration (see Fig 13.1). The dose depends on the nature and strength of the materials to be adsorbed, but it is usually the lowest dose which will give satisfactory removal; doses are usually in the range of 1.5 to 15 g/m^3 but, in extreme cases, up to 80 g/m^3 may be required. The powdered activated carbon is lost either with the sludge or with the filter backwash water, and cannot be recovered. Feeding and handling devices must be designed to avoid fouling the machinery rooms with black dust.

Granulated activated carbon is used as final filter after the water has passed through the sand filters. It can produce a high-quality water and can remove chlorine. When the adsorptive capacity of the granulated material is exhausted, it can be partially restored by treatment with steam at appropriate time intervals. At longer intervals, it can be heated in furnaces to volatilise even the persistent adsorbed materials and restore the original adsorptive capacity, but there is always a loss of carbon through burning as well as through erosion in handling.

13.10 Desalination

Desalination is the reduction of the mineral salt content of water. Other terms used to describe the same operation are desalting, demineralisation, desalinisation and deionisation.

Water with a salinity low enough to be useful for human consumption and industrial use forms about only 3 per cent of the earth's total water resources. Of this amount, much is frozen in the Arctic and Antarctic areas, and the geographical distribution of the remainder in rivers, lakes and underground aquifers does not coincide with the distribution of present water needs. The development of mining towns and the growth of commercial centres have occurred in areas which do not have adequate natural fresh water supplies. In these cases, development has been dependent on the availability of fresh water both for the people involved and for the industrial activities.

The choice has often been between (a) the construction of long water transmission lines, and (b) the treatment of brackish or salty water which may be available close at hand. The high costs of water transmission over long distances have resulted, in many instances, in desalination being chosen as the favoured method of water supply, in spite of its relatively high cost.

The usual classification of salty waters according to the concentration of total dissolved salts is

$$> 35\ 000\ \text{mg/L} \quad — \quad \text{brine}$$
$$\sim 35\ 000\ \text{mg/L} \quad — \quad \text{seawater}$$
$$1000–35\ 000\ \text{mg/L} \quad — \quad \text{brackish water}$$
$$<\ 1000\ \text{mg/L} \quad — \quad \text{fresh water}$$

A common method of removing unwanted ions is by precipitation. There are, however, ions of sodium, potassium and nitrate which do not form insoluble compounds; and ions of sulphate and chloride which form insoluble compounds only with expensive or toxic ions such as silver, barium and lead. Methods other than precipitation are therefore needed for removing sodium, potassium, sulphate, chloride and nitrate ions from water. The main processes used in commercial methods for separating soluble salts from water are: distillation, freezing, ion exchange, electrodialysis and reverse osmosis. Other processes which have not been developed on a wide basis are salt adsorption and solvent extraction.

In 1976, it was estimated that the total world desalting capacity was 2500 ML/d, and it was expanding at a rate of 16 per cent a year. Of this amount, about 80 per cent was from distillation of seawater, with the multi-flash process supplying 80 per cent of the distillation total. About 20 per cent of the world total is from brackish waters, using reverse osmosis (about 13 per cent) or electrodialysis (about 7 per cent). Although freezing appeared to have some theoretical advantages, there are practical difficulties which have prevented its widespread use. The use of ion exchange desalting has been limited to small installations where convenience and freedom from excessive maintenance is important.

In general, the use of desalting has been restricted, because of its cost, to semi-arid or hot regions without enough natural fresh water, where the cost of water supply is only secondary to the success of some other commercial venture (such as oil production).

Distillation processes

When water boils, the dissolved salts remain in the liquid and the vapour released consists of water vapour and volatile impurities. Condensation of the water vapour produces a salt-free water. A simple distillation scheme is shown in Fig 13.25(a).

Energy, as heat, is required to raise the temperature of the water and to provide the latent heat of vaporisation (about 2280 kJ/kg). Scales consisting of calcium and magnesium salts can be deposited as water containing hardness is heated and the impurities are concentrated by evaporation. The refinements added to the simple distillation process aim at both reducing the energy requirements and avoiding undue scaling problems.

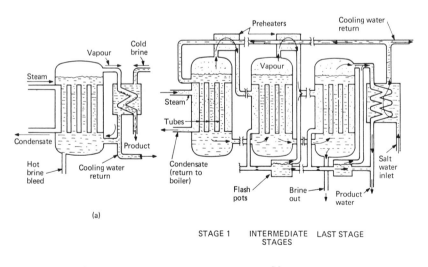

Fig 13.25 (a) Simple distillation, (b) multi-stage distillation

In *multi-stage distillation*, several boilers are in series, each operating at a lower pressure (and hence at a lower temperature) than the preceding one. The condensing vapour from one boiler contributes heat for vapour generation in the next (see Fig 13.25(b)).

In this way, some of the heat originally supplied is recovered and re-used, as condensation and vaporisation occur in the various stages. The number of stages is limited by the size and efficiency of the heating coils required for transfer of heat with a low temperature differential. In practice, a plant with between 10 and 20 stages is not uncommon.

The use of *multi-stage flash* distillation localises serious scaling problems to a single heat exchanger, while recovering most of the latent heat of vaporisation for re-use. The diagram in Fig 13.26 illustrates the principle of multi-stage flash distillation.

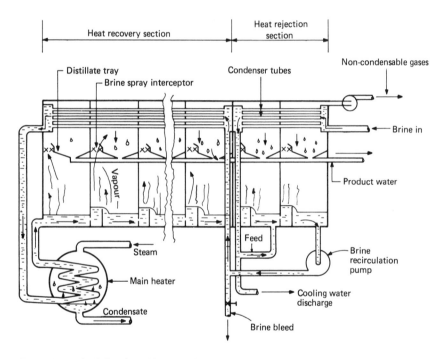

Fig 13.26 Principle of multi-stage flash distillation

The vapour pressure of water rises with increasing temperature. The temperature at which water boils is that for which its vapour pressure equals the ambient pressure. Hence, if the ambient pressure is reduced to below the vapour pressure, boiling will occur and it will continue until the temperature of the water falls to the value at which the vapour pressure equals the reduced ambient pressure.

Vapour generation or boiling as a result of pressure reduction is called *flashing*. In the multi-stage flash distillation process, the salt water is first heated and then passed through a series of compartments (usually between 25 and 50), each maintained at a pressure less than the preceding one. As the water enters each compartment through a pressure-reducing nozzle, some of it flashes to form vapour. As the vapour condenses on the condenser surfaces, its latent heat is used to preheat the brine which is being returned to the main heater, where it receives more heat before it is again directed into the first flashing compartment.

Vapour compression processes rely on the increase in pressure of the vapour to establish the temperature difference for transfer of heat. Fig 13.27 indicates the basic layout of a vapour compression distillation unit. After initial heating of the salt water, the vapour pump is operated so that the vapour under higher pressure can condense in the condenser tubes, at the same time causing the release of an equivalent amount of vapour from the brine. Heat exchangers can conserve heat from both the condensate and the waste brine. The only energy input required during operation is the mechanical energy for the vapour pump. Hot brine must be discharged at intervals to prevent the build-up of excessive concentrations of salt in the boiler.

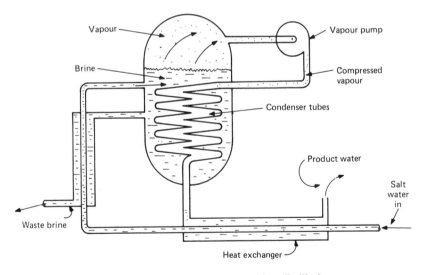

Fig 13.27 Operating principle of vapour compression distillation

Solar stills have been developed. One type was used for some years in Australia (see Fig 13.28). The production from each square metre is limited by the intensity of solar radiation, so that large areas are required to produce a moderate quantity of fresh water. The actual cost of water produced from a

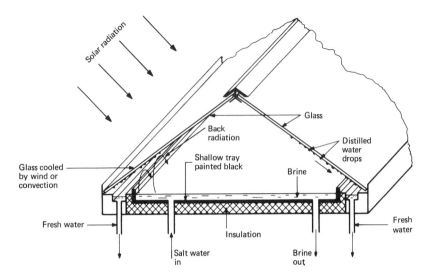

Fig 13.28 Australian solar distillation principle

prototype greatly exceeded the estimates based on laboratory studies because of high maintenance required to remove dust, to replace broken glass and to keep the draining and distribution system properly levelled in spite of the swelling clays in the foundation. The only major solar installation in Australia has now been abandoned in favour of reverse osmosis.

Freezing

When salt water freezes, only the water molecules attach themselves to the ice crystals; the salt molecules remain in solution. A method by which fresh water can be obtained from salt water is to freeze it partially, then to rinse off the salty brine and re-melt the ice crystals to yield fresh water. This process holds some theoretical advantage over distillation, because high temperatures are not needed, with the avoidance of consequent corrosion problems, and because the latent heat of fusion (ice to water) is only about 333 kJ/kg compared with 2276 kJ/kg for the latent heat of evaporation (water to vapour) — the amount of heat to be transferred for the phase change by freezing is only about 15 per cent of that needed for a phase change by evaporation of the same amount of water.

As with distillation processes, the reuse of heat through heat exchangers is needed to make this process efficient. The two main configurations for freezing desalination are those of direct freezing, in which the refrigerant is bubbled through water in a freezing compartment, and indirect freezing, in which the heat is transferred from the the water to the refrigerant through the

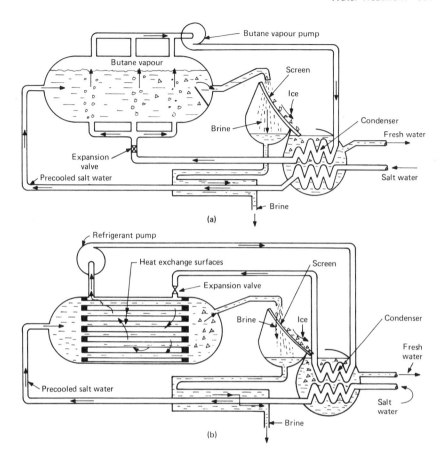

Fig 13.29 Diagram showing layout of desalination by freezing: (a) with direct freezing, (b) with indirect freezing

metal surfaces of the cooling coils (or evaporators). The layout of these types is illustrated in Fig 13.29.

Owing to practical difficulties, the freezing process has not gained much commercial support. One trouble is that the ice crystals tend to trap pockets of brine, which is later released into the product water as the ice melts. Another disadvantage is that it is more difficult to transfer an ice slurry between tanks than it is to transfer a vapour. On a large scale, serious consideration has been given to towing icebergs from Arctic or Antarctic regions, and permitting them to melt in offshore enclosures in temperate or tropical waters, to provide fresh water which could be piped ashore. However, this is not yet considered to be economically practical.

Ion exchange processes

As early as the middle of the last century, it was observed that water passing through beds of coarse soil had some ions removed and replaced by other ions. Natural zeolites were found to possess the property that calcium and magnesium ions from solution could displace sodium ions from the solid zeolite when in contact with a water containing hardness but negligible sodium, and that sodium from brine would displace the calcium and magnesium from the zeolite when it was in contact with a solution of brine.

$$Ca^{2+} + Na_2Z \rightleftharpoons 2Na^+ + CaZ$$
$$Mg^{2+} + Na_2Z \rightleftharpoons 2Na^+ + MgZ$$

where Z represents the solid zeolite complex. Early in this century, artificial zeolites were manufactured, and later various organic resins were manufactured to perform a similar function, but with much greater efficiency.

Some of the resins could be regenerated with hydrogen ions (acids) which could be replaced by any other cations. These are called *cation exchange* resins. Others were made which could be regenerated with hydroxyl ions (alkali), which could be replaced by other anions. These are called *anion exchange* resins.

With both anion and cation exchange, any electrolytes can be removed from a stream of water (see Fig 13.30). The cations in the original stream are

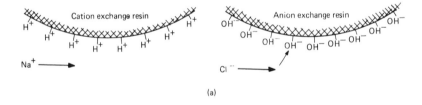

(a)

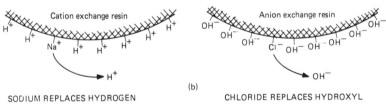

(b)

SODIUM REPLACES HYDROGEN   CHLORIDE REPLACES HYDROXYL

Overall effect: *sodium chloride* in solution replaced by *water*

Fig 13.30 Diagram illustrating anion and cation exchange principle

replaced by hydrogen ions and the anions by hydroxyl ions, thus replacing the original salt by H.OH (water). When most of the hydrogen and hydroxyl ions have been displaced from the resin, the exchange process slows down and there is an increase in the salt content of the effluent. It then becomes necessary to regenerate the resin bed.

The cation exchange resin is regenerated by passing an acid solution, and the anion exchange resin by passing an alkali solution. In large plants, the disposal of the waste regenerant can create problems.

For the reaction

$$Na^+ + HR \rightleftharpoons H^+ + NaR$$

the equilibrium coefficient is

$$\frac{[Na^+][HR]}{[H^+][NaR]} = K_e$$

The equilibrium coefficients for most of the resins are only slightly affected by temperature. However, scientists have developed resins in which the equilibrium coefficient is exceptionally sensitive to temperature changes. Increasing the temperature increases the equilibrium hydrogen and hydroxyl content of the cation and anion exchange resins respectively. This enables the use of an ion exchange process that needs no chemical regenerants, the regeneration being effected by hot water. This patented process has been called the *Sirotherm* process.

Water for ion exchange processes should be free of organic ions which may combine non-reversibly with the resins (that is, 'foul' the resins), and of ferric, manganic and aluminium ions which could produce clogging precipitates. This may require extensive pretreatment of water. In addition, water for the Sirotherm process must be free of oxygen and excessive bicarbonates.

Reverse osmosis

If two aqueous solutions are separated by a membrane which is permeable to the water but impermeable to the solute, the water will tend to flow through the membrane in the direction from the solution with the lower concentration to the solution with the higher concentration. This is known as the process of *osmosis*. If the flow is just stopped by an increase of pressure on the side where the higher concentration is, then the pressure necessary to stop the flow is called the osmotic pressure. A further increase of pressure would cause the water to flow in the direction against the osmotic pressure — that is, in a reverse direction to that induced by the osmosis. If the membrane is impermeable to the solute, this would be left behind. This is the basis of reverse osmosis as a desalting process. The principle is illustrated in Fig 13.31.

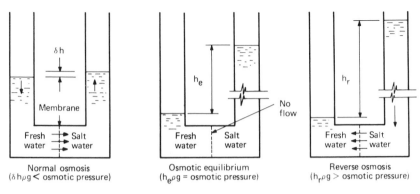

Fig 13.31 Principle of reverse osmosis

Membranes used in practice are not totally impermeable to salt and some salt leakage does occur. The solute rejection efficiency is a property of the type and grade of material used for the surface of the membrane, but it seems to be independent of the membrane thickness. The permeability of the membranes to water is inversely proportional to their thickness and so, if the membranes are thinner, less water pressure will be needed to overcome the hydraulic resistance for a given flow of water per square metre.

The pressures used in practice vary from about 3 MPa up to about 7 MPa, depending on the osmotic pressure, the type of membrane and the required yield of fresh water per square metre. Most of the pressure applied is used in overcoming the hydraulic resistance. The osmotic pressure is proportional to the combined molar concentration of dissolved molecules and ions, and is independent of the type of membrane used. For a brackish water with a total salinity of 10 000 mg/L, the osmotic pressure would be about 800 kPa.

The satisfactory application of reverse osmosis to desalt water requires a large area of very thin membrane, supported so that it will withstand high pressure. Commercial applications use membranes made either of cellulose acetate or of polyamide (a nylon-like material). The cellulose acetate membranes are made asymmetrical, with a very thin layer (0.05 to 0.25 microns) of dense material responsible for rejection of the salt, backed by a spongy underlayer (about 100 microns) which provides strength for handling, but accounts for only a small percentage of the total resistance to hydraulic flow. The polyamide membranes are made in the form of hollow tubes with an external diameter of about 0.08 mm and an internal diameter of about 0.04 mm (finer than a human hair). The cellulose acetate sheets are mounted either around porous rods (Fig 13.32(a)) or in a spiral winding (Fig 13.32(b)). The polyamide fibres are mounted in a tube as shown in Fig 13.32(c).

Provision must be made for discharging brine and for adequate turbulence near membrane surfaces to prevent a build-up of rejected salts, because such

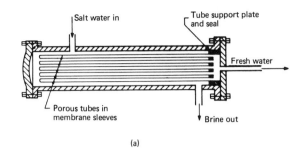

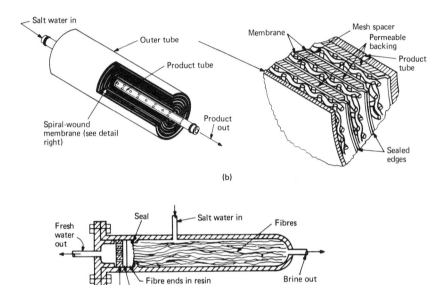

Fig 13.32 (a) Membranes mounted on porous rods, (b) membranes in spiral winding, (c) method of mounting polyamide fibres

a build-up would greatly increase the osmotic pressure and may result in membrane clogging. It is usual to remove turbidity, iron and manganese before pumping the water into a reverse osmosis unit, and also to add acid or a sequestering agent to prevent the formation of calcium carbonate scale on the membranes.

The largest reverse osmosis plants in 1978 were constructed at Riyadh in Saudi Arabia. Their total capacity from two units is 118 400 m³/d. The first unit has a capacity of 57 600 m³/d, and the second, 60 800 m³/d. In both cases, warm (55°C), brackish (1400 to 1800 mg/L TDS) water from deep wells is treated by lime-soda softening and filtering prior to reverse osmosis through hollow fibre membranes, to produce a water with less than 500 mg/L total dissolved salts.

Electrodialysis

Ionised salts can be removed from brackish water by a process known as *electrodialysis.* This uses a pair of electrodes, which are capable of maintaining an electric field in which the ions will move as in electrolysis, and two kinds of special membrane which are selectively permeable to either cations or anions. The cation-selective membrane will allow cations to pass through it freely, but will repel anions. The anion-selective membrane will allow anions to pass freely, but will repel cations. A stack of membranes (consisting of alternate cation- and anion-selective membranes, with separators about 1 mm thick between successive membranes, and an anion-selective membrane at both top and bottom) is placed between two electrodes. At the inlet end of the stack, brackish feedwater is pumped into alternate spaces between the membranes and recirculated brine is pumped into the other spaces. At the other end, there are two outlets — one for fresh water and one for brine. The receiving ducts are arranged so that the water from alternate spaces is ducted to one outlet, while that from the remaining spaces is ducted to the other outlet (see Fig 13.33).

When an electricial potential is applied across the electrodes, the cations (such as Na^+, Mg^{2+}, Ca^{2+}) move towards the cathode until they are stopped by an anion-selective membrane, and the anions (Cl^-, SO_4^{2-}, HCO_3^-) move towards the anode until they are stopped by a cation-selective membrane. The effect of these ion migrations is that alternate spaces between membranes lose ions of both types, while the remaining spaces gain ions; thus, some streams of water lose their salinity while the other streams become more saline. The salinity of the product water can be controlled by adjusting either the flow rate or the electrode current.

There may be a hundred or more membranes in a stack, and the potential difference applied to the electrodes may be of the order of 1000 V. Care must be taken to avoid leaks of either water or electricity.

Conditions tend to become alkaline at the cathode and acid at the anode. To prevent the alkaline conditions from causing the precipitation of calcium carbonate scale and other metals at the cathode, the membrane nearest the cathode is anion-selective, which prevents the approach of calcium and sodium ions; the space between this membrane and the cathode is continually washed with an acid rinse.

Organic anions can combine with the anion-selective membranes, thus neutralising their property of selectivity. Membranes thus affected must be replaced. If the concentration of salt ions in the boundary layer against a

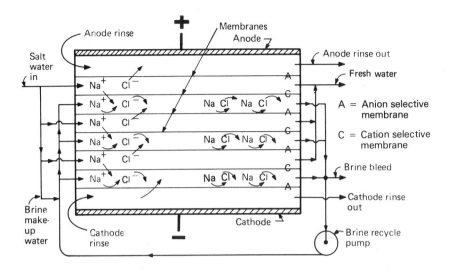

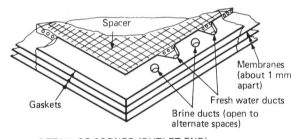

DETAIL OF CORNER (OUTLET END)

Fig 13.33 Diagram illustrating the principle of electrodialysis

membrane becomes so low that the ion migration to make up the current is that of hydroxyl ions, then there is a hazard of precipitation of calcium carbonate scales on the membranes, as well as of damage to the membrane by overheating as a result of the high local resistance.

Pretreatment for electrodialysis consists of removal of excess organic ions and hardness, and of acidifying the concentrate. In addition, care must be taken to keep the current low enough to avoid migration of hydroxyl ions rather than other anions such as Cl^-, SO_4^{2-}, and HCO_3^-.

Trends in desalting process selection

For the large-scale desalting of sea water, practically all recently-constructed units have been of the multiple flash distillation type. Some small installations have adopted vapour compression distillation.

For water with a total salinity of less than 4000 mg/L, reverse osmosis and electrodialysis are favoured. The main point of interest here is the swing towards reverse osmosis — in 1972 about 71 per cent of membrane desalting units operated on the electrodialysis process, but over the period 1972-75, the sales of reverse osmosis units were about 72 per cent of the total membrane sales.

13.11 Chemical feeders

In both water and wastewater treatment practice, it is necessary to add chemicals to the stream of water or wastewater being processed (the process stream). Some examples are the addition of coagulants, pH control chemicals and disinfectants during the treatment of water to produce a potable supply. Less frequently, chemicals are added to sewage in physico-chemical treatment plants, or to industrial wastes for some special purpose (see Chapter 15).

The design and manufacture of chemical feeding devices is a specialist activity. However, the designer of a treatment plant should have knowledge of the available options for methods of chemical feeding, and should be able to discuss process requirements with instrumentation and feed control specialists.

Many of the chemicals are very corrosive in the concentrations used for handling and feeding, and can be dangerous in respect of the escape of toxic material (such as chlorine gas) and the corrosion of tanks, pipes and equipment which may have been made from unsuitable materials. It is important that all materials used for storing and handling chemicals should be chosen for their durability under the proposed conditions of service, and that the utmost care should be used to prevent the escape of chemicals in quantities which could be dangerous.

Classification of chemical feeders

Although almost all the chemicals used in water and waste treatment are applied to the process stream as a solution or suspension (ozone is an exception), the additive at the point of measurement and control may be a *gas*, a *liquid* (solution) or a *solid* (granular or powdered). Hence, the method of application may be by gas feeder, solution feeder or dry feeder — the primary classification of feeders. If a chemical is measured and controlled as a gas or a solid, it is usually dissolved or suspended in water before being applied to the process stream, and the mixer or solution chamber is regarded as forming part of the chemical feeder.

Gas feeders
The principles used in gas feeders have already been discussed in connection

with chlorination in Chapter 10. The units used for feeding sulphur dioxide and ammonia are very similar to those used for feeding chlorine. Ozone, however, is generated by the passage of air through a silent discharge of electricity and, being sparingly soluble, it is bubbled through the process stream rather than dissolved in a small transport stream as are the more soluble gases.

Solution feeders

These are positive displacement pumps of various designs. Some are capable of variable displacement, and all can be equipped with a variable speed drive shaft, if required. The most widely used solution feeders in the water industry are diaphragm pumps, in which the diaphragm is operated by a slowly rotating cam. An adjustable stop can vary the length of the diaphragm stroke and thus affect the output per revolution. Variable speed drives can also be used. The ratio of maximum to minimum delivery of a particular piston or diaphragm pump is of the order of 10 to 1, although some models may give a modicum of accuracy over a range of 50 to 1.

Solution feeders are used for chemicals which are hygroscopic and form cakes in humid conditions, are very dusty for dry feeding or are in liquid form. In small treatment works, solution feeders can be more convenient and trouble-free than dry feeders, and even free-running granular material may be dissolved and fed in solution for the sake of convenience and economy.

Dry feeders

The next basis of classification relates more particularly to dry feeders, which are further classed according to the method of measurement: by weight (gravimetric) or by volume (volumetric). The difference between these two methods is shown in Fig 13.34.

The feeders depicted both have a chemical storage hopper equipped with an outlet gate controlling the cross-sectional size of a continuous pile of chemical, which is carried away on a belt. For the *volumetric* feeder, the gate

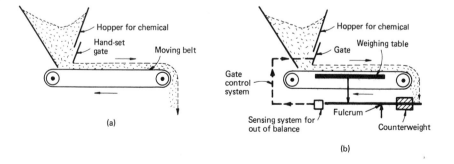

Fig 13.34 Diagram of belt feeders: (a) volumetric, (b) gravimetric

position is set by hand, thus fixing the cross-section of the chemical pile. The length of pile dispensed in a given time depends on the speed of the belt; the volume feed rate of loose chemical can therefore be estimated. Under the belt in the *gravimetric* feeder, there is a weighing platform which checks the weight of the pile of the chemical on a given length of belt. The correct weight corresponding to the desired feed rate and belt speed has been previously determined, and the counterweight set accordingly. Any deviation from correct weight is sensed by the gate control system and the gate is adjusted automatically to compensate for the error. The gate control system may be mechanical, pneumatic, electrical or electronic. The principal differences between volumetric and gravimetric feeders are: (a) volumetric feeders dispense chemicals with up to about five per cent error, whereas the error from a gravimetric feeder is likely to be less than one per cent; (b) volumetric feeders are simpler, cheaper and easier to maintain; (c) gravimetric feeders are better adapted for recording the quantities fed and for automatic control.

Various manufacturers have different designs for the volumetric feed of chemicals. They are based on rotating discs, reciprocating screws, vibrating pans, belts or other principles. Volumetric dry feeders are available in various sizes covering a range of feed rates from 30 grams per hour to over 2 tonnes per hour. Gravimetric dry feeders are not made as small as volumetric ones because the saving in chemicals resulting from the increased accuracy would not justify the much higher price; they are made for feed rates of from about 300 grams an hour to over 2 tonnes an hour. The ratio of maximum to minimum feed rates for any one feeder is about 100 to 1.

Control of feeders

Another basis of classification is according to the degree of automation provided. There are three main categories on this basis:

a Manually pre-set rate of flow
b Dose automatically changed to correct for changes in process stream flow rate (with rate of dose per cubic metre set manually)
c Two-stage (quantity-quality) automatic control, with not only automatic adjustment for flow rate compensation, but also automatic adjustment to compensate for changes in the quality of the water.

Automatic control requires some action in response to a change in a signal from a measuring device. Some of the early proportional dosing equipment operated on very simple mechanical and hydraulic principles. Many simple designs are still appropriate for use in areas where there is an absence of skilled maintenance or operating staff, such as in some developing countries. In the system depicted diagrammatically in Fig 13.35, the float and solution collector are so adjusted that the depth of flow over the solution collection weir is always proportional to the depth of flow of the process stream over its

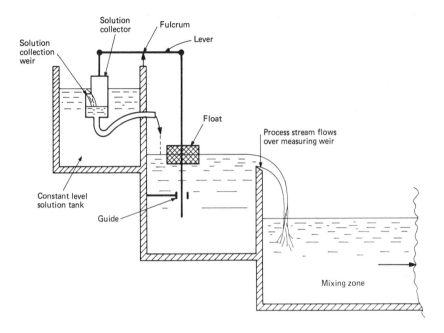

Fig 13.35 Diagram of a simple automatic solution feeder for proportional feed

weir, so that the amount of solution delivered is proportional to the main flow.

In later developments, methods other than mechanical have been used for transmitting signals (such as pneumatic pressure and electrical signals). Suitable signal converters were devised to achieve the desired motion of the control devices. For example, the control system represented diagrammatically in Fig 13.36 receives a differential water pressure from an orifice acting as a primary flow sensor. This pressure is led to a converter, where it is converted into a pneumatic pressure of greater magnitude — the pneumatic diaphragm being smaller than that for the differential pressure. The magnitude of the pneumatic pressure signal is proportional to the square of the flow rate, as was the original signal from the orifice. The pneumatic signal can be transmitted by pipeline over considerable distances, so that a distant spring-loaded piston can be displaced a distance proportional to the square of the flow through the metering orifice. A suitably-shaped cam, positioned by the piston, can be used to achieve a metering pump stroke length proportional to the water flow, and hence proportional dosing is achieved automatically. In such a system, compensation for quality variation can be achieved by varying either the speed of the pump drive shaft or the strength of the solution in the solution tank.

With two-stage (quantity-quality) automatic chemical feed control, it is

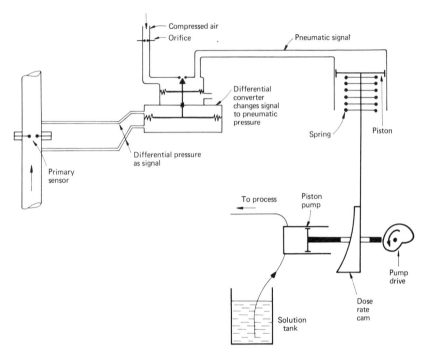

Fig 13.36 Diagrammatic representation of a method of automatic compensation for changes in flow, using pneumatic signal transmission

convenient if one parameter in the feeder is controlled by the flow rate, and the other is controlled by some sensed property, so that each may operate independently of the other. Because the flow rate is likely to change more rapidly than the water quality, the flow rate adjustment should be linked with the most readily changed parameter in the feeder, unless the maximum to minimum flow ratios are so great that this would be impracticable.

In a gas feeder, such as a chlorinator, two feeder parameters which can be controlled are the size of the metering orifice and the pressure to be maintained across it. The pressure across the orifice can readily be related to the water flow, and an apparatus for adjusting the dose rate by varying the size of the orifice can be operated at intervals by a signal created by the chlorine residual in the water after a predetermined contact time.

In a solution feeder, one paramater is usually the length of a stroke of a diaphragm pump or piston pump; the other parameter can be the rotation speed of the pump drive shaft.

With a volumetric dry feeder of the belt type, the two parameters for automatic adjustment are the positioning of the gate which releases the chemical and the speed of the belt; with a similar gravimetric unit, they are the position of the counterbalance (see Fig 13.34) and the speed of the belt.

Quality sensors for controlling chemical dosing must be appropriate to the purpose of chemical addition. For example, chlorinators would be controlled from chlorine residual analysers, pH correction chemicals from a pH sensor, and coagulation chemicals from coagulation tests.

Automatic coagulation control testing can be complex. At some water treatment plants, the jar test has been automated so that it is performed mechanically at fixed time intervals. The test takes the freshly-dosed water from the plant and arranges for three jars to be tested; one of the jars is tested as collected, one has some raw water added to reduce the concentration of coagulant, and the third has some extra coagulant added. Depending on the results of turbidity readings of the three samples after a time for flocculation and a time for settlement, the testing machine automatically increases or reduces the dose in use in the plant, or leaves it unchanged.

Another coagulation control system is based on the filtering of the dosed water through pilot filters soon after the addition of the coagulant dose. The pilot filter effluent is tested for turbidity at fixed time intervals. If the effluent turbidity exceeds the target value, the dose of coagulant is slightly increased, but if it is less than the target value, the dose is slightly decreased. In this way, the changing quality of the water is followed by a changing dose of coagulant, which is just adequate to maintain a specified turbidity at the outlet of the pilot filters; this gives maximum economy in the use of coagulant chemicals while maintaining satisfactory conditions for coagulation.

Chemical control trends

In large plants where skilled technologists can be engaged, there is a trend towards computer control of chemical dosing as well as of the overall flows and operations. Signals which can be transformed to electrical signals can be converted into digital form and fed into microprocessors, which can carry out complex calculations on the data presented and provide signals for the control of feeders, valves and other equipment. The effectiveness of such a system is limited only by lack of knowledge of data interpretation for optimum conditions, and by the reliability of the equipment — especially if it is not maintained at a high level of efficiency. The extent and sophistication of metering, chemical feeding and control should be matched to the magnitude of the works and to the skill and training of the people expected to operate and maintain it.

13.12 Conventional water treatment plant design summary

The design data and the dimensions of process units are often presented in summary form in design reports and operating manuals. A typical design summary, suitable for a conventional water treatment works, is presented below. This summary is a useful guide to the main items to be considered in a preliminary design of a plant for treatment to remove colour, turbidity and bacteria from water taken from a river or a lake.

NAME OF TREATMENT WORKS: ....

A *Population*

Ultimate	....	Stage 1	....

B *Flows*

	Per capita flow (L/d)		Total flow (ML/d)		Flow rate	
	Ultimate	Stage 1	Ultimate	Stage 1	Stage 1	(L/s)
Average day	....	....	....	......	....	
Peak day	:.........	....	....	......	....	
Design flow Stage 1						

C *Rapid-mixing chamber*

Design factors		Dimensions	
Detention	..........s	Length	........m
Volume	........m^3	Width	........m
No. of units	....	Depth	........m

D *Flocculation basins*

Design factors		Chamber dimensions	
Total detention	.......min	Length	........m
Total volume	........m^3	Width	........m
No. of flocculators	....	Depth	........m
No. of chambers each	....		

E *Sedimentation tanks*

(i) Sedimenta-
tion tanks

Design factors		No. and dimensions	
Particle sett. vel. .... mm/s		No. of tanks	....
Equiv. surf. load ...... m³/m².d		Length	.... m
Detention .... min		Width	.... m
Forward velocity .... mm/s		Depth	.... m
Weir loading .... m³/m.d		Weir length	.... m

(ii) Sludge
production

Sludge volume produced	.... L/kg alum dosed
Water loss in sludge	.... % of daily throughput

F *Filters*

Design factors		No. and dimensions	
Media:		No. of filters	....
....		Length	.... m
Loading rate	.... L/s.m²	Width	.... m
Backwash rate	.... L/s.m²	Backwash flow	.... L/s
Air scour rate	.... L/s.m²	Backwash water loss	.... %

G *Clear water storage tanks (for backwashing)*

Design factors	Dimensions	
Volume: .... × filter wash vol.	Length	.... m
.... m³	Width	.... m
No. of tanks	Depth	.... m

H *Chemical dosing*

	Chemical dose	Daily requirement		Annual requirement
		At a. flow	At peak flow	
(i) Alum (coagulant)	.... mg/L As $Al_2(SO_4)_3.16H_2O$	.... kg	.... kg	.... tonne
	As supplied .... % alum	.... kg	.... kg	.... tonne
(ii) Chlorine	.... mg/L As chlorine	.... kg	.... kg	.... tonne
(iii) Fluoride	.... mg/L as F^-	.... kg	.... kg	.... tonne
	As supplied .... % F^-	.... kg	.... kg	.... tonne
	As liquid with density ... kg/L	 L	 L	 L

Review questions

13.1 A proposed source for domestic water supply may be found to contain amounts of impurities in excess of the limits set by locally-adopted standards with regard to turbidity, colour, hardness, total dissolved salts, toxic materials or bacteriological quality. State, with reasons, which of these deficiencies can be readily corrected, and which of them require extensive or expensive treatment.

13.2 Compare and contrast the arrangement and operation of horizontal flow sedimentation tanks, sludge blanket clarifiers and mechanically-operated solids contact clarifiers.

13.3 Discuss the relative merits of different methods of applying shallow depth sedimentation.

13.4 State the main principles of flotation, and describe three sets of conditions in which flotation may be gainfully used in water treatment.

13.5 Compare the operation methods of slow sand filters, rapid sand filters and diatomaceous earth filters.

13.6 Discuss methods of backwashing rapid sand filters.

13.7 State the circumstances in which water for domestic supply should be softened, and outline the main methods of doing this.

13.8 Describe a suitable aerator to remove excess carbon dioxide and iron from groundwater. What chemicals must be added after aeration to ensure precipitation of the iron?

13.9 Summarise the methods of controlling tastes and odours in a water supply.

13.10 Outline the methods used for desalting:
a   Sea water,
b   Brackish water.
What are the main advantages and disadvantages of each method?

13.11 'Chemical feeders must be sufficiently accurate both to avoid waste of chemicals and to ensure effective treatment of the water' — discuss, and illustrate your discussion by reference to various types of feeder.

14 Wastewater Treatment

14.1 Introduction

The design of wastewater treatment works comprises the following main steps:

a Process design — selection of a suitable sequence of processes to satisfy requirements for the plant concerned

b Functional design — estimation of the capacities required for all major units, channels, pumps and pipework, and definition of control requirements. This includes design for hydraulic, organic and solids loadings

c Detailed design — structural design of units and channels, detailing of pipelines, fittings and control valves, and selection of mechanical, electrical and control equipment.

Aspects of design steps a and b are the main concerns of this chapter. It should be stressed that the complete design should be integrated. For instance, sludge treatment is discussed in Chapter 12, but it is an important part of a wastewater treatment plant.

Rational selection of treatment processes for any particular application requires knowledge of the *flow* and *characteristics* of the wastewater to be treated, as well as the desired effluent quality. General characteristics of wastewaters and some aspects of stream water quality have been discussed in Chapters 4 and 6, respectively.

Adequate information on wastewater flows and pollutant loadings and their variability is not only necessary for the *selection* of appropriate processes but is also fundamental to the estimation of the hydraulic *capacities* of treatment units, pumps, interconnecting pipework and channels, and the capacities of the biological systems and sludge removal equipment.

Design flows and pollutant loadings

Wastewater flows from various types of sewered area may be estimated by the procedures outlined in Section 3.4.

Under *dry-weather* conditions, both flow and strength of *domestic sewage* peak in mid-morning and in the evening, soon after the peak times of normal domestic activity. Lowest flow occurs early in the morning. At these times, sewage strength tends to be low, because groundwater infiltration, which is low in organic pollution, constitutes a large proportion of the sewage flow. *Industrial waste* discharges may either reinforce the diurnal pattern of domestic sewage flow, or they may increase flows throughout the whole of the day, depending on the type of industry and its pattern of operation.

In estimating design flows for treatment works, a designer commonly adopts the average dry-weather flow (ADWF), Q_a, as a base. The value of Q_a varies greatly, as noted in Section 3.4, and depends on the climate, the extent of industrial and commercial development, the per capita water supply, the age and condition of the sewer pipes and their position relative to the groundwater table. Commonly quoted per capita figures for Q_a range from less than 200 L/d in the UK to over 300 L/d in the US, while design values adopted by most Australian authorities are within ten per cent of 250 L/d. The increasing use of household appliances, such as automatic washing machines and dishwashers, and the fact that affluence results in water being used more freely, have caused wastewater flows per capita to increase. This should be taken into account when designing a system.

The expected range of flows must be defined, because this affects every unit in the treatment process. Peak dry-weather flow, Q_d, and peak wet-weather flow, Q_w, may be the initial design flows for some units. It is often necessary to limit the flow which is permitted to enter some units, such as those where excessive flow could wash away accumulated activated sludge. The excess flow may be bypassed or diverted to other treatment facilities. Minimum flow may also be important, especially in hot climates, where odours can result when detention time in the sewers is so long that biological action removes dissolved oxygen and leads to anaerobic conditions. These problems can be especially severe where treatment works are operated with very low flows — for example, in the first few years after the installation of treatment works in a new scheme.

Process loading parameters of greatest importance in the design of municipal wastewater treatment works are biochemical oxygen demand (BOD) and suspended solids (SS). Commonly adopted contributions to wastewater treatment works vary from about 50 to 100 g/d.cap for BOD and SS. The lower figure would be reasonable for a purely domestic sewage with a minimum of automated household appliances and without garbage grinders, while the higher figure would be representative of communities with a high incidence of such devices. Loadings adopted by many authorities are in the middle of the above range — about 70 g/d BOD and 80 g/d SS.

The design of biological treatment processes and sludge treatment systems is usually based on average estimates of BOD and SS loadings, but sufficient capacity must be provided to handle peak loadings in some units, such as aeration systems and equipment for the removal, treatment and disposal of sidestream products such as screenings, grit and sludges.

Problems in design and operation are likely to occur in holiday and resort areas, where the contributing population may increase during one or two days to several times its former size. Problems caused by industrial wastes are mentioned in Chapter 15.

In some cases, special conditions in the receiving waters may require that treatment works be designed to remove plant nutrients such as nitrogen and phosphorus. The loadings of the various forms of nitrogen and phosphorus, as well as the total loadings of these nutrients, should then be determined for all sources of wastewater entering the treatment plant.

Classification of treatment processes

Traditionally, treatment processes are classified under a number of broad headings related generally to the effluent quality they are expected to produce (see Fig 14.1).

Primary treatment, the simplest form, comprises simple gravity sedimentation, preceded by *preliminary treatment* processes such as screening, grit removal and sometimes prechlorination or pre-aeration. Primary treatment removes most of the obviously identifiable solids, grease and floating matter, and reduces BOD and SS concentrations from about 300 mg/L each to about 200 mg/L and 100 mg/L respectively. This standard of treatment has often been considered satisfactory for ocean disposal of effluent.

Secondary treatment is normally achieved by some form of aerobic biological process, and is aimed at further removing the non-settleable, largely organic matter to produce an effluent suitable for discharge into inland streams.

Where effluent of higher quality, such as 10/10 BOD/SS or better, is required, a further stage, *tertiary treatment*, is added. *Disinfection* for destruction of pathogenic and bacterial indicator organisms is often included under this classification. Removal of plant nutrients is sometimes classified as tertiary treatment, but this is more commonly classed as *advanced wastewater treatment* (AWT). Tertiary and advanced wastewater treatment may involve physical, chemical or biological processes or various combinations of them, depending on the impurities to be removed. Flow sheets for conventional treatment works are summarised in Fig 14.1. The stages in the works will be discussed in the same sequence as the usual treatment.

14.2 Pretreatment and preliminary treatment

A wide variety of coarse suspended matter finds its way to a municipal wastewater treatment works via the sewerage system; it is usually necessary to

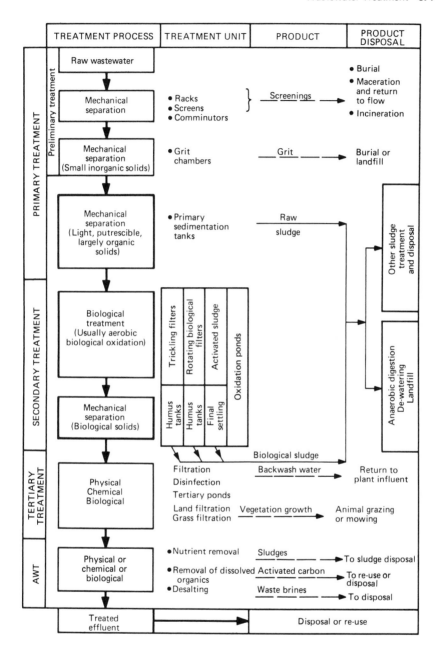

Fig 14.1   Wastewater treatment process flow sheet

remove it by pretreatment or preliminary treatment before it enters the main treatment processes.

When such processes are provided at the head of a treatment works, they constitute part of the *primary treatment* phase as shown in Fig 14.1 and are often called *preliminary treatment*. In some cases, pretreatment may also be carried out in sewers and rising mains to ensure that the wastewater is amenable to treatment and is unlikely to give rise to odour problems.

The main processes used for pretreatment in sewers and preliminary treatment at treatment works are summarised in Fig 14.2.

Pretreatment

Raw domestic sewage in a fresh state is typically light grey to brown in colour and has a not unpleasant, rather sweet odour. In it, however, the biodegradation of its organic content is constantly in progress. While a measurable amount of dissolved oxygen is maintained in the wastewater, the biodegradation process will remain aerobic and the wastewater will remain fresh. Should the rate of oxygen demand exceed the rate at which oxygen can be dissolved from the sewer atmosphere, anaerobic conditions will result — the wastewater will rapidly turn a black colour and hydrogen sulphide will be formed. Hydrogen sulphide gas evolved in sewers is a hazard to sewer maintenance personnel and is a major cause of corrosion of sewer structures; it also causes severe odour problems in the primary phase of the treatment works. These problems can be particularly severe in hot climates because of the reduced solubility of oxygen at higher temperatures and the more rapid biological action.

Pretreatment in the sewerage system is aimed at controlling conditions to avoid these problems. Aerobic conditions may be ensured by providing adequate sewer ventilation, by designing sewers with steep gradients and by minimising the total detention time of sewage in the collection system.

Where the sewerage system is very extensive, or in flat areas where frequent pumping is required, or in hot climates, it may not be economically feasible to maintain an adequate level of dissolved oxygen in the wastewater by these means. In such cases, the oxygen supply can be supplemented by aeration, injection of pure oxygen or by addition of hydrogen peroxide.

Control of H_2S evolution may be achieved by oxidising the H_2S, usually through chlorination at critical points in the sewerage system, or by adding copperas ($FeSO_4$) to precipitate the sulphide as ferrous sulphide.

Rising mains are often the critical elements as far as oxygen depletion is concerned, since they operate without a free surface in contact with the atmosphere. Because they must be sized for wet-weather flow, detention time at dry-weather flow may be several hours.

Air injection into the rising main downstream of the pumps is the usual method of keeping sewage fresh in such mains. The required air injection rate

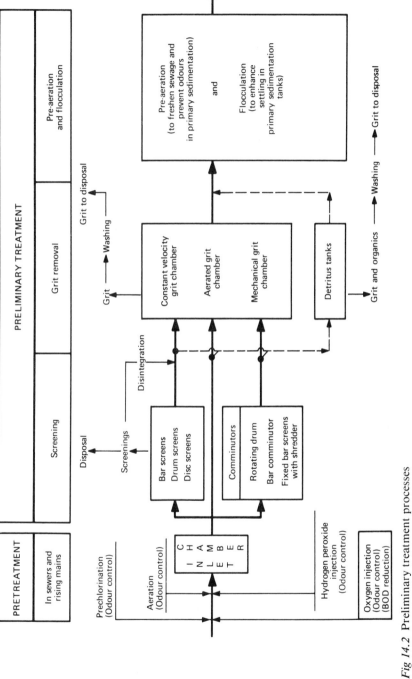

Fig 14.2 Preliminary treatment processes

depends on the rate of oxygen demand and the rate of oxygen transfer from the injected air to the sewage.

Pure oxygen injection may be considered as an alternative method of supplying the oxygen required to sustain aerobic conditions. It is doubtful whether pure oxygen is economically justifiable for use for odour control alone. Further research is required to establish the effectiveness of oxygen injection into sewers and rising mains to partially satisfy the BOD of raw sewage.

Hydrogen peroxide (H_2O_2) has been applied as an alternative method of supplementing the oxygen supply. Hydrogen peroxide is not subject to the solubility limitation of air or pure oxygen, so that injection methods can be somewhat simpler, while H_2O_2 is also a powerful oxidising agent and reacts readily with H_2S. This results in greater availability of the applied oxygen equivalent in H_2O_2 so that, although it is more expensive than the other forms of oxygen, less is required.

Prechlorination of sewage by injecting chlorine into rising mains has been quoted as an established method of avoiding H_2S odour and corrosion problems at the inlet and in primary phases of treatment works. In this case, control of H_2S is achieved by its oxidation, usually to a precipitate of molecular sulphur. Each 1 mg/L of sulphide present requires 2 mg/L of chlorine to be added. Therefore, a typical septic sewage might require 10 to 15 mg/L of chlorine for precipitation of sulphur from the sulphide. In practice, however, the chlorine demand exerted by organic material in the sewage often requires chlorine to be dosed at up to 25 mg/L.

With increasing concern over the possible formation of carcinogenic chloro-organic compounds as a result of chlorination, it seems likely that the use of prechlorination for H_2S control will decline in favour of aeration or oxygenation processes.

Preliminary treatment

The main objectives of preliminary treatment are (a) to selectively remove suspended materials which could interfere with the physical operation of subsequent treatment processes, and (b) to precondition the wastewater in order to prevent odour problems in, and to improve the treatment efficiency of, the subsequent processes.

14.3 Design of primary treatment works

Treatment processes involved in primary treatment, as shown in Fig 14.1, are sedimentation and the preliminary processes of screening, grit removal and pre-aeration.

Screen design

Screens are usually provided to remove rags and other coarse material which may become entangled in mechanical scraping equipment in grit chambers and sedimentation tanks or caught on effluent weirs. If removed with the sludge from sedimentation tanks, such material may become entangled in the impellers of sludge pumps or contribute to the formation of scum layers in digestion tanks. Balls of rags can clog sludge withdrawal pipes in digesters.

Fixed bar screens (Fig 8.1(a) and Fig 14.3(a)) are the most common type used at the inlet of municipal wastewater treatment works. Typical dimensions and applications of bar screen installations for sewage treatment are quoted in Table 14.1.

The size of screen aperture is a compromise between the need to remove coarse matter from the flow and the need to keep the volume of screenings for disposal as small as practicable. In most plants, the aperture chosen is between 20 and 25 mm. For strength and durability, the minimum bar width is usually 10 mm. The hydraulic design of screen installations must ensure that the flow velocity is controlled within an optimum range over all rates of flow, as well as satisfying the normal requirements for open channel flow in upstream and downstream channels. Head loss through the screens must also be considered at these flow rates and in all conditions, ranging from the minimum head loss when the screens are clean, to the maximum permissible head loss through the screens just before they are cleaned.

The velocity of flow through the bars should be limited to between 0.75 and 1.0 m/s at maximum flow, in order to prevent the entrapped material from being forced through the bars. Minimum velocity must also be considered in order to ensure that a cleansing velocity is maintained in the approach channel. To prevent deposition of solids, a velocity of at least 0.4 m/s is

Table 14.1 Dimensions and applications of bar screens

	Hand raked	*Mechanically raked*
Bar spacing	20 mm − 30 mm	10 mm − 40 mm
Bar size	10 mm × 50 mm − 60 mm	To manufacturer's design
Inclination	30°–45° to horizontal	Varies with method of cleaning, commonly 85° to horizontal
Cleaning frequency	Not less than 3 times daily	Automatically controlled by head loss or by time clock
Head loss	Not more than 0.8 m when clogged or 0.01 m when clean	75 mm − 150 mm
Applications	Small treatment works and bypass screens in large treatment works	Large treatment works

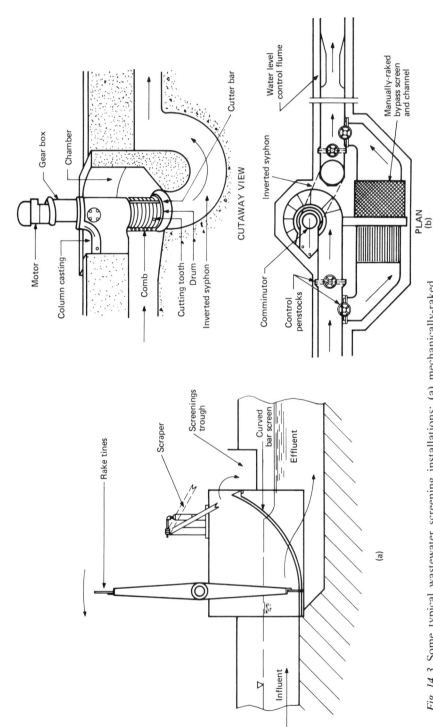

Fig 14.3 Some typical wastewater screening installations: (a) mechanically-raked curved bar screen, (b) small comminutor installation

necessary, so that the minimum velocity through the bars in a typical installation would be about 0.6 m/s.

Because the ratio of peak wet-weather flow to average dry-weather flow (Q_w/Q_a) may reach 8:1, the above velocity criteria require that the depth of flow at the screens be varied according to the flow rate. This can be readily accomplished if the screen is placed upstream of a grit chamber with a level control flume (Section 14.2), and the level of the bottom of the screen channel is carefully selected.

Head loss through clean screens at the various flow rates may be calculated with Eq 8.1, but the freeboard provided in the upstream channel must be sufficient to allow for the head loss increase during the interval between cleaning operations.

The *quantity of screenings* produced can vary widely according to the type of area served, the screen aperture and the wastewater flow. Under normal flow conditions, standard 25 mm bar screens remove 0.005 to 0.05 m³ of screenings for each megalitre of wastewater treated.

Mesh screens are seldom used at the inlet to wastewater treatment works, but fine mesh screens are often used ahead of trickling filters to protect the distribution nozzles.

Moving screens, such as drum screens and disc screens, have been used relatively infrequently for wastewater applications. Such devices usually require water cleaning, which produces very wet screenings demanding a more complex de-watering and disposal system.

Cutting screens trap the coarse material from the wastewater on the screen surface and shred it with some form of cutting mechanism into smaller pieces that will pass through the screen. Thus, these devices do not remove material from the flow and so there is no problem of screenings disposal. When these are used, there is a need for maintenance (especially renewal of cutting surfaces) and there is a tendency for shredded rags and similar materials to string together downstream of the screen. In such cases, problems may arise from fouling of mechanical equipment and pipelines and from the fact that shredded material may still cause scum problems in digesters.

A common type of cutting screen is the comminutor (Fig 14.3(b)), a slotted drum which rotates on a vertical axis, fitted with cutting bars and cutting teeth which mesh closely with a fixed comb attached to the supporting casing. The macerated screenings are carried by the flow through the apertures in the drum and out of its bottom through an inverted siphon to the outlet channel. The bar-comminutor consists of a fixed bar screen and a rotating drum mounted adjacent to the upstream face of the bar screen, with its axis at right angles to the bars. The rotating drum is fitted with cutting teeth which mesh with the bar apertures, and the drum with its submersible drive assembly is mounted on tracks parallel to the screen bars. Controls are provided to periodically start the drum rotating and lower it down the face of the bar screen.

Any material trapped on the face of the screen is then macerated until it will pass through the screen.

The *disposal* of wastewater screenings is important because they are frequently heavily contaminated with putrescible organic matter and thus attract flies. Three methods used for disposal are disintegration followed by return to the flow, burial, and incineration.

Incineration is not generally economical in small treatment works because of the high cost of incineration plant and the necessary de-watering equipment.

Example 14.1

A bar screen is to be designed for the inlet works of a sewage treatment plant which serves a population of 20 000. Per capita average dry-weather flow to the plant is 250 L/d. Peak dry-weather flow, Q_d, is twice ADWF and peak wet-weather flow, Q_w, is 4 times Q_d. Clear spacing between bars is to be 25 mm and the bars are each 10 mm wide, normal to the direction of flow. Calculate the dimensions of the approach channel cross-section and the control flume if required.

Solution

Average flow to the plant, $Q_a = 20\ 000 \times 250$ L/d
$$= 5\ \text{ML/d} = 58\ \text{L/s} = 0.058\ \text{m}^3/\text{s}$$
Peak dry-weather flow, $\quad Q_d = 2\ Q_a = 0.116\ \text{m}^3/\text{s}$
Peak wet-weather flow, $\quad Q_w = 4\ Q_d = 0.464\ \text{m}^3/\text{s}$

The minimum approach velocity to be achieved at least once each day (at Q_d) is 0.45 m/s, and maximum velocity through the bars at peak wet-weather flow is 1 m/s. Therefore, the maximum approach velocity, $V_{a_{max}}$, is calculated as follows:

$$V_{a_{max}} = V_{b_{max}} \times \frac{\text{bar spacing}}{\text{bar spacing} + \text{bar width}}$$

$$= 1.0 \times \frac{25}{25 + 10} = 0.71\ \text{m/s}$$

If depth of flow in the approach channel is the same for all flow rates, the maximum range of flows which may be handled $= V_{a_{max}}/V_{a_{min}} = 0.71/0.45 = 1.6$.

But the range of flows to be served is $Q_w/Q_d = 4$. Therefore, some form of control is required to increase the depth as the flow increases. This may be achieved by using a critical depth flume, with a discharge equation approximately as given by Eq 14.1 : $Q = 1.7\ b\ h^{3/2}$. Then, for a trial throat width of $b = 0.2$ m, and $Q = Q_d$, the flow depth, h_d is given by

$$h_d = \left(\frac{Q_d}{1.7\,b}\right)^{\frac{2}{3}} = \left(\frac{0.116}{1.7 \times 0.2}\right)^{\frac{2}{3}}$$

$$= 0.488 \text{ m}$$

Area of approach channel $= Q_d/V_{a_{min}}$ and, since $A = W\,h_d$, the width, W, of the channel is

$$W = \frac{Q}{V_{a_{min}} h_d}$$

$$= \frac{0.116}{0.45 \times 0.488} = 0.528 \text{ m}$$

At maximum flow, Q_w,

$$h_w = \left(\frac{0.464}{1.7 \times 0.2}\right)^{\frac{2}{3}} = 1.230 \text{ m}$$

and a check on the maximum approach velocity gives

$$V_{a_{max}} = \frac{Q_w}{W \times h_w} = \frac{0.464}{0.528 \times 1.230} = 0.71 \text{ m/s}$$

which is equal to the maximum permissible value calculated above, and therefore acceptable.

Therefore, overall channel depth $= 1.230$ m $+ 0.3$ m freeboard

$$= 1.55 \text{ m, say}$$

In practice, the range of depths corresponding to the range of flows from ADWF to PWWF may be considered too great. It may be preferable to provide two screens, the second to accept sewage when the flow is in excess of some predetermined value, such as 2 PDWF.

Grit chamber design

Grit chambers are provided to remove inorganic grit which may cause abrasion of comminutors and the impellers of sludge pumps, or set hard in sludge hoppers, transmision pipes and in the bottoms of digesters. All these effects may require the units concerned to be taken out of service for maintenance much more frequently than would otherwise be the case.

Grit removal is usually achieved by differential settlement, in which the flow velocity is controlled so that heavier inorganic grit particles are removed, while organic solids are retained in suspension. Grit chambers are commonly designed to remove inorganic particles down to an equivalent diameter of 0.2 mm. For sand (density 2650 kg/m³), particles of this size settling in water at 20°C have a settling velocity of about 21 mm/s. Grit particles typically behave as discrete particles and, since their concentration is usually relatively low, they provide the nearest approximation to ideal Class I settling encountered in wastewater treatment.

On the basis of the method used for controlling flow velocity, three main types of grit chamber may be distinguished:

a Constant velocity grit chambers, in which longitudinal flow velocity is controlled hydraulically

b Aerated grit chambers, in which helical rolling motion is induced by controlled introduction of air along one side of the chamber

c Mechanically-stirred tanks, in which rotary motion is produced by a system of paddles mounted on a vertical shaft in a cylindrical chamber.

The *quantity of grit* in sewage can vary widely according to the characteristics of the sewerage system, the geology of its area and the types of industry served by the system. Maximum grit loads generally occur during wet weather, in association with storm flow or infiltration into the sewers. In cold regions, areas served by combined sewers, which carry stormwater along with domestic and industrial waste, can greatly increase grit loads when the ice and snow melt after road gritting. Grit loads quoted by various authorities range from 0.002 to 0.15 m^3/ML of sewage treated. For separate sewerage systems, grit loads usually lie in the range 0.005 to 0.05 m^3/ML.

Constant velocity grit chamber installations comprise two essential components: the *grit chamber* itself and the *velocity control device*. The design involves matching these two elements so that the forward velocity in the grit chamber is practically constant at the chosen value for all rates of flow. It has been found that a forward velocity in the range 0.25 to 0.35 m/s will permit most of the grit of 0.2 mm equivalent diameter, or larger, to settle, while retaining most of the organic matter in suspension. A design velocity of 0.30 m/s has been widely adopted.

The required constant velocity can be achieved either by a parabolic grit chamber matched to a rectangular critical depth control flume, or by a rectangular grit chamber matched to a specially-shaped control weir or flume. Most installations employ rectangular flumes with approximately parabolic grit chambers (see Fig 14.4). This type of chamber is therefore chosen for detailed discussion.

For a rectangular control flume, the flow in the flume, Q_f, is related to the width, b, and depth of flow, h, by the relationship

$$Q_f = c\, b\, h^{3/2} \tag{14.1}$$

where c is a flume coefficient.

Flow through the *grit chamber* is given by

$$Q_g = A\, V_f \tag{14.2}$$

where Q_g is the flow (m^3/s); A is the cross-sectional area of the flow through the grit chamber (m^2); and V_f is the forward velocity (m/s).

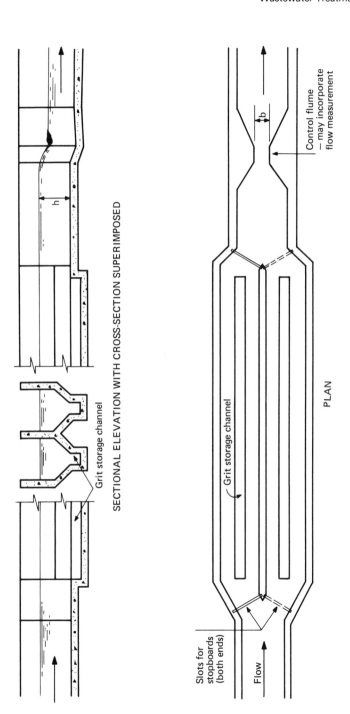

SECTIONAL ELEVATION WITH CROSS-SECTION SUPERIMPOSED

Grit storage channel

Control flume
— may incorporate
flow measurement

Grit storage channel

PLAN

Slots for
stopboards
(both ends)

Flow

Fig 14.4 Constant velocity grit chamber

The same flow passes through both the flume and the grit chamber, so that

$$Q_g = Q_f$$

Therefore

$$A\,V_f = c\,b\,h^{3/2} \tag{14.3}$$

If the grit chamber is constructed with a parabolic cross-section (Fig 14.5), with its invert at the same level as the invert of the flume, the depth of flow is related to the surface width of flow by

$$h = a\,W^2 \tag{14.4}$$

where a is a proportionality coefficient. The area of flow, A, is given by

$$A = 2/3(h \times W)$$

$$= \frac{2\,h^{3/2}}{3\sqrt{a}} \tag{14.5}$$

Substitution of this value in Eq 14.3 and rearrangement shows that the forward velocity in such a channel is independent of the depth or rate of flow:

$$\frac{2}{3\,\sqrt{a}}h^{3/2}\,V_f = c\,b\,h^{3/2}$$

$$V_f = \frac{3\,c\,b\,\sqrt{a}}{2} \tag{14.6}$$

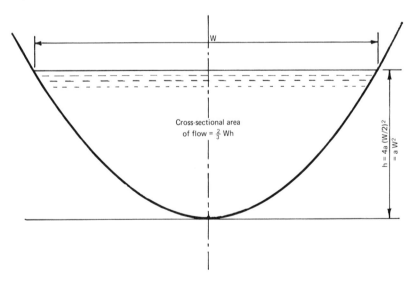

Fig 14.5 Ideal parabolic cross-section of grit chamber

The surface width of the flow in the channel for any desired forward velocity, as a function of its depth, can be determined from Eqs 14.4 and 14.6 as

$$W = 1.5 \, c \, b \, h^{1/2}/V_f \tag{14.7}$$

$$= 1.5 \, A/h \text{ (From Eq 14.5)} \tag{14.8}$$

For simplicity and economy in construction, it is usual to approximate the ideal parabolic cross-section by a simple shape such as the section shown in Fig 14.4.

The required *length* of grit chamber can be determined simply from a consideration of the discrete particle settling theory presented in Section 8.2 (Fig 8.3 (a)). Thus, for the critical particle settling path, at maximum flow

$$\frac{h_{max}}{V_s} = \frac{L}{V_f} \tag{14.9}$$

V_f is usually 0.30 m/s, while V_s for a sand particle 0.2 mm in diameter settling in water is given above as 0.021 m/s. Substitution of these values gives $L \cong 14 \, h_{max}$. To allow for the effects of turbulence and interference to particle settling, a safety factor of about 1.2 to 1.5 should be applied. Hence for practical purposes

$$L > 18 \, h_{max} \tag{14.10}$$

It is normal practice to provide a *grit storage channel* in the base of each grit chamber. Dimensions of the channel are governed by the expected grit load and the method and frequency of cleaning. In small treatment plants grit is usually removed manually, and this requires the grit chamber to be taken out of service during the cleaning operation. An extra grit chamber is provided so that each chamber can be taken out of service in turn for cleaning when required.

In larger treatment plants, either grit pumps or mechanical *de-gritting systems* are usually employed. Where bucket scrapers or screw conveyors are used, the grit channel dimensions are fixed by the requirements of these systems. Another method of grit removal is by means of a travelling pipe connected to the suction of a pump, mounted on a bridge travelling on rails fixed to the side walls of the grit chambers. In this type of chamber, the grit storage channel can be quite small if cleaning is carried out frequently.

Aerated grit chambers are designed to impart a transverse rolling motion to the flow as it passes through a channel of approximately rectangular cross-section (Fig 14.6). The required intensity of motion should permit grit to settle, while organics are retained in suspension. This is achieved by injecting air at a controlled rate near the base of one longitudinal wall of the chamber.

Helical flow is promoted by the filleted or rounded corners of the chamber cross-section, while grit collection and removal is facilitated by sloping the

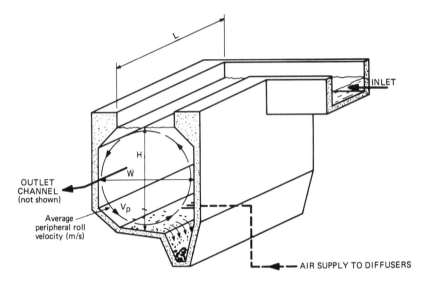

Fig 14.6 Diagram of aerated grit chamber

tank floor so that the rolling motion moves the grit towards hoppers along one side of the tank.

To promote the desired helical flow, aerated grit chambers should be proportioned so that the width and depth are about equal while, to prevent short-circuiting, the length should be greater than twice the width.

Critical velocities to be considered are the minimum scour velocity to move settled grit towards collecting hoppers, the maximum velocity before settled grit is re-suspended, and the velocity required to keep organics in suspension.

A velocity of about 0.4 m/s at the floor of the grit chamber should result in efficient removal of grit with a reasonably low organic content. Since it has been observed that the velocity near the floor of the chamber is about 75 per cent of the surface velocity, the required surface velocity will be 0.5 to 0.6 m/s. To achieve these velocities, it has been reported that an air supply rate of 0.3 m³/minute for each metre of tank length is required when the air is admitted at a height of 0.6 to 1.0 m above the grit hoppers. The air supply should be metered and capable of adjustment to allow flexibility in obtaining optimum grit removal.

For satisfactory grit removal, it is usually considered that the *detention time* in the grit chamber should be long enough to ensure that at least two spirals are completed. A common design criterion for aerated grit chambers is a detention time of 2 to 3 minutes at maximum wet-weather flow.

The main *methods of grit withdrawal* are air lift pumps, centrifugal pumps and mechanical scraper systems. Air lift pumps are prone to blockage by rags unless effective pre-screening is provided. Grit pumps are usually of the torque flow type, with minimum contact between the abrasive grit and impeller surfaces. Mechanical systems are usually either screw conveyors or continuous chain and bucket elevators.

Several types of *mechanically-stirred grit chamber* are available from manufacturers of mechanical equipment. Velocity control in grit chambers of this type is usually achieved by paddles on a vertical shaft, which rotate in a specially-profiled circular chamber. The inlet channel is built so that it discharges tangentially in the direction of rotation. Grit settles to the chamber floor, which is sloped so that the grit moves towards a hopper in the centre and can then be removed.

Another approach to the problem of grit removal is to use *detritus tanks*. The tanks are designed to operate at a velocity lower than for normal grit chambers. This not only results in removal of finer grit than that from other types of chamber, but it also permits some organic solids to settle out. Such chambers are usually equipped with a grit-washing system to wash out the organics and return them to the flow downstream of the detritus tanks.

Example 14.2

Calculate the main dimensions of a set of constant velocity grit chambers for the treatment plant data given in Example 14.1.

Solution
The simplest installation will comprise one duty grit chamber with one standby, controlled by a single critical depth flume.

Control flume:

As a first trial, adopt the same dimensions and discharge equation as those for the screen control flume in Ex 14.1: $Q = 1.7\,b\,h^{3/2}$, $b = 0.2$ m. Then flow depths upstream of the flume are $h_a = 0.308$ m, $h_d = 0.488$ m and $h_w = 1.230$ m.

Grit chamber:

Cross-sectional area, $A = Q/V_f$
For constant velocity, $V_f = 0.3$ m/s, and at Q_a

$$A_a = \frac{0.058}{0.3} = 0.193 \text{ m}^2$$

Similarly, at Q_d, $A_d = 0.387$ m², and at Q_w, $A_w = 1.547$ m²

Width of grit chamber is given by Eq 14.8

$$W_a = 1.5\,A_a/h_a = \frac{1.5 \times 0.193}{0.308}$$

$$= 0.94 \text{ m}$$

Similarly, $W_d = 1.189$ m and $W_w = 1.886$ m

For the three flows, calculated values of h and W can be plotted to give the 'ideal parabolic' cross-section, and a suitable trapezoidal approximation developed.

Length of grit chamber is obtained from Eq 14.10

$$L \cong 18 \, h = 18 \times 1.23 \cong 22m$$

Grit collecting channel:

Estimated grit load $\cong 0.005$ to 0.05 m³/ML
At Q_w, total grit load $= 40 \, (0.005 \text{ to } 0.05)$
$$= 0.2 \text{ to } 2.0 \text{ m}^3/\text{d}$$

Cross-sectional area of grit channel

$$= \frac{\text{Volume}}{\text{Length}} = \frac{2.0}{22} = 0.09 \text{ m}^2$$

A channel 0.3 m $\times$ 0.3 m would give an area of 0.09 m², and should be adequate to ensure that cleaning is only required once each day at PWWF.

Pre-aeration

Pre-aeration is provided where wastewater reaches the treatment works in a stale condition, particularly in hot climates. This increases the dissolved oxygen concentration and thus lessens the odour problems in the primary treatment phase of the works. Detention time in the pre-aeration tanks for this purpose should be at least 20 minutes. Pre-aeration may also be effective in assisting *flocculation* of sewage solids and enhancing SS and BOD removal efficiency in primary sedimentation tanks. Somewhat longer detention times — about 45 minutes — are considered necessary for effective flocculation. Improved flocculation can be achieved with shorter detention times by the use of chemical coagulants or polymers, but this increases the mass of sludge solids for disposal.

Design of primary sedimentation tanks

Sedimentation is generally the main unit operation in the primary phase of municipal wastewater treatment. It can remove all the readily settleable matter from the wastewater, achieving an overall SS removal of 50 to 70 per cent. Along with this suspended matter, a proportion of the organic oxygen-demanding material is removed, so that BOD is reduced by 25 to 40 per cent. A considerable proportion of the suspended particles of grease and fatty material floats to the surface to form a scum which can be removed.

The design of primary sedimentation tanks is based on the principles set out for design of Class II sedimentation tanks in Chapter 8, Section 8.2.

Concentration of SS at about 200 to 500 mg/L is fairly dilute and, since they are largely organic, the solids tend to be flocculent. Surface loading rate ($Q/A = V_p$) is generally considered to be the major design parameter — commonly adopted values for all types of primary tank lie in the range of 20 to 40 m^3/m^2.d. The *depth*, H, or *detention time*, t, needs to be considered, as set out in Chapter 8, because of the flocculent nature of the solids. The mean depth is usually between 2.5 and 4 m. For economy of construction, rectangular and circular tanks are usually less than 5 m deep at their deepest point. From Eq 8.8, using the extreme values of the above-quoted ranges for Q/A and H, the corresponding detention times would be 1.5 to 4.8 hours. The values of t commonly adopted are 1.5 to 3 hours at design flow. Once the values of the major design parameters are chosen, the dimensions can be chosen from Fig 8.7.

Table 14.2 presents a summary of data for various types of primary

Table 14.2 Typical design criteria for primary sedimentation tanks (based on UK practice)

	Type of tank		
	Horizontal flow (rectangular)	*Radial flow*	*Upward flow*
Surface loading (m^3/m^2.d)	30 at max flow. < 45 if design max flow > 3 ADWF	≯ 45 at max flow	≯ 43 often ≅ 29
Detention time (hours)	2 for max sewage flow + return liquors	2 at max flow. 1.5 if max flow > 3 ADWF	2–3
Dimensions	Small tanks depth ≮ 1.5 m L/W 4:1 Large tanks depth ≮ 3 m L/W 2:1	Diameter: 5 m fixed bridge to 50 m rotating bridge. Side depth: ≮ 1.5 m; 1/6 to 1/10 diameter	Pyramidal shape: side slope ≮ 60° 5 m–9 m square. Conical shape: side slope ≃ 45°
Weir overflow rate (m^3/m.d)	450 max; 300 preferred	Where max rate < 100 m^3/m^2.d use V-notch weirs	V-notch weirs to overcome low O/F rates
Performance	SS > 100 mg/L SS removal ≃ 40–75% Sludge 3–7%	SS > 100 mg/L SS removal ≃ 50–75% Sludge 3–6.5%	SS removal ≃ 65% Sludge 3–4%

sedimentation tank in the UK. Some modification to these data is necessary when designing tanks for warmer climates, especially in the choice of *design flow*. Whereas it is common practice in cooler climates, such as in the UK, to design for three times average dry-weather flow (3 ADWF), it is frequently found in warmer climates that the resulting long detention time at average flow can result in the sewage becoming septic, with consequent odour problems. Therefore, it is common in countries with warm to hot climates to design primary sedimentation tanks for ADWF or PDWF. In such cases, wet-weather flows of up to six times ADWF are passed through primary sedimentation. Although this results in reduced sedimentation efficiency at high flows, it has been found that more than 50 per cent of normal efficiency can still be achieved, provided that a detention time of at least 20 minutes is available.

Where reduced efficiency is not acceptable at peak flow, *storm sedimentation tanks* can be provided to treat the sewage in excess of the maximum permitted flow to the primary sedimentation tanks. These storm sedimentation tanks are normally kept empty and act as storage tanks for low-volume overflows. Once they are filled, they serve simply as auxiliary sedimentation tanks. They may be of relatively cheap construction and are frequently not provided with sludge scraping equipment. Sludge is allowed to accumulate in them during the period of storm flow, and once flow returns to normal, their contents are pumped back to the treatment works inlet.

Rectangular horizontal flow tanks
These are commonly used for primary sedimentation, since they occupy less space than circular tanks and can be economically built side-by-side with common walls. Fig 14.7 (a) shows a typical tank. The maximum *forward velocity* to avoid the risk of scouring settled sludge is 10 to 15 mm/s, indicating that the *ratio of length to width*, L/W, should preferably be about 3:1 (Fig 8.7).

The maximum *weir loading rate*, to limit the influence of draw-down currents, is preferably about 300 m³/m.d; this figure is sometimes increased where the design flow is greater than 3 ADWF. To achieve this low figure, it is usually necessary to provide multiple suspended weir troughs. *Inlets* should be baffled to dissipate the momentum of the incoming flow and to assist in establishing uniform forward flow. *Sludge* is removed by scraping it into collecting hoppers at the inlet end of the tank. In small plants, sludge is usually removed by gravity under the visual control of the operator, while in large plants it may be pumped from the hoppers; sludge density meters are used to assist in controlling the sludge withdrawal operation. *Scum removal* is essential in primary sedimentation tanks because of the grease and other floating matter which is present in wastewaters. The sludge scrapers can return along the length of the tank at the water surface. As they move towards

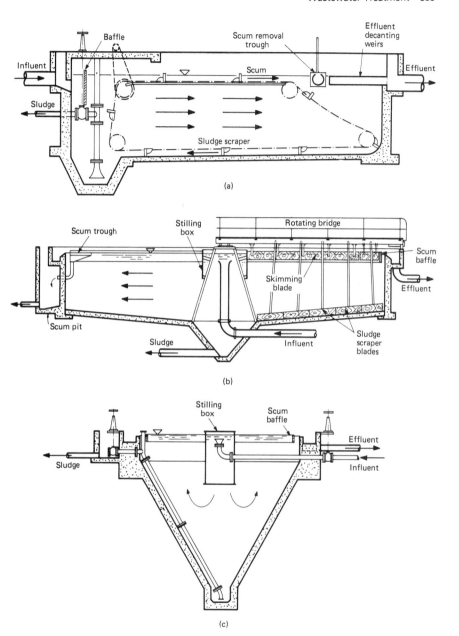

Fig 14.7 Typical primary sedimentation tanks: (a) rectangular horizontal flow tank, (b) circular radial flow tank, (c) upflow tank

the outlet end of the tank, the flights then move the scum towards a skimmer located just upstream of the effluent weirs.

Circular radial flow tanks

These are also used for primary sedimentation. Fig 14.7(b) shows a typical tank. Careful design of the *inlet stilling well* is needed to achieve a stable radial flow pattern without causing excessive turbulence in the vicinity of the central sludge hopper. The weir length around the perimeter of the tank is usually sufficient to give a satisfactory *weir loading rate* at maximum flow, but at low flows, very low flow depths may result. To overcome the sensitivity of these tanks to slight errors in weir level and wind effects, it is common to provide V-notch weirs. *Sludge removal* is effected by means of a rotary sludge scraper which moves the sludge into a central hopper, from which it is withdrawn. *Scum removal* is carried out by a surface skimming board attached to the sludge scraper mechanism and positioned so that scum is moved towards a collecting hopper at the surface.

Upflow tanks

Upflow tanks, usually square in plan and with deep hopper bottoms, are common in small treatment plants. Fig 14.7(c) shows a typical tank. Their main advantage is that *sludge removal* is carried out entirely by gravity, and no mechanical parts are required for cleaning them. The steeply-sloping sides — usually 60° to the horizontal — concentrate the sludge at the bottom of the hopper. This also means, however, that *scum removal* is a manual operation, requiring daily attention. *Weir loading* rate is a problem only at low flows, so that V-notch weirs are desirable. The required upflow pattern is maintained by weir troughs adjacent to the inlet stilling well in addition to those at the tank perimeter. True upflow tanks have a disadvantage in that hydraulic overloading may have more serious effects than in a horizontal flow tank. Any particles with a velocity lower than $V_p = Q/A$ will not be removed in an upflow tank, but will escape in the effluent. In a horizontal flow tank, assuming that such particles were uniformly distributed throughout the flow, particles with $V_p' < Q/A$ would still be removed in the proportion V_p'/V_p.

Example 14.3

Two rectangular primary sedimentation tanks are to be designed for the treatment plant whose data are given in Example 14.1. Determine suitable dimensions for these tanks if the surface loading rate is 35 m^3/m^2.d at peak dry-weather flow, detention time is not to exceed 4 hours at ADWF and forward velocity at a maximum flow of 3 ADWF is not to exceed 5 mm/s (flows in excess of 3 ADWF are to be diverted upstream of the primary sedimentation tanks).

Solution
Flows:

$$Q_a = 5 \text{ ML/d} = 58 \text{ L/s}$$

$$\text{Design flow} = Q_d = 10 \text{ ML/d} = 116 \text{ L/s}$$

$$3 \text{ ADWF} = 15 \text{ ML/d} = 174 \text{ L/s}.$$

Surface loading rate:

Given as 35 $\text{m}^3/\text{m}^2.\text{d} = \dfrac{35}{86.4} = 0.4 \text{ L/m}^2.\text{s}$ (equivalent to a theoretical particle settling velocity of 0.4 mm/s)

Surface area of each tank (Eq 8.12), for n = 2 tanks

$$A = Q_d/[(Q/A)n] = \frac{116}{0.4 \times 2} = 145 \text{ m}^2$$

Detention time t = $\forall/Q$ = 4 hours at ADWF, Then,

$$\forall = Q_a\, t_a = Q_d\, t_d$$

Therefore

$$t_d = \frac{Q_a\, t_a}{Q_d} = \frac{t_a}{2} = 2 \text{ hours}$$

Tank depth:

From Eq 8.8, t $= \dfrac{H}{Q/A}$ (H in metres for t in days, Q/A in $\text{m}^3/\text{m}^2.\text{d}$)

Therefore

$$H = tQ/A = 2 \times 35/24 = 2.92 \text{ m}$$

Forward velocity:

From Eq 8.15, $V_f = \dfrac{L}{3.6\, t}$

At $3Q_a$, $V_f = 5$ mm/s

Hence, at $Q_d = 2Q_a$, $V_f = 3.33$ mm/s

Therefore, L $= 3.6\, t V_f = 3.6 \times 2 \times 3.33 = 24$ m

Tank width W $= A/L = 145 \text{ m}^2/24 \text{ m} = 6$ m

Check length/width ratio, $\alpha = 24/6 = 4$

Therefore, suitable tank dimensions are: length = 24 m, width = 6 m, depth = 3 m.

Note: The above solution could also have been obtained directly by use of Fig 8.7.

14.4 Secondary treatment

The main objective of secondary treatment is to remove most of the fine suspended and dissolved degradable organic matter which remains after primary treatment, so that the effluent may be rendered suitable for discharge. In many cases, reduction of the BOD to below 20 mg/L and SS to below 30 mg/L is acceptable, and conventional secondary treatment can achieve this quality.

A second objective in some cases is the reduction of ammonia toxicity and nitrification oxygen demand in the stream. This is achieved by oxidation of most of the ammonia to nitrate during treatment (nitrification). Nitrification is possible with aerobic biological processes if they are operated at low organic loading rates — hence the units must be larger than those which would be required for oxidation of carbonaceous matter alone.

The principles of aerobic biological oxidation, and their application to various forms of fixed film, suspended growth and some recently-developed hybrid processes are set out in Chapter 11. Of the processes discussed in that chapter, the most widely used in municipal treatment systems are trickling filters, rotating biological filters, activated sludge and oxidation ponds (as in Fig 14.1). Aerated lagoons are sometimes used for municipal treatment and for pretreating industrial effluents. These five processes have been selected for discussion in the following sections on designing biological treatment systems. The principles set out in Chapter 11 are most directly applicable to the suspended growth systems — particularly the activated sludge process. Since this process is now the most widely used in newly-installed municipal treatment systems, it is discussed first and in greatest detail. This provides a standard with which the design requirements of the other processes can be compared.

14.5 Design of activated sludge systems

From the description of the activated sludge process given in Chapter 11, it may be seen that its design involves details of sizing and operation of the following main elements:

a Aeration tank (reactor) — capacity and dimensions
b Aeration system — oxygen requirements and oxygen transfer system
c Final sedimentation tank (clarifier)
d Return activated sludge system
e Excess activated sludge withdrawal system and subsequent treatment and disposal of the waste sludge.

Since the whole process takes place in a liquid medium, the hydraulic regime, especially in the aeration tank and the final sedimentation tank, needs to be carefully considered. The main system elements are discussed below.

The aeration tank

The aeration tank serves as a reactor in which the processes of biological growth and biodegradation take place. Therefore, conditions in the tank must satisfy the requirements for biological growth. Hence both capacity, as determined by process loading, and configuration, as dictated by hydraulic requirements, must be considered.

Aeration tank capacity is often determined simply on the basis of empirical values of food-to-micro-organism ratio, irrespective of the hydraulic regime provided. For this purpose, F/M ratio (F) can be expressed as

$$F = \frac{\text{Mass of BOD entering the aeration tanks/day}}{\text{Total mass of MLVSS under aeration}}$$

$$= \frac{\text{kg BOD/day}}{\text{kg MLVSS}} \tag{14.11}$$

(Strictly speaking, the total MLVSS in the aeration tanks and final settling tanks should be used. Many design loading parameters, however, are quoted in terms of MLVSS in the aeration tank only.)

In terms of normal design variables,

$$F = \frac{QL_i}{VX_v} \tag{14.12}$$

where Q is the sewage flow rate (m^3/d); L_i is the BOD concentration (mg/L); V is the aeration tank volume (m^3); and X_v is the MLVSS concentration (mg/L); and the aeration tank volume is given by

$$V = \frac{QL_i}{FX_v} \tag{14.13}$$

In Eq 14.13, Q and L_i, or their product, are usually given, while values of F and X_v must be chosen according to the required effluent quality and operating characteristics of the system. For the conventional activated sludge process, values of F and X_v are usually in the ranges of 0.20 to 0.50 kg BOD/kg MLVSS.d and 1500 to 3000 mg/L respectively.

It may also be seen from Eq 14.12 that F/M ratio encompasses a number of other commonly-quoted loading parameters. Apart from MLVSS concentration, which is the term X_v, mean *sewage detention time*, t, in the aeration tanks is present as V/Q, while *volumetric organic loading rate* in g.BOD/m^3.d is QL_i/V. Thus, comparison of plant loading data in terms of any of these other parameters is valid only as long as the other terms included in the expression for F/M ratio are constant.

Performance of activated sludge processes is affected not only by the biological reactions in the aeration tanks but also by the *hydraulic flow pattern* through the tanks. At one extreme, flow may approximate to ideal *plug flow*, where each element of fluid entering the aeration tank retains its identity without intermixing with adjacent elements of fluid. At the other extreme, flow may be *completely mixed*, where the incoming flow is rapidly mixed with the whole of the tank contents.

Plug flow systems are characterised by conditions which vary along the length of the reactor. At the inlet end, substrate concentration is at its highest and both reaction rate and rate of oxygen use are at a maximum. As the mixed liquor passes along the aeration tank, substrate concentration declines and sludge mass increases. At the effluent end of the tank, substrate concentration is reduced to a very low value and sludge activity is therefore at its lowest, the oxygen use being due mainly to respiration of sludge organisms.

Completely mixed systems are characterised by uniform concentrations of substrate and activated sludge solids as well as by a constant rate of oxygen use throughout the mixed liquor. Hence the concentration of substrate and sludge solids in the effluent from the aeration tank is the same as that in the mixed liquor. These features give completely mixed systems some advantages in treating shock loads of toxic materials or organics, since the whole of the aeration tank volume is available to dilute the sudden input.

It is apparent that the ideal aeration tank geometry must be quite different for the two flow patterns. Plug flow reactors should be very long and narrow to prevent longitudinal mixing, while completely mixed reactors should be either circular or square to promote mixing of the tank contents. In most practical cases, the actual flow pattern is somewhere between the two ideal patterns. The completely mixed condition is generally simplest to achieve.

In recent decades, much research has been carried out in an effort to develop mathematical models of the activated sludge process. Generally speaking, these models have indicated that, theoretically, plug flow systems should give slightly better treatment than completely mixed systems under normal operating conditions. Some studies of full-scale plants employing plug flow and completely mixed flow patterns in parallel, treating the same waste, gave very similar performances under normal operation, while the completely mixed system was found to have superior response to shock loads. For these reasons, and because it is much simpler to describe mathematically, the completely mixed activated sludge process has been selected for closer study in the following section.

The completely mixed activated sludge process

A definition sketch for the completely mixed activated sludge (CMAS) process is shown in Fig 14.8. For the CMAS system, it is possible to develop a number of useful correlations between food-to-micro-organism ratio and other design parameters. For these correlations, however, it is necessary to

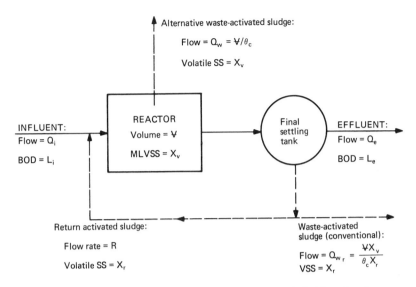

Fig 14.8 Completely mixed activated sludge process — definition sketch

use a modified form of the food-to-micro-organism ratio, U, defined in terms of the *BOD removed* by the process, rather than the BOD applied. Thus

$$U = \frac{\text{Mass of BOD removed each day}}{\text{Total mass MLVSS under aeration}} = \frac{[L_r]_T}{[X_v]_T} \qquad (14.14)$$

or

$$U = \frac{Q(L_i - L_e)}{\Psi X_v} \qquad (14.15)$$

where L_e is the effluent BOD concentration (mg/L).

Implicit in Eq 14.15 is the further assumption that the flow rate of waste-activated sludge is small relative to the influent flow rate. Hence, Q_e and Q_i are for practical purposes assumed to be equal and are represented simply by the general term Q.

Sludge production per unit mass of sludge solids in the system, $[\Delta X_v]_T/[X_v]_T$, can be correlated with U, as shown in Fig 14.9(a).

The term $[\Delta X_v]_T/[X_v]_T$ is the inverse of the mean cell residence time (MCRT) — also known as the sludge age, θ_c. The correlation between θ_c and U is expressed by Eq 14.16, shown in Fig 14.9(a). For estimation of sludge production, Eq 14.16 may be rearranged to give Eq 14.17, also shown in Fig 14.9(a).

At very low values of U, as in extended aeration plants, the linear correlation expressed by these equations does not apply. Hence, at low

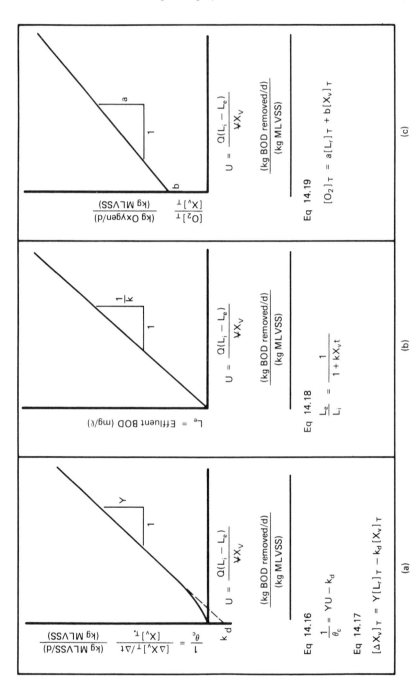

Fig 14.9 Completely mixed activated sludge process: correlations between modified F/M ratio, U, and: (a) mean cell residence time, (b) effluent BOD concentration, (c) oxygen requirements

loading rates corresponding to large values of θ_c, Eqs 14.16 and 14.17 can be applied only if the values of Y and k_d are adjusted for the particular loading range.

Another method of taking into account the variation in sludge production rate at low loadings is to express it in terms of an observed yield coefficient Y_{obs}. Then

$$\frac{[\Delta X_v]_T}{[X_v]_T} = Y_{obs}U \qquad (14.20)$$

In this case, Y_{obs} is a non-linear function of θ_c, and, for a given waste, the form of the relationship must be determined from laboratory or pilot scale studies.

Effluent BOD, L_e, can be correlated with U, as represented by Fig 14.9(b). The first-order reaction Eq 14.18, shown in Fig 14.9(b), can be derived from this. It should be noted that the value of L_e given by these relationships is the BOD which remains dissolved in the effluent, and hence it corresponds to the BOD of filtered effluent. Effluent from practical wastewater treatment plants always contains a small amount of fine activated sludge solids. In such cases, the total effluent BOD will be represented by the sum of the soluble BOD, L_e, and the BOD of the escaping sludge solids.

Oxygen requirements for *carbonaceous oxidation*, expressed as the oxygen required per unit mass of activated sludge, $[O_2]_T/[X_v]_T$, can be correlated with U, as shown in Fig 14.9(c), whence the total oxygen consumption in carbonaceous oxidation can be determined (Eq 14.19 in Fig 14.9(c)). Alternatively, the oxygen demand for carbonaceous oxidation can be estimated from the expression

$$[O_2]_T = [L_{ur}]_T - 1.42[\Delta X_v]_T \qquad (14.21)$$

where $[L_{ur}]_T$ is the total mass of ultimate BOD removed each day $(\cong 1.46[L_r]_T$ for domestic sewage) and the second term represents the approximate oxygen equivalent of the influent carbon which is synthesised into new cells and is thus removed as waste-activated sludge.

The oxygen demand for *nitrification* must be estimated separately. In general, 4.6 kg of oxygen are required for each kilogram of ammonia nitrogen oxidised.

The aeration system should have sufficient oxygenation capacity to transfer the oxygen needed to satisfy the total oxygen demand for the required degree of carbonaceous and nitrogenous oxidation, while maintaining the DO concentration in the mixed liquor at, or above, the minimum acceptable value. At least 1 mg/L of DO is required to ensure that organism activity is not inhibited and to prevent the growth of filamentous organisms. If nitrification is required, the DO concentration should be at least 2 mg/L.

In the design of the aeration system, it is important to consider not only the average but also the *peak hourly* rate of oxygen demand; this may be 50 to 100 per cent or more above the average rate of oxygen demand.

The values of the *process coefficients,* Y, Y_{obs}, k_d, k, a and b, in Eqs 14.16 to 14.20 depend on many factors, such as the biodegradability and oxidation-reduction state of the organic carbon and the predominant micro-organism species. These values, therefore, tend to be specific to the type of waste being treated. Wherever possible, they should be evaluated by laboratory or pilot scale tests. Some typical values which have been reported for domestic wastewater systems are: Y = 0.5 to 0.7 kg VSS/kg BOD removed; k_d = 0.04 to 0.07 per day; k = 0.025 L/mg.d; a = 0.57 kg O_2/kg BOD removed; and b = 0.1 kg O_2/kg MLVSS.day.

The parameter θ_c can be used as a simple *control parameter* by the withdrawal of $1/\theta_c$ of the aeration tank contents each day. The liquor so withdrawn should be thickened, and the supernatant returned to the aeration tank.

Aeration system

If all other factors are the same — type of waste, power input, system of aeration, temperature and impurities — the rate of oxygen transfer is proportional to the difference between the saturation concentration and the actual concentration (Section 8.4).

If the concentration of oxygen is lowered, more oxygen can be transferred for the same expenditure of power on the same equipment. Therefore, it is desirable, from this point of view, to operate with a low oxygen concentration. However, too great a reduction of the oxygen concentration affects the efficient operation of the biological process. A suitable design target value, with air at atmospheric pressure as an oxygen source, is 2 mg/L. For oxygen gas, with its much higher partial pressure and a saturation concentration of about 40 mg/L or more, a higher target concentration may be used to advantage.

Aeration devices commonly used in activated sludge systems include diffused air systems (with porous or non-porous diffusers), mechanical surface aerators (horizontal or vertical shaft) and turbine aerators.

Many activated sludge systems use *diffused air*, in which air is introduced through some apparatus to form bubbles which rise through the water. Diffused air aeration has been developed as an obvious way to create air-water interfaces, but not because of any significant technical advantage. In its application, distinction should be made between circumstances where mixing is of primary importance (aerated grit chambers and channel aeration) and those where oxygen transfer is the primary aim.

A diffuser unit for oxygen transfer should be chosen on the basis of maximum efficiency. This should not be measured merely as kg/kW.h, but as the cost per kilogram of oxygen transferred, including power, maintenance and replacement costs, and amortisation of capital cost of diffusers, ancillary equipment and standby aeration tanks, if required.

Porous diffusers
These must be operated continuously, with an airflow less than that which could damage the diffuser but always more than the minimum recommended flow, so that clogging will not occur too rapidly. This requires the provision of standby air compressors. Porous diffusers mounted between three and four metres deep in tanks about seven metres wide have given oxygen transfer efficiencies of 8 to 16 per cent. In terms of power requirement, porous diffusers operating in a 1.5 metre band of aeration in a spiral flow tank, at a pressure of 49 kPa, have a *theoretical* oxygen transfer rate of about 2.8 kg/kW.h.

Porous diffusers may be made of ceramic material, and they are available in the shape of plates, domes or tubes. They may also be made of plastic material, either fabric or moulded. Fabric diffusers are generally lightweight and they can be readily cleaned.

Non-porous diffusers
These have been developed with the objectives of

a Elimination of diffuser clogging problems
b Reduction of equipment capital cost (but there is a loss in efficiency as compared with fine bubble porous diffusers).

Many types of jet, valved orifice and turbulence disc are now available. A system which uses slotted pipes with a shallow immersion of about 0.9 m and a large volume of air at low pressure has been developed. In these conditions, compressors can be replaced by fans and the holes in the pipes are so large that they seldom block. Power efficiency is in the range of 1.0 to 2.25 kg/kW.h.

Some diffusers consist of a plastic or metal base with a hole covered by a spring-loaded plate. Air pressure from within will raise the plate and allow medium-sized bubbles to escape. When the air pressure drops, the spring-loaded plate is pressed down over the hole by the combined action of the spring and the water pressure to prevent solids from gaining access to the pipeline. This type of diffuser permits intermittent operation of compressors to meet varying organic loads on a daily or seasonal basis.

Most diffused air systems require a supply of air at a pressure of 50 to 80 kPa. Porous diffuser systems require air to be well filtered and oil-free to prevent clogging of diffusers.

Turbine aerators
These have submerged turbines with air released from spargers immediately

below them. They have been used where the required oxygen input per unit of volume is greater than can be conveniently obtained with diffused air. Their oxygen transfer capacity is in the range of 1.5 to 2.0 kg/kW.h.

Mechanical surface aeration
This is achieved by mechanically breaking up the water surface to produce a large water-air interface as drops and by producing turbulence throughout the aeration tank to keep the solids in suspension. This has the advantages of simplicity of equipment and comparative ease of maintenance. In recent years, the designs of surface aerators have been refined to increase reliability and efficiency and to prevent interference by foreign objects such as rags.

Aerators have been designed with vertical shafts and with horizontal shafts. The transfer efficiencies are similar for both types; the choice depends on system layout, first cost and maintenance costs.

Vertical shaft mechanical aerators have a rotor at the surface of the water, where the oxygen transfer takes place through surface turbulence, splashing and air bubble entrainment. The oxygen transfer capacity depends on the design of the equipment, the depth of immersion, the shape and size of the aeration tank, the energy input per unit volume of tank and the rate of rotation; some of these factors are interrelated. The oxygen transfer rates under average operation conditions are of the order of 2 to 3 kg/kW.h. It is important that the aerators mix the tank contents to avoid a build-up of anaerobic sludge on the bottom, as well as to provide oxygen.

The power absorbed and the oxygen transferred by a vertical shaft aerator can be varied by changing the degree of immersion of the impeller, by varying the speed of rotation, or by intermittent operation. The degree of immersion of a unit mounted on a fixed platform can be altered either by variation in the level of the water (such as with an adjustable weir) or by the use of a telescopic shaft.

Horizontal shaft surface aerators with various types of *brush* and *cage* rotor have been designed since the use of *Sheffield paddles* in the early days of activated sludge treatment (1920). They provide not only aeration but also a horizontal pumping effect to maintain circulation and mixing. They may be used in tanks of moderate depth to provide a rolling circulation, but the most common use is in oxidation ditches and for supplementing oxygen supply in maturation ponds or oxidation ponds.

A typical cage rotor of 700 mm diameter could be operated at a speed of 75 rev/min, to give an oxygen transfer of 2.9 to 3.5 kg/kW.h, depending on depth of immersion. These rotors may be mounted on floats which slide in guide-boxes at each end, so that a constant depth of immersion is maintained. This depth may be varied by the addition or removal of ballast in the floats.

U-tube aeration

This has been developed from a requirement to aerate water to near-saturation without involving a high power cost. With surface aerators adding oxygen to clean water initially devoid of oxygen, the rate of transfer is proportional to the difference between the saturation concentration and the actual concentration. As the actual concentration approaches saturation, the transfer rate slows down. If the saturation concentration is 8 mg/L, it takes as much energy to increase the concentration by 1 mg/L from 6 mg/L to 7 mg/L as it does to raise it 4 mg/L from zero concentration.

In U-tube aeration, however, the partial pressure of the oxygen can be doubled or trebled by passing the water, with diffused bubbles entrained, through a U-tube with its lower portion 10 to 20 metres or more below the hydraulic grade line. This increases the partial pressure and hence the instantaneous saturation concentration, and speeds up the transfer of oxygen. Further increase of partial pressure of oxygen can be obtained by using oxygen gas for the bubbles.

Molecular oxygen can be used instead of air to increase greatly the partial pressure of the oxygen. If the atmosphere in contact with the sewage under treatment is oxygen, the partial pressure of the oxygen approaches that of the atmosphere and creates a much greater driving force to transfer it into the liquid. In this way, the saturation concentration at atmospheric pressure changes from 8 to 10 mg/L, which is the usual range for water in contact with air, up to 40 to 50 mg/L. This makes it practicable to maintain higher concentrations of DO in the liquor.

Where 'pure' oxygen is used for waste treatment, it has to be obtained from such a source as cylinders, bulk tankers or reticulated oxygen from suppliers, cryogenic oxygen distillation plant at the works, or the residual left when nitrogen is adsorbed from air into a packed bed of special zeolite.

It has been claimed that activated sludges grown under conditions of plentiful dissolved oxygen (such as 4 to 6 mg/L) will settle more rapidly than those grown in liquors containing only 1 to 2 mg/L of dissolved oxygen. More rapid settling means smaller settling tanks, or allows higher concentrations of sludge, thus requiring smaller aeration volume. The savings in capital costs of plant and the probable higher efficiency of treatment which may give more completely nitrified effluents have to be offset against the increased running cost, and the reliability of oxygen supply.

Final sedimentation tank

The final sedimentation tank has to serve two major functions in activated sludge systems: clarification and thickening.

Unless the final settling tank is correctly designed and operated for its *clarification* function, activated sludge solids may escape, resulting in a highly turbid effluent with a high suspended solids concentration. Because the escaping sludge solids are biological in nature, they exert an oxygen demand, directly by their respiration and indirectly as they die and are degraded by other organisms.

For clarifiers, the most important characteristic of the activated sludge suspension is its settling velocity, V_s, because this fixes the maximum surface loading rate, Q/A, on the settling tank, as discussed in Section 8.2.

Because of their high concentration, activated sludges exhibit the form of hindered settling known as *zone settling*. In this case, the parameter $V_s = Q/A$ represents the settling velocity of the interface between the settling suspension and the clarified liquid. In Section 8.2 it was noted that, according to hindered settling theory, the interface settling velocity decreases as concentration increases. For activated sludges, settling velocity is also related to the growth state of the activated sludge organisms and other factors, and hence to the organic loading rate in the process. Clarifier design is therefore based on empirically-determined values of Q/A, typically 30 to 40 m³/m².d.

Since clarifiers are required to perform effectively at all flows, the *design maximum* surface loading rate should be applied to the *maximum flow rate* which may be admitted to the biological treatment system. It should be noted that in calculating the surface loading rate, only the sewage flow need be considered since the return sludge flow is drawn off in the underflow from the settling tank and does not have to pass up through the interface between the sludge and the supernatant.

In addition to producing a clarified effluent, final settling tanks are required to thicken the settled sludge so that it can be returned at a sufficiently high concentration to maintain the designed MLSS concentration in the aeration tank. The design parameter which relates to thickening capacity of the final settling tanks is the solids loading rate, S_x. For a given surface loading rate, Q/A in m³/m².d, S_x, is given by Eq 14.22:

$$S_x = (Q/A)\left(\frac{X}{1000}\right)\left(1 + \frac{R}{Q}\right) \tag{14.22}$$

where R is the flow rate of return activated sludge in the same units as Q. The factor $(1 + R/Q)$ is included because the total solids loading rate must be considered; it is equal to the product of (X) and the total flow to the final settling tanks $(Q + R)$, or $Q(1 + R/Q)$.

In practice, the thickening characteristics of the activated sludge may be the controlling factor in the performance of final settling tanks at MLSS concentrations above 2000 mg/L. For this MLSS concentration, with return sludge flow rate set at 50 per cent of the incoming sewage flow rate and a surface loading rate of 40 m³/m².d, the solids loading rate would be 120 kg/m².d, or 5 kg/m².h. The latter unit of expression for S_x is sometimes preferred since the critical condition for plant performance is likely to occur at the peak hourly flow rate.

Depth, detention time, weir loading rate and *inlet arrangements* should be considered, as with other types of sedimentation tank (see Sections 8.2 and

14.3). The minimum depth of tank below the outlet weirs should normally be 3 metres. For a design surface loading rate of 30 to 40 $m^3/m^2.d$, the detention time would be 1.5 to 2 hours (from Eq 8.8). For a design flow of 3 ADWF, this would result in a hydraulic detention of 4.5 to 6 hours at ADWF. A very efficient sludge removal system is essential, therefore, in order to reduce the time that the settled activated sludge solids remain in the clarifiers. Excess sludge detention can lead to anoxic conditions, the reduction of nitrates to nitrogen gas, the attachment of the resulting bubbles to the sludge solids causing them to float, and the loss of sludge solids in the effluent. For this reason, it is desirable also to provide scum removal equipment in the final settling tanks, especially in nitrifying activated sludge plants. In very small plants, it is often difficult to achieve the recommended depth below the outlet weirs. Depth may be reduced in such cases, but it is also desirable to adopt a conservative value for the surface loading rate, such as 20 $m^3/m^2.d$.

Weir overflow rates, Q/W_L, should be restricted to prevent the development of local currents which may interfere with the hydraulic flow pattern through the tank. In small tanks, sufficient weir length, W_L, should be provided so that the weir loading rate at maximum flow does not exceed 250 $m^3/m^2.d$.

Circular tanks are the most common type used for final sedimentation. The design of the inlet stilling and distribution box is similar to that of circular primary tanks. If the effluent weir is suspended at a distance of about one-third of the tank radius from the outer wall, some of the problems caused by stray currents will be reduced.

The required rapid removal of sludge can be achieved either by means of rotary scrapers, which move the sludge to a central hopper, or by a set of rotary suction heads, which operate under a slight vacuum, to withdraw the sludge to a collection well adjacent to the inlet chamber.

Rectangular tanks have been used for final settling where site restrictions, such as limited land area or poor soil conditions, compel the most efficient use of the available area. General requirements are similar to those of primary tanks. The required rapid removal of settled activated sludge solids is achieved by the location of the hopper to collect sludge halfway along the tank, and the provision of a separate, chain-mounted, horizontal flight scraper to clean each end of the tank. Operation of the scrapers is continuous, rather than intermittent as in primary tanks.

Return activated sludge system

The activated sludge from the underflow of the final settling tanks should be returned to the inlet of the aeration tanks at a rate sufficient to maintain the MLSS concentration at the design value. The flow rate needed for return sludge is determined from the incoming sewage flow rate and the concentration at which the sludge is withdrawn from the final settling tanks. Hence, a simple measure of the underflow concentration from the settling tanks is required. The parameter conventionally employed for this purpose is the sludge volume index, SVI, which is defined as the volume occupied by sludge containing 1.0 g of sludge solids (dry weight) after 30 minutes' settling, and thus it has the units mL/g. The same result can be expressed as sludge density index, SDI = 100/SVI, which has the units of g/100 mL.

The sludge volume index is measured by taking a standard volume of the mixed liquor from the outlet of the aeration tank (usually 1 L) and letting it settle for 30 minutes in a graduated cylinder. The volume occupied by the settled sludge mass is measured at the end of that period. The MLSS concentration of the sludge sample before settling is also measured. The sludge volume index can then be calculated from

$$SVI = \frac{\text{Settled volume of sludge after 30 minutes (mL/L)}}{\text{Mixed liquor suspended solids concentration (g/L)}}$$

$$(14.23)$$

For example, consider the case where the sludge solids in a 1.0 L sample of mixed liquor having an initial MLSS concentration of 2000 mg/L (2.0 g/L) settle to a volume of 200 mL; the sludge volume index, from Eq 14.23, is 100 mL/g.

There are some problems in relating the measured settling characteristics, as given by SVI, to the performance of full-scale settling tanks, as there are wall effects in the settling cylinders and the SVI is a batch test, whereas settling tanks operate as continuous thickeners. To account for these effects, measured values of SVI are sometimes corrected by multiplying by an empirical factor, determined by experience.

Once the SVI and operating MLSS concentration, X, are known, the required rate of activated sludge return can be calculated by Eqs 14.24 and 14.25, derived from a solids mass balance around the aeration tanks and final settling tanks:

$$r = 100 \left/ \left[\frac{10^6}{(X)(SVI)} - 1 \right] \right. \qquad (14.24)$$

where r is the return sludge flow rate as a percentage of the incoming sewage flow, whence

$$R = \left(\frac{r}{100} \right) Q \qquad (14.25)$$

where R is the return sludge flow rate (ML/d for Q in ML/d).

Theoretically, return sludge pumps should have adjustable pumping rates to cover the extremes of sludge settleability and the full range of sewage flow rates. For example, the SVI may vary from 50 to more than 200, while the sewage flow rate could range from about ½ ADWF to 3 ADWF. At an MLSS concentration of 2500 mg/L, it will be seen from Eqs 14.24 and 14.25 that this would require the return sludge pumps to be able to deliver from 7 per cent to 300 per cent of ADWF. It is seldom considered economical to provide for the full theoretical range of pumping rates. Also, there is evidence that limitations on the capacity of the final settling tank to effectively thicken the sludge at higher flow rates make very high return rates impracticable. As a practical compromise, it is therefore common to provide for return sludge flow rates of about 20 to 150 per cent of ADWF. At the critical condition of maximum SVI and wet-weather flow, it may be necessary to divert flows in excess of 1.5 to 2 ADWF to avoid excessive loss of sludge solids in the effluent.

Example 14.4

Settled sewage at an average dry-weather flow rate of 5 ML/d with 200 mg/L BOD and 100 mg/L SS is to be treated in a completely mixed activated sludge plant to produce an effluent with not more than 10 mg/L BOD. Kinetic coefficients for the sewage are $k = 0.03$ L.mg.d, $Y = 0.65$ kg VSS/kg BOD_r, $k_d = 0.07$ d^{-1}, $a = 0.55$ kg O_2/kg BOD_r and $b = 0.10$ kg O_2/kg MLVSS. Calculate

a The aeration tank volume and dimensions, assuming two tanks square in plan with MLVSS concentration of 2000 mg/L
b The mass and volume of excess activated sludge produced each day, assuming that sludge is wasted from the return sludge system at 99 per cent moisture content
c The operating values of θ_c and F/M ratio
d The daily oxygen requirements for oxidation of carbonaceous matter
e The return activated sludge flow rate if the SVI ranges from 70 to 150 mL/g
f The dimensions of the final sedimentation tanks (two) if the maximum surface loading rate, Q/A, is 40 m^3/m^2.d, the maximum solids loading rate, S_x, is 150 kg/m^2.d, and the detention time at ADWF is less than 6 hours (if possible).

Solution

a Aeration tanks
The average sewage detention time is given by Eq 14.18

$$\frac{L_e}{L_i} = \frac{1}{1 + kX_vt}$$

Substitution from the data gives

$$\frac{10}{200} = \frac{1}{1 + (0.030 \times 2000 \times t)}$$

or   t = 0.32 d

Volume, Ψ = Qt = 5 ML/d × 0.32 d = 1.6 ML = 1600 m³

For two tanks, and an assumed depth of 5 m the side length is

$$\sqrt{\frac{1600}{2 \times 5}} = 12.6 \text{ m, say 13 m square to allow for corner fillets.}$$

b   Sludge production

Daily production of volatile solids is given by Eq 14.17

$$[\Delta X_v]_T = Y[L_r]_T - k_d[X_v]_T$$
$$= 0.65[(200 - 10)5] - 0.07[1.6 \times 2000] = 394 \text{ kg VSS/d}$$

Non-volatile solids production, $[\Delta X_{Nv}]_T$, can be estimated from the amount of non-volatile solids present in the SS in the settled sewage feed, usually 25 to 30 per cent of the SS.

$$[\Delta X_{Nv}]_T = \frac{25}{100} \times (100 \times 5) = 125 \text{ kg NVSS/d}$$

Therefore, total excess sludge solids = $[\Delta X_v]_T + [\Delta X_{Nv}]_T$

$$= 394 + 125 = 519 \text{ kg/d}$$

The percentage of VSS in activated sludge solids is 394/519 × 100 = 76 per cent.

Volume of waste-activated sludge is approximately (from Chapter 12)

$$V_{sw} = \text{Mass sludge solids} \left[\frac{100}{\% \text{ mass of solids}}\right]\left[\frac{1}{\text{wet sludge density}}\right]$$

$$= 519 \times \frac{100}{1} \times \frac{1}{1} = 51\,900 \text{ L/d}$$

c   Loading factors

Mean cell residence time is

$$\theta_c = \frac{[X_v]_T}{[\Delta X_v]_T} = \frac{1.6 \times 2000}{393} = 8.14 \text{ days}$$

F/M ratio is

$$F = \frac{QL_i}{\Psi X_v} = \frac{5 \times 200}{1.6 \times 2000} = 0.31 \text{ kg BOD/kg MLVSS.d}$$

Note that for a high degree of BOD removal, as in this case,

$$U = \frac{Q(L_i - L_e)}{\Psi X_v} = \frac{5 \times 190}{1.6 \times 2000} = 0.30 \sim F$$

It may be seen, therefore, that the size could have been calculated by the use of a conventional loading factor of F = 0.30.

d   Oxygen requirements for oxidation of carbonaceous matter

$$[O_2]_T = a[L_r]_T + b[X_v]_T$$
$$= 0.55 \, [(200 - 10)5] + 0.10[1.6 \times 2000] = 843 \text{ kg } O_2/d.$$
$$= 35.1 \text{ kg } O_2/\text{hour} \equiv 22 \text{ g } O_2/m^3.\text{hour}$$

Note that the oxygenation equipment would be required to have the capacity to transfer oxygen at a rate sufficient to meet the peak oxygen demand.

e   Sludge recycle

The recycle rate as a percentage of the settled sewage flow is given by Eq 14.24

$$r = 100 \Big/ \left[\frac{10^6}{(SVI)(X)} - 1 \right]$$

From (b) above

$$X = \frac{X_v}{76/100} = \frac{2000}{0.76} = 2632 \text{ mg/L}$$

For $SVI_{min} = 70 \text{ mL/g}$

$$r_{min} = 100 \Big/ \left[\frac{10^6}{70 \times 2632} - 1 \right] = 22.6 \text{ per cent}$$

Similarly, for $SVI = 150 \text{ mL/g}$, $r_{max} = 65.2$ per cent

Ideally, the return sludge pumps should be capable of returning sludge at a controlled rate to maintain the required MLVSS concentration in the aeration tanks over the full range of flow rates (say from ½ ADWF to 3 ADWF).

From Eq 14.25

$$R = \frac{r}{100} Q$$

Then

$$R_{min} = \frac{r_{min}}{100} Q_{min} = 0.226 \times 2.5 = 0.6 \text{ ML/d}$$

and

$$R_{max} = \frac{r_{max}}{100} Q_{max} = 0.652 \times 15 = 9.8 \text{ ML/d}$$

Under average conditions, $SVI = 100$, $Q = Q_a$, therefore

$$R_{ave} = \frac{r_{ave}}{100} Q_a = 0.357 \times 5 = 1.8 \text{ ML/d}$$

f   Final sedimentation tanks

Design flow = Maximum flow to aeration tanks

$$= 3 \, Q_a \text{ (assumed)} = 15 \text{ ML/d}$$

Given $(Q/A)_{max} = 40 \text{ m}^3/\text{m}^2.\text{d}$ and $S_{xmax} = 150 \text{ kg solids}/\text{m}^2.\text{d}$

From Eq 14.22

$$S_x = Q/A \times \frac{X}{1000} \times 1 + \frac{R}{Q}$$

At maximum recycle rate, $R/Q = 0.652$, therefore,

$$S_x = Q/A \times \frac{2632}{1000} \times 1.652$$

For $S_x = 150 \text{ kg}/\text{m}^2.\text{d}$, $Q/A = 34.5 \text{ m}^3/\text{m}^2.\text{d}.$

Since this is less than the maximum permissible surface loading rate (40 $\text{m}^3/\text{m}^2.\text{d}$), the solids loading rate controls the design.

$$\text{Total surface area } A = Q/(Q/A) = \frac{15\,000}{34} = 441 \text{ m}^2$$

For two circular tanks, diameter $= 16.8 \text{ m}$

For detention of 6 hours at ADWF, at 3 ADWF, $t = 2$ hours

Depth, from Eq 8.8

$$H = tQ/A = \frac{2}{24} \times 34 = 2.83 \text{ m}$$

Practical tanks should have some allowance made for the sludge scraper mechanism. They normally have conical bottoms, and preferably should have a minimum of 3 m below the outlet weirs. It is desirable therefore to increase H to at least 3 m, plus conical bottom, so increasing the effective detention time.

Variations of the activated sludge process

Since its introduction in 1914, the activated sludge process has undergone many variations and adaptations. In some cases, these adaptations have resulted from basic research into the principles of the process, but more usually they have arisen as empirical solutions to particular problems in plant operation. Thus, development of the theory of activated sludge has generally followed practice, but nevertheless the understanding of the process has been considerably deepened. The main objective of many modifications has been to increase the loading capacity of the basic plug flow activated sludge plant by provision of optimum conditions.

Design parameters for different variations are summarised for comparison in Table 14.3. It is worthy of note that five modifications — tapered aeration, step aeration, the CMAS process, the pure oxygen system and the deep shaft process — all aim at either the improvement of oxygen transfer efficiency or the efficient distribution of available oxygen to match demand. A flow sheet of most of the commonly-used variations is similar to that for conventional activated sludge.

Conventional activated sludge

This process consists of a reactor (aeration tank), a final sedimentation tank and a return sludge system as illustrated in Fig 14.10(a–i). Settled sewage and return sludge are admitted at one end of an aeration tank, in which the mixed liquor is aerated for a nominal 6 to 12 hours detention at ADWF. Aeration and mixing are achieved at a fairly uniform rate over the length of the aeration tank. This leads to an oxygen shortage at the inlet end of the tank (Fig 14.10(a–i)). Reaction may be oxygen-limited, and hence process efficiency may be impaired. Near the outlet end, there may be more than ample oxygen for process requirements. Nitrification may be achieved at the

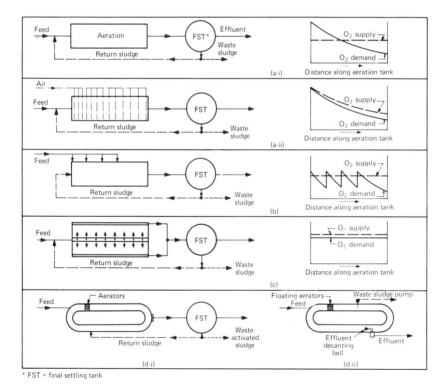

* FST = final settling tank

Fig 14.10 Comparison of simple modifications to the activated sludge process: (a-i) conventional layout, (a-ii) tapered aeration, (b) step aeration, (c) completely mixed (CMAS), (d-i) continuous oxidation ditch, (d-ii) intermittent oxidation ditch

lower end of the conventional process loading range. Excess activated sludge is usually wasted from the return sludge system.

Tapered aeration
This is a simple development of the conventional process. It seeks to adjust the rate of oxygen supply throughout the length of the tank to the rate of demand. Hence a higher proportion of the total air supply is introduced at the inlet end of the aeration tank and the rate of supply is reduced, or tapered, towards the tank outlet — see Fig 14.10(a–ii).

Step aeration
This is another method of equalising oxygen supply and demand rates. In this system, instead of varying the rate of oxygen supply along the aeration tank, partial equalisation of demand rate is achieved by the admission of the settled wastewater at several points along the tank — Fig 14.10(b). It is evident that this process could more appropriately be called 'step feed'.

Completely mixed activated sludge (CMAS) process
In this, the flow pattern and mixing intensity are such as to ensure uniform distribution of influent wastewater, activated sludge and oxygen throughout the aeration tank. To achieve this ideal, the aeration basin could be circular or square, but efficiency in land use and construction economy is achieved in large plants by employing long aeration tanks with influent and effluent arranged along opposite sides of the tank — Fig 14.10(c). The natural flow pattern induced by mechanical surface aerators makes them very suitable for the CMAS process. In a small treatment plant, the size of the aeration tank results in a close approximation to a completely mixed flow pattern.

High rate activated sludge processes
Sometimes called modified aeration, these operate at very much higher F/M ratios than conventional processes. This high loading rate is achieved by means of a much reduced hydraulic detention time and a lower MLSS concentration. As a consequence, θ_c is much shorter than in the conventional process. Cell synthesis and, hence, excess sludge production are higher per unit mass of BOD removed and the waste sludge is less stable. Effluent BOD is much higher than in the case of the conventional process, so that the high rate process is only applicable where a lesser standard of treatment is required — for example, to produce an effluent for ocean discharge. Because more of the incoming organic matter is synthesised to sludge organisms, total oxygen requirements are somewhat less than in the conventional process, but the rate of oxygen demand is higher per unit mass of MLVSS.

Extended aeration
This process is a variation of the basic activated sludge process, usually

employing a completely mixed flow pattern. It is characterised by very low values of F/M ratio, low net sludge yield and hence high values of θ_c, achieved by providing a much longer hydraulic detention time and a higher concentration of MLSS than in the conventional process. The flow sheet of the extended aeration process is similar to that of the conventional process, as given in Fig 14.10(a). Primary sedimentation is usually omitted when extended aeration is used, so that the only sludge for disposal is the excess activated sludge.

Pasveer oxidation ditch
This is a relatively low-cost adaptation of the extended aeration process, especially developed for small installations (Fig 14.10(d)). Essential elements in the process, as in any activated sludge process, are

a An aeration tank (ditch)
b An aeration system
c A means of separating the activated sludge from the effluent
d A return sludge system
e An effluent discharge system and
f A means of withdrawing excess sludge solids.

The two major variations of the process may be distinguished by the way in which the elements of the system are arranged and operated — continuous and intermittent ditches.

Continuous oxidation ditches
These differ from other extended aeration systems only in their use of a racetrack-shaped aeration basin and horizontal shaft cage aerators (Fig 14.10(d–i)). Sewage flows continuously into one part of the ditch, where it is mixed with the activated sludge and circulated around the ditch by the action of the aerators at such a velocity that sewage and sludge solids are kept in suspension. Mixed liquor is displaced over the outlet weirs by the incoming sewage, and it flows to a final sedimentation tank. Settled activated sludge is pumped back to the ditch while the clarified effluent is discharged. Waste sludge is withdrawn either from the return stream or directly from the ditch.

Intermittent oxidation ditches
These carry out both biological oxidation and settling in the ditch itself (Fig 14.10(d–ii)). Effluent discharge is intermittent, however, and the water level varies throughout the operating cycle. To accommodate this variation in water level, while maintaining the required immersion depth of the rotors, the aerators are mounted on a floating platform. Sewage is admitted to the ditch throughout the operating cycle while effluent is withdrawn by a decanting bell during a 30-minute period at the end of each cycle. A typical cycle takes 4 hours, consisting of 2.5 hours aeration, 1 hour settlement and

0.5 hour effluent removal. There is also a short period at the end of the aeration cycle when the aerators are reversed, to slow down the circulation in the ditch so that effective settling can take place. An electrode is set at top water level (TWL), and arranged to return the timer to the beginning of the cycle if TWL is reached before the expiry of the normal operating cycle, as, for example, under storm conditions.

Typical design parameters for the intermittent oxidation ditch are listed in Table 14.3. Dimensions of the ditch should be carefully matched to the aerators used, so as to achieve a circulation velocity of about 0.3 m/s in the ditch and maintain the sludge in suspension. For typical 700 mm diameter cage rotors, a trapezoidal cross-section, having a base width of 2.9 m, 45° side-slopes, a 1.5 m depth to TWL and 1.2 m depth to bottom water level, has proved successful.

The aeration system is designed to transfer oxygen equivalent to 2.4 times the BOD of the incoming wastewater. This allows for both carbonaceous oxidation and nitrification. If one aerator breaks down, the full oxygen requirements can be satisfied by immersing the remaining unit(s) to the maximum depth, and varying the cycle so that the aerators will run for up to 15 hours each day.

At the very low F/M ratio adopted — equivalent to about 0.04 kg BOD/kg MLSS.d — and in the presence of a plentiful supply of dissolved oxygen, a highly-nitrified effluent is produced. Each kilogram of ammonia nitrogen, when oxidised to nitrate, uses about 7 kg of alkalinity to neutralise it. With low-alkalinity wastewater, the pH of the mixed liquor can become low (sometimes less than 5) and cause inhibition of biological activity. It has been found that this problem can be reduced by alteration of the aeration cycle to encourage denitrification in the ditch. In this way the alkalinity requirement can be reduced by about 40 per cent. To achieve denitrification, the aerators are stopped during the cycle to allow the DO to drop to zero; then the heterotrophic sludge organisms use the oxygen from nitrates for respiration. This results in the reduction of nitrates to nitrogen gas and the total nitrogen in the effluent can be reduced to less than 5 mg/L.

Sludge removal from the intermittent oxidation ditch can be achieved by daily pumping of the required volume of mixed liquor from the ditch during the aeration cycle. The sludge is fairly well stabilised and can be satisfactorily discharged to open sludge lagoons.

Following the success of the intermittent extended aeration process in oxidation ditches, the process has recently been applied with floating vertical shaft mechanical aerators in a rectangular concrete structure; this can meet the needs of 4000 people.

Contact stabilisation
This makes use of the observed phenomenon that much of the BOD removal in activated sludge processes occurs within 20 to 40 minutes of mixing the

Table 14.3 Typical design parameters for activated sludge processes

Process modification	θ_c, d	F $\dfrac{kg\ BOD_5/d}{kg\ MLVSS}$	Volumetric loading $\dfrac{kg\ BOD_5}{m^3.d}$	MLSS mg/L	Detention time $\mathbf{V}/Q$,h	RAS rate R/Q
Conventional	5-15	0.2-0.4	0.3-0.6	1500-3000	4-8	0.25-0.5
Complete mix	5-15	0.2-0.6	0.8-2.0	3000-6000	3-5	0.25-1.0
Step aeration	5-15	0.2-0.4	0.6-0.9	2000-3500	3-5	0.25-0.75
High rate	0.2-0.5	1.5-5.0	1.2-2.0	200-500	1.5-3	0.05-0.15
Contact stabilisation	5-15	0.2-0.6	0.9-1.2	Contact unit 1000-3000 Stabilisation unit 4000-10 000	0.5-1.0 3.6	0.25-1.0
Extended aeration	20-30	0.04-0.15	0.15-0.4	3000-6000	18-36	0.75-1.50
Oxidation ditch (intermittent)	30+	~0.03	0.12-0.18	4000-6000	~24	see text
Kraus process	5-15	0.3 - 0.8	0.6 -1.6	2000-3000	4-8	0.5 -1.0
Pure oxygen systems	8-20	0.25-1.0	1.6 -4.0	6000-8000	1-3	0.25-0.5

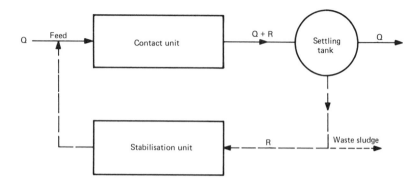

Fig 14.11 Flow sheet for the contact stabilisation process

return sludge with the wastewater flow (Fig 14.11). Separation of the activated sludge at this point in the process therefore results in a substantial degree of BOD removal from the effluent. Aeration of the activated sludge for a further 3 to 4 hours is required, however, to permit oxidation of the organics adsorbed by the sludge organisms during the contact period. Since this second-stage aeration, or stabilisation, can be carried out on the return sludge stream at about twice the concentration of the mixed liquor, the volume of the aeration tank is reduced. Even with a contact period of 1.5 to 2 hours to provide for fluctuations in wastewater flow rate, the total volume of aeration tanks is 30 to 40 per cent less than for the conventional process at an equivalent F/M ratio.

Contact stabilisation can be achieved in step aeration activated sludge plants, if the air supply rates to the different sections of the tank can be

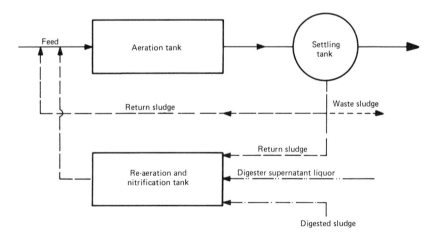

Fig 14.12 Flow sheet for the Kraus process

adjusted. By admitting wastewater at inlets about half way along an aeration tank, the whole of the front end of the tank can be used as a re-aeration zone for the return sludge before it comes into contact with the wastewater inflow.

Kraus process

This was developed to overcome nitrogen deficiencies in the treatment of high carbohydrate wastes which give rise to sludge with very poor settling characteristics. The Kraus process (Fig 14.12) comprises a conventional flow pattern with an additional small sidestream, drawn off the return sludge line to a re-aeration tank. To this re-aeration tank is added a portion of the ammonia-rich supernatant and digested sludge from the sludge digesters and the mixture is aerated for 24 hours to achieve nitrification; it is then returned to the aeration tanks, thus adding nitrogen to correct the deficiency in the waste, while the digested sludge solids act as a weighting agent to improve the settling characteristics of the activated sludge.

Pure oxygen systems

These have been developed to increase the oxygen transfer efficiency into the mixed liquor. In this process, completely mixed chambers are used in series and each chamber is covered (Fig 14.13). The oxygen content in the atmosphere above the aeration tanks can be increased from the normal 20 per cent in air to upwards of 80 per cent, resulting in four times the rate of oxygen transfer attainable in air systems (see Section 14.5). Efficiency in the use of oxygen is improved by recirculating the oxygen-rich gas from above the aeration tanks. It is necessary to bleed off some of the recirculating gas to prevent the accumulation of CO_2. The increased rate of oxygen transfer makes it possible to maintain higher MLSS concentrations (5000 mg/L), enabling the same standard of treatment to be achieved in a much smaller

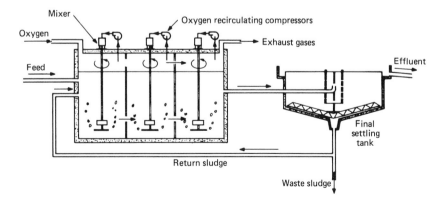

Fig 14.13 Typical arrangement of pure-oxygen activated-sludge process

aeration tank volume. Further reduction in aeration tank volume may be achieved because the sludge activity is reputed to be greater. Other advantages claimed for pure oxygen systems are reduced sludge accumulation, better sludge settling characteristics and more efficient nitrification.

Deep shaft process

This was developed as a result of research into methods of improving oxygen transfer in diffused air systems. This can be achieved by an increase in oxygen partial pressure and by an increase in the total pressure applied to the system. In the deep shaft process, a circular shaft is drilled to a depth of 60 to 150 metres, lined and fitted with a second liner concentric with the first but suspended clear of the floor of the outer shaft (Fig 14.14). A circulating flow can be induced in this sytem by injection of air or oxygen into the outer annulus. Once the circulating flow pattern is developed, air can be injected into the down-flowing liquid in the centre tube. This air is then carried down-

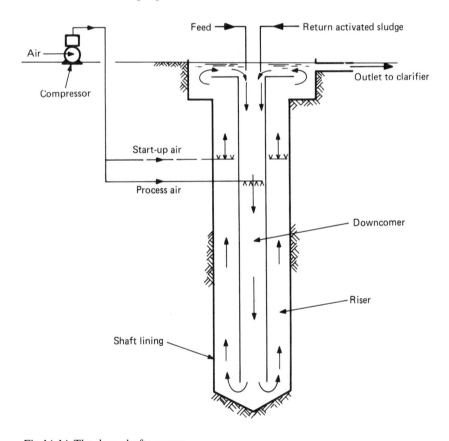

Fig 14.14 The deep shaft process

wards towards the bottom of the shaft, undergoing a steadily increasing pressure and an enhanced rate of solution into the surrounding liquid. Oxygen transfer rates are correspondingly enhanced, so that such a system is able to sustain a higher rate of aerobic biological activity than is a normal activated sludge system.

14.6 Design of aerated lagoons

The technology of aerated lagoons has developed from attempts to increase the oxygenation of overloaded algal oxidation lagoons by the use of surface aerators or air diffusion systems. Aerated lagoons provide a method of low-cost biological treatment for municipal and industrial wastewaters in areas where land is not too expensive, where seepage pollution of groundwater is not an issue, and where the necessary earthworks can be effected economically. Depending on the size, type and disposition of the aerators, an aerated lagoon may be a fully-mixed aerobic lagoon or there may be some areas where solids settle to the bottom and decompose anaerobically. The soluble products of the anaerobic decomposition would be, in turn, oxidised in the upper aerobic layers of the lagoon.

The behaviour of a fully-mixed aerated lagoon is, in principle, similar to that in the activated sludge process, but there is no recycling of sludge solids. The mean cell residence time is therefore equal to the hydraulic detention time. To prevent wash-out of active bacteria, the detention time should not be too short. From two to five days' detention is the general order of the size of aerated lagoons. This range will produce bioflocculation of the sludge for later settling, if required.

The main advantages of aerated lagoons over activated sludge systems are

a Ability to handle shock loads, because of the greater volume available to dilute the influent immediately
b Ability to treat biodegradable toxins, such as phenols, even when received intermittently
c No sludge recycle requirements
d In suitable terrain, construction consists mainly of cheap earthworks.

But the disadvantages, when compared with activated sludge systems, are

a More land area required for implementation
b Only about 80 per cent maximum BOD removal is possible
c More sensitive to air temperature variations with inhibition of action at low temperatures
d More turbid effluents.

For some industries, where the effluent quantity and quality may change rapidly — sometimes hot, sometimes cold, sometimes acid, sometimes alkaline, strong or weak — an aerated lagoon with its mixing ability and its size as a buffer against the sudden changes of quality of influent is the logical initial stage of treatment. Often it can produce an effluent acceptable for discharge into a public sewer (probably during off-peak hours), or one of fairly uniform quality and flow rate for treatment by subsequent processes.

Removal kinetics for mixed lagoon

Section 14.5 dealt with the kinetics for activated sludge treatment and Eqs 14.16, 14.17 and 14.18 can be used to estimate the sludge concentration and BOD removal in a fully-mixed aerated lagoon. The symbols used here are as previously defined.

The *equilibrium MLVSS concentration* can be found from a sludge mass balance for the lagoon. The total mass of MLVSS in the lagoon is given by

$$[X_v]_T = \Psi X_v/1000 \, kg \qquad (14.26)$$

where Ψ is the volume of lagoon (m^3).

Since the effluent concentration is the same as that of the mixed liquor in the lagoon, the total daily discharge of suspended solids is

$$[\Delta X_v]_T = QX_v/1000 \, kg \qquad (14.27)$$

$$
\begin{aligned}
\text{Sludge age} \;\; &= \text{(total MLVSS)/(daily removal of MLVSS)} \\
&= [X_v]_T/[\Delta X_v]_T \\
&= (\Psi X_v/1000)/(QX_v/1000) \\
&= \Psi/Q = T \qquad (14.28)
\end{aligned}
$$

The value of θ_c, the mean cell residence time, or sludge age, is therefore equal to the hydraulic detention time, as stated above.

From Eq 14.17

$$[\Delta X_v]_T = Y[L_r]_T - k_d[X_v]_T \qquad (14.29)$$

This symbolic statement merely says that the amount of solids to be removed daily is equal to the yield from the conversion of BOD to solids less the loss due to endogenous action. Substitution of symbols for the lagoon operation gives

$$QX_v = Y(L_i - L_e)Q - k_d\Psi X_v \qquad (14.30)$$

from which

$$X_v = Y(L_i - L_e)/(1 + k_d t) \qquad (14.31)$$

The *soluble effluent BOD* can be determined by consideration of the BOD removal in conjunction with the solids balance. From the definition of U given in Fig 14.9

$$(L_i - L_e) = U\Psi X_v/Q = UX_v t \qquad (14.32)$$

The substitution of this for $(L_i - L_e)$ in Eq 14.31, the elimination of X_v and rearrangement give

$$U = (1/t + k_d)/Y \tag{14.33}$$

and, from the diagram in Fig 14.9(b),

$$U = kL_e \tag{14.34}$$

Hence, for a first-order reaction with volatile suspended solids, the rate of BOD removal by a particle of volatile suspended solids is proportional to the BOD present. (Note that the BOD of the effluent is the same as the BOD of the liquid anywhere in the lagoon.)

Combining Eqs 14.33 and 14.34 gives

$$L_e = (1 + k_d t)/ktY \tag{14.35}$$

This equation implies that the effluent concentration of soluble BOD is independent of the initial BOD. Higher initial concentrations of BOD result in a higher quantity of suspended volatile solids and higher BOD removal rates. From this equation, for large values of t, L_e tends to k_d/kY, indicating a theoretical limit to BOD removal. It is valid only as long as the equilibrium concentration of volatile solids, given by Eq 14.31, remains in suspension. Also, it can be valid only when the properties of the suspended solids are independent of sludge age, which is seldom the case. There are limitations which result from the lack of specific data for the kinetic constants and the variation of these with temperature.

Total effluent BOD will be the sum of the BOD in solution and the BOD exerted by the suspended volatile solids. The amount of suspended volatile solids may be estimated from Eq 14.31. The BOD contribution from these solids is a function of the food-to-micro-organism ratio, F, which was given in Eq 14.12 as

$$F = \frac{QL_i}{\Psi X_v}$$

Substituting t for Ψ/Q, and the value of X_v from Eq 14.31 gives

$$F = (1 + k_d t)/[tY(1 - L_e/L_i)]$$

which is of the order of $1.5/tY$, indicating that, for a yield coefficient of about 0.6 and a 6-day detention, the F value would be about 0.4. The total effluent BOD is then given by

$$L_{et} = L_e + rX_v \tag{14.36}$$

where L_{et} is the total effluent BOD (mg/L); L_e is the soluble effluent BOD (mg/L); r is the BOD contribution of unit mass of MLVSS (ratio); and X_v is the concentration of MLVSS (mg/L).

The value of r can be expected to vary from about 0.3 kg BOD per kg MLVSS at F = 0.1 up to about 0.6 kg BOD per kg MLVSS at F = 1.0 when treating ordinary domestic wastes.

Oxygen requirements

There are two distinct approaches to estimating the oxygen requirements for aerated lagoons:

a Oxygen required for removal of soluble BOD *plus* oxygen required for respiration and breakdown of cells
b Oxygen required for removal of total BOD without reference to the relative contributions by soluble and solid components.

The first of these approaches has been explained in Section 14.5, where the Eq 14.19 was given as

$$[O_2]_T = a[L_r]_T + b[X_v]_T \tag{14.37}$$

where L_r is the BOD removed. The values of a and b in this formula are functions of the food-to-micro-organism ratio. Well-fed organisms respire faster than not-so-well-fed ones. For ordinary sewage, the value of a is about 0.5 for F values greater than 0.5, and it varies from 0.5 at F = 0.5 up to 0.65 at F = 0.15; for aerated lagoons, a value of 0.5 would be reasonable, because the F values are usually more than about 0.4. The value of b for ordinary sewage at normal temperature varies from 0.07 at F = 0.1 up to 0.15 at F = 1.0.

For a lagoon, Eq 14.37 can be rewritten as

$$M_O = (aQL_r + b \forall X_v)/1000 \tag{14.38}$$

where M_O is the daily requirement of oxygen (kg). This can be shown to be equivalent to

$$M_O = QL_r[a + btY/(1 + k_d t)]/1000 \tag{14.39}$$

In the second type of determination, the overall BOD reduction can be estimated, and the oxygen requirement is approximately equal to the reduction in BOD_{ult}. If the influent and effluent BOD values are given in terms of BOD_5, the oxygen requirement is

$$M_O = Q(L_i - L_{et}) \times \frac{BOD_{ult}}{BOD_5} \bigg/ 1000 \tag{14.40}$$

$$= L_{et}K_o t \times \frac{BOD_{ult}}{BOD_5} \bigg/ 1000 \tag{14.41}$$

When the detention time is more than four or five days, the oxidation of nitrogenous material is likely to occur and an allowance for this should be added to the figures obtained by either of the above methods.

Lagoon not fully mixed

If a lagoon is not fully mixed, allowance must be made for the settlement of some solids with anaerobic decomposition and the return of soluble BOD to the pond liquor.

Temperature effects

Temperature variations affect all biological processes. The speed of reaction with aerobic mesophilic bacteria increases with temperature until reaching an optimum between 25° and 30°C. The effect of temperature on the reaction rate, over the usual range encountered in aerated lagoons, can be expressed in terms of a modified Van't Hoff-Arrhenius equation

$$k_T = K_{20}\theta^{(T-20)} \tag{14.42}$$

where k_T is the reaction rate at temperature T°C; and θ is the temperature coefficient.

The value of the temperature coefficient has been reported as 1.074 to 1.085, but recently a value of 1.035 has been reported for aerated lagoons. It appears that the higher values are more applicable to activated sludge conditions, where both the concentration of sludge and turbulence are relatively high, whereas in a lagoon the sludge particles at low concentration and low turbulence are less sensitive to temperature variations.

Because of its large surface area compared with conventional activated sludge, the lagoon will have a temperature which more closely follows that of the air. Therefore, the lagoon volume, oxygen requirements and aerator oxygenation capacity should be calculated for both summer and winter conditions.

In general, the *volume* required in a lagoon is governed by its behaviour under winter conditions when bacterial action is slower. The *aeration capacity* required will be governed by the summer temperature because the bacterial activity, and hence oxygen requirements, will be higher, and the saturation levels will be lower. The *mixing* requirements are not directly related to lagoon temperature, except as temperature affects the settling characteristics of the biological flocs formed.

Mixing requirements

The effectiveness of aerators as mixers to maintain sludge in suspension must depend on the actual configuration of the impeller and guide vanes (if any) on the aerator, and on the torque and horizontal velocity imparted to the surface water. The comparison of mixing capacity on a basis of watts per cubic metre is valid only when the aerators compared are of a similar type.

In many cases, the mixing requirement rather than the oxygen transfer capability will control the power input required for a lagoon. If such is the case, aerators should be chosen for efficiency as mixers rather than for oxygen transfer efficiency.

Aerators

Aeration in general has been dealt with in Chapter 8 and Section 14.5. The commonest method of aerating lagoons is by the use of surface aerators with vertical shafts.

Nutrients

The micro-organisms which make up the flora and fauna of the volatile suspended solids need a balanced diet for optimum activity, as noted in Chapter 11. This diet should be related to their overall average composition. An empirical 'average' formula for cell material has been given as

$$C_{106} \ H_{108} \ O_{45} \ N_{16} \ P_1 + \text{other minor constituents}$$

Domestic sewage provides a well-balanced diet but many industrial wastes do not. Sometimes, they are deficient in nitrogen, phosphorus or both. However, wastes, such as those from meatworks, are often deficient in carbon, compared with the amounts of nitrogen (protein) and phosphorus available. Shortage of nutrients can reduce the rate of treatment by over 80 per cent. As a general rule, the ratios BOD:N:P should be about 100:5:1. The nutrient needs for the micro-organisms vary from about 6 to 15 per cent nitrogen, and from 2 to 5 per cent phosphorus (based on the dry weight of living micro-organisms) during the phase of growth. The supplemental addition of nutrients may be necessary.

14.7 Design of waste stabilisation ponds

Waste stabilisation or oxidation ponds, in common with simpler processes such as land treatment, have fallen into disfavour for large communities because they require much greater areas of land than do the more compact trickling filter and activated sludge processes. Many small communities, however, find the investments in capital and labour required by these more sophisticated processes beyond their means. Therefore, waste stabilisation ponds still offer these communities the attraction of low capital outlay and relatively low operation and maintenance costs, at the price of a relatively small loss in treatment standard. Thus, both bacteria and virus concentrations in pond effluents may be similar to those in conventional chlorinated secondary effluents. The aesthetic quality of pond effluents may be lower than that produced by other secondary processes, because algae contribute high concentrations of both SS and BOD, while plant nutrients such as nitrogen and phosphorus may be present in high concentrations in pond effluent. Where effluent can be used for irrigation, these factors may be an advantage, but they may not meet current standards for stream discharge.

The design of ponds has, until recently, has been based on empirical values of average liquid detention time, areal organic loading, or both, with little rational basis for varying the design for areas having differing climatic conditions. The principles of pond processes and some of the methods available for pond design are discussed below; a climatically-based procedure for sizing the first pond in a series is also described.

Pond classification

Many criteria have been used to classify waste stabilisation ponds. These include

a The type of waste treated — domestic, industrial or septic tank wastes
b The place of the pond in the conventional treatment sequence — primary, secondary or tertiary
c The principal biological reaction phases — aerobic, anaerobic or aerobic/anaerobic (facultative)
d The principal mode of water loss from the pond — infiltration, evaporation or flow-through.

Other terms commonly applied are 'lagoon' and 'oxidation pond'. In this text, the nomenclature adopted is based on the principal biological reactions, while discussion will be confined to ponds which treat raw or settled domestic sewage, and which operate as flow-through systems. The range of biological reactions occurring in pond systems is conventionally represented as shown in Fig 14.15, from which it is seen that three basic types of pond may be distinguished:

a Aerobic (high-rate) ponds in which there is no significant anaerobic or sludge zone
b Anaerobic ponds in which the contribution of any possible aerobic surface layer is small
c Oxidation (so-called facultative or aerobic/anaerobic) ponds, in which the whole range of reactions is present. This is the predominant type of pond in municipal treatment systems.

High-rate aerobic ponds
These act essentially as carbon conversion systems. Influent waste organic matter is broken down by bacteria and the resulting products are used by algae to synthesise new algal cells by photosynthesis. Oxygen released by algae in this process is the major source of the oxygen required to satisfy the demand in the aerobic biodegradation process. The combined and mutually-beneficial action of algae and bacteria in this process is termed *algal-bacterial symbiosis*. It is apparent that there is no net loss of influent carbon in this

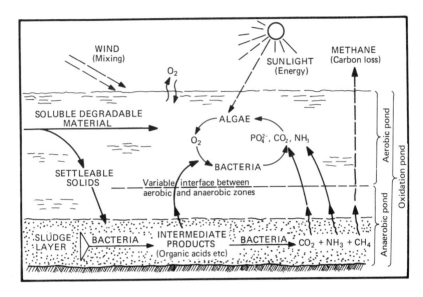

Fig 14.15 Principal pond reactions related to pond classification

system — only a transformation of waste organic matter into living cells, especially algae.

Unless the algae are harvested, the total carbon in the effluent will be similar to that in the influent, although the full BOD will not be exerted on the receiving waters unless the algae die. These ponds are necessarily less than 0.5 metres deep to permit light penetration, and they need to be stirred regularly to prevent sedimentation of the organics and algae. At present, processes for harvesting algae are too expensive to encourage widespread use of this system. Recent research has shown that it may be feasible, by careful design and operation of a facultative pond followed by a stirred aerobic pond, to promote the growth of larger algal species which can be removed by settling.

Anaerobic ponds
These cause odour problems and so they are not usually employed in municipal installations although, in recent years, they have been used in some countries as pretreatment ponds in order to reduce the total land area required. Their main use is in the treatment of concentrated industrial wastes in isolated places. Effluents from anaerobic systems require aerobic treatment before they are discharged to surface waters.

Oxidation ponds (facultative ponds)
These are the most frequently encountered type. Much of the volume of these ponds can be either aerobic or anaerobic at various times so that growth of facultative organisms, which are able to adapt to either condition, is favoured.

Table 14.4 Empirical pond design criteria

Type of pond	Efficiency in BOD removal (%)	Surface area of pond (ha)	Depth of pond (m)	BOD load[1] (g/m².d)	System detention time (d)
Aerobic[2]	80-90	0.2-0.3	0.2-0.3	15-20	2-6
Anaerobic[3]	70-80	≈ 1	2.5-5	25-40	8-40
Oxidation[4] (facultative)	70-95	1-20 (or more)	1-2.5	2-5	20-100

[1]BOD is ultimate carbonaceous BOD for domestic waste.
[2]Aerobic pond: must be periodically mixed. V_{mix} = 0.3 to 0.5 m/s (usually by recirculation); must be lined to prevent scour and must harvest algal mass.
[3]Anaerobic pond: must be followed by aerobic pond to produce effluent suitable for discharge to surface water.
[4] Oxidation pond: at least two ponds should be provided in series — figures given are total for all ponds in series.

Empirical methods for designing ponds

Pond systems of all types have traditionally been designed on the basis of average liquid detention time (t), organic loading per unit surface area of ponds (g BOD/m².d), or both. These have been determined largely by trial and error. Table 14.4 summarises typical values of these and other empirical design parameters quoted by various authorities for sizing pond systems.

Problems have arisen when ponds have been designed using factors developed for locations with markedly different climates.

Where insufficient attention has been paid to the loading rate on the first pond in a system comprising several oxidation ponds in series, severe odour problems can occur if that pond becomes completely anaerobic. Hence the design of such systems purely on the basis of average areal BOD loading or total detention time is inadequate; the first pond must not be overloaded. A method of taking this into account in design is discussed below.

Kinetic-based method of oxidation pond design

An expression for oxidation pond kinetics can be developed on the basis of the following simplifying assumptions:

a The pond may be approximated as a completely mixed system
b Degradation of organic matter as measured by ultimate BOD can be represented as a first-order reaction ($dL_t/dt = -kL_t$), where L_t is the ultimate BOD at time t
c Evaporation and infiltration losses are small.

A completely mixed system is represented in Fig 14.16. The BOD mass balance around the reactor is

$$\begin{bmatrix} \text{Total mass of} \\ \text{influent BOD} \end{bmatrix} = \begin{bmatrix} \text{Mass of} \\ \text{effluent BOD} \end{bmatrix} + \begin{bmatrix} \text{Mass of BOD} \\ \text{removed in reactor} \end{bmatrix}$$

which may be written as

$$QL_i = QL_e + k\Psi L_p \qquad (14.43)$$

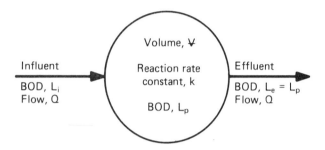

Fig 14.16 Completely mixed pond

For a completely mixed system, the effluent BOD will be the same as the BOD of the pond contents, that is $L_e = L_p$.

The substitution of L_e for L_p and $t = \Psi/Q$, and then simplifying, gives

$$\frac{L_e}{L_i} = \frac{1}{1 + kt} \qquad (14.44)$$

This equation is reported to correlate well with observed BOD reduction in the *first pond in a series*, but correlation for the second and later ponds was poor. Correlation in terms of coliforms and faecal bacteria, however, was good for all ponds in the series.

In order to design the first pond in a series using Eq 14.44 for a given influent waste BOD, it is necessary to estimate values of L_p, the pond liquid BOD and k, the reaction rate constant. Since in a first-order reaction the reaction rate is proportional to the concentration of reactants remaining, the higher the value of L_p, the higher will be the rate of BOD removal per unit volume. Hence, for economy in pond design, it is desirable to keep the BOD concentration in the first pond as high as possible, without risking the onset of permanent anaerobic conditions and consequent odour problems.

The maximum allowable pond BOD has been estimated from observations of operating ponds in different climates. If a plot of pond BOD (L_p mg/L) against pond depth (D m) were made for those circumstances in which any of the ponds had become wholly anaerobic, the lower envelope of the plotted points would be given approximately by

$$L_p = 1000/(2D + 8)$$

To provide some safety margin for design purposes, a designer can use a relationship of the form

$$L_p = X/(2D + 8) \qquad\qquad (14.45)$$

where $X < 1000$ (usually $600 - 750$), and L_p is the maximum allowable design BOD for the pond. Note that L_p is expressed in terms of a single variable — pond depth. This implies that the net effect on L_p of all other interacting variables, such as temperature, solar radiation intensity and wind action is constant and included in the value of X. Although this is an oversimplification, it may be seen qualitatively that the results of changes in some of these variables tend to be self-compensatory. Increased intensity of solar radiation leads to increased pond temperature and results in both higher rates of oxygen production by photosynthesis and higher rates of oxygen demand by biodegradation. Wind action may be important in mixing pond contents and in promoting transfer of oxygen from the atmosphere. However, the critical condition for the onset of anaerobic conditions is likely to occur during periods of calm.

Increase in pond depth will decrease light penetration to the deeper layers and reduce the average rate of photosynthetic re-oxygenation of the pond contents. In these circumstances, the permissible BOD concentration in the pond should be reduced if an aerobic surface layer is to be maintained. This is in agreement with the trend given by Eq 14.45. Although further work is required to elucidate the effects of climate on maximum permissible pond BOD concentration, the empirically-derived Eq 14.45 appears to give a reasonable fit to data collected from ponds in areas with quite different climates. To provide a safety factor against odour problems, a value of $X = 600$ appears reasonable, while, if climatically-determined values of the reaction rate constant are used, a somewhat higher value, say $X = 700$, would be warranted.

Of the climatic factors discussed above, *temperature* is most likely to have the greatest effect on the rate of biological activity. Because complex interactions occur between the aerobic surface layer and the anaerobic liquid and sludge layers, it is unlikely that a simple temperature correction could adequately account for the effects of temperature on oxidation ponds. For example, it has been observed that effluent BOD is not always lowest during summer, when biological activity would be expected to be greatest — probably because there is also a much higher rate of anaerobic degradation of accumulated organic material in the sludge layer, with an accompanying increase in the feedback rate of soluble organics to the pond liquid. This effectively increases the total BOD load on the aerobic surface layers of the pond. It has been found that the range of temperatures at a given locality can be adequately represented by the *average daily maximum temperatures for the warmest and coldest months*, with a sinusoidal interpolation between them. A dynamic model has been used to simulate long-term operating data for a typical pond. From the model output, the highest effluent BOD data in a single test were selected and substituted into Eq 14.44, together with the loading data and dimensions used in the pond simulation; a value of the *equivalent reaction rate*, k_e, was calculated. Values of k_e obtained from a large number of such simulations were plotted against the corresponding values of the warmest and coldest months' average daily maximum temperatures to give a convenient design chart, as shown in Fig 14.17.

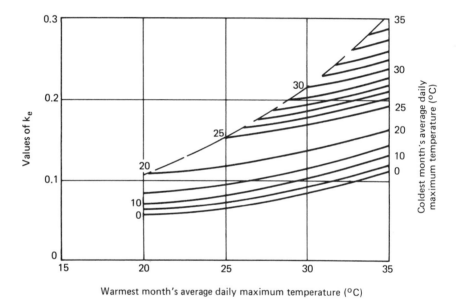

Fig 14.17 Values of k_e as a function of temperature

For the design of the first pond in a series, Eq 14.44 may be rewritten in terms of k_e as

$$\frac{\max L_e}{L_i} = \frac{1}{1 + k_e t} \qquad (14.46)$$

Simplified design procedure
In practice, the problem confronting the designer at any particular location is to determine the required pond area and depth for a particular waste flow and

strength. For this purpose, Eqs 14.45 and 14.46 can be combined to give a single expression for pond detention time:

$$t = \frac{1}{k_e \cdot} \left[\frac{L_i(2D + 8)}{X} - 1 \right] \tag{14.47}$$

The substitution of AD/Q for t and transposition give a direct expression for pond surface area:

$$A = \left[\frac{1}{k_e} \right] \left[\frac{L_i(2D + 8)}{DX} - \frac{1}{D} \right] Q \tag{14.48}$$

If the substitution $Y = \left[\dfrac{L_i(2D + 8)}{DX} - \dfrac{1}{D} \right]$ is made,

$$A = \left[\frac{1}{k_e} \right] \left[Y \right] Q \tag{14.49}$$

where A is in square metres, D is in metres and Q is in m³/d.

The value of k_e can be determined as outlined above if the average daily maximum temperatures for the coldest and warmest months are known. To simplify the use of Eq 14.49, the factor Y is plotted in Fig 14.18 as a function of the sewage influent BOD and pond depth. Fig 14.18 is based on X = 700.

Selection of pond depth

The normally recommended minimum depth to prevent the growth of emergent vegetation is 1 metre, while the maximum depth for oxidation ponds is usually 2.0 to 2.5 metres. For temperate to hot climates, where the heat loss from ponds during winter is not severe, a shallower depth of about 1.0 metre is usually adopted. For ponds which treat raw sewage, natural mixing is frequently not sufficient to prevent deposition of a large proportion of the solids in the immediate vicinity of the inlet. To accommodate these settled solids, without excessive reduction in water depth, the pond depth in that location can be increased.

Careful design of the pond inlet can ensure that the energy of the incoming flow is usefully employed to promote mixing of the pond contents and to assist in the prevention of stratification; hence, closer conformity to the design assumption of complete mixing can be assured.

Design of second and subsequent ponds

The second and subsequent ponds in a series are intended partly to remove some BOD, but mostly to reduce the bacterial count. The second pond should be of a similar size to the first, so that it can be used as a first pond if the regular one is out of service. Third and subsequent ponds should be smaller,

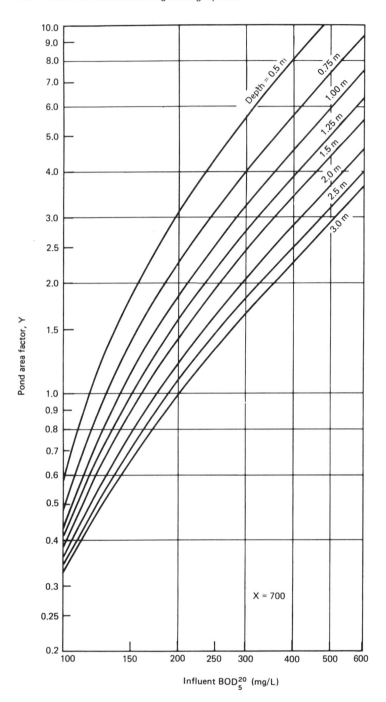

Fig 14.18 Pond area factor, Y, for various values of sewage BOD and pond depth

and designed for bacterial removal efficiency.

The bacteria removal in each pond has been found to follow a rule given by

$$\frac{N_e}{N_i} = \frac{1}{1 + K_B t} \tag{14.50}$$

where N_e and N_i are the numbers of coliforms in the effluent and influent respectively, and K_B is the bacterial reduction rate constant, which is reported to have a value of about 2 for most conditions.

14.8 Design of trickling filters

Trickling filters are suitable both as a complete secondary treatment method and as a roughing treatment to reduce the load on some other biological processes. Although trickling filters have lower power and operating costs than activated sludge, their relatively higher capital cost has made them unpopular in many countries, especially for larger treatment works. With rising energy costs and the development of improved types of filter medium, there may be a reversal of this trend.

A general description of trickling filtration is given in Section 11.3 and the main components of a typical trickling filter installation are indicated on Fig 14.19. The main aspects to be considered in designing trickling filter systems are

a Pretreatment requirements
b Dosing system for applying wastewater to the filter
c Filter bed — volume, type and dimensions of the medium
d Underdrainage system for collecting filter effluent
e Ventilation system for supplying the oxygen
f Final sedimentation for removing biological solids washed off the filter medium.

Pretreatment

This is required to remove all grease and coarse suspended matter which could otherwise clog the small nozzles in the distributor. Therefore, screening *and* primary sedimentation are necessary both to protect the filters and to reduce the organic loading. Fine mesh screens are sometimes provided in the inlet channels to the filter dosing system to remove any rags or solids which may have passed through primary treatment.

Dosing equipment

This distributes the settled sewage regularly and evenly over the filter bed. A *circular filter* has a multiple-arm rotary distributor supported on a central bearing, which incorporates the inlet to the distributor. Rotation of the

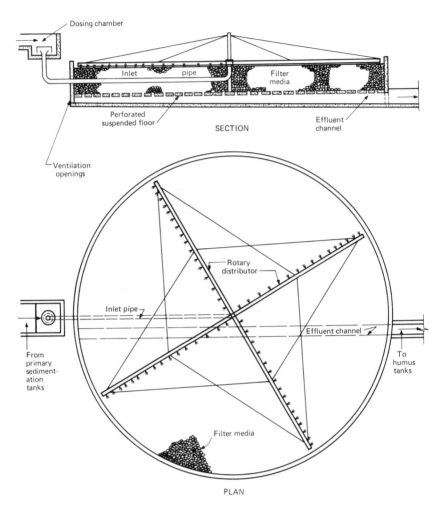

Fig 14.19 Arrangement of a trickling filter

distributor is induced by the jet reaction of the flow from nozzles along one side of the distributor arms. This requires that the settled sewage flow rate be controlled to prevent the rotation from becoming too rapid at high flows and to limit static dribbling at times of low flow. With gravity-fed systems, a *dosing syphon* and chamber are provided to hold back the flow until a sufficient volume is stored to ensure effective operation. Large distributors are sometimes fitted with wheels running on the top of the filter wall to support the outer ends of the arms. Electric motor drives may be provided in such systems to ensure positive control of the speed at which the distributor rotates. Some *rectangular filters* have motor-driven distributors, but tipping distributors have been used in small units. Motor-driven systems are fed by a pump with which the operation of the distributors is synchronised.

Filter beds

These are usually circular in small-to-medium-sized installations, while large units are sometimes rectangular to reduce the area of land required. The *media* used in trickling filters must provide a suitable environment for the growth of an active mixed microbial film, which is responsible for removing organic matter from the applied wastewater. It must be durable and not subject to physical erosion or chemical or biochemical attack. The processes set out in Section 11.3 as contributing to effective biological treatment in filters are summarised in Fig 14.20. Organic matter must be absorbed from the flowing wastewater and then diffused to the organisms within the film;

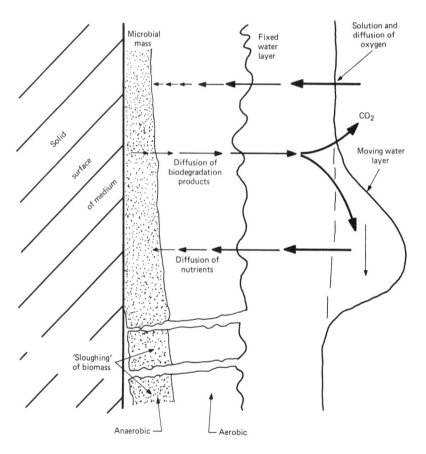

Fig 14.20 Action in a trickling filter

oxygen must be dissolved in the liquid and diffused throughout the aerobic biomass; products of biodegradation must diffuse out of the biomass and either be carried away by the liquid flow, or pass from solution into the air which circulates through the bed. Although recent research has contributed much towards the understanding of trickling filters, it is not yet possible to apply the results obtained directly to filter design, mainly because of the difficulty of estimating both the total micro-organism mass and the environmental conditions prevailing in it. It is evident, however, that there must be regular and effective contact between the biological film and the applied wastewater as well as effective oxygen transfer to the biomass. Both are related to the configuration of the medium and the hydraulic loading rate on the filter. Oxygen transfer is also dependent on adequate ventilation of the bed and the DO of the applied wastewater.

Within the deeper layers of the microbial film, the reaction rate is governed by the limited amount of organic matter and nutrients available. Where the film is very thick, limitations on the oxygen diffusion rate probably lead to anaerobic conditions and the production of gases of decomposition. As a result, sections of the biomass lose their adhesive ability, 'slough off' the medium, and are washed from the filter in the effluent. These solids represent the net biomass increase in the filter.

Ideal filter media to provide for all the above processes should therefore have

a A large area of surfaces on which biomass may grow
b Voids with sufficient volume and size to allow for the growth of biomass without clogging, while permitting free circulation of air
c An internal structure which effectively distributes the applied wastewater over all surfaces within the bed, with a maximum of turbulence to promote oxygen transfer.

In the case of gravel, crushed rock or other granular media, although the total surface area for a given mass of medium increases as particle size decreases, the void size requirements to satisfy condition (b) usually restrict the minimum size of particles to 40 to 50 mm. Traditional trickling filters are packed with stones of 50 to 100 mm size, to a *depth* of approximately 2 m. The stones are contained by a concrete wall and supported by a suspended perforated floor.

Underdrainage
This collects the effluent and usually consists of an impervious base beneath the perforated filter floor, graded towards one or more collecting channels. The capacity of the underdrainage should be great enough to accommodate the maximum flow rate while maintaining adequate air space.

Ventilation
This is achieved by natural air circulation through the bed, induced by the heating or cooling effect of the applied wastewater. Sufficient openings should be provided at the base of the filter to allow air to flow into or out of the space under the suspended filter floor. In temperate climates, adequate ventilation can be assured by providing plentiful inlets around the base of the filter wall. In very cold climates, it is desirable to control the inflow rate of cold air in order to minimise heat loss and so reduce low-temperature inhibition of biological activity. Hot, dry climates may require the air circulation rate to be limited to prevent the biofilm from drying out when the sewage flow is low.

Biomass production
In trickling filters, biomass production is related to the organic loading rate (Chapter 11). This biomass is sloughed from the surfaces of the medium during normal operation but many filters tend to accumulate biomass during the colder months and to slough large amounts of solids in the spring. Too much biomass, which may result either from organic overloads or from low biological activity in winter, leads to clogging of the filter voids, ponding of sewage over parts of the filter surface, restriction of air circulation and reduced process efficiency. Odour problems may therefore be increased.

Final sedimentation (humus) tanks
These are essential if a good-quality effluent is required; without these tanks the variable concentration of biological solids causes the effluent to have an SS concentration little better than that of settled sewage as well as a high BOD. Design criteria and the general configuration of humus tanks are similar to those for primary sedimentation tanks. Circular tanks with sludge rakes are usually adopted for large works. Because humus solids are more readily settleable than many of the fine organics in raw wastewaters, surface loading rates up to 50 per cent higher than those for primary sedimentation tanks have been used for some small works. Scum removal equipment is often not provided, but care should be taken to limit the time the humus sludge remains in the tank. A few hours would be the maximum, under temperate conditions, to avoid the risk of gas formation and sludge carry-over in the effluent.

Dosing syphons and distributors are normally purchased from specialist manufacturers. Design parameters for various types of filter are discussed below.

Types of filter and typical loading rates

Factors affecting the efficiency of trickling filters include organic loading rate, hydraulic loading rate, depth of filter medium, and type, shape and total surface area of the medium. Although organic loading rate can be expressed in terms of a ratio (kg BOD/kg biological solids.day) as shown in Chapter 11, it is not possible to obtain a practical measure of biological solids mass in a filter, or the net area of biological film in contact with the wastewater. Therefore, it is customary to include all these effects within the one conveniently-determined parameter: the gross volume of the filter medium, V_m (m³). *Organic loading rate*, F_m, is then expressed in kg BOD/m³.d. For a settled sewage flow rate, Q (m³/d), and influent BOD, L_i (mg/L), this is given by

$$F_m = \frac{QL_i}{1000 V_m} = \frac{QL_i}{1000 A_m H} \tag{14.51}$$

where A_m is the horizontal area of the trickling filter (m²), and H is the depth of the medium (m).

Hydraulic loading rate, Q_h (m³/m².d), is given by

$$Q_h = \frac{Q}{A_m} \tag{14.52}$$

This is important because it affects the wetting of the surfaces within the filter bed and, hence, the total area upon which active biomass may grow. It also affects turbulence of the flow through the bed and the rate at which the flow is broken up and re-formed. This, in turn, affects the rate of oxygen transfer from the air to the liquid (see Chapter 8) and, hence, to the biomass. For this reason, recirculation of effluent back to the trickling filter usually improves filter performance. If the effect of the recirculation flow rate, R, is included, the gross hydraulic loading rate is given by

$$Q_h = \frac{Q + R}{A_m} \tag{14.53}$$

Several design formulae, derived from plant operating data, have been proposed as a basis for taking account of the effects of changing the magnitude of the various loading factors outlined above. There is wide disagreement about the relative importance assigned to each factor. The only conditions about which there is general agreement are at loading rates similar to those in conventional standard-rate filters. Even here, predicted filter efficiencies vary from 80 to 90 per cent. No formula has been generally accepted, and the design of most trickling filters is based on *empirical loading parameters*. Typical values of parameters commonly used are given in Table 14.5.

Low (standard) rate filters
These have low hydraulic and organic loading rates, usually without recirculation (Fig 14.21(a)). They give a 20/30 effluent which can be well nitrified. Single-pass units can be gravity fed without any source of external power.

Table 14.5 Typical loading parameters for trickling filters

Filter type	Organic loading kg BOD / $m^3.d$	Hydraulic loading $m^3/m^2.d$	Effluent recircu-lation ratio	Depth of filter medium m	Effluent BOD/SS mg/L
Low-rate	0.07-0.10	0.25-1.2	Not usually provided	2	20/30 (well nitrified)
High-rate		3.5		$\simeq 2$	20/30 (no nitri-fication)
	Up to 1.0	10-20	2:1 to 10:1	1-2	30/40 and greater
High-rate plastic media	1.8	12 $m^3/m^3.d$	Varies	Several metres	BOD removal 60-70%
Alternating double filtration	0.24	3	—	2	20/30

Some recent filter designs of 'low'-rate filters have included provision for high rates of recirculation (Fig 14.21(b)). This has improved the loading capacity, the effluent quality produced or both, at the cost of providing the extra pumps and the power required to run them.

High-rate filters
These have loading factors which are significantly higher than those of low-rate filters. Recirculation must be included, and so pumping and power facilities are necessary. Recirculation rates of 4:1 have commonly been employed. The effluent is less likely to be nitrified and the effluent quality depends upon filter loading.

Alternating double filtration
This process (Fig 14.21(c)) uses two filters in series. The effluent from the first filter passes to a humus tank from which the settled effluent is dosed to a second filter and subsequently to a second humus tank. The first filter is sub-jected to high organic loads and accumulates a heavy biomass growth, while the second filter is lightly loaded. The filters are alternated on a weekly or monthly basis, depending on local loading or conditions. When the flow pattern is changed, the previously lightly-loaded filter begins to grow a

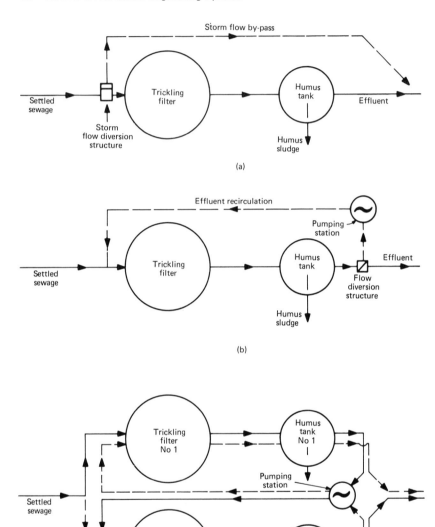

Fig 14.21 Operating principle of a rotating biological filter: (a) conventional, (b) with recirculation, (c) alternating double filtration

greater biomass and the previously highly-loaded filter now sheds biomass as the loading is not sufficient to maintain the growth. Loadings are between those of low- and high-rate filters, while effluents are usually of at least 20/30 standard. This method requires pumping to effect the second dosing. It is very useful for highly variable or very difficult wastewaters, but is unsuitable for small works. The humus tanks can be of similar design to that of conventional ones; additional effective capacity can be included to allow for the higher solids loading.

High-rate, plastic media filters
These have specially-moulded plastic media instead of the traditional stone media. A solid stone medium exposes only the stone surface as a potential microbial site. A range of plastic products which present a larger surface area per unit volume of filter space than does stone is available. The medium can be in the form of sheet material designed to split the flow and so expose the settled sewage to the maximum biomass, or a randomly packed medium, comprising small units such as rings. Plastic media are of light weight, and they can be used in deep beds or towers. The constructional requirements for such units are less than for traditional media. Plastic media can be used at high or low loading rates, but they have found most application in high-rate processes, with high recirculation rates. A particular application is as a roughing unit for concentrated wastes which can be reduced to a strength suitable for conventional biological treatment, or discharge to sewers.

Performance of trickling filters

Trickling filters have been used for many decades and the plants in current operation range from old low-rate processes to modern high-rate processes; they are made from a range of materials. This makes quantitative performance data difficult to compare.

Trickling filters are particularly suited to treating difficult and variable wastewaters. The fixed film is not prone to wash out at times of high hydraulic flow, as is the sludge in a suspended growth process. The high proportion of biomass attached to the medium gives a good reserve against variable organic loads. The process is quiet and does not foam, but it is prone to some fly and odour nuisance. These problems are more marked in single-pass, low-load processes; high rates of recirculation reduce these difficulties. The area required for a traditional circular filter is greater than that for an equivalent activated sludge plant. The actual filter area is approximately four times that of an activated sludge unit with similar capacity, while the area of the complete plant is between 50 and 100 per cent larger, although high-loading or deep filters reduce this disparity. Capital costs for a trickling filter unit are usually higher than those for an activated sludge plant (10 to 50 per cent). The differential cost depends on local factors. Running costs are usually lower — gravity-fed plants require no power, others require power only for recirculation or for the distributor drive. Electrical costs are therefore less than those required for an activated sludge plant. Operational requirements are relatively low. Trickling filters require a period of several weeks to mature — that is, to establish a useful biomass. The process therefore cannot be started up rapidly but, once established, it is tolerant of variations in flow and strength of sewage.

14.9 Rotating biological filters

The RBF process is briefly described in Section 11.3 and is illustrated in Fig 14.22. The development of this process as a commercially-viable treatment method has occurred only since 1960, although the principle was developed before 1920 and a few units were built and tested by 1930. The use of heavy materials, such as wood, galvanised iron and asbestos cement for constructing the discs, however, led to cumbersome plants with high running costs. These factors, combined with the general shortage of finance before and during the Second World War, stopped further development. Interest in the process revived in the 1960s, when lightweight, non-biodegradable plastic materials became available for constructing the discs. This led to the development of the current range of designs. Materials such as polystyrene, polypropylene and expanded wire mesh are now used. Multiple-disc assemblies made from these materials are compact, are easily rotated, have low power requirements and are particularly suitable for small installations.

Principles of operation

In the RBF unit, the discs are spaced so as to allow the film to grow to a

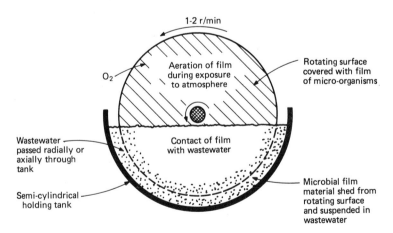

Fig 14.22 Operating principle of a rotating biological filter

thickness of a few millimetres. *Primary settlement* is therefore necessary to prevent bridging between discs by gross solids. This settlement may be in a conventional settlement tank, but one of the chief criteria for small works is that desludging should be required as seldom as possible. The settled sewage enters the *RBF zone*, which is usually trough-shaped, with only a small clearance between the invert and the discs to reduce short-circuiting (Fig 14.22). The discs are usually grouped into four or five stages which, at small works, are supported on one shaft. The rotation of the shaft allows adsorption of sewage onto the film, followed by aeration while that part of the disc contacts the atmosphere. Some of the film intermittently sloughs off the discs and must be removed in a *secondary settlement tank*. A pump can be used to transfer the secondary sludge to the primary settlement tank. In addition, effluent recirculation can be included, particularly for plants where there are long periods of very low flow.

In the *RBF stage*, the processes of adsorption and aeration occur in regular short cycles as the discs rotate. The discs are usually from 1 m to 3 m in diameter and are rotated with a peripheral speed of 0.07 to 0.14 m/s. The rotation rate is constant and this avoids the problems associated with the drying out of the microbial film at low flows. The microbial oxidation of the adsorbed material is mainly aerobic. As the film thickness increases, anaerobic conditions may occur close to the disc surface. The resulting gas production and increased weight of the thick film (2 to 3 mm) cause areas of the biomass to drop off. The film left on the disc then becomes aerobic and the cycle is repeated. This process denudes only small areas at any particular time, and the efficiency of the oxidation process is therefore almost constant.

The degree of longitudinal mixing in the RBF stage is kept low by baffling each stage, or group, of discs. The first discs receive the greatest pollutional load and the final stage discs are only lightly loaded. As the applied load per unit of disc area reduces through the plant, the film growth becomes less. An average film biomass of 197 g/m² disc area has been measured; this is equivalent to approximately 50 000 mg/L mixed liquor volatile suspended solids. These figures are difficult to apply to treatment plant design. Such high values of biomass offer some protection against slug loads of toxic or inhibitory wastes. In practice, these wastes appear to poison mainly the outer layers of the film, which then slough off the discs and leave the underlying layers of film to carry on the oxidation process. As with all aerobic treatment processes, it is necessary to ensure an adequate concentration of oxygen in the biological unit. The optimum concentration of dissolved oxygen is similar to that for the activated sludge process — approximately 1.5 mg/L.

Design criteria

The RBF process configuration sometimes adopted follows the conventional pattern of a primary settlement tank followed by the RBF unit and then a secondary settlement tank. In these plants, the design of the *primary settlement* stage may be based on conventional practice. For small plants, the primary settlement tank takes the form of a septic or Imhoff tank. One design for small communities incorporates both primary and secondary settlement within the one unit (Fig 14.23). This has the advantage that the film shed from the first two RBF stages, where the growth is more rapid, can pass through slots into the 'main' primary settlement tank (Fig 14.23). In the later stages, which produce less excess film, the shed material remains in suspension until the secondary settlement stage. Cold digestion occurs in the primary tank, the sludge being similar to that from a septic tank. The primary settlement stage has a nominal retention time of approximately 20 hours at DWF in tanks designed in the UK. If a separate septic tank is used, the retention time is likely to be between 15 and 30 hours. Such a tank will remove at least 50 per cent of the suspended solids but only approximately 25 per cent of the BOD_5. The per capita BOD_5 which will be passed to the RBF stage is often estimated as 40 to 50 g/d.

Design of the RBF unit usually takes into account both BOD and hydraulic loading. These units are sized on the basis of empirical curves produced by manufacturers for their particular ranges of equipment. These curves relate BOD removal efficiency to the disc area per unit flow for a given BOD_5 concentration, with various corrections to allow for the loading pattern and the number of stages provided. For larger plants, maximum BOD_5 loading to the

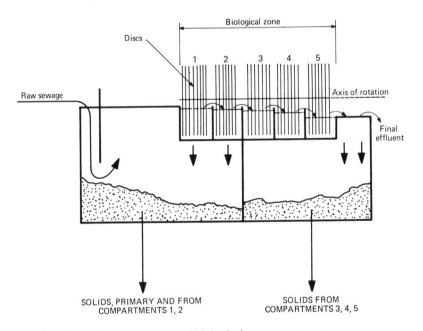

Fig 14.23 Possible arrangement of biological treatment zones

first-stage discs is 100 $g/m^2.d$. In smaller plants, it may be as low as 6 to 8 $g/m^2.d$. For plants serving fewer than 100 persons, a disc area of 6 m^2 per person has been quoted for design.

Secondary settlement is required to remove the film which is shed by the RBF stages. This film biomass is in a form which settles well and, therefore, conventional overflow rates may be used. In many small plants, hydraulic shock loads are pulsed through the plant and cause sludge washout. The weir overflow rate can be kept lower than 90 $m^3/m.d$ to reduce this effect.

Operation

Because of their simple construction, RBF plants are easy to operate and require very little operator attention. The only moving parts in the plant are the slowly rotating discs, which are usually driven by an electric motor.

Performance

A well-designed and well-operated plant will easily meet the 20:30 BOD_5:SS Royal Commission standard. Although plants usually produce a good reduction of carbonaceous BOD and suspended solids, the degree of nitrification depends on the loading and operating factors. Provision of units in addition to those required for BOD_5 reduction combined with oxygen concentrations at or above 2 mg/L in the later stages usually results in some nitrification.

The system operates in a plug flow condition, and therefore an increased hydraulic load on the biological stage will displace only the treated liquids from the final stages of the unit. The plants allow several hours' retention in the disc sections under dry-weather flow conditions, so that poorly-treated liquors will be apparent only after some hours of increased flow. More frequently, poor final effluents result from hydraulic overload of the final settlement unit. For prolonged flows in excess of 3 ADWF, deterioration of the effluent is to be expected.

The RBF unit is silent and requires only a small electric motor to turn the shaft. The process does not foam, froth, bulk or attract insects. The units are compact and usually have a cover to retain heat in colder climates and to act as a safety barrier.

Overall, the RBF process offers a reliable low maintenance wastewater treatment process which, despite its high initial cost, warrants consideration — especially where loads are variable and a minimum of attention is desired.

14.10 Design of anaerobic digesters

For most of this century, anaerobic digestion has been the main process used for stabilising the concentrated organic sludges produced in municipal wastewater treatment works. It is likely to retain its position as the basic method of sludge treatment, although other treatment methods may assume increasing importance in situations where sludge must be transported long distances for final disposal. Some other methods of wastewater sludge treatment may become economically competitive with anaerobic digestion — for example, aerobic digestion in extended aeration package plants. Although anaerobic digestion requires more costly structures and closer operator attention than aerobic digestion, it produces combustible methane gas. This has some attraction in the present climate of concern about energy resources. At present, however, the majority of plants either discharge this methane to the atmosphere or burn it as waste.

Anaerobic digestion produces a sludge which is well stabilised and suitable for drying on open sand beds without odour nuisance and without attracting flies. Methods of dewatering and disposing of digested sludge, together with alternative methods of treatment, are discussed in Chapter 12.

Approach to design

General descriptions of the various types of anaerobic digester are given in Section 11.4. Digestion systems are the most controlled of the conventional anaerobic processes, and therefore the biological principles set out in Section 11.2 are most readily applied to them. Design of a digester to account for these factors involves

a Sizing the digester to suit the volume and characteristics of the sludges to be treated
b Selection of the environmental conditions, especially temperature and mixing intensity, to be provided
c Choice of ancillary equipment and control systems for achieving the required conditions.

In practice, the size of the digester depends on the chosen environmental conditions, which in turn govern the choice of ancillary equipment. Therefore, optimum design is essentially an attempt to find the best compromise between the cost of providing larger structures with less environmental control, and the cost of providing more effective control of environmental conditions with a saving on the required digester capacity. Cost analysis should also take into account the higher costs of energy, operation and maintenance for the more sophisticated systems. In general, simple systems with a minimum of control equipment are preferred for small treatment works, while the more complex but more compact systems are more suitable for large works where workshop facilities and constant supervision can be provided. Detailed consideration of costs and design of the environmental control equipment for digesters is outside the scope of this text; the following discussion is confined to methods of determining *digester capacity* to satisfy process requirements.

Methods of designing anaerobic digesters range from the use of simple empirical factors, such as volume/capita served, to approaches based on the kinetics of the anaerobic biological process. Where correctly applied, all are capable of yielding satisfactory results provided the design constants and factors chosen are appropriate for the characteristics of the sludge to be treated.

Kinetic basis for digester design

It was noted earlier that, hydraulically, anaerobic digesters approximate a completely mixed system without recycle (that is, $\theta_c = t$). Anaerobic growth processes can be described in terms of Eq 14.16, developed for the aerobic activated sludge processes in Section 14.5:

$$\frac{1}{\theta_c} = YU - k_d$$

The problem which arises is how to measure both the food and microorganism concentrations. Although BOD can be used for measuring the food concentration, the difficulty of representatively sampling sludges, together with the very large dilution factors required for such concentrated materials, makes the BOD test unsuitable. For this reason, *volatile solids* is the most commonly used measure of sludge organic strength. Similarly, volatile solids in the digester contents is the best available indication of organism content.

An appropriate form of the modified F/M ratio is

$$U_s = \frac{\text{Mass of volatile solids destroyed in the digester daily}}{\text{Total mass of volatile solids in digester}} \qquad (14.54)$$

where the subscript 's' signifies the loading of volatile solids.

For anaerobic digestion, Eq 14.16 can be written as

$$\frac{1}{\theta_c} = \frac{1}{t} = YU_s - k_d \qquad (14.55)$$

It is difficult to apply Eq 14.55 directly to the design of anaerobic digesters because values of the yield coefficient, Y, and the constant, k_d, are not well established, and the terms in both the numerator and denominator of the Eq 14.54 defining U_s are themselves dependent on the loading rate and environmental conditions in the process. However, the above considerations are useful in providing a basis for the various empirical design factors widely used for estimating the capacity of municipal sludge digestion systems.

Because of the difficulty of determining the mass of volatile solids *removed* daily from digesters, it is more convenient for design purposes to use the mass of volatile solids *added* to the digesters daily. This gives a factor which is analogous to the F/M ratio, F, presented in Chapter 11 and applied in Section 14.5 to the activated sludge process. On a volatile solids basis, the F/M ratio for anaerobic digesters, F_s, is given by

$$F_s = \frac{\text{Mass of volatile solids } \textit{added} \text{ daily (kg/d)}}{\text{Mass of volatile solids in digester (kg)}} \tag{14.56}$$

Anaerobic digestion generally destroys about 40 to 60 per cent of the volatile solids in the feed sludge. It is important to note that the form of the remaining volatile matter is such that the digested sludge is a non-putrescible, relatively stable humus-like material with reasonable dewatering properties and that, once dried, it does not readily liquefy on re-wetting.

Empirical design factors

The following design factors have been developed over many years of digester design and operation, and apply to all types of sludge digestion system.

Volatile solids loading
Volatile solids loading, F_s, per unit mass of volatile solids in the digester is a practical way of describing the process loading for anaerobic digesters (Eq 14.56).

Volatile solids loading per unit volume of digester is a simplification of the volatile solids loading, which avoids the need to define the volatile solids content in the digester. It can be shown that the equilibrium mass of volatile solids in the digester is related to the volatile solids concentration in the feed sludge. For any given system at equilibrium, the volatile solids concentration in the digester remains constant; hence, each unit volume of digester contents will contain a constant mass of sludge solids. This leads to a simple expression of the volatile solids loading rate in volumetric form

$$F_{s\Psi} = \frac{\text{Volatile sludge solids added daily (kg)}}{\text{Digester volume (m}^3)} \tag{14.57}$$

In terms of the variables given in Section 12.4, and considering solids mass and volume to apply *per head of population*,

$$F_{s\Psi} = \frac{(Pv/100)S_s}{\Psi} = \frac{\text{Volatile solids per head.day (kg)}}{\text{Digester volume per head (m}^3)} \tag{14.58}$$

Average liquid detention time
Average liquid detention time, t, is dependent on U_s as shown by Eq 14.55, and thus on F_s, as shown above. It is therefore also dependent on $F_{s\Psi}$.

For a given digester volume, $\Psi\,(m^3)$, and a given feed sludge flow rate, Q_s (m^3/d),

$$t = \frac{\Psi}{Q_s} \qquad (14.59)$$

The parameters t and $F_{s\Psi}$ are related in terms of the sludge moisture content, P_M.

It can be shown that the wet sludge volume, $\Psi_w\,(m^3)$, is given, in terms of the daily sludge solids mass, S_s, sludge moisture, P_M, and volatile solids content, P_v, and the densities of these various sludge constituents, as follows:

$$\Psi_w = S_s\left[\frac{P_v}{100\,\rho_v} + \frac{100 - P_v}{100\,\rho_f} + \frac{1}{\rho}\left(\frac{P_M}{100 - P_M}\right)\right] \qquad (14.60)$$

where ρ_f is the density of the fixed fraction of dry sludge solids (kg/m^3); ρ_v is the density of the volatile fraction of dry sludge solids (kg/m^3); and ρ is the density of water (kg/m^3).

With S_s and Ψ_w taken as *per head of contributing population*, Ψ_w can be substituted for Q_s in Eq 14.59. If the substitution $\Psi = [(P_v/100)S_s]/F_{sV}$ is also made, the following expression results:

$$t = \frac{P_v/100}{F_{s\Psi}\left[\dfrac{P_v}{100\,\rho_v} + \dfrac{100 - P_v}{100\,\rho_f} + \dfrac{1}{\rho}\left(\dfrac{P_M}{100 - P_M}\right)\right]} \qquad (14.61)$$

For a given treatment works, P_v, ρ_f, ρ_v and ρ can be considered to remain reasonably constant, so that Eq 14.61 reduces to the general form

$$t = f(P_M/F_{s\Psi}) \qquad (14.62)$$

For any given value of P_M, a plot of t against F_{sV} results in a rectangular hyperbola. Fig 14.24 presents such a plot for the range of moisture contents commonly encountered in municipal wastewater sludges. Values assumed for the other parameters in Eq 14.61 are $P_v = 70$ per cent, $\rho_f = 2650\,kg/m^3$, $\rho_v = 1400\,kg/m^3$ and $\rho = 1000\,kg/m^3$.

Digester volume per head of population
Digester volume per head of population is a convenient design parameter which incorporates all the above parameters. Volumetric volatile solids loading, F_{sV}, was defined by Eq 14.58 as $F_{s\Psi} = (P_v/100)S_s/\Psi$. This equation

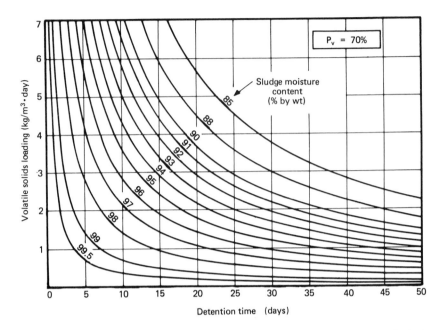

Fig 14.24 Relationship between solids loading rate, detention time and sludge moisture content in anaerobic digestion

will give $\mathcal{V}$ in terms of $F_{s\mathcal{V}}$ and S_s, the daily per capita mass of sludge solids produced:

$$\mathcal{V}_c = \frac{(P_v/100)S_s}{F_{s\mathcal{V}}} \tag{14.63}$$

Hence, the digester volume/capita parameter, $\mathcal{V}_c$, can be rationally derived from the same data which are required to apply the other, more fundamental, loading factors outlined above. It is important in applying such parameters to consider the types of sludge and the degree of environmental control prevailing in the system where these were derived.

Typical ranges of values adopted for volumetric volatile solids loading rate, average detention time and per capita digester volume for both standard-rate and high-rate digesters are listed in Table 14.6.

Volume reduction method for standard-rate digesters

The chief operational difference between standard-rate and high-rate digesters is that in standard-rate digesters, stratification results in separation of much of the sludge moisture from the digested sludge solids. This excess water is then withdrawn as *supernatant liquor*, while the digested sludge is

Table 14.6 Typical design and loading parameters for sludge digesters

Parameter	Standard-rate digestion	High-rate digestion
	kg volatile solids/cubic m of digester.d	
Solids loading volumetric	0.5–1.5	2.5–4.0 up to 6.5
Digestion period required	30–60 days	10–15 days
Per capita digester volume	*cubic m of digester space/capita*	
a Primary	0.06–0.09	0.04–0.06
b Primary + humus	0.12–0.15	0.08–0.10
c Primary + activated	0.12–0.18	0.08–0.12

drawn off the bottom of the digester in smaller volumes, at a considerably increased concentration. Thus, some preliminary separation of sludge solids and water takes place in the digester itself.

By contrast, there is no stratification in high-rate or other completely mixed digesters, and therefore no preliminary thickening of digested sludge. On the contrary, since digestion destroys up to 40 per cent of the total sludge solids, the digested sludge drawn from high-rate digesters has a lower solids content than that of the incoming raw sludge. Separation of the supernatant and solids in high-rate systems is therefore carried out in separate settling units, in the form of either secondary digesters or sludge lagoons.

During digestion in standard-rate digesters the sludge structure is broken down, allowing the separation of water from the sludge solids. At the same time, 50 to 60 per cent of the volatile solids are gradually destroyed by digestion. These two processes have the combined effect of reducing the volume occupied by the sludge solids in the digester. If the released supernatant liquor is drawn regularly from the digester, the total volume occupied by the sludge is gradually reduced. This volume reduction with time follows an approximately exponential curve. The total digester volume required for a continuous process would be the area under this time-volume curve divided by the hydraulic detention time, t, provided in the digester. Therefore, the per capita volume required for the active digestion zone in standard-rate digesters is approximately

$$\Psi_a = \frac{t}{3}\,(\Psi_f + 2\Psi_d) \tag{14.64}$$

where Ψ_a is the volume of active digestion zone, per person (m³); Ψ_f is the daily volume of fresh sludge produced per person (m^3); and V_d is the volume of digested sludge per person, after time t (m^3).

The time required for substantially complete digestion depends on the temperature at which the digester is operated. Some widely-quoted figures are shown in Table 14.7.

Table 14.7 Time for 90 per cent digestion of primary sludge

	Mesophilic range					Thermophilic range				
Temperature, °C	10	16	21	27	32	38	43	49	54	60
Digestion time, days	75	56	42	30	25	24	26	16	14	18

Additional volume must be allowed for in unmixed standard-rate digesters to accommodate the scum, supernatant and digested sludge zones. Total volume is typically twice the calculated volume of the active digestion zone.

Energy production by anaerobic digestion

During anaerobic digestion, the volatile content of the solids in the feed sludge (typically about 70 per cent in raw primary sludge and about 80 per cent in waste activated sludge — Chapter 12) is reduced by 50 to 60 per cent. The gas volume produced by degradation of this volatile matter is about 0.4 to 0.5 m^3 (at normal temperature and pressure) per kilogram of volatile solids added. This is equivalent to about 1 m^3 per kilogram of volatile solids destroyed in digestion. This gas usually contains about 60 to 70 per cent of methane (heat value about 36 000 kJ/m^3 at standard temperature and pressure), and the remainder is mainly carbon dioxide, with traces of hydrogen gas and hydrogen sulphide. Sludge gas therefore has a heat value of 22 000 to 25 000 kJ/m^3.

Sludge gas is commonly burnt to provide heat for maintaining the digesters at constant temperature, usually in the optimum mesophilic range of 30° to 35°C. In many larger treatment plants, sludge gas has been used in dual fuel engines coupled to electric generators that are used to generate electric power for use in the treatment plant. In many cases, however, the high costs of labour associated with the maintenance and continuous supervision of the engines and generating equipment, together with the cost of supplying the small amount of fuel oil required to supplement the sludge gas supplied to the engines, has led to abandonment of the use of sludge gas for power generation.

14.11 Tertiary treatment — effluent polishing

The conventional sequence of primary treatment and biological secondary treatment normally removes 85 to 95 per cent of the primary pollutants, BOD and SS. Secondary treatment of a sewage containing about 300 mg/L BOD and 300 mg/L SS will therefore produce an effluent with 15 to 30 mg/L BOD and 20 to 40 mg/L SS. If dilution in the receiving stream is low or there is some reason for special protection of the water quality in it, the effluent must be of a higher standard than that obtainable by secondary treatment. Although it is sometimes possible to achieve effluent BOD/SS concentrations less than 15/20 mg/L from a well-designed and carefully-operated secondary treatment plant, it is usually necessary to provide *tertiary treatment* if a consistently high quality effluent is required.

The main objective of tertiary treatment is *effluent polishing* (the removal of fine suspended solids). Because these suspended solids are mostly organic, their removal results in a reduction in the effluent BOD. In the case of standard-rate trickling filters, about 1 mg/L BOD is removed for each 2 to 3 mg/L reduction in SS concentration while, in conventional activated sludge effluents, the ratio is about 1 mg/L BOD to 1 mg/L SS removed. A second objective of tertiary treatment is *disinfection*, to reduce the concentrations of pathogenic and indicator bacteria and other pathogens which could be a health hazard to downstream users.

Other materials remaining in secondary effluents include non-bio-degradable organic compounds, surfactants (detergents), inorganic dissolved salts and dissolved plant nutrients — particularly nitrogen and phosphorus. Conventional tertiary treatment processes have little effect on these materials, whose removal generally requires more sophisticated processes, classified as *advanced wastewater treatment* (AWT).

Principles of tertiary treatment processes

Effluent polishing can be carried out by the simple *physical* separation of suspended solids from the effluent or by more complex processes which involve biological as well as physical action. Physical separation of suspended matter is usually achieved by one of four main mechanisms — prolonged settling, straining through a fine mesh, filtration through granular media or irrigation over grassed surfaces. These processes remove the bacteria and other pathogens associated with the suspended solids which are removed; single organisms are generally too small to be captured, so that little disinfection is achieved by simple separation. By contrast, in some tertiary processes involving biological action, bacterial reductions of 80 to 90 per cent have been achieved.

Where a high degree of disinfection is required, this is usually achieved by treatment with a *chemical* such as chlorine or ozone or by ultraviolet irradiation. The efficiency of disinfectants is enhanced by the prior removal of small particles that could shield pathogens from effective contact with the disinfectant. Disinfection is discussed in Chapter 10.

Physical separation processes

Devices which effect the simple physical separation of suspended solids from secondary effluent include microstrainers and various types of filter, ranging from slow sand filters to rapid sand, dual media and mixed media filters. Filters may also differ as to flow pattern, ranging from conventional down-flow to upflow or even biflow filters. Such filters are similar to those used in water treatment and described in Chapter 13. Typical loading rates and performances of various types of filter used for tertiary treatment are given in Table 14.8.

Filter developments are aimed at improving filter performance by increasing the permissible loading rate, increasing the time of filter run between backwashes, or both. In the development of surface filtration devices from the early slow sand filters to rapid sand filters, the increased efficiency which resulted from more efficient cleaning methods reduced the economic cleaning interval from 1 to 2 months to a day or less.

Recently-developed filter systems (such as *dual media, mixed media and upflow filters*) have further improved filtration economy because they effect in-depth filtration. In this case, instead of solids being removed only within the surface layers of the filter, as in surface filtration devices, a much greater depth of medium is used in removing impurities. In-depth filters have a much greater volume available within the pores of the filter medium in which to store the removed material, without causing excessive head loss. This results in the greater loading rates or longer filter runs commonly observed in such systems. It is particularly noteworthy that gelatinous biological solids, whose tendency to quickly blind the surface of filtration systems can result in low filtration rates, are particularly suited to treatment by in-depth filters. High backwash rates with air-scour assistance are required to ensure effective scouring of entrapped solids.

Microstrainers

These are a type of surface filtration or straining device developed to con-centrate a large filter surface area into a small space (see Section 8.1). They require less space than any other tertiary device, and they are capable of efficient solids removal when treating a good secondary effluent. Their performance deteriorates markedly under heavy loads, such as may occur during the seasonal heavy sloughing of solids from trickling filters or when plant upsets produce poorly-settling sludge in the activated sludge process.

Pebble-bed clarifiers

These have frequently been used in the UK for improving final effluent from small treatment plants. This system uses a bed of 5 to 10 mm size pea gravel, 150 to 200 mm deep, mounted 300 mm below the water surface near the effluent weirs in a humus tank. Effluent is forced to flow upwards through

Table 14.8 Typical loading rates and operational characteristics of tertiary filters, microstrainers and pebble-bed clarifiers

Treatment method	Loading rate $m^3/m^2.d$	Average performance		Other features	Cleaning		Washwater requirement % of flow
		SS removal %	BOD removal %		Method	Frequency	
Slow sand filter	Up to 3	~ 60	~ 40	40-70% reduction in coliform bacteria. Small reduction in ammonia	Removal of surface layer of sand	Once a week to once a month	–
Rapid sand filter	120-250	70-80	50-70		Air-scour with water backwash at ~ 8 L/s.m²	Once a day (rate of increase of head loss: 1-2 m/d)	2-3
Upflow sand filter	200-300 (up to 400)	Up to 80	Up to 70	Some loss of dissolved oxygen during passage through filters	Ditto at ~ 14 L/s.m²	Once or twice each day	3-5
Mixed media filter	300-400	70-90	50-70		Ditto at ~ 14 L/s.m²	Once or twice each day	3-5
Pebble-bed clarifier	10-20	40-60	25-40		By lowering water level beneath pebble-bed and hosing down	Twice a week to once a month	
Microstrainer	350	50-75	25-50	Maximum permissible head loss ~ 150 mm. UV light essential	High-pressure water jets (plus chemical cleaning about once a month)	Continuous	Up to 5%

the pebble-bed towards the weirs. Flocculation is promoted by the gentle agitation of the suspended solids as they pass through the bed so that they settle in the bed or on its surface. Cleaning is carried out at intervals of a few days to a few weeks, according to the quality of the effluent being treated. For cleaning, flow to the humus tank is interrupted and the water level is dropped below the bottom of the bed, so that much of the entrapped material is drawn back into the humus tank. Final cleaning is completed by hosing the bed with effluent.

Tertiary processes involving biological action

Effluent polishing processes which involve some form of biological action include tertiary ponds, grass filtration and land filtration. Typical design and operational data for these systems are given in Table 14.9.

Table 14.9 Typical design and operational data for tertiary ponds, grass filtration and land filtration

Treatment method	Configuration	Loading rate $m^3/m^2.d$	Average performance		
			SS removal %	BOD removal %	Coliform bacteria removal %
Tertiary ponds	Depth 1-2 m Detention 2–20 days, plug flow, 2 to 4 ponds in series	< 0.15 to 0.5	25–70	30–70	70–96 (Greater removals possible)
Grass filtration	Grass plots – gradient 1:100 preferred. 1:60 maximum. Uniform flow distribution	0.1–0.8	60–80	50–75	80–95
Land filtration	Grass plots, permeable soils, gradient as above. Under-drainage may be provided	< 0.1	> 80	> 75	> 95

Tertiary ponds
These provide an opportunity for prolonged settling. Suspended solids which settle to the bottom of the pond undergo anaerobic degradation. Other solids undergo normal aerobic degradation in the pond liquid and by-products of this process support algal photosynthesis. Algae which do not settle in the pond are discharged in the effluent so that net SS changes in the ponds are

highly variable. Effluent BOD is therefore variable also, although the full potential BOD of the escaping algae will be exerted only if they die and decompose in the receiving water. Growth of algae is stimulated by warm conditions and sunlight and it increases with increasing detention time in the pond. In the UK, lagoons with short detention times — about 3 days — have been found to give optimum SS removal. Longer detention times, however, give greater bacterial reductions. In warm, temperate climates about 10 days' detention gives an acceptable compromise between bacterial reduction and algal growth. Some nitrogen and phosphorus removal occurs in ponds, mainly by incorporation into biological cell material.

Grass filtration
This involves the distribution of secondary effluent onto grass plots which are gently graded towards a collection channel at the lower end. As the effluent flows through the lush growth which develops, much of the suspended solids content is strained or settled out, later being degraded by soil bacteria. Some of the nutrient content becomes incorporated into new grass growth. Effluent from grass filtration may be very low in SS and BOD and may show some reduction in nutrient concentration. Often it is brown in colour. Good reductions in bacterial numbers are also frequently observed, and dissolved oxygen concentration may be increased. Grass growth should be mowed and disposed of at intervals.

Land filtration
In land filtration, effluent is applied to prepared land surfaces at lower loading rates than in grass filtration. Much of the water infiltrates and percolates through the soil mantle towards drainage ditches, some is lost by evaporation and some by transpiration of growing plants. Suspended matter is deposited on the soil and removal of nutrients which can be used by plants may be considerable. Bacteria removal should also be very good, especially where most of the effluent reaches the drains through the soil. The net growth of vegetative cover should be removed periodically. Where permitted by health regulations, controlled grazing by cattle or sheep, after a suitable drying-out period, may be practised.

14.12 Conclusions

This chapter has dealt in some detail with particular parts of a municipal wastewater treatment plant. It should be stressed that, in practice, it is very important that all the required processes are integrated into a treatment system. This includes the disposal of sludge and, perhaps, effluent disinfection, which are dealt with in other chapters. Additionally, a designer will have to account for particular problems on sites, including the hydraulic flow through the plant and plant layout. The plant should be easy to operate with a minimum of difficult or unpleasant tasks.

14.13 Wastewater treatment plant design summary

Presentation of design data

In design reports and operating manuals, it is often convenient to include a summary of the main process design criteria and the dimensions of each of the major treatment units. Where required, details of the interconnecting pipework and channels, pumps and other mechanical equipment, as well as the electrical and control systems can be included, but such details are beyond the scope of this text. A form of summary which is suitable for most conventional trickling filter or activated sludge plants is set out below. This summary is based on the design approach set out in the text, and will be found useful not only as an aid in presenting plant design data, but also as a guide to the major aspects which should be considered in designing these types of treatment plant.

For simplicity in presentation, only the major flow streams are included in the design summary. In practice, return flows, such as digester supernatant and tertiary filter backwash water, should be taken into account as they may increase both the flow and pollutant loadings to the treatment plant.

Typical design summary plan

NAME OF TREATMENT WORKS ....

A *Effluent quality objectives*

BOD.......mg/L	SS..........mg/L	Nitrogen	Other ....

B *Equivalent population*

	Residential population	Industrial EP	Total EP
Stage 1	....	....	....
Ultimate	....	....	....

C *Design flow and loadings*

(i) Flows

	Daily flow per EP (L)		Total flow (ML/d)		Stage 1 equivalent flow rate (L/s)
	Stage 1	Ultimate	Stage 1	Ultimate	
ADWF	....	....	....	....	....
PDWF	....	....	....	....	....
3ADWF	....	....	....	....	....
PWWF	....	....	....	....	....

(ii) Loadings

	Daily contribution per EP (g)	Total daily loading (kg)
BOD loading	....	....
SS loading	....	....

D *Screens and approach channels*

(i) Screens

	Number	Bar spacing (mm)	Bar width (mm)	Velocity at PWWF (m/s)
Duty units	....	....	....	....
Bypass units	....	....	....	....

(ii) Water level control

....

(iii) Approach channels

	Velocity (m/s)		Depth (m)		Width (m)
	At PWWF	At PDWF	At PWWF	At PDWF	
Duty units	....	....	....	....	....
Bypass units	....	....	....	....	....

E1 *Aerated grit chambers and pre-aeration tanks*

	No.	Detention time (minutes)	Volume (m³)	Dimensions		
				Depth (m)	Width (m)	Length (m)
(i) Aerated grit chambers	...	.... (At PWWF)	....	....	....	....
(ii) Pre-aeration tanks	...	.... (At ADWF)	....	....	....	....

E2 *Constant-velocity grit chambers and control flume*

(i) Control
flume

No.	Throat width (m)	Depth at various flow rates (m)			
		PWWF	3ADWF	PDWF	ADWF
. . .	. . . .	. . . . . .	. . . .	. . . . . .	. . . . . .

(ii) Grit
chambers

Number		Design forward Design particle velocity (m/s) settling velocity (mm/s)
Duty units	Standby units	
. . . .	. . . .	. . . .

Length (m)		Dimensions of ideal cross-section at various flows			
		PWWF	3ADWF	PDWF	ADWF
. . . .	Depth (m)	. . . . . .	. . . .	. . . . . .	. . . . . .
	Width (m)	. . . . . .	. . . .	. . . . . .	. . . . . .

F *Primary sedimentation tanks*

(i) Primary
sedimentation
tanks

Design loadings		No. and dimensions	
Design flow	. . . . m³/d	No. of tanks	. . . .
Surface loading	. . . . m³/m².d		
Detention time	. . . . . . hours	Length	. . . . m
Forward velocity	. . . . . . mm/s	Width	. . . . m
		Depth	. . . . m
Weir loading rate	. . . . m³/m.d	Weir length	. . . . m

Estimated removal efficiency	BOD	. . . . %
	SS	. . . . %

(ii) Primary
sludge
production

Mass of sludge solids produced	. . . . kg/d
Volatile content of sludge solids	. . . . %
Mass of volatile sludge solids	. . . . kg/d
Wet sludge moisture content	. . . . %
Wet sludge density	. . . . kg/L
Volume of wet sludge produced	. . . . L/d

G *Flows and loadings to secondary treatment*

Maximum flow rate	. . . × ADWF: . . . . ML/d
BOD loading (average)	. . . . kg/d
SS loading (average)	. . . . kg/d

H1 *Activated sludge*

(i) Aeration tanks

Design factors	No. and dimensions	
Food/micro-organisms ratio . . . . kg BOD/kgMLVSS.d	No. of tanks	. . . .
MLVSS concentration . . . . mg/L	Length Width Depth	. . . . m . . . . m . . . . m

(ii) Air supply

Total air supply . . . . . m³/d	Peak rate	. . . . . m³/s

(iii) Excess sludge production

Volatile solids net production . . . . kg/kg BOD removed	
Mass volatile solids produced Mass non-volatiles added in settled sewage Total excess sludge produced	. . . . kg/d . . . . kg/d . . . . kg/d
Sludge moisture content . . . . . . % ⎪ Sludge density . . . . kg/L	
Volume of excess sludge produced	. . . . L/d

(iv) Mean cell residence time

. . . . days

(v) Final sedimentation tanks

Design loadings		No. and dimensions	
Design flow Surface loading Solids loading Detention time	. . . . . m³/d . . m³/m².d . . kg/m².d . . . . hours	No. of tanks	. . . .
		Diameter Side-wall depth Bottom slope	. . . . m . . . . m . . . . °
Weir loading rate	. . . m³/m.d	Weir length	. . . . m

(vi) Return sludge pumps

	Theoretical requirements		
	SVI(mL/g)	Sewage flow (ML/d)	RAS flow (ML/d)
Maximum Minimum Normal	. . . .	. . . .	. . . .

H2 *Trickling filters*

(i) Trickling filters

Design factors	No. and dimensions	
Organic Loading	No. of filters	. . . .
. . . . kg BOD/m³.d	Volume	. . . . m³
Hydraulic Loading at ADWF	Depth	. . . . m
	Diameter	. . . . m
. . . . m³/m².d		
Recirculation factor . . . . to 1		

(i) Humus tanks

Design loadings		No. and dimensions	
Design flow	. . . . m³/d	No. of tanks	. . . .
Surface loading	. . . . m³/m².d		
Detention time	. . . . hours	Diameter	. . . . m
		Side-wall depth	. . . . m
Weir loading		Bottom slope	. . . . °
rate	. . . . m³/m²d	Weir length	. . . .

I *Tertiary treatment*

(i) Granular media filters

Design factors		No. and dimensions	
Media:		No. of filters	. . . .
Design flow	. . . . m³/d	Length	. . . . m
Loading rate	. . . . m³/m².d	Width	. . . . m
Backwash rate	. . . . m³/m².d	Backwash flow	. . . . L/s

(ii) Disinfection

(a) Chlorination contact tank

Design factors		No. and dimensions	
Design flow	. . . . . . × ADWF	No. of tanks	. . . .
	. . . . m³d		
Detention	. . . . min.	Length	. . . . m
		Width	. . . . m
Volume	. . . . m³	Depth	. . . . m

(b) Chlorine dosing

Chlorine residual required . . . . mg/l

	Flow rate	Chlorine dose	Chlorine required
ADWF	. . . . m³/d	. . . . mg/L	. . . . kg/d
3ADWF	. . . . m³/d	. . . . mg/L	. . . . kg/d
PWWF	. . . . m³/d	. . . . mg/L	. . . . kg/d

J *Sludge treatment and disposal*

(i) Sludge production

Sludge type	Volatile solids	Volume
Primary Secondary	.... kg/d .... kg/d	.... L/d .... L/d
Total	.... kg/d	.... L/d

(ii) Anaerobic digesters

(a) Primary

Design factors		No. and dimensions	
Volatile solids loading	.... kg vs/m³.d	No. of tanks	....
Total volume	.... m³	Side-wall depth Centre depth	.... m .... m
Detention	.... d	Diameter	.... m

(b) Secondary

		No. of tanks	....
		Side-wall depth	.... m
Total volume	.... m³	Centre depth	.... m
Detention	.... d	Diameter	.... m

(iii) Sludge disposal

(a) Lagoons

Design factors		No. and dimensions	
Volume per capita	.... m³	No.	....
Side batters	⊿	Depth Length Width	.... m .... m .... m
Total volume	.... m³	Surface area	.... m²

(b) Drying beds

Area per capita	.... m²	No. of beds	....
Total area	.... m²	Length Width	.... m .... m

Review questions

14.1 Describe the sewage flow and quality data required for the design of a sewage treatment works incorporating grit removal, primary settling and activated sludge stages. What is the significance of each of the items in the data in respect to the proportioning of the treatment units?

14.2 Outline the objectives of sewage pretreatment, and the methods which may be used to attain those objectives.

14.3 Discuss the various types of screen and grit chamber which may be used to remove large objects and grit from sewage prior to primary sedimentation.

14.4 Explain the significance of detention time, forward velocity, surface loading rate and weir loading rate in the design of sedimentation tanks for sewage treatment.

14.5 Explain the probable fate of dissolved organic matter which is fed into an activated sludge system.

14.6 Derive Eqs 14.16, 14.18 and 14.19 from the information shown on the graphs in Fig 14.9.

14.7 Discuss and compare the methods of maintaining the dissolved oxygen to ensure continued aerobic conditions in activated sludge processes.

14.8 Explain some of the disadvantages of the conventional activated sludge process, and describe the essential features of modifications which have been made to improve operation in some situations.

14.9 Explain the operation of aerated lagoons and oxidation ponds. In what conditions can either of these types of treatment be appropriate?

14.10 Compare the method of operating a trickling filter with that of an activated sludge plant. Considering first cost and power consumption, comment on the probable future development of fixed-film processes.

14.11 Discuss the circumstances in which anaerobic processes may be economically used in sewage treatment, having regard to both the generally slow rate of anaerobic reactions and the avoidance of the need to provide dissolved oxygen.

14.12 If the quality of the effluent from secondary treatment is not good enough for discharge in some specific situation, such as into a stream in a recreation reserve, what further steps can be taken to upgrade the effluent?

15 Industrial Water Supply and Wastewater Treatment

15.1 Introduction

The water supply and wastewater treatment and disposal systems of most communities involve the supply of water to industrial premises and the treatment and disposal of industrial liquid wastes. The industrial load on the systems in regard to quantity and quality, and their variation with time, may have significant effects on the design and operation of these systems. Industrial processes are subject to regulations imposed by public health authorities, particularly in the food and beverage industries, and by sewerage authorities in regard to the quality of wastes discharged to the sewers, and/or by authorities empowered to maintain surface water quality.

Some industrial processes may require pretreatment of water drawn from the municipal system or treatment of a particular internal water stream for a specific water use. In this chapter, some of the problems of industrial water supply and wastewater treatment are discussed.

While the water used by all industrial consumers may amount to a significant percentage of the total supply, the amount used by each individual industrial concern is usually small. For example, a large factory using 5000 m³/d would represent, in terms of water supply and wastewater treatment and disposal, a population equivalent of less than 20000. Compared with the requirements of a city of several hundred thousand or more people, this is a small load. Hence the scale of the majority of industrial treatment processes required at the individual factory would be considerably smaller than that of a city's treatment works.

The variations in municipal water supply and wastewater flow rates can be predicted from established diurnal and seasonal patterns and, for large systems, the distribution and collection systems act as storage buffers, smoothing out the variations in the demand, in the flow rates and in the quality of the wastewater. On the other hand, demands and discharge flow rates for individual factories are more variable over a 24-hour period. A plant may operate intermittently or for one or two shifts, so that the water demand and the quality and quantity of wastewater may be subject to wide variation.

The opening or closing of a factory, or the introduction or the cessation of a process, can cause sudden changes in the average water demand and the average flow and quality of the wastewater from an industrial site. This can be contrasted with the gradual changes which take place in domestic demand and wastewater characteristics. For example, water demand per head tends to increase and phosphate concentrations have increased in domestic wastewaters with the advent of detergents which have partly replaced traditional soaps. These changes are relatively slow, particularly when compared with the changes from industrial sites.

The differences between industrial and municipal water demands and wastewater generation tend to influence the choice of treatment processes for waters and wastewaters and the operation of these processes. For some industrial sites, the treatment processes can be operated effectively on a discontinuous basis, but municipal plants usually operate continuously. The smaller size of industrial treatment plants and the uncertainty of continuity of manufacturing processes make it economic to provide less massive and less durable methods of construction. Thus, while the majority of municipal plants are constructed as inground units of concrete, designed to be serviceable for several decades, industrial plants are more likely to be above ground and to rely upon lighter weight construction materials such as steel or plastics. The life of the plant is likely to be dictated by the expected commercial viability of the manufactured product.

The other major factor is an economic one. Industrial operations are established to make a profit. *From a purely economic standpoint*, the treatment of wastewater represents unproductive capital and often involves a commitment of manpower and running costs. While in certain cases some return is possible in terms of water re-use or material recovery, most industrial wastewater treatment is carried out for non-economic reasons. The requirements of maintaining or establishing a 'clean' environment have resulted in the formation of statutory bodies which control effluent discharges. The conventionally-accepted criterion that the 'pollutor pays' for wastewater treatment (in the first instance) has meant that many industrial companies are now required to carry out some form of wastewater treatment on the premises.

The degree of treatment required for water used in industrial processes, and for the wastewater generated, is a function of the use to be made of the water by the industry and the subsequent uses to be made of the stream which receives the wastewater. It is at these points that interaction between municipal and industrial processes and treatment becomes most important. In many cases, municipal drinking water supplies are used for industrial purposes, even if the water is of higher quality than actually required (see Section 15.2). Some wastewaters are re-used within the industrial site, with or without additional treatment; most are discharged to sewers or to surface waters. For internal use, it is most convenient to re-use water for a process which requires a lower water quality. Unless the water is likely to contact a product governed by an outside authority, such as one responsible for health standards in the food and beverage industries, the quality standards and treatment processes tend to be internal issues for a particular industrial site. If the industrial wastewater is to be discharged to a sewer for eventual treatment at a municipal wastewater treatment plant, the discharge to the sewer is controlled by the municipal authority that operates the sewers and treatment plant. The requirements for discharge to the sewer are less stringent than for discharge to surface waters (see Section 15.3). If the industrial wastewater must be treated before being permitted to enter a sewer or water body, it probably contains either toxins or inhibitors or is highly polluting. The wastewater treatment processes are designed to remove toxins and inhibitors or to reduce the pollutional load from a high level to that comparable with domestic wastewaters. The plants to reduce organic loads are usually designed for loading factors higher than for municipal plants discharging to surface waters. If the industrial wastewaters are discharged to a watercourse or body of water, the quality of the effluent will be controlled by a regulatory body. The standards for effluent quality and treatment processes are similar to those for municipal treatment processes, but with a greater emphasis on removal of toxic or inhibitory materials which result from industrial processes.

As industrial concerns usually have to buy water used on a site and may be charged or suffer penalties if they do not treat their wastewaters to the appropriate standard, there is an increasing tendency to re-use waters within a site and, therefore, the segregation of wastewater streams is very important. The separation of highly-polluted water which will require treatment and 'clean' wastewater minimises the cost of any wastewater treatment plant and maximises the possible savings of water re-use. These factors will reduce any adverse impact industrial development may have on municipal water supply and wastewater treatment.

It is not intended that this chapter will provide a detailed description of all industrial water and wastewater treatment processes. The diversity of industrial operations, as opposed to domestic operations, precludes all but a brief introductory description of some industrial treatment processes. The following sections provide illustrations of the previous statements regarding industrial treatment, particularly the difference between industrial and municipal practice and the mutual interaction of the two practices. They are largely descriptive, and do not give detailed design information.

15.2 Industrial water quality and treatment

The quality of water required for industrial processes reflects the uses made of the water. In general terms, industrial waters are required to be non-corrosive, low in suspended solids and low in microscopic life, with a minimum of colour and turbidity. The quality of water required for many industrial processes is clearly not as high as that for drinking water. For certain processes, such as cooling and washing down, this water merely has to satisfy these general standards. For many industrial processes, especially those concerned with the food and beverage industries where the water can contact or be included in materials for human consumption, the quality must be similar to or better than that required for drinking water. Certain industries require particular water qualities. In beer making, it is necessary to extract flavouring agents from hops, and this is facilitated if there are significant amounts of calcium and magnesium in the water; if the water is soft, it is therefore preferable for calcium and magnesium salts to be added. The standards and treatment required vary from industry to industry and from location to location but, generally, the treatment processes are similar to those employed for domestic treatment.

Water to be used in boilers may require special treatment. Water in boilers will be heated and the major criteria are the prevention of scale formation and corrosion within the boiler. Heating water which contains temporary hardness leads to the formation of calcium carbonate deposits, which seriously affect the performance of the boilers. Boiler waters therefore require the hardness to be low, and softening is usually necessary. The higher the operating pressure of the boiler, the more stringent are the requirements. High-pressure boilers require control of the silica concentration (< 0.5 mg/L). Conditioning agents can be added to further inhibit scale formation. It is also necessary to ensure that the waters are non-corrosive; this is partially achieved if alkaline conditions (pH 7 to 8) are maintained. The other major control for corrosion is to remove oxygen which is required for many corrosion processes. Oxygen can be removed by preheating and spraying the water at an elevated temperature ($> 100°C$) or lower temperatures under a vacuum, so that atmospheric gases dissolved in water are expelled (O_2 and CO_2 are of most concern). Oxygen can be removed by chemical means; the most common reagents are sodium sulphite (Na_2SO_3) and hydrazine (N_2H_4), both of which react chemically with oxygen.

It should be stressed that the re-use of industrial waters within a plant, and the use of lower quality waters for certain processes, can make significant economic savings. Application of good housekeeping techniques and effective wastewater segregation is often a critical factor in industrial management of water and wastewater. Excessive use of water, for example in washing down plants or premises, combined with poor segregation, entails paying for the water and for treatment and/or disposal of the resulting wastewater.

15.3 Industrial wastewater treatment

The treatment of industrial wastewaters is usually carried out to meet standards for discharge either to a watercourse or to the sewers. The standards required for discharge to a watercourse are similar to those for municipal plants, minimising oxygen demand, solids and toxin loadings to the watercourse. Discharge to the sewers is limited by factors which affect the health and safety of persons working in the sewers, the structural strength of the sewers and the treatability of the wastewater on arrival at the treatment works. Typical standards for wastewater discharge to sewers limit the discharge rate, BOD_5^{20} and SS (< 600 mg/L) to prevent overloading the capacity of the sewers or treatment plant. For similar reasons, limits are imposed on grease, oil and nitrogen compounds. Controls on the discharge of harmful, explosive, toxic or potentially toxic materials, acids and alkalis, sulphide, cyanide, toxic metals and herbicides are to prevent hazard to personnel in the sewers and prevent inhibition of treatment processes. Other standards are required to protect the structure of the sewers, such as that for sulphate (< 1000 mg/L) and pH (6 to 10).

The wide range of industrial manufacturing processes employed yield a wide range of wastewaters. It is not the aim of this book to present detailed discussion of the treatment required for all types of wastewater; the treatment of a few representative types will be discussed. Even within this restricted group, individual practices or local conditions can modify wastewater characteristics or treatment methods. The following sections refer to oily wastewaters, wastewaters which contain toxic metals and cyanide, and wastewaters from the food and beverage industries. The examples cover a high percentage of industrial wastewaters and illustrate certain general principles.

15.4 Oil-water separation

The widespread use of oil as a fuel and of oil-based products produces large volumes of oil-water mixtures. An oil-water mixture containing a small amount of oil may be stable as an emulsion, which is a suspension of one liquid in another liquid, in this case oil in water. Oils are composed of long-chain hydrocarbon molecules. The hydrocarbon structure is non-polar and has little affinity for the polar structure of water molecules. The molecules in oils therefore tend to group together, forming oil layers if in large amounts, and small spheres if a small amount is dispersed in water. A sphere of oil minimises the surface contact with the water, for which the oil has no affinity. In order to maintain a high concentration of oil in water, the emulsion must be stabilised. This is achieved by the addition of compounds such as detergents, containing a large hydrocarbon tail, which has affinity for the oil, and a polar 'head' which can align with the surrounding water. In this manner, higher concentrations of oil in water can be achieved, such mixtures having an important industrial use as cutting oils, so that the treatment, disposal and/or re-use of these oils is important.

Simple oil-water mixtures which do not contain stabilisers for the emulsion

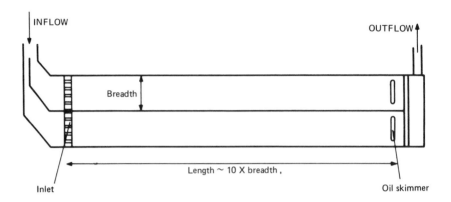

Fig 15.1 API oil separator (plan view)

can usually be separated by a flotation process. Oils tend to be less dense than water and so have a natural tendency to rise. This tendency is used in a horizontal flow separator, usually referred to as an American Petroleum Institute (API) separator (Fig 15.1). The separator permits sufficient retention time for the majority of oil droplets to reach the surface and coalesce before being discharged; the general concepts are similar to those outlined for horizontal settlement tanks in Chapter 8, except that they rely on flotation rather than settlement of the oil.

The flotation process can be modified by the installation of a series of inclined parallel plates which provide a shorter rise for the oil droplets. On reaching a plate, they coalesce and can be collected at the upper edge (Fig 15.2). As the distance required for the droplets to rise is less than in a horizontal flow system, parallel plate systems are more compact. The general principles of this system are similar to the settlement units described in Chapter 8. The plates are constructed with corrugations so that oil or solids are removed at points of optimum flow.

The velocity of rise of the oil droplets can be increased if bubbles of air can be attached to the oil droplets. Air flotation methods rely on releasing small air bubbles in the solution. The air bubble-oil droplets rise rapidly to the surface, where the oil can be collected. The process is described in Section 8.5. The successful application of this technique depends on the ability of the air bubbles to adhere to the oil droplets, and it therefore depends upon the characteristics of the oil.

Stabilised oil-water emulsions require chemical treatment to break the physical and chemical structure of the emulsion. The addition of a coagulant or acidification is often sufficient to separate the oil and water fractions. This process is usually referred to as *cracking* the emulsion. Once cracked, the oil

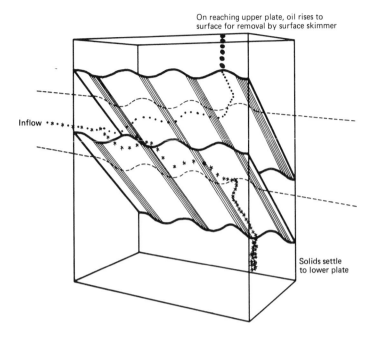

On reaching upper plate, oil rises to
surface for removal by surface skimmer

Inflow

Solids settle
to lower plate

Fig 15.2 Schematic representation of oil and solids/separation in a corrugated plate interceptor *(Courtesy: Environmental Engineering Pty Ltd)*

can be removed by the processes already described. The quantity of acid required to crack a particular emulsion depends on its inherent stability. Simple oil-water-detergent emulsions can be cracked at a pH of approximately 5, while oil-water mixtures formulated to form a stable emulsion may require pH < 2. Discharge standards usually specify an effluent close to neutral pH, and so it is necessary to readjust the pH of the water phase prior to discharge.

The oil layers which are produced by these separation processes can usually be removed by a surface skimming device and the oil can then be processed, recycled or disposed of. The relative ease of combustion of oils makes incineration a useful disposal method.

15.5 Wastewaters containing toxic metals and cyanide

Many metallic ions (Cu, Zn, Hg, Cd, Cr, Pb . . .) are toxic, and are therefore not suitable for waterborne discharge. The specified discharge limit is often below 1 mg/L for any single toxic metal. Despite their potential toxicity, many of these metals are widely used and particular industries rely on solutions of the metallic ions. Electroplating processes are employed to provide a range of goods such as automobile components and printed board circuitry for the electronics industry. The wastewaters from these processes contain toxic metals, often as a mixture of metallic ions in acidic solution. Cyanide formulations are employed in several industries, including electroplating. Cyanide solutions are maintained in alkaline solution to prevent the evolution of the poisonous gas hydrogen cyanide (HCN).

As an illustration of a possible treatment scheme, consider the processes required to treat an alkaline cyanide wastewater stream and a stream which contains chromium in the hexavalent form (Cr^{6+}) and copper and zinc ions. Small concentrations of cyanide ions can be oxidised by micro-organisms. As cyanide ions (CN^-) are composed only of carbon and nitrogen, microbial oxidation produces innocuous carbon and nitrogen compounds. The high concentration of cyanide in industrial wastewaters usually necessitates a chemical oxidation process. Strong chemical oxidants like chlorine, hydrogen peroxide and ozone will detoxify cyanide into innocuous products. The overall reaction (Eq 15.1) between cyanide ions and chlorine produces gaseous nitrogen, carbon dioxide and chloride ions.

$$2CN^- + 5Cl_2 + 8OH^- \rightleftharpoons 10Cl^- + 2CO_2 + N_2 + 4H_2O \qquad (15.1)$$

Some of the products of this reaction are gaseous, and the reaction will go almost completely to the right-hand side (see Section 5.4). The residual cyanide concentration after a reasonable reaction time will be very small.

Many toxic metal ions can be precipitated as their hydroxides. The

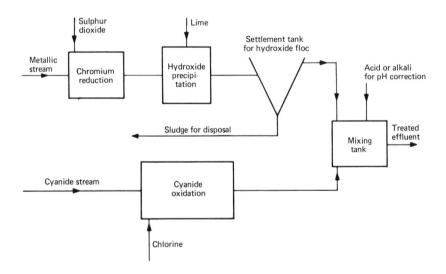

Fig 15.3 Schematic representation of the treatment of toxic metal and cyanide wastewaters

solubility product (K_{sp}) of copper hydroxide is 1×10^{-20}, and of zinc hydroxide 3×10^{-17}. In both cases, most of the metal will be precipitated if the hydroxide ion (OH^-) concentration is high (see Section 5.4). Therefore, if the pH of the wastewaters is raised by adding alkali, the toxic metals precipitate. Lime ($Ca(OH)_2$) is usually the most suitable alkali. Chromium present as hexavalent chromium (Cr^{6+}) does not precipitate under normal high pH conditions. It is necessary to reduce the hexavalant chromium to trivalent chromium (Cr^{3+}), which does form an insoluble hydroxide ($K_{sp} = 1 \times 10^{-30}$). The reduction is conveniently carried out with sulphur dioxide or sodium bisulphate. The overall treatment of a toxic metal and cyanide wastewater is summarised in Fig 15.3.

The precipitated mixed metal hydroxide ($Cr + Zn + Cu$, in this case) can be withdrawn and further dewatered, for example in a filter press; the dewatered sludge requires safe disposal. The toxic metals cannot be fully detoxified as can cyanide ions; they can be converted to a form more suitable for disposal and may return to more toxic states if not adequately controlled.

15.6 Wastewaters from the food and beverage industries

Many industries involved in the production of foods and beverages produce effluents which require separate treatment and/or disposal. The manufacturing processes are diverse and produce a range of possible effluent characteristics. Certain industries are present in many locations (abattoirs, soft drink manufacture); others tend to be found mainly in urban areas (breweries), or near particular geographical locations (distilleries, fruit and vegetable processing), while some products are relatively specialised and are made at only a limited number of locations.

The methods of wastewater treatment which have been outlined in previous chapters are usually applicable to wastewaters from the food and beverage industries. The materials in the wastewaters tend to be of 'natural' origin and so tend to be degradable and amenable to biological treatment. Particular wastewaters may contain an excess or a deficiency of specific nutrient material for useful microbiological growth. Wastewaters from the production of soft drinks or canned fruit are likely to contain a high percentage of carbohydrates (sugar) and a low percentage of protein. These wastewaters contain little nitrogen and phosphorus, and therefore biological growth in such media is below optimum and favours species which require little nitrogen and phosphorus — usually species such as fungi, which have poor settlement characteristics. It is therefore advisable to add sources of nitrogen and phosphorus to provide a reasonable balance between the carbon, nitrogen and phosphorus and to encourage the growth of species with good settling properties. This can often be achieved by mixing with domestic wastewater.

The wastewaters can be much stronger than domestic wastewaters: suspended solids and BOD_5^{20} concentrations greater than 1000 mg/L are not uncommon. It is often necessary therefore to carry out roughing processes, which receive very high loads and reduce the strength of the wastewaters towards that of domestic wastewaters. In certain industries, this reduction can be achieved by recovery of a saleable by-product; fats can be recovered and reprocessed for consumption or for use as tallow; grains and yeast from fermentation processes can be used as animal or human foodstuffs. In all cases, removal and recycling are facilitated if internal wastewater streams are segregated. This minimises the contamination of potentially useful materials, reduces the volume of wastewater which requires treatment and often prevents pollution of wastewater by toxic materials.

Some of these principles are illustrated in the treatment of abattoir wastewaters. These reflect the practices within the abattoir, the number and type of animals killed and processed, and the extent of segregation of flows. Wastewater may contain approximately 3000 mg/L BOD_5^{20} and 1000 mg/L fat and grease, together with appreciable amounts of nitrogen and blood. The treatment possible for such a sample depends on the location of the abattoir. In a non-urban area, distant from habitation and where there is adequate sunlight, a series of oxidation ponds can provide adequate treatment. The first of the ponds is designed as an anaerobic pond to remove high oxygen demands; later ponds are facultative to provide an acceptable effluent (Chapter 11) and the effluent may be disposed of by irrigation. Such a system requires considerable land areas and the anaerobic ponds are prone to give offensive odours; but they provide a low-cost method of treatment.

Abattoir wastewaters can be treated in a compact scheme without producing odours, as is illustrated in Fig 15.4. The screening processes are to remove large objects from the wastewater flow and air flotation is to remove fats and some suspended solids. The wastewater is acidified (to pH 5) to facilitate fat/water separation (subsequent neutralisation is needed) and treated with polyelectrolyte to aid separation and flotation to remove the fat. The process is operated by dissolving air under pressure in a portion of the flow. When this portion is mixed with the main stream and returned to atmospheric pressure the dissolved air is forced out of solution, releasing small air bubbles. These tend to form on the available particles in the sample (fat globules and suspended solids); the particles and air bubbles will then rise to the surface, where they can be collected.

The fat which accumulates on the surface can be removed for reprocessing or disposal. An air flotation unit is relatively compact; the retention time is of the order of 30 minutes and the effluent from the flotation would be low in fat and grease content and would have a BOD_5^{20} of approximately 2000 mg/L.

The removal of fats makes the wastewater suitable for conventional biological treatment, and either fixed-film or suspended-growth processes can be employed. The processes are designed and operated according to the

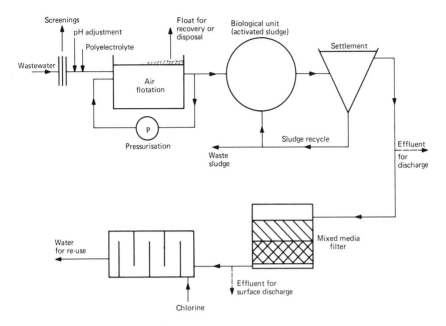

Fig 15.4 Schematic representation of a system for the treatment of wastewaters from an abattoir (major processes only)

principles outlined in Chapter 11. If the effluent is to be discharged to a sewer, the biological and settlement stages would be designed as a roughing process, reducing the effluent to a BOD_5^{20} and an SS of less than 600 mg/L. If a higher quality effluent is required, a larger capacity is necessary in the biological stage; or a two-stage biological process may be needed, in which a roughing process is followed by a conventionally loaded process. The former alternative is less expensive to construct but would not produce as reliable an effluent quality as a two-stage process. The effluents from the aerobic biological process followed by settlement would contain suspended solids and a BOD_5^{20} of between 15 and 50 mg/L, depending on the loading to the units. The effluent quality is therefore suitable for ocean discharge and will approach that suitable for discharge to surface waters. Filtration will further improve the quality of the effluent. Rapid sand filters and/or multimedia filters remove most of the remaining suspended solids and the associated BOD_5^{20}. This water would now be suitable for disinfection by chlorine and re-use.

The processes required are therefore dictated by the intended fate of the effluent — discharge to a sewer, to the sea, to surface water, to irrigation, or re-use. The separated solids include screenings, which have no value and are dumped, fats, which can be processed and represent a valuable by-product (tallow), and waste biological sludge which requires dewatering and disposal.

15.7 Conclusions

The interaction between industrial water use and the subsequent generation of wastewater reflects the type of industrial processes being carried out. Industries tend to be situated near centres of population, and so have access to municipal water supply and sewer systems, or they are required to produce a high quality effluent to prevent pollution of surface water. The supply of water and the treatment and disposal of wastewaters should therefore be considered as an integrated whole, not as separate units. The nature of manufacturing processes as compared with the domestic 'operations' which consume water and generate wastewater lead to differences of scale and of operation between industrial and domestic practices; the underlying principles are nevertheless similar.

Review questions

15.1 What are the differences between the characteristics of industrial and domestic wastewaters?

15.2 Why are restrictions placed on the discharge of industrial wastes to municipal sewers?

15.3 What advantages can be gained by internal re-use of waters within an industrial site?

15.4 Why is oxygen removed from boiler feedwater?

15.5 Why are plate interceptors efficient oil separation units?

15.6 What problems may be encountered in the treatment of wastewaters from the following processes? How could these problems be overcome?
   i Sugar refining
   ii Machinery degreasing
   iii Copper plating
   iv Machining of metals
   v Manufacture of sulphuric acid
   vi Preparation of fresh turkeys for sale at Christmas.

16 Advanced Wastewater Treatment and Reclamation

16.1 Objectives of advanced wastewater treatment

Tertiary treatment of wastewaters followed by disinfection can give good removal of BOD, SS and bacteria (Chapter 14), but the effluents may still contain other impurities which could either cause problems in receiving waters, or interfere with some subsequent uses of those waters. These impurities include: nutrients, such as various forms of inorganic nitrogen (30 to 60 mg/L) and phosphorus (5 to 20 mg/L), residual dissolved organic compounds (15 to 30 mg/L as organic carbon), including surfactants (0.5 to 5 mg/L), and dissolved inorganic salts (400 to 800 mg/L of total dissolved solids, TDS). Methods of removing these impurities are usually classified as Advanced Wastewater Treatment. Some typical AWT processes are discussed below; because these processes add so much to the cost of wastewater treatment, it is only in exceptional circumstances that they are used. Where AWT is required, however, it may often be more economical to reclaim the resulting high-quality effluent for some form of direct re-use, rather than simply to discharge it to the environment.

16.2 Nitrogen control and removal

Nitrogen is present in raw sewage mainly as organic nitrogen and ammonia, much of which results from hydrolysis of urea, a major constituent of urine. In biological treatment, some of this nitrogen is incorporated in new cell growth and is removed as biological sludge, while most of the remaining nitrogen is discharged in the plant effluent. This effluent nitrogen may be either in the form of ammonia or, depending on conditions in the plant, in the oxidised form, nitrate, and to a lesser extent, nitrite. Some organic nitrogen also remains in the effluent, mainly in the suspended solids. Tertiary processes designed to remove suspended solids therefore remove much of the organic nitrogen but have little effect on the dissolved ammonia, nitrite and nitrate. Table 16.1 summarises the microbial transformations in the nitrogen

Table 16.1 Nitrogen transformations and removal

Form of nitrogen	Responsible micro-organisms	Representative equations	Control and removal process
Organic – N (Protein) ↓	Aerobic Heterotrophs	See Sections 4.3, 4.4	Ammonia stripping Breakpoint chlorination Ion exchange
Ammonia – N NH_3 ↓	Aerobic Autotrophs *Nitrosomonas*	$2NH_3 + 3O_2 \longrightarrow 2NO_2^- + 2H^+ + 2H_2O$	Biological nitrification for control
Nitrite – N NO_2^- ↓	*Nitrobacter*	$2NO_2^- + O_2 \longrightarrow 2NO_3^-$	
Nitrate – N NO_3^- ↓	Anaerobic Heterotrophs	$3NO_3^- + CH_3OH \longrightarrow 3NO_2^- + 2H_2O + CO_2$	Biological denitrification for removal
Nitrite – N NO_2^- ↓		$2NO_2^- + CH_3OH \longrightarrow N_2 + H_2O + 2OH^- + CO_2$	
Nitrogen gas N_2			

cycle as they affect nitrogen control and removal. The biological secondary treatment process must be operated to control the form in which the nitrogen appears in the effluent so as to suit the nitrogen removal process adopted.

Ammonia stripping

Ammonia stripping involves raising the pH to about 11 (see Section 8.4), usually by addition of lime and passing the effluent down through a tower somewhat similar to a cooling tower, while forcing ammonia-free air upwards through it. The resulting effluent ammonia concentration is reduced but is usually greater than 2 mg/L. Ammonia stripping is successful only at temperatures well above freezing point.

Breakpoint chlorination

Breakpoint chlorination can also be used for removing ammonia nitrogen. By dosing with chlorine to the breakpoint (see equations in Chapter 10), most of the ammonia nitrogen is converted to gaseous and other volatile compounds which are driven off. The chlorine dose required to reach the breakpoint, however, is about 10 times the concentration of ammonia nitrogen present. To remove concentrations of up to 20 to 30 mg/L of NH_3-N would therefore require about 200 to 300 mg/L of chlorine, obviously economically prohibitive for any but a very small flow or in an emergency situation. The most likely application of this process is in removing small residual ammonia concentrations following other processes such as ammonia stripping.

Ion exchange

Ion exchange uses clinoptilolite, a natural zeolite mineral which preferentially takes up NH_4^+ ions from solution in the presence of other cations. From available reports, it seems to be too expensive to compete with other processes at present.

Denitrification

Denitrification, following *biological nitrification*, is the process widely regarded as offering the most economical and efficient method of nitrogen removal (Table 16.1). *Nitrification* involves the action of two types of autotrophic, chemosynthetic bacteria to oxidise ammonia nitrogen sequentially through nitrite to nitrate. Simplified equations for these oxidations are given in Table 16.1. For nitrification to be maintained, the net growth rate of biomass should not exceed that of the nitrifying organisms; otherwise, the nitrifying organisms will be washed out of the system. From the fact that net growth rate is equal to the reciprocal of mean cell residence time, θ_c, the condition for nitrification is then given by

$$\frac{1}{\theta_c} \leqslant \frac{1}{\theta_{cN}} \text{ or } \theta_{cN} \leqslant \theta_c$$

where θ_{cN} represents the critical mean cell residence time for maintaining nitrifying organisms in the system.

In general, reasonable nitrification can be achieved in activated sludge systems having $\theta_c > 10$ days and $F/M < 0.3$, provided that the environmental requirements of temperature, pH and absence of toxins are satisfied.

For those situations where simply converting the ammonia nitrogen to the oxidised form is not considered adequate, the further stage of *biological denitrification* for removing the oxidised nitrogen may be required (see Table 16.1). This is effected by normal aerobic heterotrophic organisms under anoxic conditions. These organisms, which use molecular DO as the electron acceptor in their respiration processes under normal conditions, are able to use the oxygen from nitrate and nitrite for this purpose if molecular oxygen is absent (Section 4.4).

Under denitrifying conditions, the organisms also require a source of carbon, represented in the equations as methanol. This source can also be raw sewage. The denitrification rate is affected by temperature, pH and the nitrate concentration itself. Denitrification, which may be carried out either in a submerged filter or in a suspended growth reactor, restores about half the alkalinity used in the process of nitrification.

16.3 Removal of phosphorus

Phosphorus is present in raw wastewaters in various organic and inorganic forms, both in solution and in suspension. Soluble forms include inorganic orthophosphates and condensed phosphates and some organic orthophosphates. Biological treatment results in such a transformation that 50 to 90 per cent of the total phosphorus remaining in the effluent is in soluble orthophosphate form, which is more readily available for organism growth and is easier to remove by chemical treatment.

The main process used for phosphorus removal is *chemical precipitation*, although some *biological methods* have also been suggested.

Chemical precipitation

Chemical precipitation using lime, iron or aluminium salts may be carried out by dosing (a) prior to primary sedimentation, (b) into the aeration tanks of activated sludge systems, or (c) after secondary sedimentation. The most commonly used process is *lime precipitation*, either in the primary sedimentation tanks or after secondary sedimentation. The optimum pH for lime precipitation is 10.5 to 11.5. The dose required to raise the pH to this level depends mainly on the alkalinity of the wastewater, rather than on the phosphorus content. Such a high pH is not suitable for subsequent biological treatment, but it is ideal for ammonia stripping. Thus, the high pH lime process has been used in AWT as a method of phosphorus removal in conjunction with air stripping of ammonia. Lime precipitation in primary sedimentation has the advantage that it does not need an additional clarifier for settling out the precipitate, but additional complexity is introduced in treating the mixed chemical and organic sludge. In the process, the pH is raised only to about 9, and iron salts may also be added to improve the settling properties of the precipitate. Trivalent iron and aluminium salts may be used to precipitate soluble phosphorus as ferric or aluminium phosphate under slightly acid conditions (pH 5 to 6).

Some further aspects of lime and the various iron and aluminium salts and other compounds, such as polymers, which may be used in wastewater treatment as well as in water treatment, are discussed in Chapter 9. Details of some chemical dosing systems are given in Chapter 13.

Biological removal

Biological phosphorus removal in conventional wastewater treatment generally occurs only to the extent that phosphorus is taken up in new cell growth and removed from the system with the excess biological sludge. Maximum removal by this means is normally only 20 per cent. Although removals of up to 90 per cent have been reported in a number of activated sludge plants, this is believed to be the result of various precipitation phenomena rather than true biological uptake. Removals of over 90 per cent have been achieved in an adaptation of the activated sludge process developed for combined biological phosphorus and nitrogen removal. In this system, the reactor is divided into four compartments in series, providing for an anoxic zone at the inlet end (3 hours' detention), an aerobic carbonaceous oxidation/nitrification zone (6 hours), a further anoxic denitrification zone (2 hours) and a final re-aeration zone (1 hour).

16.4 Removal of residual organics

Where effluent is to be reclaimed for high quality use, it is often necessary to remove as much of the residual organic matter as possible. This is usually achieved by *activated carbon adsorption* although, where otherwise required for removing inorganic dissolved solids, some *desalination* processes are also effective in reducing small amounts of organic matter. Removal of surfactants (detergents) can be achieved by *foam fractionation*. With the introduction of soft detergents there is seldom any need for separate removal of these materials. Activated carbon adsorption is similar to that discussed in Section 13.9. In advanced wastewater treatment, carbon adsorption is usually the final treatment operation (other than disinfection) to ensure that as much of the suspended and dissolved organic matter as possible has been removed by other processes.

16.5 Removal of dissolved inorganic salts

Each cycle of municipal water use normally results in an increase of 300 to 400 mg/L in TDS over that of the water supply to the area, a factor which places a practical limit on the number of times water may be re-used for potable supply purposes (compare with the World Health Organisation drinking water standard of 500 mg/L TDS). Already, a number of communities are facing the need to reclaim sewage effluent for municipal re-use by about 1990. If this is done by returning reclaimed effluent to the common municipal water supply system, the maximum rate of effluent recycle which would be possible without a gradual build-up of the TDS content would be about 50 per cent of the wastewater flow.

Where a greater rate of recycle is necessary, *desalination* will be required to control salt build-up. Similar processes to those discussed in Chapter 13 are applicable to wastewater desalination. *Reverse osmosis* has been used for AWT. It requires very careful pretreatment to prevent fouling of the membranes. *Distillation* processes also require special attention to the avoidance of scale formation as well as to corrosion problems.

16.6 Reclamation

Industries in some countries use water several times over. The increase of water re-use as a general practice is brought about by economic pressures due to the increased price of water owing to scarcity or difficulty of collection and transmission, or the increased price of effluent disposal. In recent times, many interested people have expressed concern not only for the environmental effects of water storage and diversion to provide for the needs of the ever-growing cities, but also for the effective disposal of the resulting wastes from the houses and factories which those cities contain. This concern is about the amount of water which must be collected so that the needs of the communities can be met, and pollution of water by the effluents from the cities.

Water re-use is an obvious way to reduce the amount of water which must be extracted from the surface water sources. It should not be introduced for domestic supply without a prior detailed understanding of the health and other hazards which may occur. Municipal wastes have been treated and directly re-used as domestic supply, both under emergency conditions when the regular water supply was interrupted, and under regular conditions in desert areas where the amount of surface and groundwater has proved inadequate for growing cities.

Although there may be no apparent ill-effects where sewage is treated and pumped back into the city's water supply mains, there are some unanswered questions about the probable effects of long-term exposure to trace amounts of the chemicals which are not removed by the treatment. In addition, such a system requires constant vigilance on the part of the engineers and plant operators to ensure the proper treatment and production of a safe drinking water.

Industrial use of treated domestic wastes has been practised for years; for example, some steel mills use treated sewage for cooling and quench water.

Indirect water re-use has been practised for many years in Europe, where the rivers receive the wastes of the towns and also serve as sources of water supply. In some cases, where there is a possibility of either illegal or accidental discharge of toxic materials, fish may be used to provide a continuous bio-assay.

In some towns where large quantities of water are used for gardening or where the available supply is scarce or of poor quality, dual or even triple water supply systems have been installed to provide water for (1) drinking and cooking, (2) laundering and ablutions, (3) gardening and (4) firefighting and WC flushing. The economics of such systems depend on the availability and quality of raw water sources, treatment costs and the amount of water used for each of the various purposes, and will therefore not be the same for all places. Where such systems are practicable, treated water from a good source may be supplied for drinking and cooking and, possibly, laundering and ablutions, but reclaimed water may be suitable for WC flushing, garden watering and firefighting.

During the last century, when the *real* price of water was much higher than it is now, water could have been used up to four times over, within the household, for non-consumptive purposes before being used for consumptive irrigation use. The amount of waste discharged was therefore at a minimum.

In a 21st-century home, it may be that automatic washing machines will be equipped with tanks for temporary storage of water so that the last rinse from one wash may be saved for the first rinse in the next wash, and the effluent from the first rinse may be used for toilet flushing or garden watering. In addition, regular arrangements may be made for using bath water or shower water for lawn watering. During droughts in some cities, the use of laundry, bath, and roof water for garden watering can be encouraged.

The cost of buying new water is often small compared with the combined cost of the inconvenience and equipment to conserve water in the household. But this may not always be so.

The most promising avenue for the limited re-use of water is to reclaim it and re-use it in the factories where it is first taken from the public supply. This is called 'in-plant re-use' of water. In this way, the water is not contaminated with a great many unknown materials before treatment for re-use.

In-plant re-use may be effected either by *direct re-use*, in which some slightly soiled waters may be used again for some purpose not requiring such a high quality, or by *re-use after treatment* in which some relatively easily treatable water may be kept separate from the general waste stream, and treated to bring it up to a standard suitable for some purpose within the factory, or by *recycling*, in which it is used again and again for the same purpose until the quality is degraded beyond acceptable limits.

Under these conditions, where a selected waste is separated for treatment for a specified purpose (unlike where mixed sewage is treated for general domestic and industrial re-use), not only are the contaminants known, but also the quality required for the specified re-use may not be as high as that for drinking water.

On the one hand, direct re-use and recycling require only a minimum of capital outlay and extremely low running costs. The possibilities should be closely examined by an industry. On the other hand, the economically desirable amount of treatment for re-use depends on the nature of the wastes, the costs of water supply and wastewater disposal, and the possibility of obtaining by-products from some of the wastes which may be recovered. In some industries, treatment to recover wastes as by-products can be financed by the sale of those products.

In planning a water reclamation project, a selection can be made from appropriate processes as described in Chapters 8 to 15. The type of treatment to be used in any particular circumstance depends on the nature and concentration of the contaminants, the purpose for which the water is to be re-used and the possibility of salvaging useful materials. There are many unexplored possibilities where re-use of water could prove to be economical.

The community benefits of re-use, apart from possible economies for individual industries and the purchasers of their products, are reduced volumes of wastewater flows (and hence less possibility of sewer overloading or stream pollution), reduced quantities of water diverted from the supply streams (and hence less environmental impact on those streams) and reduced quantities of water transmitted and distributed (and hence a lower cost of pipelines and storages).

Further Reading

For the student wishing to continue with the study of water supply and wastewater engineering, the following list of books is suggested for reference. The list is arranged alphabetically by author.

American Waterworks Association, *Water Quality and Treatment; A Handbook of Public Water Supplies*, McGraw-Hill, 3rd edn, 1971

Barnes, D. and Wilson, F., *Chemistry and Unit Operations in Sewage Treatment*, Applied Science, London, 1978

Barnes, D. and Wilson, F., *Chemistry and Unit Operations in Water Treatment*, Applied Science, 1980

Benefield, L.D. and Randall, C.W., *Biological Process Design for Wastewater Treatment*, Prentice-Hall, 1980

Bouwer, H., *Groundwater Hydrology*, McGraw-Hill, 1978

Cox, C.R., *Operation and Control of Water Treatment Processes*, WHO, 1964

Department of the Environment, *Analysis of Raw, Potable and Waste Waters*, HMSO, 1972

Fair, G.M., Geyer, J.C. and Okun, D.A., *Water and Wastewater Engineering*, 2 vols, Wiley, 1971

Grace, R.A., *Marine Outfall Systems: Planning, Design and Construction*, Prentice-Hall, 1978

Hawkes, H.A., *The Ecology of Waste Water Treatment*, Pergamon, 1963

Henderson, F.M., *Open Channel Flow*, Collier Macmillan, 1966

Holden, W.S., *Water Treatment and Examination*, Churchill, 1970

Ives, K.J. (Ed), *The Scientific Basis of Flocculation*, Sijthoff and Noordhoff, 1978

Klein, L., *River Pollution*, 3 vols, Butterworths, 1966

Linsley, R.K., Kohler, M.A. and Paulhus, J.L.H., *Hydrology for Engineers*, 2nd edn, McGraw-Hill, 1974

McKinney, R.E., *Microbiology for Sanitary Engineers*, McGraw-Hill, 1962

Metcalf and Eddy Inc., *Wastewater Engineering: Collection, Treatment, Disposal*, McGraw-Hill, 1972

Mitchell, R. (Ed), *Water Pollution Microbiology*, Wiley-Interscience, 1972

Nemerow, N., *Liquid Wastes of Industry: Theories, Practice and Treatment*, Addison-Wesley, 1971

Parker, H.W., *Wastewater Systems Engineering*, Prentice-Hall, 1972

Sawyer, C.N. and McCarty, P.L., *Chemistry for Sanitary Engineers*, 2nd edn, McGraw-Hill, 1978

Steel, E.W. and McGhee, T.J., *Water Supply and Sewerage*, 5th edn, McGraw-Hill, 1979

Stephenson, D., *Pipeline Design for Water Engineers*, Elsevier, 1976

Twort, A.C., Hoather, R.C. and Law, F.M., *Water Supply*, 2nd edn, Edward Arnold, London, 1974

Water Pollution Control Federation, *Manuals of Practice*

Webb, T. and Gould, B.W., *Water Hammer*, University of New South Wales Press, 1978

Problems

1 Water demand and sources of supply

1.1 For town A in Example 1.1, determine the errors that would have been made if, in 1940, the 1970 population had been predicted by each of the following methods

    a Geometric growth rate, based on the 1890 and 1940 populations
    b Arithmetic growth rate based on the 1920 and 1940 populations
    c Graphical extension of the 1890–1940 growth curve.
    (+ 16.5%; + 8.9%; + 12.6%)

1.2 On the assumption that the population of town A in Example 1.1 is approaching a saturation value of 23 000 in accordance with Eq 1.5, estimate the population in 1980 on the basis of the 1940 and 1970 values. (19 960)

1.3 A concrete gravity dam on the site described in Example 1.2 has its storage over a particular period of one month modified by

    a River inflow, 40.55 ML
    b Downstream release, 80 ML
    c Town water supply draft, 210.25 ML
    d Rainfall on the storage, 25 mm
    e Evaporation, 96 mm
    f Infiltration, average of 44 mm over the inundated area.

If the water level at the beginning of the period was 85.52 metres, find the level at the end of the period. (Calculate the curves in Example 1.2 and plot to a larger scale to provide an accurate answer.) (85.00)

1.4 For the portion of the mass diagram shown in Fig 1.2, what is the maximum safe rate of draft and what would be the minimum useful storage required for a reservoir to provide such a draft? What storage would be required if the draft were 85 per cent of this maximum value? (2400 ML/yr; 1000 ML; 800 ML)

1.5 The dam in Fig 1.3 has a height of 46 metres and a base width of 34 metres. When the dam is full, the thrust, T, on the base is inclined at 66° to the horizontal, cutting the base 4.5 metres downstream of the centre. Its magnitude is 25.5 MN per metre length of dam. Find the normal stresses on the foundation at the heel and the toe of the dam. (Heel stress 0.141 MPa; toe stress 1.229 MPa)

1.6 The hydraulic conductivity of a confined aquifer 28 metres in thickness is 125 m/d and its storage coefficient is 0.00055. Flow in the aquifer is steady and uniform, with a potentiometric gradient of 0.55 m/km.

   a Estimate the flow velocity and the volumetric flow rate per metre width of the aquifer
   b What volume of water would need to be pumped from the aquifer to lower the potentiometric surface by an average of 2.5 metres over an area of 20 km²?
   c What is the transmissivity of the aquifer?
   (0.069 m/d; 1.93 m³/d.m; 2.75 ML; 3500 m²/d)

1.7 The static level of the water table in an unconfined aquifer was 33.5 metres above the underlying impermeable stratum. A 150 mm well, penetrating the aquifer to its full depth, was pumped at the rate of 20 L/s. After several weeks of pumping, the drawdowns in observation wells 20 metres and 50 metres from the well were 3.55 metres and 2.27 metres, respectively, and the observed drawdowns were increasing very slowly.

   a Assuming equilibrium conditions, estimate the hydraulic conductivity and the transmissivity of the aquifer
   b Estimate the drawdown just outside the pumped well (Hint: As an approximation, take r_1 as the well radius and r_2 as the distance to either of the observation wells.)
   c What would be the yield of a 300 mm diameter well which would produce the same drawdowns just outside the well and at the 50 metre distant observation well as in b? What would be the drawdown at the nearer observation well?
   (6.44 m/d, 215.6 m²/d; 13.01 m; 22.4 L/s, 3.70 m)

1.8 If the details in problem 1.7 refer to a confined aquifer of thickness 33.5 metres after six hours of pumping, estimate K and T, assuming equilibrium conditions. (5.88 m/d, 197 m²/d)

1.9 A bore in a confined aquifer 26 metres thick is pumped at a steady rate of 28 L/s and the drawdowns in two observation wells, A and B, 96 metres and 192 metres respectively, from the bore were as follows:

Time from commencement of pumping (min)	Drawdown A (m)	Drawdown B (m)
2	0.16	0.02
4	0.23	0.06
8	0.32	0.12
15	0.42	0.18
20	0.47	0.23
30	0.53	0.29
40	0.58	0.33
60	0.64	0.40
80	0.69	0.45
100	0.72	0.48
125	0.76	0.52
150	0.79	0.55
200	0.83	0.59

Develop two estimates of the hydraulic conductivity of the aquifer material and of the transmissivity and the storage coefficient of the aquifer. (44.8 m/d, 46.7 m/d; 1165 m²/d, 1215 m²/d; 0.00021, 0.00024)

2 Transmission and distribution of water

2.1 A long, circular, concrete-lined tunnel 3 metres in diameter with a slope of 0.0010 conveys a flow of 10.24 m³/s. What are the flow depth and velocity, if n = 0.013? (Calculations are simplified if the capacity of the pipe flowing just full is determined and Fig 3.6 is used to find the part-full conditions.)
(2.10 m, 1.91 m/s)

2.2 A mortar-lined trapezoidal canal, with a bottom width of 1.50 metres and side slopes 1:1, has a bed slope of 1 in 950. If the flow depth is to be 0.75 metres, estimate the velocity and flow rate, assuming that Manning's n is 0.014. If the actual n value were (a) 0.013, (b) 0.015, find the percentage error in your estimate of the flow rate. (1.39 m/s, 2.35 m³/s; −7.14%, +7.14%)

2.3 For the canal in Problem 2.2, with a flow depth of 0.75 metres and a Manning's n of 0.014, what bed slope would result in critical depth flow? (The criterion for critical depth flow is $Q^2/g = A^3/T$, where A is the cross-sectional area and T is the top width of the flow cross-section.)
(0.0030 or 1 in 333)

2.4   Water is to be conveyed at a maximum rate of 11.5 m³/s in hilly country from a storage reservoir to a delivery point 7.90 km away, measured in a straight line. The available head is 18.0 metres. Determine the minimum conduit dimensions to the nearest 10 mm, and the corresponding velocities, for each of the following alternative forms of conduit:

a Pressure tunnel, length 7.90 km, k = 3.0 mm
b Pressure pipeline, length 8.05 km, k = 0.5 mm
c Lined canal, length 10.80 km, n = 0.020, bed-width = depth, side-slopes 1:1.
(2490 mm, 2.36 m/s; 2320 mm, 2.72 m/s; 1740 mm, 1.91 m/s)

2.5   If, in Problem 2.4, topographical and other factors require 1.5 km of circular tunnel, 2.5 km of pipeline and 4.5 km of canal:

a How should the head loss be distributed for minimum cost, assuming that the curves in Fig 2.2 apply to the above lengths of tunnel, pipeline and canal respectively?
b For this distribution, what would be the common incremental cost per metre of head loss and the total cost of the supply line?
c What would be the diameters of the tunnel and the pipeline and the depth of flow in the canal if the depth equals the bed-width and side-slopes are 1:1? What would be the velocities in the three sections of the line?
(Tunnel, 8.0 m; pipeline, 5.2 m; canal, 4.8 m; $19 000/m, $825 000; 2130 mm, 2190 mm, 2040 mm; 3.23 m/s, 3.05 m/s, 1.38 m/s)

2.6   If the cumulative curve of demand on a one-day service reservoir for the maximum daily consumption is as shown in Fig 2.3, show qualitatively, by means of sketches, a comparison between equalising storages required for a steady 24-hour supply and for a steady supply between 6 am and 8 pm.

2.7   Revise the calculations in Example 2.1 to meet the following conditions:

a Design period for service reservoir, pipeline and dam, 30 years
b Equalising storage, 25 per cent of maximum daily demand
c Emergency and fire storage, 100 per cent of average daily demand.

2.8   In Fig 2.6, if the discharge for single pump operation is 220 L/s, what is the size of the pump? If the static head is 15 metres, estimate, by scaling from the figure, the percentage increases in discharge and operating head for two similar pumps in series and in parallel. (300 mm; series: Q 25%, H 19%; parallel: Q 40%, H 34%)

3 Wastewater collection

3.1 Estimate the maximum dry-weather and wet-weather flow rates for a 300 ha residential area from the following data:

Population density, 60 persons per ha; average daily water supply, 200 L/cap; waste/supply ratio, 0.67; average length of sewer and service lines, 0.65 km/ha; peak flow rate due to infiltration 0.7 L/s.km. (84 L/s, 220 L/s)

3.2 By reference to Fig 3.10, determine the slopes, velocities and Darcy f values for a flow of 100 L/s which just fills pipes of diameter 230, 250, 300, 380 and 460 mm.
(For D = 230 mm: 4.4%, 2.41 m/s, 0.033)
(For D = 460 mm: 0.11%, 0.60 m/s, 0.027)

3.3 Find the slope of a 460 mm pipe (k = 1.5 mm) which would carry 142 L/s with a depth/diameter ratio of 0.70. What would be the area ratio and the velocity of flow? (0.43%, 0.75, 1.14 m/s)

3.4 If the full-pipe cleansing velocity is 0.70 m/s, what is the flattest permissible grade for a 460 mm sewer pipe which is to carry a peak wet-weather flow of 85 L/s with an area ratio not exceeding 0.75 and a self-cleansing minimum flow of 25 L/s? (0.20%)

3.5 Revise the sewer design presented in Example 3.7, allowing for the following changes in the design data:

Population density, 70/ha; average dry-weather flow, 330 L/s per person; infiltration allowance, 0.8 L/s.ha; peak dry-weather and wet-weather flows entering manhole 8 from Pamina Parade are 35 L/s and 105 L/s, respectively. (Note that Q_f no longer equals P/33, so that the P scale in Fig 3.10 should not be used.)

3.6 Estimate the probable peak flow rate at a point in a drainage system for a 5-year return period, if the tributary area is 6.5 ha, the inlet time is 18 minutes and the flow time is 4.5 minutes. Assume that Fig 3.12 is applicable to the region and that C = 0.5.
(650 L/s)

3.7 Revise the pipe-drain design in Example 3.10 to provide for a design frequency of once in 10 years and an overland flow time of 18 minutes.

5 Characterisation of waters and wastewaters

5.1 What is the pH of solutions which contain the following concentrations (mole/L) of protons at 25°C: 10^{-5}, 2×10^{-6}, 9×10^{-11}? (5, 5.7, 10.05) Under similar conditions, what is the pH of solutions which contain the following hydroxide ion concentrations: 10^{-6}, 2×10^{-10}, 7×10^{-2}? (8, 4.3, 12.85)

5.2 What is the pH of a solution of 0.1 M acetic acid and 0.3 M sodium acetate? (5.24)

5.3 What is the pH of a one litre solution of 0.1 M acetic acid and 0.1 M of sodium acetate to which 20 mL of 2 M H_2SO_4 is added? (4.39)

5.4 ror an ultimate BOD of 400, calculate the one-day and five-day BOD for a rate constant of $0.05d^{-1}$, $0.3d^{-1}$ and $1.0d^{-1}$. (43.5, 175.1, 199.5, 387.4, 360, 400 mg/L)

5.5 For a BOD_5^{20} of 300 mg/L ($k = 0.1d^{-1}$), calculate the one-day BOD. (90.2 mg/L)

6 Environmental pollution

6.1 Domestic wastewater from a city of 50 000 inhabitants at a per capita flow rate of 200 L/d and a per capita BOD_5^{20} contribution of 60 g/d, together with a flow of 0.05 m^3/s of industrial wastewater at a BOD_5^{20} concentration of 400 mg/L, is treated at a municipal wastewater treatment plant. The plant removes 94 per cent of the BOD and the effluent is discharged with a DO of 6 mg/L into a stream which has a dry-weather flow of 1.5 m^3/s, a BOD of 2 mg/L and a 90 per cent saturation with DO. Temperature is 20°C throughout, and corresponding saturation DO concentration is 9.17 mg/L.

For the mixture of stream water and effluent immediately downstream of the effluent outfall, calculate the BOD_5^{20} concentration, the DO concentration and percentage saturation, and the oxygen deficit. (3.77 mg/L; 8.03 mg/L; 88 per cent; 1.14 mg/L)

6.2 A flow of 0.25 m^3/s of wastewater effluent with 20 mg/L BOD_5^{20} and saturated with DO is discharged into a stream which has a flow of 2 m^3/s, a BOD_5^{20} of 1.5 mg/L and a DO of 9.0 mg/L. The temperature of the effluent and stream water is 20°C, saturation DO is 9.17 mg/L, and for the mixture $k_1 = 0.1$ d^{-1} and $k_2 = 0.35$ d^{-1}. Average velocity of the stream is 0.14 m/s.

What is the critical DO concentration and at what distance downstream of the outfall does it occur? (8.24 mg/L, 24.75 km)

6.3 A stream with a flow of 1.5 m³/s, 2 mg/L BOD_5^{20}, and 9 mg/L DO receives an effluent discharge of 0.3 m³/s, 20 mg/L BOD_5^{20} and 5 mg/L DO. Temperature is 20°C throughout, saturation DO is 9.17 mg/L, k_1 for the effluent/water mixture is 0.1 d⁻¹, k_2 is 0.2 d⁻¹ and stream velocity is 0.1 m/s. Plot the DO sag curve against distance downstream of the outfall, and determine the critical DO concentration and the distance below the outfall at which it occurs. (7.11 mg/L, 21.45 km)

6.4 A flow of 0.25 m³/s of sewage effluent with 5 mg/L DO and 20 mg/L BOD_5^{20} is discharged, at point A, into a stream which under both summer and winter conditions has a minimum flow of 1.25 m³/s, a DO deficit of 0.5 mg/L and a BOD_5^{20} of 2.5 mg/L. At point B, 18.5 km downstream of point A, a further flow of 0.5 m³/s of sewage effluent with 6 mg/L DO and 10 mg/L BOD_5^{20} is discharged to the stream. Temperature of the mixtures of stream water and effluent is 15°C in winter and 25°C in summer. At 20°C, k_1 for the mixture is 0.1 d⁻¹ and k_2 is 0.2d⁻¹. Average stream velocity is 0.1 m/s. Assume saturation DO is 10.14 mg/L at 15°C and 8.40 mg/L at 25°C.

a What is the *maximum DO deficit*, where does it occur, and during what season?

b What is the *minimum DO concentration* in the stream, where does it occur, and during what season?

(a 2.80 mg/L, 8.73 km downstream of B, in winter, and 9.90 km downstream of B, in summer; b 5.60 mg/L, 9.90 km downstream of B, in summer)

8 Physical treatment processes

8.1 Calculate the length required for a microstrainer 3 metres in diameter, if the flow to be treated is 10 ML/d and the loading rate based on projected area (length × diameter) is 1000 m³/m².d. (3.33 metres)

8.2 A screen is placed upstream of an outlet which has been designed so that the depth of flow in the channel is proportional to $Q^{2/3}$. If the range of flow rate is from 50 L/s to 400 L/s, the width of channel is 0.5 metres and the velocity at all flows must be between 0.4 m/s and 0.8 m/s, calculate the maximum depth of flow. (1.0 metre)

What would be the velocity if the flow rate were 30 L/s or 500 L/s? (0.34 m/s, 0.86 m/s)

8.3 Calculate the loss of head through a vertical clean bar screen fitted with 10 mm × 30 mm rectangular bars at 40 mm centres, if the approach velocity is 0.8 m/s. (18 mm)

8.4 What would be the settling velocities of the following particles in water at 15°C (μ = 1.1 $\times$ 10^{-3} N.s/m^2), if it is assumed that they are spherical?

Material	Relative density	Diameter (mm)	
Clay	2.65	0.01	(0.08 mm/s)
Fine grit	2.65	0.10	(7.36 mm/s)
Organic detritus	1.001	0.50	(0.12 mm/s)

8.5 Calculate the theoretical surface area (based on ideal performance) of a horizontal flow sedimentation tank to remove particles having a settling velocity of 1.5 mm/s from a flow of 330 L/s. (220 m^2) Under practical conditions, what area should be provided? (330-440 m^2)

8.6 A suspension of uniform fine grit has a hindered settling velocity of 6.22 mm/s when the volumetric concentration is 0.1 and 3.66 mm/s when it is 0.2. Calculate the hindered settling velocity when the volumetric concentration is 0.25, if the velocity can be expressed by $V_s = V_p (1 - c)^n$. (2.74 mm/s)

8.7 A circular radial flow tank, 30 metres in diameter, has an inlet tower 3 metres in diameter. If the outlet weir is on the outside wall and the flow rate is 700 L/s, calculate the surface overflow rate and the weir loading rate. (86.43 m^3/m^2.d, 642 m^3/m.d)

8.8 The surface layer of a filter, after some time of operation, contains 0.01 m^3 of impurities per cubic metre of sand bed. The filter is operating at a rate of 2.0 L/m^2.s, and the unfiltered water has a concentration of 80 mg/L of suspended impurities (density 1003 kg/m^3). If, using Eq. 8.21, the rate parameters for the system are f_o = 0.4, λ_o = 10 m^{-1}, c = 1.2 mm^{-1} and ϕ = 22 mm^{-1}, estimate the volumetric concentration of impurities at the surface of the sand bed 15 minutes later. (0.0121 m^3/m^3)

8.9 A clean filter has a bed consisting of water-worn sand grains with an effective size of 0.5 mm. The bed is 0.8 metres thick and has a porosity of 0.38. If the flow rate is 2 L/s.m^2 and the viscosity of the water is 1.15 $\times$ 10^{-3} N.s/m^2, estimate the loss of head. (1.17 metres)

8.10 Calculate the saturation concentration of dissolved oxygen in clean water at 12°C at an elevation of 1000 metres above sea level. (9.65 mg/L)

8.11　An aerator rated to transfer 26 kg of oxygen an hour into clean water devoid of oxygen at 10°C at sea level is to be installed at an elevation of 500 metres above sea level to oxygenate sewage and maintain a concentration of 2.5 mg/L at 15°C.

　　　If the saturation level of the sewage is 0.85 times that of clean water and the transfer factor is 0.9, estimate the rate of oxygen transfer. (12.9 kg/h)

9 Coagulation and flocculation

9.1　Chemicals are added to water just before it flows over a measuring weir into a mixing basin. Calculate the fall required for hydraulic mixing with an energy dissipation of 5 J/L. (0.51 metres)

9.2　If a treatment plant has a maximum capacity of 50 ML/d, calculate the volume of a mixing chamber required for a detention of 30 seconds. (17.36 m^3)

9.3　In a jar test, the optimum results are obtained with 1.3 mL of a 10 g/L alum solution mixed in a jar with 500 mL of sample. Calculate the dose rate in mg/L, and the mass of alum needed to treat 40 ML. (26 mg/L, 1040 kg)

9.4　A flocculator treating 30 ML/d has a total volume of 630 m^3, and it achieves an average velocity shear gradient of 20 s^{-1}. If the viscosity of the water is 1.15×10^{-3} N.s/m^2, calculate
　　　a　Detention time in flocculator　　　　　　　　　　(30.2 min)
　　　b　Camp number (Gt)　　　　　　　　　　　　　　(3.63×10^4)
　　　c　Electrical power input required if the overall efficiency of motor and gearing is 70 per cent.　　　　　　　　　　　　(414 W)

9.5　A rapid mixer treating a flow of 20 ML/d has a detention period of 2 minutes and a shaft power input of 1 kW. Estimate the average velocity shear gradient attained if $\mu = 1.1 \times 10^{-3}$ N.s/m^2 (180.9 s^{-1}), as well as the power input per litre. (4.32 J/L)

10 Disinfection

10.1　For E coli, calculate the contact time required to achieve a 99 per cent kill for chlorine concentrations of 0.05 mg/L, 0.2 mg/L, 1 mg/L, 5 mg/L and 10 mg/L. (3.2, 0.96, 0.24, 0.06 and 0.03 seconds)

10.2　Calculate the contact time required to achieve a 99.99 per cent kill for a disinfectant micro-organism system with a rate constant (to the base 10) = 5×10^{-2} s^{-1}. (80 seconds)

11 Biological treatment processes

11.1   A town of 25000 persons has an average per capita daily contribution of 280 L of sewage and 70 g of BOD_5. About 30 per cent of the BOD_5 is removed by primary sedimentation, and the settled sewage is applied to four trickling filters each 50 metres in diameter and 2 metres deep. Calculate the organic and hydraulic loading rates. (0.078 $kg/m^3.d$, 0.89 $m^3/m^2.d$)

11.2   Settled sewage flowing at an average rate of 4.5 ML/d, with a BOD_5 of 200 mg/L, is discharged into a pond 10 ha in area and 1 metre deep. Calculate the average detention time and the areal organic loading rate. (22.2 days, 90 kg/ha.d)

11.3   Settled sewage at an average flow rate of 2 ML/d and with a BOD_5 of 250 mg/L is treated in an activated sludge plant in a single aeration tank 15 metres square and 4 metres deep. The mixed liquor volatile suspended solids concentration is 2500 mg/L. Calculate the nominal average detention time, the volumetric organic loading rate and the F/M ratio. (10.8 h, 0.56 $kg/m^3.d$, 0.22 kg/kg.d)

12 Sludge treatment and disposal

12.1   Calculate the volume of primary sludge produced per day from a town of population 100 000 with a per capita daily wastewater flow of 200 L, an SS concentration of 300 mg/L and primary settlement tanks which remove 70 per cent of the suspended solids to give a sludge of moisture content 95 per cent. (84 m^3)

12.2   A wastewater treatment plant produces 50 000 kg of primary sludge per day on a dry solids basis with a moisture content of 94 per cent and 20 000 kg of secondary sludge per day on a dry solids basis with a moisture content of 99.2 per cent. Calculate the total volume of wet sludge produced each day. (3333 m^3)

12.3   A digested sludge has a moisture content of 97 per cent. To what moisture content must the sludge be dewatered to reduce the volume to 15 per cent of the original? (Assume density of sludge solids = 1000 kg/m^3.) (80 per cent)

12.4   In a specific resistance test on a mixed sludge, the following values were obtained:

Time, s	0	60	120	180	300	900	1200
Filtrate volume, mL	0	2.7	3.8	4.5	5.9	10.5	12.1

Find the specific resistance value for the sludge, given

Filtrate viscosity, μ $= 1 \times 10^{-3}$ Ns/m^2
Filter area, A $= 5 \times 10^{-3}$ m^2
Suspended solids concentration $= 20$ kg/m^3
Vacuum, P $= 50$ kN/m^2

(10^{12} m/kg)

13 Water treatment

13.1 A travelling belt screen is installed in a channel 1.0 metre wide, and is to screen a maximum flow of 45 ML/d. If the velocity through the screen at maximum flow is to be 0.6 m/s, calculate the depth of flow. (0.87 metres)

13.2 A rectangular presedimentation tank is to be installed at a treatment works where the maximum flow rate is 400 L/s. If the surface loading rate is to be 2 L/s.m^2 and the length/width ratio is to be 2, calculate the surface dimensions of the tank. (L $=$ 20 metres, W $=$ 10 metres.)

13.3 A sludge blanket clarifier is operating with a sludge having settling properties described by

$$V_s = 2(1 - c)^{4.5} \text{ mm/s}$$

Calculate the proportionate increase in the slurry pool volume if the upflow velocity of the water is increased from 1.0 to 1.3 mm/s. (56.4 per cent)

13.4 A solids contact clarifier of 25 metres diameter has a central secondary mixing and reaction zone 10 metres in diameter. The rate of throughput is 400 L/s. Calculate the surface loading rate at the slurry pool surface. (0.97 L/s.m^2)

13.5 A flotation unit to treat a maximum flow of 200 L/s is designed to provide for 10 minutes flocculation and 20 minutes flotation. If the flotation surface loading rate is 1.4 L/s.m^2 and both tanks are the same depth, calculate the surface area and depth of each tank. (Flocculation area $=$ 71.4 m^2, flotation area $=$ 142.9 m^2, depth $=$ 1.68 metres)

13.6 A slow sand filter or a rapid sand filter is to be used for filtering a flow of 300 L/s. If the loading rates are 400 L/s.ha and 1.5 L/s.m² respectively, calculate the area required in each case. (SSF: A = 0.75 ha = 7500 m²; RSF: A = 200 m²)

13.7 A rapid sand filter operates at 1.6 L/s.m² for 26 hours before it requires a backwash. The backwash cycle takes 30 minutes, which includes 10 minutes of actual washing at a rate of 9 L/s.m². Estimate the percentage of filtered water lost in backwashing, and the average net throughput rate of the filter. (3.61 per cent; 1.51 L/s.m²)

13.8 A sand has the following grading:

Sieve size (mm)	0.3	0.42	0.60	0.84	1.00
Per cent passing	2	10	36	60	80

What is its effective size and uniformity coefficient? (ES = 0.42 mm; UC = 2.0)

13.9 A rapid sand filter, 4 metres × 6 metres in size, is to be backwashed at a rate of 9 L/s.m². Calculate the required capacity for backwash pumps. (216 L/s)

13.10 Calculate the capacity required for a chemical feed pump to feed a saturated solution of sodium fluoride into a flow of 200 L/s to give a concentration of 1 mg/L of fluoride. (10.92 mL/s)

13.11 In a split-flow softener treating water with a total hardness of 5 me/L including a magnesium hardness of 2 me/L, the flow is split equally between the two streams. In the high-pH stream, 95 per cent of the magnesium hardness is removed. The calcium hardness of the final effluent is 1.0 me/L. Estimate the final total hardness. (2.05 me/L)

13.12 A reverse osmosis plant operates at a pressure of 5 MPa. If the cost of power is 3 cents per kWh and the combined efficiency of the pump and motor is 60 per cent, calculate the cost of power per cubic metre of water produced. (6.95c)

14 Wastewater treatment

14.1 A town with a present population of 10 000 is expected to grow to 20 000 in the design period of a sewage treatment works. Present average dry-weather flow (ADWF) is 240 L/cap.d, which is expected to increase to 280 L/cap.d. The ratio between peak wet-weather flow (PWWF) and ADWF is expected to remain constant at 8:1. In the screen chamber, it is desired that the velocity at times of PWWF at the end of the design period should be not more than 0.9 m/s, and that at times of ADWF at present it should be not less that 0.3 m/s. If the width of the screen channel is 0.5 metres, calculate the desired depth of flow under these two extreme design conditions. (1.152 metres 0.185 metres)

14.2 For the flow conditions described in Problem 14.1, calculate the volume of an aerated grit chamber that has 3 minutes detention during PWWF at the end of the design period. (93.4 m³)

14.3 Estimate the surface area of a primary sedimentation tank designed for 3 ADWF at the end of the design period, if the adopted surface loading rate is 30 m³/m².d and the design population is 30 000 with a design flow rate (ADWF) of 280 L/cap.d. (840 m²)

14.4 An activated sludge plant is to serve a population of 25 000 persons, with an ADWF of 270 L/cap.d and a BOD_5 per capita contribution of 70 g/d. The MLVSS concentration is to be 3000 mg/L, and the F/M ratio has been chosen by the designer as 0.30. If 30 per cent of the BOD is removed by primary treatment, calculate the volume required for the aeration tank. (1361 m³) What is the minimum detention time in the aeration tank if flows in excess of 3 ADWF are bypassed? (1.61 h)

14.5 An oxidation ditch, with no preliminary settlement, operates at an F/M ratio of 0.05 kg BOD/kg MLVSS.d. If the contributing population is 4000 persons with a per capita BOD contribution of 75 g/d, calculate the volume required below bottom water level if the maximum operating MLVSS concentration is 4500 mg/L. (1334 m³) What would be the oxygen transfer capability of the aerators provided for such a ditch if they normally run for 10 hours each day? (72 kg O_2/h)

14.6 Flow data for a wastewater treatment plant at two-hourly intervals over a three-day period are tabulated on page 498 in terms of ratios to the average dry-weather flow rate.

Flows on day 4 and following may be assumed as for day 1. (Data for days 2 and 3 are estimated to correspond to a storm with a recurrence interval of 5 years.) For these flows:

a What size of storage basin would be required to equalise the flows passing to treatment in *dry weather*? (5.2 hours at ADWF)

			Ratio of flow to AWDF at 2-hourly intervals					
	Day	am/pm	12	2	4	6	8	10
dwf	1	am	0.5	0.3	0.3	0.3	1.0	2.0
		pm	1.7	1.3	1.0	1.2	1.4	1.0
wwf	2	am	0.5	0.3	1.0	2.0	4.0	7.0
		pm	8.0*	8.0*	7.5	6.0	5.0	4.0
wwf	3	am	3.0	2.4	2.0	1.7	2.0	2.8
		pm	2.3	1.7	1.3	1.4	1.5	1.0

* Equivalent to the capacity of sewers entering the treatment works

b   What volume of *storm detention* basins would be required if all flow in excess of 3 ADWF is to be diverted into them to await later treatment? (2.1 days at ADWF)

c   Storm return pumps are provided to pump the stored wastewater back to the treatment plant, commencing 6 hours after the flow drops below 3 ADWF, and operating at a rate that will maintain the flow through the works at 3 ADWF until all storm flow has been returned. At what time will the storm detention basins be empty? (Approximately 1230 on day 4)

14.7   For the data given in Problem 14.6, if storm detention tanks are provided with a total capacity of one day's flow at ADWF

a   What would be the total volume of storm effluent discharged from the tanks? (1.1 days at ADWF)

b   What would be the maximum storm effluent flow rate, and when will it occur? (5 ADWF; 1400 hours on day 2)

c   For how long will storm effluent discharge continue? (From 1400 to 2400 hours on day 2)

14.8   An existing biological filtration wastewater treatment plant serving a community of 10 000 people is to be provided with a new inlet works to include a set of two constant-velocity grit chambers (one duty with one standby). A 150 mm throat-width critical depth flume installed as a measuring flume in the works will be retained and used as the downstream control flume for the new grit chambers. If the ADWF is 250 L/d per person, $Q_d/Q_a = 2.5$ and $Q_w/Q_d = 4$, calculate the depth and surface width of flow in a suitable ideal parabolic cross-section for the grit chambers, at flows of Q_a, Q_d and Q_w. (At Q_a, h = 0.234 m, W = 0.617 m; at Q_d, h = 0.432 m, W = 0.838 m and at Q_w, h = 1.088 m, W = 1.330 m)

14.9 A settled sewage with ADWF of 6 ML/d and 210 mg/L BOD_5 is treated in an activated sludge plant which provides 8 hours detention in the aeration tanks.

   a If operating MLSS is 2000 mg/L and dry sludge solids are 75 per cent volatile matter, calculate the F/M ratio. (0.42)

   b If the mean cell residence time is to be maintained at 5 days, what volume of mixed liquor would need to be pumped from the aeration tanks each day? Alternatively, what volume of sludge would need to be pumped from the return activated sludge system (concentration 0.8 per cent) in order to maintain the same value of MCRT (θ_c)? (0.4 mL/d, 0.1 ML/d)

   c For a maximum flow of 3 ADWF and an SVI of 200, calculate the required return activated sludge flow rate. If the maximum surface loading rate on the final sedimentation tanks is 35 m^3/m^2.d, what is the maximum solids loading rate? (12 ML/d, 117 kg/m^2.d)

14.10 A flow of 2 ML/d of domestic sewage with a BOD_5 of 350 mg/L is to be treated in an oxidation pond system. Calculate the detention time and surface area (neglecting bank slopes) of the first pond in the series, if its depth is 1.0 metre and mean daily maximum temperatures for the warmest and coldest months are 30°C and 10°C respectively. (40 days, 8 ha.)

    If the second pond has a surface area exactly half that of the first pond, how many further polishing ponds each with a surface area of 2 ha would be required to reduce an E coli concentration from 5×10^6 MPN per 100 mL in the raw sewage to 200 MPN per 100 mL if K_B for the pond system may be assumed to be 1.8? (One pond)

    What is the areal BOD loading on the first pond alone and on the pond system? (8.75 g BOD/m^2.d, 5 g BOD/m^2.d)

14.11 Mixed primary and humus sludge is added to a heated, well-mixed primary anaerobic digester at a rate of 30 000 litres each day. Sludge moisture content is 96 per cent, and the dry sludge solids contain 70 per cent volatile matter. If average detention time in the digester is 20 days, what is the volatile solids loading rate? (1.4 kg VS/m^3.d)

    If the supernatant is not separated from the sludge in the primary digester and 40 per cent of the volatile matter is converted to gas during digestion, what is the moisture content of the sludge as it leaves the primary digester? (97.1 per cent)

14.12 The primary sedimentation of wastewater from a town of 15 000 people (250 L/d flow and 80 g/d SS loading per person) results in the removal of 60 per cent of the SS load and the production of a primary sludge with 95 per cent moisture content. Dry sludge solids contain 70 per cent volatile matter. Calculate the mass of volatile solids produced each day and the total daily volume of primary sludge (wet sludge density may be assumed to be the same as that of water). (504 kg/d; 14 400 L/d)

If secondary treatment is provided in an activated sludge plant which provides an aeration tank volume equivalent to 6 hours detention at ADWF, an operating MLVSS concentration of 2000 mg/L and a mean cell residence time of 8 days, calculate the mass of volatile solids and total volume of the excess activated sludge produced each day. Assume that the moisture content of excess activated sludge is 99 per cent and the dry sludge solids contain 80 per cent volatile matter. (234 kg/d; 29 300 L/d)

What volume of primary anaerobic digester would be required to treat the primary and secondary sludges at a volatile solids loading of 1.5 kg/m³.d, and what would be the resulting average detention time in the digester? (492 m³; 11.26 days)

If excess activated sludge is returned to the works inlet for settlement with the primary sludge, what would be the maximum moisture content of the combined sludge if the minimum detention time in the primary digester is to be 15 days? (96.9 per cent)

Index